Reporting Technical Information

Second Canadian Edition

Kenneth W. Houp
Late, The Pennsylvania State University

Thomas E. Pearsall
Emeritus, University of Minnesota

Elizabeth Tebeaux
Texas A&M University

Susan Cody
Ryerson Polytechnic University

Ann Boyd
Ryerson Polytechnic University

Fotios Sarris
Ryerson Polytechnic University

CONTRIBUTING AUTHORS:

Sam Dragga, *Texas Tech University*

Janice C. Redish, *President, Redish & Associates, Inc., Bethesda, Maryland*

Allyn and Bacon Canada
Scarborough, Ontario

Canadian Cataloguing in Publication Data

Reporting technical information

2nd Canadian ed.
ISBN 0–205–29774–9

1. Technical writing.   I. Houp, Kenneth W., 1913 – .

T11.R46 1999   808'.0666   C99–932310–2

Allyn and Bacon, Inc., Needham Heights, Massachusetts
Prentice-Hall, Inc., Upper Saddle River, New Jersey
Prentice-Hall International (UK) Limited, London
Prentice-Hall of Australia, Pty. Limited, Sydney
Prentice-Hall Hispanoamericana, S.A., Mexico City
Prentice-Hall of India Private Limited, New Delhi
Prentice-Hall of Japan, Inc., Tokyo
Simon & Schuster Southeast Asia Private Limited, Singapore
Editora Prentice-Hall do Brasil, Ltda., Rio de Janeiro

ISBN 0–205–29774–9

Vice-President, Editorial Director: Laura Pearson
Acquisitions Editor: David Stover
Executive Developmental Editor: Marta Tomins
Associate Editor: Susan Ratkaj
Copy Editor: Sharon Kirsch
Production Editor: Melanie M. Meharchand
Production Coordinator: Wendy Moran
Permissions/Photo Research: Susan Wallace-Cox
Art Director: Mary Opper
Cover Design: Lisa LaPointe
Cover Image: Pakwa Engineering—Tim K. L. Lee, photography and editing;
                       Jeff Richardson, computer modelling
Page Layout: Kyle Gell Art and Design

Original English Language edition published by Allyn & Bacon,
Needham Heights, Massachusetts

3 4 5   WEB   03 02

Printed and bound in Canada.

Visit the Prentice Hall Canada Web site! Send us your comments,
browse our catalogues, and more. **www.phcanada.com** Or reach us
through e-mail at **phabinfo_pubcanada@prenhall.com**

For our colleagues,

friends, and students

BRIEF CONTENTS

CONTENTS

9 Design Elements of Reports 201

10 Graphical Elements 233

Part V: Handbook 484

Communication textbooks for technical students commonly emphasize the importance of writing for the reader, and of ensuring that method is guided by purpose and situation. Yet the usual approach is heavy on prescription and light on example and discussion. *Reporting Technical Information* is based on the premise that students are best prepared for the communication tasks of the workplace by seeing how and why technical writers make the many and varied decisions that result in a successful communication. We believe that students must be dramatically engaged in the situational analysis as well as equipped with a knowledge of reporting tools.

As technology continually transforms how work is done and as the tools of communication multiply, prescriptive formulas will necessarily fall short. The student who understands how to read his or her readers and how to assess the complex interdependent elements of the situation will be better able to meet the communication challenges that arise out of change.

As with the first edition, our task as authors of the second Canadian edition of *Reporting Technical Information* was to retain the in-depth discussion and the wealth of examples that are the strengths of this popular text, while ensuring that they reflect distinctly Canadian content and context. Yet what is distinctly Canadian? For many who ask that question, Canada remains a country in the making. One feature that *has* emerged—as prominently as regionalism and multiculturalism—is an international outlook and influence. This edition reflects current developments in the increasingly international nature of industry linkages and the communications associated with them.

In adapting an American text for Canadian readers, even such apparently obvious changes as bringing spellings into line with Canadian practice and converting to metric measurements created subtle problems. We soon decided that to impose rigid consistency would be misguided and also futile. Canadians who are used to writing for American markets have in many cases chosen to use American spellings. Similarly, Canadian practice has been to adopt metric measures for some things, but still to refer to 8 1/2" x 11" paper or a one-inch nail. So readers of this book will find some of that doubleness, so distinctly Canadian, reflected in its pages.

Reporting Technical Information features up-to-date Canadian examples, representing the demographic and regional realities of this country and showcasing Canadian achievement in an international context. A broad range of technical fields is represented: most engineering specialties, including electrical, nuclear, mechanical, industrial, aerospace, and metallurgical fields; geology; computer technology (E-mail, Internet, multimedia CD-ROM); food and agriculture; transportation; energy; health and welfare; forestry; and health sciences. Examples of graphics, reports, technical descriptions, etc., come from industry, business, government, and from organizations across the country.

The text also reflects the current role of electronic media in the workplace as well as in educational endeavours. Hints to help students write, edit, design, and format on the computer are given throughout the chapters. In addition, the References section contains updated electronic resources, including indexes, detailed annotations, and Internet addresses. This will be a highly valuable research tool, not only for undergraduates, but also for academics and authors.

Finally, the chapters contain comprehensive checklists that summarize chapter information while providing guidelines for students' own work. Weblink resources are now provided for each chapter focus. The exercises allow students to try out the techniques in realistic contexts.

Plan of the Book

CHAPTER 1, AN OVERVIEW OF TECHNICAL WRITING.   Chapter 1 defines technical writing and describes the world of workplace writing—the forms that technical reporting takes and the problems that writers of technical information encounter.

PART I: BASICS.   In Part I, emphasis falls on the composing process. Chapter 2, "Composing," explains how to analyse a writing situation; how to discover, arrange, write, revise, and edit the information you will need; and how to deal with ethical concerns. With this chapter begins the emphasis on audience that is central to this book. Chapter 3, "Writing Collaboratively," deals with how to compose technical writing in collaboration with others. Chapter 4, "Writing for Your Readers," discusses, within a global context, some of the ways you can adapt your writing to various audiences. Finally, Chapter 5, "Achieving a Readable Style," shows you how paying attention to elements of your style at the paragraph, sentence, and language levels can make your writing more readable.

PART II: TECHNIQUES.   In Part II we build on the basic concepts of Part I. Chapter 6, "Arrangement Strategies," now incorporates material formerly contained in three separate chapters. It describes and demonstrates the techniques you will need to inform, describe, define, and argue. With these techniques you can arrange, draft, and revise much of the writing you will do as a professional in your field. As in Part I, we emphasize the need to consider audience and purpose no matter what technique you are using. Chapter 7, "Electronic Communication," describes the role that new channels of communication—such as e-mail, electronic discussion lists, synchronous discussion groups, FTP (file transfer protocol) sites, and World Wide Web sites—play in the workplace, detailing their limitations as well as their virtues. This chapter will help writers make informed decisions about which medium is most effective for each task they undertake as technical communicators.

PART III: DOCUMENT DESIGN.   Part III deals with document design and graphics. Good design—creating a format that helps readers find information and read selectively—is vitally important in technical writing. Chapter 8, "Document Design," focuses on the format and appearance of both electronic and print documents. Chapter 9, "Design Elements of Reports," tells you how to construct all those elements that full reports need, such as covers, tables of contents, abstracts, introductions, discussions, and summaries. Chapter 10, "Graphical Elements," tells you how to use tables, graphs, drawings, and photographs to inform your reader about such things as concepts, processes, trends, relationships, and objects. Technical writing is marked by an extensive use of graphics.

PART IV: APPLICATIONS.   The first six chapters of Part IV put all the basics, techniques, design features, and graphics of the first three parts to work. The chapters of Part IV discuss correspondence, the job hunt, and reports such as feasibility reports, instructions, progress reports, and proposals. Chapters 13 and 14, in particular, show you how to deal with any kind of report, no matter what it is called. Chapter 17 discusses how to put the principles and techniques of this book to work in oral reports. In short, Part IV covers most of the kinds of reports, written and spoken, that professionals in every field have to deliver.

PART V: HANDBOOK.   Any living language is a growing, flexible instrument with rules that are constantly changing by virtue of the way it is used by its speakers and writers. Only the rules of a dead language are unalterably fixed. Nevertheless, at any point in a language's development, certain conventions of usage are in force. Certain constructions are considered errors that mark the person who uses them as uneducated. It is with these conventions and errors that this handbook deals. It also contains information on documentation—including electronic sources—as well as sections on outlining and avoiding sexist language.

APPENDICES.   The appendices guide you to technical reference sources in your own field. These will, in turn, lead you to other sources for the many subjects covered in *Reporting Technical Information*.

Instructor's Manual

With the Canadian Edition, we offer a comprehensive Instructor's Manual to complement the text.

Acknowledgments

In preparing this new Canadian edition, many colleagues and friends have helped us, and we would like to acknowledge their contributions here: Sue Giles of the Ryerson Polytechnic University Library, Renée Lemieux of Ryerson's Computing Services; Nancy Trefiak of the Ryerson Career Centre;

Dr. Douglas White and Nensi Palu from our own Department of Business and Technical Communication; Dr. Linda Schofield; Bill Kershaw of Ontario Hydro; Public Affairs staff of Spar Aerospace; Les Duhasky of Publications Ontario; Peter Dance, Director of Operations, City of Orillia; Don Klepp, Okanagan University College; Lance Moen, Saskatchewan Institute of Applied Science and Technology; and Jan Shepherd, University of Western Ontario; along with many others who responded generously to our requests for advice and gave us an array of fine examples of Canadian technical writing. Our deep gratitude is expressed here as well to Melanie Meharchand and Sharon Kirsch for their skillful assistance and calm capability in taking this work through production. We are particularly pleased to be able to offer in this edition a revised and expanded electronic resources section, which Jey Wolofsky of the Ryerson Polytechnic University Library created for us. The book's dedication reflects our most personal indebtedness.

AN OVERVIEW OF TECHNICAL WRITING

This first chapter is intended to give you the broadest possible view of technical writing. Beginning with Chapter 2, we go into details, but in order to be meaningful, these details must be seen against the background given here.

Some Matters of Definition

As you work your way through this book, you will see that technical writing is essentially a problem-solving process that involves the following elements at one or more stages of the process:

- A technical subject matter that is peculiar to or characteristic of a particular art, science, trade, technology, or profession.
- A recognition and accurate definition of the communication problem involved.
- The beginning of the solution through the establishment of the role of the communicator and the purpose and audience (or audiences) of the communication.
- Discovery of the accurate, precise information needed for the solution of the problem through thinking, study, investigation, observation, analysis, experimentation, and measurement.
- The arrangement and presentation of the information thus gained so that it achieves the writer's purpose and is clear, useful, and persuasive.

The final product of this problem-solving process is a piece of technical writing that may range in size and complexity from a simple memorandum to a stack of books. To expand our overview of technical writing, we discuss it under these five headings:

The Substance of Technical Writing
The Nature of Technical Writing
The Attributes of Good Technical Writers
The Qualities of Good Technical Writing
A Day in the Life of Two Technical Writers

The Substance of Technical Writing

Organizations produce technical writing for internal and external use. Internally, documents such as feasibility reports, technical notes, and memorandums go between personnel at different reporting levels and between colleagues at the same level. If documents move in more than one direction, they may have to be drafted in more than one version. Company policy, tact, and the need to know are important considerations for intracompany paperwork.

Many examples come to mind. The director of information services studies and reports on the feasibility of providing middle management with personal computers. The research department reports the results of tests on new products. The human resources department instructs new employees about company policies and procedures. In fact, the outsider cannot imagine the amount and variety of paperwork a company generates simply to keep its internal affairs in order. Survey research indicates that university-educated employees spend about 20% of their time on the job writing.[1] In fact, most university-educated workers rank the ability to write well as very important or critically important to their job performance.[2]

Externally, letters and reports of many kinds go to other companies, to the government, and to the users of the company's products. Let us cite a few of the many possibilities: A computer company prepares instructional manuals to accompany its computers. A university department prepares a proposal offering to provide research services to a provincial government. An architectural firm prepares progress reports to inform clients of the status of contracted building programs. An insurance company writes letters accepting or denying claims by its policyholders.

The manufacture of information has become a major industry in its own right. Much of that information is research related. Many government agencies, scientific laboratories, and commercial companies make research their principal business. They may undertake this research to satisfy their internal needs or the needs of related organizations. The people who conduct the research may include social scientists, computer scientists, chemists, physicists, mathematicians, psychologists—the whole array of professional specialists. They record and transmit much of this research via reports. The clients for such research may be government agencies or other institutions that are not equipped to do their own research. Reports may, in fact, be the only products of some companies and laboratories.

Much technical writing goes on at universities and colleges. Professors have a personal or professional curiosity that entices them into research. If they believe that their findings are important, they publicize the information in various ways—books, journal articles, papers for professional societies. Students assigned research problems present what they have done and learned in laboratory reports, monographs, and theses.

Many reports are prepared for public use. For example, provincial ministries of natural resources are entrusted not only with conserving our woodlands, wetlands, and wildlife but also with making the public aware of these resources. Agricultural extension services have as a major responsibility the preparation and dissemination of agricultural information for interested users. Profit-earning companies have to create and improve their public image and also attract customers and employees. Airlines, railways, distributors of goods and services, all have to keep in the public view. Pamphlets, posted notices, and radio and television announcements are commonly used to meet these needs.

Myriad applications such as these—company memos and reports, government publications, research reports, public relations releases—create a great flood of paperwork. Some of it is only of passing interest; some of it makes history. Some of it is prepared by full-time professional writers, but most of it is prepared by professionals in a technical field who are writing about their own work.

The Nature of Technical Writing

Technical writing, whether done by professional writers or professionals in a technical field, is a specialty within the field of writing as a whole. It requires a working knowledge of the technical subject matter and terminology. People working with technical documents need to learn about document design, standards for abbreviations, the rules that govern the writing of numbers, the uses of tables and graphs, and the needs and expectations of people who use technical documents.

And yet a broad and sound foundation in other writing is a tremendous asset for those who write technical documents, for it gives them versatility both on and off the job. They can write a good letter, prepare a brochure, compose a report. In this comprehensive sense, they are simply *writers*. The same writing skills that are important in a college classroom are important on the job. Surveys show that workers rank writing skills in this order of importance:[3]

1. Clarity
2. Conciseness
3. Organization
4. Grammar

They understand, too, that not all writing is done in the same tone and style. As writers, they have not one style but a battery of them:

... the very nice plant my mother had on her table in the front hall.	Everyday, homey diction; much depends on the reader's imagination
... in a shaft of yellow sunlight, a white-flowering begonia in a red clay pot.	Pictorial, vivid, sensory; shows, rather than tells
... a 12-inch begonia propagated from a 3-inch cutting; age, 42 days.	Specific, technical, factually informative

As someone who writes technical documents, whether part-time or full-time, you may have to use all of these styles, for your job will be to convey your message to your intended readers. By playing the right tune with these styles in different combinations, and by adding other writing skills in generous measure, you can produce leaflets, proposals, brochures, sales literature, reports to shareholders, and a great variety of letters.

In writing intended for your professional colleagues, you will be nearer to the third begonia example than to the first two. Your diction will be objective and accurate. By relying on this style, you can produce operating manuals, feasibility reports, research reports, progress reports, and similar materials. When your audience and purpose are appropriate for this style, your writing is likely to have these characteristics:

- Your purpose is usually spelled out in the opening paragraph or two. All included information bears upon the accomplishment of the stated purpose. For example, a technical paper on smoke detectors may set forth only one major objective: to determine the relative effectiveness of photoelectric and ionization chamber types in detecting smoldering fires, flaming fires, and high temperatures. Other major topics would be reserved for other papers.
- The vocabulary tends to be specialized. Some of the terms may not appear in general dictionaries. If the audience shares the writer's specialization, such terms may not be defined within the text, on the assumption that professional colleagues will be familiar with them. At other times, the terms may be listed and defined in accompanying glossaries.
- Sentences are highly specific and fact-filled.
- When appropriate to the material, numbers and dimensions are numerous.
- Signs, symbols, and formulas may pepper the text.
- Graphs and tables may substitute for prose or reinforce and expand upon the surrounding prose. Figures and illustrations of all sorts are widely used, sometimes to supplement prose, sometimes to replace it.
- Documentation and credits appear in notes and bibliographies.

As this list makes clear, audience analysis is tremendously important to successful technical writing. What is appropriate for your professional colleagues may be inappropriate for the general public. In matters of definition, for example, terms are not normally defined if the audience is expected to know them. But the indispensable corollary to that proposition is that terms *have to be defined* when your audience, for whatever reason, cannot be expected to know them. Sentences can be fact-filled when the audience is highly professional and highly motivated. However, when your readers do not share your motivation, profession, and enthusiasm, you should slow your pace and make your prose less dense. In technical writing, you have to know your audience as well as your objectives and adapt your style and material to both.

The Attributes of Good Technical Writers

To write clear and effective reports, you build upon the natural talents you have in communicating ideas to others. How can you build successfully? What skills, characteristics, and attitudes are of most value to the technical writer? From experience, we can summarize some of the major attributes that will stand you in good stead:

- Be reasonably methodical and painstaking. Plan your work for the day and for the rest of the week. Look up from time to time to take stock of what you and others are doing, so that you do not squander your time and energy on minor tasks that should be put off or dispensed with altogether. File your correspondence. Keep at your desk the supplies you need to do your work. Keep a clear head about ways and means of accomplishing your purpose.
- Be objective. Try not to get emotionally attached to anything you have written; be ready to chuck any or all of it into the wastebasket. While reading your own prose or that of your colleagues, do not ask whether you or they are pleased but whether the intended audience will be pleased, informed, satisfied, and persuaded.
- In your research, keep in mind that most of what you do will eventually have to be presented in writing. Do your work so that it will be honestly and effectively reportable. Keep a notebook, a computer journal, or a deck of note cards. Record what you do and learn.
- Remind yourself frequently that *clarity* is your most important attribute. Until the sense of a piece of writing is made indisputably clear, until the intended reader can understand it, nothing else can profitably be done with it.
- As someone who writes, understand that writing is something that can be learned, even as chemistry, physics, and mathematics can be. The rules of writing are not as exact as those of science, but they can never be thrown overboard if you are to bring your substance home to your reader.

One writer, who knew well the nature and substance of technical writing, summed up the way to be successful with three imperatives that underlie much of this book:

1. Know your reader.
2. Know your objective.
3. Be simple, direct, and concise.[4]

The Qualities of Good Technical Writing

Because the qualities of good technical writing vary, depending upon audience and objective, we cannot offer you a list that applies equally to everything you write. However, some qualities are apparent in good technical writing:

Good technical writing ...

- Arrives by the date it is due.
- Is well designed. It makes a good impression when it is picked up, handled, and flipped through.
- Has the necessary preliminary or front matter to characterize the report and disclose its purpose and scope.
- Has a body that provides essential information and that is written clearly without jargon or padding.
- When appropriate, uses tables and graphs to present and clarify its content.
- Has, when needed, a summary or set of conclusions to reveal the results obtained.
- Has been so designed that it can be read selectively: for instance, by some users, only the summary; by other users, only the introduction and conclusions; by still other users, the entire report.
- Has a rational and readily discernible plan, such as may be revealed by the table of contents and a series of headings throughout the report.
- Reads coherently and cumulatively from beginning to end.
- Answers readers' questions as these questions arise in their minds.
- Conveys an overall impression of authority, thoroughness, soundness, and honest work.

Beyond all these basic characteristics, good technical writing is free from typographical errors, grammatical slips, and misspelled words. Little flaws distract attention from the writer's main points.

A Day in the Life of Two Technical Writers

To summarize, let us describe two representative writers, whom we shall identify as Marie Doucette and Ted Freedman.

Marie Doucette: Computer Specialist and Occasional Technical Writer

Marie has a bachelor's degree in engineering technology. She works in the information services division of a small electronics company that employs some 400 people. Marie has been with the company for a little over a year. Since her childhood, she has been recognized as a whiz at mathematics. In university, she was drawn to the use and design of computing systems. Her major responsibility is to provide technical support for computer systems users in the company.

Marie's first project with the company was a design for an automated system for the shipping department. She interviewed the supervisors and workers in the department to establish the department's needs. She then matched the needs to available off-the-shelf equipment and programs and designed a system to automate much of the department's work. After finishing her design, she had to prepare a written report and oral briefing describing it for the shipping department and her boss. She had a ghastly time the next two weeks. She found, as do many novices at writing, that she knew what she wanted to say but not where or how to say it. The 10-page report did somehow get written and, after a thorough overhaul by Ted Freedman (whom we'll meet next), was presented. Her oral report was a summary of the written report, and it was well received. Her system design was accepted and will be implemented in several months.

Marie's first experience with on-the-job technical writing taught her four important things: (1) An engineer is not simply a person whose only product is a new design or a gadget that works; (2) things that go on in your head and hands are lost unless they are recorded; (3) writing about what you have thought and done is a recurring necessity; and (4) technical writing, strange and difficult as it may seem at first, is something that can be learned by anyone of reasonable intelligence and perseverance.

Marie's present project is a set of instructions for the accounting department to help them use an automated system that was installed over a year ago. Marie's predecessor had installed the equipment and furnished the accountants a set of the manuals produced by the computer and program manufacturers. The manuals are well written, but because they are written by different manufacturers for a general audience, they do not integrate the components of the system in a way meaningful to the accountants. Marie has studied the system and interviewed the users to determine their needs. She has drafted a 20-page booklet that supplements the manufacturers' manuals and shows the accountants how to use the new equipment and programs in their work. She has sent the draft to Ted Freedman for his comments.

Ted Freedman: Technical Writer and Company Editor

Ted Freedman was hired three years ago by the company as a technical writer-editor. He holds a bachelor's degree in science with a specialization in technical communication. His office is a sparsely furnished cubicle down the hall from the publications and mailing departments. His office possessions include an old typewriter, a brand-new personal computer and printer, a four-foot shelf of dictionaries and reference manuals, and an extra-large wastepaper basket.

At 8:45 this morning Ted is scheduled for a project review session in the company auditorium. He arrives at the auditorium with five minutes to spare. For the next hour he studies flip charts, slide projections on the huge screen, chalkboard plans for company reorganization (minor), and staffing proposals for three new projects totalling $578 400. From the platform, Chief Scientist Muldoon requests that Ted develop research timetables and preview reporting needs.

At 10:20 he meets with a commercial printer to examine the artwork and layout for a detailed report the company is preparing for a royal commission. The work looks good but needs a little typographical variety, he suggests.

At 12:55, back from lunch in the company cafeteria, Ted glances over the memos that collected on his desk during the morning—nothing urgent. Then he opens the manila envelope lying in his mail rack. In it is a computer disk that contains Marie's instructional booklet and a printout of the booklet.

At 1:30 he calls Marie and arranges for a meeting at 3:00 so that they can run through the draft together. In the meantime he looks over the printout. He notices some computer jargon. He is pretty sure the accountants would not have a clear idea of the distinction between Standard Generalized Markup Language (SGML) and American Standard Code for Information Interchange (ASCII). He circles both phrases. Reading on, he finds a spot where the text should be supported by a graphic. He makes a note of it in the margin. He realizes that the booklet would be more accessible to the reader with more headings in it. He puts Marie's disk into his word processor and, scrolling through her text on the screen, inserts headings that fit her arrangement and material. Thus, the afternoon wears on.

At 3:00, Marie arrives and the two confer, make changes, and plan later alterations in the draft. As before, they work amicably together. They intersperse their writing and editing with an occasional trip to the water cooler, a chat with a department head, and a trip to the library to consult a specialized reference work.

Ted is good at his work and considered to have a great future with the company.

Marie and Ted are roughly representative of many thousands of technical writer-editors, most of them, like Marie, part-time as the need arises. To gain a more rounded understanding of their duties and behaviour, we would have to pay them many additional visits; however, certain things are evident even from this brief visit. Like most writers on the job, they work in collaboration with others. Also, much of the time they are not writing at all, in the popular sense. Some of the time they are simply listening hard to what people are saying to one another—trying to clarify, simplify, and translate into other terms. A generous portion of their time is spent on tasks that have little direct connection with writing but eventually provide grist for the writing mill. The techniques, tools, and processes that writers such as Ted and Marie need to accomplish their work are the subject matter of this book.

 **Weblinks**

Canadian Jobs Catalogue
www.kenevacorp.mb.ca

Technical Writing: Books and References Sources
www.interlog.com/~ksoltys/twritres.html

Technical Writing
civil.engr.siu.edu/intro.techwrite.htm

Exercises

1. As your instructor directs, bring to class one or more documents that you believe to be technical. In what respects is the writing technical? Subject matter? Purpose? Tone? Specialized vocabulary? How has the writer used numbers, formulas, tables, and graphs? Are there headings and transitional features that guide readers through the document? Is it easy to scan the document and select certain parts of it for more intensive reading?

2. Rewrite a brief paragraph of technical prose (perhaps a document submitted in Exercise 1) to substantially lower its technical level. Explain what you have done and why.

3. With the help of *Ulrich's International Periodicals Directory* and a professor in your field, find several periodicals in that field. Examine one or more copies of them. In what ways and to what extent does your examination of these periodicals confirm or change your first impressions of technical writing?

4. On a two-column page, list your present assets and limitations as a technical writer.

5. Turn to the job advertisements section of a large metropolitan newspaper. What advertisements for technical writers do you find? What qualifications are demanded of them?

6. Talk with a professional person—if possible, one in a field you would like to enter. Ask how much writing he or she does and what kinds. Ask how much importance is attached to good writing on the job. Write a short report of what you learn for your instructor.

PART I

BASICS

In Part I, the emphasis falls on the composing process. Chapter 2, "Composing," discusses how to analyse a writing situation, and how to discover the information you will need, arrange it, write it, revise it, and edit it. With this chapter begins the emphasis on audience that is central to this book. Chapter 3, "Writing Collaboratively," deals with how to compose technical writing in collaboration with others. Chapter 4, "Writing for Your Readers," discusses some of the ways you can adapt your writing to various audiences. Finally, Chapter 5, "Achieving a Readable Style," shows you how paying attention to elements of your style at the paragraph, sentence, and language level can make your writing more readable.

COMPOSING

The composing process is similar to all high-level reasoning processes in that we do not understand it completely. Most researchers in artificial intelligence—the use of computers to replicate human reasoning—have concluded that no general rule of reasoning works for all problems. As one of them put it, "The human brain ... has an incredibly large processing capacity, much greater than several Cray computers [one of the new generation of supercomputers], and it is beyond our understanding in its ability to connect, recall, make judgments, and act. Thus, all experiments to discover a generalized problem-solving system were, in a practical sense, failures."[1] Another researcher put it more bluntly: "There is no reason but hubris to believe that we are any closer to understanding intelligence than the alchemists were to the secrets of nuclear physics."[2]

Just how complex is the human brain that is "much greater than several Cray computers"? As one authority points out, "There are more neurons in the human brain than stars in the Milky Way—educated estimates put the number of neurons at about 10^{12} or one trillion. Each of those cells can 'talk' to as many as 1000 other cells, making 10^{15} connections."[3] Given that level of complexity and those kinds of numbers, no one can map out completely how any complex, high-level problem-solving process works. And the composing process is precisely that: a complex, high-level problem-solving process.

Since classical times we have understood some things about the composing process. Aristotle, for example, recognized the wisdom of taking one's audience into account. In recent years, empirical research has revealed additional useful facts about the process. What we tell you in this chapter is based upon those classical concepts that have stood the test of time and modern research. We don't pretend to have all the answers, or even that all our answers are right for you. But we can say that the process we describe draws upon the actual practices of experienced writers, and it works for them.

For most skilled and experienced writers, the composing process breaks up into roughly five parts. The first part involves **situational analysis**, that time when you're trying to bring a thought from nowhere to somewhere. It's a time when you think about such things as your audience, your topic, and your purpose. In the second stage, you "discover" the material you need to satisfy your purpose and your audience. That **discovery** process may go on completely within the trillion cells of your brain or, as is often the case in technical writing, in libraries, laboratories, and workplaces as well.

When the discovery stage is almost complete, you pass into a stage where you **arrange** your material. That is, before writing a draft, you may rough out a plan for it or even write a fairly complete outline.

With your arrangement in hand, you are ready for the fourth part of the composing process, the **drafting** and **revising** of your document. For many competent writers, drafting and revising are separate steps; for others, they are almost concurrent.

In the final stage of the writing process, you **edit** your work to satisfy the requirements of standard English and proper format.

Time spent on these five parts is usually not equal. Situational analysis, discovery, and arrangement for a complicated piece of work may take 80% or more of the time you spend on the project. For an easy piece of routine writing, these first three stages may take a few minutes, and drafting and revising may take up the bulk of the time. Some situations call for careful, scrupulous editing; others do not.

The process is often not linear. If the drafting bogs down, you may have to return to the situational analysis stage to resolve the problem. Drafting and revising may alternate as you write for a while, then stop to read and revise. But, in rough outline, what we have described for you is the competent writer's composing process. Throughout this book, we frequently deal with the process. We remind you again and again of the needs of your audience and provide you ways to discover material to satisfy different purposes and topics. In the rest of this chapter we provide some strategies you can use to develop a competent writing process of your own. Because any part of the process can be done in cooperation with others, we provide information on how to write collaboratively (Chapter 3). Also, because technical writers must be ethical, we provide a section in this chapter on **ethical considerations**.

Situational Analysis

In this section we discuss situational analysis, dealing first with topic and purpose, and then with audience and persona.

Topic and Purpose

The topics covered in technical documents are many. You may have a mechanism or process to explain; that is your topic. You may have to define a term or explain a procedure. You may have to report the results and conclusions of a scientific experiment or a comparison shopping study. New research has to be proposed. Delayed work has to be explained. All these and many more are the topics of technical writing.

Although the topics of technical writing are varied, the purposes are more limited. Generally, your purpose is either to inform or to argue. Most topics can be handled in one of these two ways, depending upon the situation. Often, you are simply informing. For example, the situation may call for you to describe a mechanism so that someone can understand it. As you will see in Chapter 6, "Arrangement Strategies," mechanism description will often call for you to divide the mechanism into its component parts and then describe these parts, perhaps as to size, shape, material, and purpose. As another example, you may have to define a term from your discipline. In your definition, you may tell what category the thing defined belongs to and what distinguishes it from other members of the same category. You may give an example of the thing described.

On the other hand, when dealing with your mechanism or definition, you may really be mounting an argument. You may not merely be describing a mechanism; you may be attempting to demonstrate its superiority to other mechanisms of the same type. To do so, you'll need to argue, perhaps by showing how your mechanism is more economical and easier to maintain than other mechanisms. In the same way, you may not simply be defining a term; you may be arguing that your definition is more comprehensive or more correct than previous definitions of the same term.

Be sure to have your topic and purpose in hand before you proceed with your writing project. It's good practice to write them down, something like this:

> I will define alcoholism in a way that reflects recent research. Further, I will demonstrate that my definition, which includes the genetic causes of alcoholism as well

as the environmental ones, is more complete and accurate than definitions that deal with environmental causes alone.

Will the topic and purpose change as you proceed with your project? That depends on the situation. Frequently, the situation may call for you to stick closely to a narrow topic and purpose: *We have to explain to our clients our progress (or lack of progress) in installing the air conditioning system in their new plant.* Or, in another typical situation, *We have to provide instructions for the restaurant staff who will use the computer consoles we have installed.* Although the way you handle such topics and purposes is subject to change as you explore them, the topics and purposes themselves really are not subject to change. On the other hand, the situation may call for you to explore a topic—perhaps the effect the rising age of the Canadian population may have on the restaurant business. Although you have defined your topic well enough to begin your exploration, the precise topic and the purpose may have to wait until you discover more information about your subject.

Audience and Persona

Writers make important decisions about content and style based upon consideration of the audience and the persona the writer wants to project. **Persona** refers to the role the writer has or assumes when writing. It relates to, among other things, the position of the writer and his or her relationship to the audience and the situation. For example, a bank lending officer might assume one persona when writing to a loan applicant and a different persona when writing to a supervisor to justify a loan that has been made.

Professional people consider both audience and persona seriously when composing, as this quote from a hydrology consultant at an engineering firm indicates:

> We write about a wide range of subject matters. Some things are familiar to a lay audience. Most people can understand a study about floods. They can understand a study that defines a 100-year flood plain. They can imagine, say, water covering a street familiar to them. But other subjects are very difficult to communicate. We work with three-dimensional models of water currents, for example, that are based upon very recondite hydraulic movements. We also have a wide audience range. Some of our reports are read by citizen groups. Sometimes we write for a client who has a technical problem of some sort and is only interested in what to do about it. And sometimes we write for audiences with high technical expertise … [They] expect a report to be written in a scientific journal style, and they even want the data so they can re-analyze it. A lot of times the audience is mixed. A regulatory agency may know little about the subject of one of our reports, but they may have a technically trained person on the staff who does. In any case, we must understand what it is that the client wants, and we must be aware of what he or she knows about the subject. We must convince clients that we know what we are doing. We depend upon return business and word-of-mouth reputation, and we must make a good impression the first time. Much of the technical reputation of this company rides on how we present ourselves in our technical reports.[4]

Here are some questions you need to ask about your audience and persona when you are preparing to write.

WHAT IS THE LEVEL OF KNOWLEDGE AND EXPERIENCE OF YOUR READERS? In technical writing, the knowledge and experience your readers possess are key factors. Do your readers understand your professional and technical language? If they do, your task is easier than if they do not. When they do not, you have to be particularly alert to your word choice, choosing simpler terms when possible, defining terms when simpler choices are not possible. There are whole concepts that a lay audience may not have. Geologists, for example, thoroughly understand the concept of plate tectonics and can assume that geologists in their audience understand it equally well. When addressing a lay audience, however, the geologist writer should assume the reader has little understanding of the concept and take time to explain it in a way that the audience can grasp.

WHAT IS THE READER'S POINT OF VIEW? Point of view relates to the reader's purpose and concerns. Suppose that you are writing about a procedure. People may read about procedures for many reasons. In one case, the reader may wish to perform the procedure. In another, the reader may have to make a decision about whether to adopt the procedure. In yet another, readers may simply want generalized information about the procedure, perhaps because they find it interesting.

Each case calls for a different selection of content and a different style. Readers wishing to perform the procedure need a complete set of step-by-step instructions. The decision maker needs to know the criteria used to evaluate the procedure and why, under these criteria, it is a better choice than other procedures. Readers for interest want the general concept of the procedure explained in language they can understand.

WHAT IS YOUR RELATIONSHIP TO THE READER? Are the readers your supervisors, clients, subordinates, peers, or students? If you are a public employee, are you writing to a taxpayer who contributes to your salary? Writers in the workplace, when interviewed about how they write, reveal that they pay a good deal of attention to the effect of such relationships on tone, as these quotations demonstrate:[5]

- Writing to my boss, I try to pinpoint things a little more.
- When you have something as personal as a phone call or a conversation back and forth ... I feel free to use "I" rather than "we."
- We always want them to realize they can call on us if they have any questions.
- This [referring to a statement] is a bit more on a personal level ... The other [statement] is much too formal.
- Just to say "Send his address," would, I think, be a little too authoritarian.

The roles writers find themselves in also affect their choice of content. Imagine the difference in approach between a Ford sales representative trying to sell a fleet of Fords to a company, and a young executive of the same company reporting to his or her superiors that the results of a feasibility study demonstrate Fords to be the best purchase. In the first instance, the sales representative is likely to be more enthusiastic about Fords than other makes. The decision makers would expect and understand such enthusiasm and would allow for it. In the second instance, the decision makers will expect a more balanced approach from the young executive.

WHAT IS YOUR READER'S ATTITUDE TOWARD WHAT YOU ARE GOING TO SAY?   Audiences can be suspicious and hostile. They may be apathetic. Of course, they may be friendly and interested. Their attitude should affect how you approach them. If you have an unfriendly audience, you must take particular care to explain your position carefully in language that is understandable but not patronizing. You may need more examples than you would with a friendly audience. A friendly audience may be persuaded with less information. With a friendly audience, you may present your conclusions first and then support them. With an unfriendly audience, it's a sound idea to present your support first and then your conclusions.

Readers may also have attitudes about the language you use. For example, public health officials have had a difficult time expressing how to avoid exposure to AIDS. Such advice, to be effective, must refer very explicitly to sexual practices. Newspapers have had to change their usual practice to allow such language to be printed, and some readers have found the language offensive. In most cases, the interest in AIDS prevention has won out over reader sensibilities, but the problem illustrates well the social context of audience analysis.

WHAT PERSONA DO YOU WISH TO PROJECT?   If you have read scientific journals, you have probably noticed that they have a certain tone about them, a tone to which words such as *objective, formal,* and *restrained* readily apply. Scientists, to find acceptance in such journals, must adopt such a tone. A breezy, light journalistic style, though it might be just as clear, would not be acceptable. In the same way, bankers must present themselves in a careful, formal way. We're not likely to give our money for safekeeping into the hands of someone who comes on like the stereotype of a television used-car dealer. Young executives writing to their bosses are likely to be a bit deferential. The bosses, in turn, want to sound firm but reasonable and not authoritarian. What has come to be called "corporate culture" plays a role in the persona a writer may adopt. In writing, you must project the values and attitudes of the organization you work for. You may want to look over past correspondence and reports to see what practices have been used, and what sort of tone writers in the organization have adopted.

Taking on a persona when you write is something like taking on a persona when you dress. The student who exchanges his blue jeans and running shoes for a business suit and leather shoes when he reports for a job interview is slipping out of one persona into another. The teacher who exchanges a comfortable sweater and skirt for a businesslike dress when she leaves the classroom to consult in industry is exchanging one persona for another. It's a common enough experience in life, and you should not be surprised to find such experiences in writing situations. Both dressing and writing have their own rhetorics. However, don't misinterpret anything we have said as a rationale for being obscure or jargony. You should be clear no matter what persona you adopt.

Discovery

At some point in your writing process you must "discover" the material you will use in your writing. Discovery is teasing out of your mind the information you will use and modify to meet the needs of your topic, purpose, audience, and persona. Discovery is making connections. It's the putting together of two pieces of information to create a third piece that didn't exist before the connection. A mind that is well stocked with information will probably be successful at discovery. Those trillion neurons need something to work with; the more you read, observe, and experience, the better you are likely to be at writing.

Of course, not all the material you need may be in your mind when you begin. Discovery includes using libraries and laboratories to fill in the gaps in your knowledge. You may also use interviews, on-site inspections, letters of inquiry and the like to gather information. The techniques we discuss here will enable you to explore your own mind.

Brainstorming

In brainstorming you uncritically jot down every idea about a subject that pops into your head, without thought of organization. The key to successful brainstorming is that you do not attempt to evaluate or arrange your material at the first stage. These processes come later. Evaluation or arrangement at the first critical stage may cause you to discard an idea that could prove valuable in the context of all the ideas that the brainstorming session produces. Also, avoiding evaluation at this point prevents the self-censorship that often blocks a writer.

Because brainstorming is a fairly painless process, it's a good device to break down the normal resistance most of us have to hard thinking. It can result in your writing down a good deal more information than you ever thought you possessed. It can quickly reveal holes in your knowledge, which can be filled with information you gather later.

Using Arrangement Patterns for Discovery

Although you do not arrange your material in the discovery stage, you can use familiar arrangement patterns as aids in discovering your material.[6] For example, suppose your purpose is to write a set of instructions for a reader who wishes to perform the procedure. As we will see in Chapter 15, a set of instructions often lists and sometimes describes the tools that must be used to perform the procedure. Furthermore, instructions normally describe the steps of the procedure in chronological order. Knowing what is normally required for a set of instructions, you can brainstorm your material in a more guided way.

You can begin by writing down the tools that will be needed for the procedure. Think about what you know about your audience. Are they experienced with the tools needed? If so, simply list the tools. If they are not experienced, jot down some information they'll need to use the tools properly.

When you are done with the tools, write down the steps of the procedure. Keep your readers in mind. Are there some steps so unfamiliar to your readers that you need to provide additional information? If so, list what that information might be.

As in brainstorming, in very little time you can get information out where you can see it. Also, as in brainstorming, if there are gaps in your knowledge, you can discover them early enough to fill them.

Another task frequently encountered in technical writing is arguing to support an opinion. In discovering an argument, you can begin by stating your opinion clearly: for example, "Women should get equal pay for equal work." Next, you can turn your attention to the subarguments that might support such an opinion. For example, you would have to establish first that a problem really does exist: in many instances women are *not* getting equal pay for equal work. Then you might think of a philosophical argument: Ethically, women have a right to equal pay for equal work. You might think of an economic argument: Women's need to support themselves and their families equals that of men. And so forth.

As you consider these and other subarguments, you can begin to think about the information you will need to support them. Some of it you may have; some you may need to research. The very form and needs of your argument serve as powerful tools to help you discover your material.

Other Successful Discovery Techniques

Most experienced writers develop their own discovery techniques. In the workplace, writers often use past documents of a similar nature to jog their minds. Many professional writers keep journals that they can mine for ideas and data. Scientists keep laboratory notebooks that can be invaluable when it's time to write up the research. In the workplace, people talk to each other to discover and refine ideas.

Asking questions, particularly from the reader's point of view, is a powerful discovery technique. Suppose you were describing the use of the Internet for research. What questions might the reader have? *Do I have to be an expert on computers to use the Internet? What are the advantages of the Internet? The disadvantages? How do I judge its effectiveness? What does it cost to subscribe? Will the Internet make research easier?* As you ask and answer such questions, you are discovering your material.

When you have established your topic and purpose, analysed your audience, and discovered your material, it's time to think about arrangement.

Arrangement

When you begin your arrangement, you should have a good deal of material to work with. You should have notes on your audience, purpose, and persona. Your discovered material may take various forms. It may be a series of notes produced by brainstorming or other discovery techniques. You may have cards filled with notes taken during library research or notebooks filled with jottings made during laboratory research. You may have previous reports and correspondence on the topic you are writing about. You may have ideas for graphs and tables to use in presenting your material. In fact, you may have so much material that you do not know where to begin.

You can save yourself much initial chaos and frustration if you remember that certain kinds of reports (and sections of reports) have fairly standard arrangements. The same arrangement patterns that helped you discover your material can now serve you as models of arrangement. For instance, you might divide your subject into a series of topics, as we have done with the chapters of this book. If you're describing a procedure and know that your readers wish to perform that procedure, you may use a standard instruction arrangement: introduction, tool list and description, and steps of the procedure in chronological order. If you are arranging an argument, you have your major opinion, often called the major thesis, and your subarguments, often called minor theses. You'll probably want to consider the strength of your minor theses when you arrange your argument. Generally, you want to start and finish your argument with strong minor theses. Weaker minor theses you'll place in the middle of your argument.

Documents such as progress reports, proposals, and empirical research reports have fairly definite arrangements that we describe for you in Part IV, Applications. Not all the arrangements described will fit your needs exactly. You must be creative and imaginative when using them. But they do exist. Use them when they are appropriate.

How thorough you are at this stage depends upon such things as the complexity of the material you are working with and your own working habits. Simple material does not require a complicated outline. Perhaps nowhere else in the writing process does personality play such a prominent role as it does at the arrangement stage. Some people prepare fairly complete arrangement patterns; others do not.

An article by Blaine McKee, "Do Professional Writers Use an Outline When They Write?" explores the outlining practices of professional technical writers.[7] Dr. McKee found that only 5% of the writers used no outline at all, and only 5% reported using an elaborate sentence outline. Most reported using some form of topic outline or a mixture of words, phrases, and sentences. Most kept their outlines flexible and informal, warning against getting tied to a rigid outline too early. But all but 5% did feel the need to think through their material and to get some sort of arrangement pattern down on paper before beginning the first draft of a report.

Most experienced writers are thorough but informal in writing down their arrangement patterns. However, if you need a formal outline and need instruction in preparing one, look in Part V under "Outlining."

In technical writing, graphs and tables are important techniques for presenting material. It's not too early to think about them while you are arranging your material. For help in planning and selecting graphs and tables, see Chapter 10, "Graphical Elements."

Drafting and Revising

When you have finished arranging your material, you are ready to draft and revise your report. Keep in mind that writing is not an easy mechanical job. But we do give you suggestions that should make a tough job easier.

The Rough Draft

Writing a rough draft is a very personal thing. Few writers do it exactly alike. As you have seen, most write from a plan of some sort; a few do not. Some write at a fever pitch; others write slowly. Some writers leave revision entirely for a separate step. Some revise for style and even edit for mechanics as they go along, working slowly, trying to get it right the first time. All we can do is describe in general the practices of most professional writers. Take our suggestions and apply them to your own practices. Use the ones that make the job easier for you and revise or discard the rest.

Probably our most important suggestion is to begin writing as soon after the prewriting stage as possible. Writing is hard work. Most people, even professionals, procrastinate. Almost anything can serve as an excuse to put the job off: one more book to read, a movie that has to be seen, anything.

The authors of the Ontario Hydro Management Training Section *Report Writing Guide* attribute writer's procrastination to "perfection paralysis"—the condition in which you feel you shouldn't write anything down unless it's perfect, but since your first attempt can never be perfect, you don't write anything down. They note that this condition can eat up whole days of valuable time.[8]

The solution is to begin and the sooner the better. Find a quiet place to work, one with few distractions. Choose a time of day when you work well, and go to work. What writing tools should you use? The original authors of this book used as tools for their first draft a yellow, legal-sized pad and a can filled with pencils. We have trained ourselves to compose directly on the word processor (and we encourage our students to do the same). Canadian author Mordecai Richler is known to have a fondness for an Olivetti manual typewriter—now virtually impossible to get. The moral of all this is that the tools used are a matter of individual choice. There is something a bit ritualistic about writing, and most competent writers insist upon their own rituals.

Where should you begin? Usually, it's a good strategy to begin not with the beginning but with the section that you think will be the easiest to write. If you do so, the whole task will seem less overwhelming. As you write one section, ideas for handling others will pop into your mind. When you finish an easy section, go on to a tougher one. In effect, you are writing a series of short, easily handled reports rather than one long one. Think of a 1500-word report as three short, connected 500-word reports. You will be amazed at how much easier this attitude makes the job. We should point out that some

writers do prefer to begin with their introductions and even to write their summaries, conclusions, and recommendations (if any) first. They feel this sets
their purpose, plan, and final goals firmly in their minds. If you like to work
that way, fine. Do remember, though, to check such elements after you have
written the discussion to see whether they still fit.

How fast should you write? Again, this is a personal choice, but most
professional writers write rapidly. We advise you not to worry too much
about phraseology or spelling in a rough draft. Proceed as swiftly as you can
to get your ideas on paper or on the screen. Later, you can smooth out
your phrasing and check your spelling, either with your dictionary or your
word processor's spelling checker. However, if you do get stalled, reading over
what you have written and tinkering with it a bit is a good way to get the
flow going again. In fact, two researchers of the writing process found that
their subjects spent up to a third of their time pausing. Generally, the pauses
occurred at the ends of paragraphs or when the writer was searching for examples to illustrate an abstraction.[9]

Do not write for more than two hours at a stretch. This time span is
one reason why you want to begin writing a long, important report at least
a week before it is due. A report written in one long five- or six-hour
stretch will reflect the writer's exhaustion. Break at a point where you are sure
of the next paragraph or two. When you come back to the writing, read
over the previous few paragraphs to help you collect your thoughts and
then begin at once.

Make your rough draft very full. You will find it easier to delete material
later than to add it. Nonprofessional writers often write thin discussions because they think in terms of the writing time-span rather than the reading
time-span. They have been writing on a subject for perhaps an hour and
have grown a little bored with it. They feel that if they add details for another
half-hour they will bore the reader. Remember this: At 250 words a minute,
average readers can read an hour's writing output in several minutes. Spending
less time with the material than the writer must, they will not get bored.
Rather than wanting less detail, they may want more.

Don't infer from this advice that you should pad your report. Brevity is
a virtue in professional reports. But the report should include enough detail
to demonstrate to the reader that you know what you're talking about. The
line between conciseness on one hand and completeness on the other is
often a tightrope.

As you write your rough draft, indicate where your references will go. Be
alert for paragraphs full of numbers and statistics and consider presenting
such information in tables and graphs. Be alert for places where you will
need headings and other transitional devices to guide your readers through
the report. (See Part III, Document Design.)

Whether your planning has been detailed or casual, keep in mind that
writing is a creative process. Discovery does not stop when you begin to
write. The reverse is usually true. For most people, writing stimulates discovery. Writing clarifies your thoughts, refines your ideas, and leads you to new

connections. Therefore, be flexible. Be willing to revise your plan to accommodate new insights as they occur.

Revision

Some writers revise while they are writing. For them, revision as a separate step is little more than minor editing, checking for misspellings and awkward phrases. For other writers, particularly those who write in a headlong flight, revising is truly rewriting and sometimes even rearranging the rough draft. Some writers can do this comfortably directly on the computer screen; others still need a hard copy, the feeling of paper in hand. Naturally, there are almost as many gradations as there are writers. However you revise, you should be concerned about arrangement, content, logic, style, graphics, and document design. In some situations you may want to show your work to others and seek their advice.

ARRANGEMENT AND CONTENT   In checking your arrangement and content, try to put yourself in your reader's place. Does your discussion take too much for granted? Are questions left unanswered that the reader will want answered? Are links of thought missing? Have you provided smooth transitions from section to section, paragraph to paragraph? Do some paragraphs need to be split, others combined? Is some vital thought buried deep in the discussion when it should be put into an emphatic position at the beginning or end? Have you avoided irrelevant material or unwanted repetitions?

In checking content, be sure that you have been specific enough. Have you quantified when necessary? Have you stated that "In 1997, 52% of the workers took at least 12 days of sick leave," rather than, "In a previous year, a majority of the workers took a large amount of sick leave"? Have you given enough examples, facts, and numbers to support your generalizations? Conversely, have you generalized enough to unify your ideas and to put them into the sharpest possible focus? Have you adapted your material to your audience?

Is your information accurate? Don't rely on memory for facts and figures. Follow up any gut feeling you have that anything you have written seems inaccurate, even if it means a trip back to the library or laboratory. Check and double-check your math and equations. You can destroy an argument (or a piece of machinery) with a misplaced decimal point.

LOGIC   Be rigorous in your logic. Can you really claim that A caused B? Have you sufficiently taken into account other contributing factors? Examine your discussion for every conceivable weakness of arrangement and content and be ready to pull it apart. All writers find it difficult to be harshly critical of their own work, but a critical eye is essential.

STYLE   After you have revised your draft for arrangement and content, read it over for style. (We treat this as a separate step, which it is. But, of course, if you find a clumsy sentence while revising for arrangement and content, rewrite it immediately.) Use Chapter 5, "Achieving a Readable Style," to help you. Rewrite unneeded passive voice sentences. Cut out words that add nothing to your thought. Cross out pretentious words and substitute simpler ones. If you find a cliché, try to express the same idea in different words. Simplify; cut out the artificiality and the jargon. Be sure the diction and sentence structures are suitable to the occasion and the audience. Remember that you are trying to write understandably, not impressively. The final product should carry your ideas to the reader's brain by the shortest, simplest path.

GRAPHICS   Much technical information is presented in tables and graphs. When dealing with content that has visual components, you should probably present at least some of that content graphically. When you have numerous statistics, particularly statistics that you are comparing to each other, consider using a table, graph, or chart. (For help in such matters, see Chapter 10, "Graphical Elements.")

DOCUMENT DESIGN   Good document design—the use of tables of contents, headings, the right typeface, proper spacing, and so forth—is integral to good technical writing. We offer detailed guidance in this area in Chapter 8, "Document Design" and Chapter 9, "Design Elements of Reports."

SHARING YOUR WORK   In actual workplace situations, writers often share their drafts with colleagues and ask for their opinions. Often, someone who is not as close to the material as the writer can spot flaws far more quickly than can the writer. As you'll see when we discuss revising and editing with word processing, you may also share your work with your personal computer.

When you are writing instructions, it's an excellent idea to share an early draft with people who are similar in aptitude and knowledge to the people for whom the instructions are intended. See if they can follow the instructions. Ask them to tell you where they had trouble and to point out specific sections that threw them off track.

Editing

Editing is a separate step that follows drafting and revising. It's the next-to-final step before you release your report to its intended audience. When drafting and revising a manuscript, you may have to backtrack to the discovery or the arranging stage of the process. But if you are editing, it means you are either satisfied with your draft or you have run out of time.

In the editing stage you make sure your report is as mechanically perfect as possible, that it meets the requirements of standard English and whatever format requirements your situation calls for. If you are working for a large organization or the government, you may have to concern yourself with things such as stylebook specifications, distribution lists, and code numbers.

Checking Mechanics

Begin by checking your mechanics. Are you a poor speller? Check every word that looks the least bit doubtful. Some particularly poor spellers read their draft backwards to be sure that they catch all misspelled words. Develop a healthy sense of doubt and use a good dictionary or the spelling checker of your word processing program. Do you have trouble with subject–verb agreement? Be particularly alert for such errors. In Part V, we have provided you with a handbook that covers some of the more common mechanical problems. A word processor can help by providing a check for some of the errors a computer program is able to detect. (Be aware, though, that a spelling checker has limitations: it will not notice if you have written "too" instead of "to," or "combing" instead of "combine.")

Checking Documentation

When you are satisfied with your mechanics, check your documentation. Be sure that all notes and numbers match. Be sure that you have used the same style throughout for your notes. For help in documentation see "Documentation" in Part V, Handbook.

Checking Graphics

Check your graphics for accuracy, and be sure you have mentioned them at the appropriate place in the report. Are your graphics well placed? If they are numbered, be sure that their numbers and the numbers you use in referring to them match.

Checking Document Design

In your drafting and revision, you should have made sure that your design made your document readable and accessible for your readers. In your editing, check for more mundane but nevertheless important things. For instance, is your table of contents complete? Is it accurate? Does it match the headings you have used? Do your headers and footers accurately describe your material?

When you are satisfied you have done all that needs to be done, print your final draft, then proofread it one more time before you turn it over to your audience. The author of a report is responsible for all errors, no matter how the report is prepared.

Editing with Word Processing Programs

To help the writer with editing, spelling checkers and grammar and style checkers are available in word processing programs.

Spelling Checkers

You may have a spelling checker in your word processing program or one that you have bought separately. Spelling checkers compare every word in your text with the dictionary included in the program. Most spelling checkers have no sense of grammar or usage. They will stop on a correctly spelled word if that word does not happen to be in the program's dictionary, as is true of many technical terms. More important, they will *not* stop at a word that is in the program's dictionary when that word is used incorrectly in context.

A spelling checker won't catch errors like these:

The *student's* all came to class today.

They wanted to *here* your speech.

They wanted to hear *you* speech.

For a list of words that sound alike but have different spellings and meanings, such as *weather* and *whether*, see "Spelling Error" in Part V, Handbook. Use a spelling checker first, but then make sure to proofread as well.

Grammar and Style Checkers

You can get programs that check your work for grammar, punctuation, and style. Some will flag passive sentences, long sentences, wordy phrases, double words (such as *and and*), unmatched pairs of quotation marks, and other problems. Some also flag problems with subject-verb agreement, incorrect possessives, and other grammatical faults. Some give your text a "readability rating" according to one or more formulas.

Grammar and style checkers can be helpful. They can make you more aware of your writing style. If you tend to write in the passive voice, they'll press you to change to active voice. If you tend to use wordy phrases or unnecessarily long words, they'll give you shorter, crisper alternatives.

Use grammar and style checkers with great caution, however. Some current text-analysis programs are too rule-bound to be flexible, and some of the rules may be of doubtful validity. As one authority says, "Syntax writers that can truly evaluate a user's writing style await future breakthroughs in artificial intelligence."[10]

Think about the advice they give you in light of the purpose and audience for your document. Not every passive voice sentence should be rewritten in the active voice. Not every sentence of more than 22 words is too long. Grammar and style checkers work only at the sentence and word level, but the most serious problems with many documents are in their content and overall organization. If you change words and sentences here and there without considering larger issues of content and arrangement, you may actually be making your document less useful and understandable.

Ethical Considerations

Because technical writing often has consequences for large numbers of people, ethical considerations frequently play a role in the writing process.[11] For example, it is sometimes tempting in a feasibility report to soft-pedal results that do not support the recommendation the writer wishes to make. It may seem advantageous in a proposal to exaggerate an organization's ability to do a certain kind of research. A scientist may be too willing to ignore results that do not fit his or her theory and report those that do. Each of these acts would be unethical.

Understanding Ethical Behaviour

What makes an act unethical? Why should we be ethical? We'll briefly answer those two questions and then offer a few suggestions about how to behave ethically.

WHAT MAKES AN ACT UNETHICAL?   Most of us carry around ethical rules in our heads. Most of us, no doubt, would agree that it is unethical to lie, cheat, and steal. Further, we would likely agree that it is wrong to make promises we don't intend to keep or to plagiarize a paper. Where do such ethical rules come from? In part, they are learned at home or in a religious setting or simply in the rough-and-tumble of growing up. The loss of friends who catch one in a lie can be a lasting ethical lesson. Philosophers have long attempted to devise theories to support ethical behaviour. Most embrace either logic, consequences, or some combination of the two.

Logically, as the 18th-century German philosopher Immanuel Kant proposed, we should not act in a way that we cannot will to be universal behaviour. For example, if you make a promise that you have no intention of keeping, you cannot will that to be universal behaviour. For if you did, all promises would be worthless, and it would be pointless to make a promise, false or otherwise.

Another group of philosophers, the utilitarians, make consequences their test for ethical behaviour. An act should do the greatest good for the greatest number of people or, conversely, create the least amount of evil for the fewest people. For example, causing an industrial plant to clean up its smokestack emissions may be an economic evil for the company and its shareholders but it is also the greatest good for the many people who must breathe those emissions. Medical scientists who fudge their data may win promotion for themselves but injure unsuspecting people who are mistreated as a result of the deception.

No matter how philosophers explain ethical behaviour, one thing seems clear: Acting ethically often involves putting one's own selfish interests aside for the sake of others. George F. R. Ellis, a modern-day student of ethics, stated this as a universal principle of ethical behaviour:

> The foundational line of true ethical behavior, its main guiding principle valid across all times and cultures, is the degree of freedom from self-centeredness of thought and behavior, and willingness freely to give up one's own self-interest on behalf of others.[12]

Most of us have sufficient ethical knowledge to act ethically if we want to. Why should we want to?

WHY SHOULD WE ACT ETHICALLY?   We don't have to act ethically. We don't have to will that our acts become universal behaviour as Kant would have us do. Despite the utilitarians, we don't have to worry about the greatest good for the greatest number of people. We can act in our own selfish interests if we want to. If acting ethically is a voluntary act, why bother?

We can list some pragmatic, nonaltruistic reasons for acting ethically. For one thing, some unethical acts are also illegal. You can end up in prison for stealing or otherwise bilking people of money. Furthermore, organizations that intend to prosper in the long term need to build a reputation for ethical behaviour. Professionals must act with integrity to survive in their work environments. Unethical acts can help an organization or an individual initially, but in the long run, they usually do more harm than good.

Professionals, such as engineers and scientists, must act with integrity to survive in their work environments. For that reason most professional groups have a professional code that calls for ethical behaviour.

The code of the Society for Technical Communication (STC) is an example of such a professional code. It reads, in part, as follows:

> As a technical communicator . . . I am committed to excellence in performance and the highest standards of ethical behavior . . . My commitment to professional excellence and ethical behavior means that I will
>
> - Use language and visuals with precision.
> - Prefer simple, direct expression of ideas.[13]

The Code of Ethics for the International Association of Business Communicators states that "Communication specialists will not condone any illegal or unethical act related to their professional activity, their organization and its business or the public environment in which it operates."[14]

However, perhaps the most important justification for acting ethically is less obvious than these individual and organizational reasons. Acting ethically is a price we pay for living in a free, civilized society. The ideal reflected in our social system is a balance of legislative constraint with individual and corporate conscience. We would not need environmental laws if every company voluntarily acted in the best interests of the people. But a government that attempted to control all unethical behaviour would be overly restrictive, even totalitarian.

Recognizing Unethical Communication

Perhaps the first step to communicating ethically is recognizing the ways in which people can be unethical when they communicate. Chief among the ways are plagiarizing, deliberately using imprecise or ambiguous language, making false implications, manipulating data, and using misleading visuals.

PLAGIARISM   Ethical writers acknowledge the sources of the words, ideas, and findings they use. In some forms of writing—journalism, for example—the acknowledgment may be in the text in a statement like, "As Dr. Ken Olson discovered, it's possible to vaccinate mosquitoes to prevent their developing and passing dengue on to human beings."

In more formal and scholarly writing, some system of documentation—notes and citations—would be used to show the source of the information and to give full credit to Dr. Olson. (See "Documentation" in Part V, Handbook.) To pass off the words and work of others as your own is plagiarism. It's a form of lying and is highly unethical. Take every precaution to avoid even the appearance of plagiarism. For example, make sure that even your acknowledged paraphrases and summaries do not track the originals so closely that they border on stealing others' words.

DELIBERATELY USING IMPRECISE OR AMBIGUOUS LANGUAGE   The STC code calls for the "simple, direct expression of ideas." In Chapter 5, "Achieving a Readable Style," we discuss ways to write clearly and help your readers to understand you. We urge you to write with precision and to avoid ambiguous language. Unclear writing usually results from a faulty style, but not always. It can result from a deliberate attempt to mislead or manipulate the reader by hiding unfavourable information.

The principal meaning of *ambiguous* is "capable of having two meanings." The word *majority*, for instance, means "the greater part of something" and "a number more than half of the total." Imagine the writer of a feasibility report who wishes to recommend a change in company policy. He takes a survey of all the workers in the company and finds that 50.1% of the 20% who returned his survey favour the change. In his report he writes, "A majority of those who returned the survey favour the change." By counting on the ambiguity of *majority*, he makes a stronger case for change than if he reported the actual bare majority the survey revealed. In addition, by not revealing that this "majority" represents only 10% of the company's workers, he further strengthens what is actually rather weak support for his case. He has not lied, but through ambiguity he has certainly misled the audience.

MAKING FALSE IMPLICATIONS   Writers can imply that things are better than they are by manipulating language. For example, a writer answering an inquiry about her company's voltage generator could reply, "Our voltage generator is designed to operate from the heat of Saudi Arabian deserts to the frozen tundra of Greenland." It may be true that the generator was *designed* that way, but if it only *operates* properly between Atlanta and Ottawa, the writer has made a false implication without telling an outright lie.

For another example, imagine a mutual fund that led its market in returns for 10 years. In the eleventh year, the original fund manager retires and a new manager takes over. In that year and the next, the fund drops to the bottom tenth of its market in returns. The writer of an advertising brochure for the fund writes the following: "Our fund has led the market for ten of the last twelve years." The writer has avoided an outright lie, but clearly has made an unethical statement.

MANIPULATING DATA   In a discussion of honour in science, a scientific research society lists three ways scientists can present their results unethically:

- *Trimming:* smoothing irregularities to make the data look extremely accurate and precise.
- *Cooking:* retaining only those results that fit the theory and discarding others.
- *Forging:* inventing some or all of the research data that are reported, and even reporting experiments that were never performed.

Only the last of these three manipulations is clearly a lie, but all misrepresent the data and are unethical.[15]

USING MISLEADING VISUALS Like words, visuals can misrepresent data and mislead unwary readers. The fundamental principle in constructing an ethical visual is to represent the data accurately and proportionally.[16]

Writing Ethically

We are probably most tempted to write unethically when our own interests or the interests of our organization are at stake. For example, you may be writing a proposal for your research laboratory to do a significant and costly piece of research for a large government agency. A proposal is a sales document, after all. It's sensible practice to cast your laboratory in its best light. But the temptation to go too far is always present. You may be tempted to exaggerate the expertise of the scientists who will carry out the job. Through imprecise language you may hide the deficiencies of your laboratory or overstate its attributes.

On the other hand, you may write unethically simply by not recognizing the consequences of what you have written. A way to bring the consequences of your writing to the foreground is to construct a fault tree diagram at the point in your planning or writing at which you recognize that there are various options open to you. As you construct your fault tree, draw each of your possible options as a branch. List the consequences for each branch or option. If any of the listed consequences leads to another consequence, draw another branch showing that consequence, and so on, until you have exhausted all reasonable options. Let us illustrate.

Imagine yourself to be a newly graduated civil engineer. You are hired by a land developer to develop plans for streets and sewage disposal for a large parcel of land on which he plans to build 45 houses. In walking the parcel, you discover that about half of it is a waste dump filled with trees and other vegetation covered with several feet of soil. When you draw this to the developer's attention, he tells you that while building other housing developments, he used this parcel of land as a dump. Upon further questioning, he reveals that he has never sought a permit for the dump from the county, so you are dealing with an unauthorized dump. You realize that a dump filled with vegetation may create substantial amounts of highly explosive methane gas. You recognize three possible options you can recommend to the developer:

1. Proceed with the development as planned.
2. Delay the building until the contents of the dump have been removed.
3. Cancel the development plans.

To help yourself sort out the consequences of the actions, you develop the fault tree shown in Figure 2-1.

Your fault tree makes it clear that you cannot ethically recommend option 1. Option 2 looks good, despite some possible negative consequences.

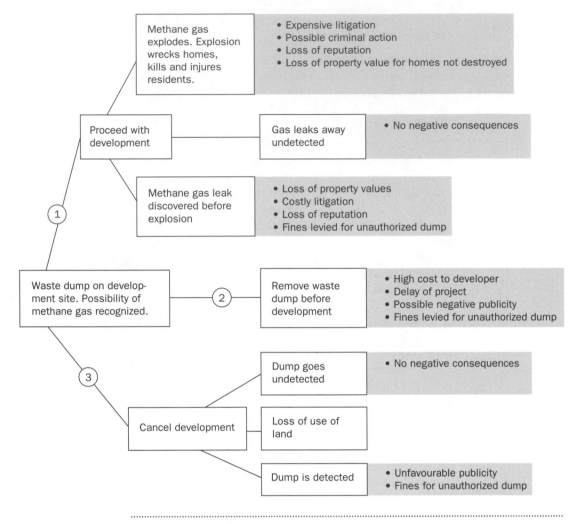

Figure 2-1   FAULT TREE

You realize you'll need some further work to determine the cost of removing the dump. Option 3 is ethical but probably not cost effective. If the developer chooses option 2 or 3, you have fulfilled your ethical duty. If the developer decides to go ahead with the development, you have another ethical choice. Should you keep a copy of your report to protect yourself but remain quiet, or should you blow the whistle on the developer? Given the possible cost in human misery if the developer goes ahead, there seems to be little choice; you'll have to blow the whistle.

In this section, we have made you aware of some of the ethical difficulties you may encounter when writing and given you ways to deal with them. However, no amount of reading about ethics can make you ethical. To be ethical, you must have a good will, good judgment, moral sense, and, frequently, courage.

Planning and Revision Checklists

These questions are a summary of the key points in Chapter 2, and they provide a checklist when you are composing.

Situational Analysis

- What is your topic?
- Why are you writing about this topic? What is your purpose (or purposes)?
- What are your readers' educational levels? What knowledge and experience do they have in the subject area?
- What will your readers do with the information? What is their purpose?
- Do your readers have any expectations as to style and tone? Serious? Light? Formal?
- What is your relationship to your readers? How will this relationship affect your approach to them?
- What are your readers' attitudes toward what you are going to say?

Discovery

- What discovery approach can you use? Brainstorming? Arrangement patterns? Other?
- Are there documents similar to the one you are planning that would help you?
- Do you have notes or journal entries available?
- What questions are your readers likely to want answered?
- Do you have all the information you need? If not, where can you find it? People? The library? Laboratory research?
- What tables, graphs, diagrams, or other graphic aids will you need?

Arrangement

- Are there standard arrangement patterns that would help you, such as instructions, arguments, or proposals?
- Will you need to modify a standard pattern to suit your needs?
- Do you need a formal outline?
- When completed, does your organizational plan fit your topic, material, purpose, and audience?
- What headings and subheadings will you use to reveal your organization and content to your readers?
- Is everything in your plan relevant to your topic, purpose, and audience?
- If you have a formal outline, does it follow outlining conventions? Are entries grammatically parallel? Is each section divided into at least two parts? Is the capitalization correct? Are the entries substantive?

continued >>

Drafting

- Do you have a comfortable place to work?
- Where in your organizational plan can you begin confidently?
- Where will your graphical elements be placed?

Revision

- Have you stated clearly and specifically the purpose of the report?
- Have you put into the report everything required? Do you have sufficient supporting evidence? Have you stated the implications of your information clearly?
- Are all your facts and numbers accurate?
- Have you answered the questions your readers are likely to have?
- Does the report contain anything that you should cut out?
- Does your organization suit the needs of your content and your audience?
- Are your paragraphs clear, well organized, and of reasonable length? Are there suitable transitions from one point to the next?
- Is your prose style clear and readable?
- Is your tone appropriate to your audience?
- Have you satisfied the needs of an international audience?
- Are all your statements ethical? Have you avoided making misleading, ambiguous statements or statements that deliberately lead the reader to faulty inferences?
- Are your graphs and tables clear and accurate? Are they well placed? Do they present your information honestly?
- Is your document readable, accessible, and visually effective?
- Are there people with whom you should share your draft—for example, members of the target audience—before going on to a final draft?

Editing

- Have you checked thoroughly for misspellings and other mechanical errors?
- Have you included all the formal elements that your report needs?
- Are design elements such as headings, margins, spacing, typefaces, and documentation consistent throughout the draft?
- Are your headings and titles clear, properly worded, and parallel? Do the headings in the text match those in the table of contents?
- Is your documentation system appropriate and complete? Have you documented wherever appropriate? Do the numbers in the text match those in the notes?
- Have you keyed the tables and figures into your text and have you sufficiently discussed them?
- Are all parts and pages of the manuscript in the correct order?
- Will the format of the typed or printed report be functional, clear, and attractive?
- Does your manuscript satisfy stylebook specifications governing it?
- Have you included required notices, distribution lists, and identifying code numbers?

continued >>

- Do you have written permission to reproduce extended quotations or other matter under copyright? (Necessary only when your work is to be published or copyrighted.)
- While you were composing the manuscript did you have any doubts or misgivings that you should now check out?

- Have you edited your manuscript for matters both large and small?
- What remains to be done, such as proofreading final copy?

 ## Weblinks

Grammar, Punctuation, and Spelling: A Handbook for Technical Writers
www.sti.larc.nasa.gov/html.Chapt3/Chapt3-TOC.html

Online Technical Writing: Online Textbook
www.io.com/~hcexres/tcm1603/acchtml/acctoc.html

CoreCOMM's Worst-Technical-Writing-Sample-of-the-Month Contest
www.corecomm.com/worst.html

Exercises

1. Describe accurately and completely your current writing process. Be prepared to discuss your description in class.

2. Interview someone who has to write frequently (such as one of your professors). Ask about the person's writing process. Base your questions upon the process described in this chapter; that is, ask about situational analysis and arranging, drafting, revising, and editing techniques. Take good notes during the interview, and write a report describing the interviewee's writing process.

3. Choose some technical or semitechnical topic you can write about with little research—perhaps a topic related to a hobby or to an academic subject you enjoy. Decide upon a purpose and audience for writing about that topic. For example, you could instruct students in some laboratory technique. You could explain some technical concept or term to someone who doesn't understand it—to one of your parents, perhaps. Analyse your audience and persona following the suggestions in this chapter. With your purpose, audience, and persona in mind, brainstorm your topic. After you complete the brainstorming, examine and evaluate what you have. Reexamine your topic and purpose to see if information you have thought of during the

brainstorming has changed them. Keeping your specific topic, purpose, audience, and persona in mind, arrange your brainstorming notes into a rough outline. Do not worry too much about outline format, such as roman numerals, parallel headings, and so forth.

4. Turn the informal outline you constructed for Exercise 3 into a formal outline. (See "Outlining" in Part V.)

5. Write a rough draft of the report you planned in Exercises 3 and 4. Allow several classmates to read it and comment upon it. Revise and edit the rough draft into a final, well-written and well-designed draft. Submit all your outlines and drafts to your instructor.

6. Read the following case and write a memo as discussed at the end of the case. For information on writing memos, see Chapter 11, "Correspondence."

Radon is an odorless radioactive gas produced by the breakdown of uranium in the soil. It is particularly prevalent in granite areas and exposure to it can cause lung cancer. Health Canada recommends radon removal measures when the annual coverage concentration in the living area of a house exceeds 800 becquerals per cubic metre of air (Bq/m3). Imagine that you live in an area where radon is a potential health threat in people's houses. Because of the threat, people frequently hire radon removal contractors to test for radon levels in their houses and, when necessary, to install radon removal systems.

You obtain summer employment with one such contractor. His name is John May and his firm is called May Radon Removal. Typically, the contractor tests the house for radon and then presents a proposal to the householder detailing the work to be done and setting a price for the work. To obtain more information about radon and its reduction, you read a booklet prepared by the Canada Mortgage and Housing Corporation titled *Radon Control in New Homes*.[17] In the booklet, you learn that the most expensive radon reduction systems are needed for houses that are built on concrete slabs or with basements. Systems for such houses can run as high as $3000. In houses built over crawl spaces, homeowners can reduce radon to safe levels simply by increasing the ventilation of the crawl space. This remedy is a sixth of the cost of the system. You realize that you have been helping Mr. May install expensive systems, suitable for houses with basements and concrete slabs, in houses built over crawl spaces.

You look at a proposal being presented to a person who owns a house with a crawl space. In the proposal, you find that Mr. May has recommended suction depressurization, a system normally used under basements or slabs. It requires an expensive installation of pipes and fans in the soil under the house to trap and suck away radon. He offers no alternatives to this system. In the proposal, Mr. May justifies the suction depressurization system with this statement: "Suction depressurization is the most common and usually the most reliable radon reduction method." From your research on radon, you know this is a true statement.

Is the contractor being unethical? If so, in what way? Construct a fault tree to answer these two questions. When you have arrived at an answer, write a memo to your instructor stating your opinion and a justification for that opinion. If you found the contractor to be unethical, propose how you plan to handle the problem. Include a copy of your fault tree with your memo.

WRITING COLLABORATIVELY

As we point out in Chapter 2, you can write collaboratively as well as individually. Organizations conduct a good deal of their business through group conferences. In a group conference, people gather, usually in a comfortable setting, to share information, ideas, and opinions. Organizations use group conferences for planning, disseminating information, and, most of all, problem solving. As a problem-solving activity, writing lends itself particularly well to conferencing techniques. In fact, collaborative writing is common in the workplace.[1]

In this chapter, we discuss some of the ways that people can collaborate on a piece of writing. We conclude with a brief discussion of group conferencing skills, skills that are useful not only for collaborative writing, but for any conference situation you are likely to find yourself in.

People cooperate in many ways in the workplace. One of the ways they cooperate is by sharing their writing with one another. Someone writing a report may pass it to a co-worker and ask for general comments or for specific feedback on the report's style, tone, accuracy, or even grammar.

However, the collaborative writing we discuss in this chapter is more complex than a simple sharing. Rather, it is the working together of a group

Planning	Drafting	Revising	Editing
• Keep all discussions objective.	• Choose a drafting plan:	• Revise for content, organization, style, and tone.	• Edit for format and standard usage.
• Record discussion.	—Divide the work.	• Be concerned with accuracy and ethics.	• Check and double-check for inconsistencies in such things as margins, typeface, documentation, and headings.
• Analyse situation and audience.	—Draft in collaboration.	• Make criterion-based comments.	
• Establish purpose.	—Choose a lead writer.	• Make reader-based comments.	
• Discover content.	• Consult with group when needed.	• Be objective in discussion, not personal.	
• Organize content.	• Stick to deadlines.	• Remember, people get attached to their writing.	
• Agree on style and tone.		• Accept criticism gracefully.	
• Agree on format.		• Don't avoid debate, but keep discussions as friendly and positive as possible.	
• Choose coordinator.		• Know when to quit revising.	
• Seek opinion on plan from outside group.		• Seek an opinion from outside the group.	

Figure 3-1   THE COLLABORATION PROCESS

over an extended period of time to produce a document. In producing the document, the group shares the responsibility for the document, the decision making, and the work. Figure 3-1 shows the major steps of the collaborative process. Collaborative writing can be two people working together or five or six. Writing groups with more than seven members are likely to be unwieldy. In any case, all the elements of composing—situational analysis, discovery, arrangement, drafting and revising, and editing—generally benefit by having more than one person work on them.

Groups sometimes digress and wander off the point of the discussion. Therefore, it helps to have set procedures that guide discussion without stifling it. To that end, we have provided planning and revision checklists at the end of this chapter and many others. The checklist provided at the back of this book combines the Chapter 2, "Composing," checklist with key elements from the checklist that follows this chapter. These checklists raise questions about topic, purpose, and audience that will keep the individual or the group on track.

Planning

The advantage of working in a group is that you are likely to hit upon key elements that working alone you might overlook. The collaborative process greatly enhances situational analysis and discovery. Shared information about audience is often more accurate and complete than individual knowledge. By hammering out a purpose statement that satisfies all its members, a group heightens the probability that the purpose statement will be on target.

The flow of ideas in a group situational analysis and in a discovery brainstorming session will come so rapidly that you risk losing some of them. One or two people in the group should serve as recorders to capture the thoughts before they are lost. It helps if the recording is done so that all can see—on a chalkboard, a pad, an easel, or a computer screen. During the brainstorming, remember to accept all ideas, no matter how outlandish they may appear. Evaluation and selection will follow.

The group can take one of the more organized approaches to discovery. For instance, if instructions are clearly called for, the group can use the arrangement pattern of instructions to guide discovery. If discovery includes gathering information, working in a group can speed up the process. The group can divide the work to be done, assigning portions of the work according to the expertise of each group member.

When the brainstorming and other discovery techniques are finished, the group must evaluate the results. This is a time when trouble can occur. When everyone is brainstorming, it's fun to listen to the flow. There is a synergy working that helps to produce more ideas than any one individual is likely to develop working alone. When the time comes to evaluate and select ideas, however, some ideas will be rejected, and tension in the group may result. Feelings may be ruffled. Keep the discussion as open but as objective as you can. As much as possible, divorce the ideas from those who offered them. Evaluate the ideas on their merits—on how well they fit the purpose and the intended audience. Whatever you do, don't attack people for their ideas. Again, someone should keep track of the discussion in a way that the group can follow.

In collaborative writing, a good way of evaluating the ideas and information you are working with is to arrange them into an organizational plan. The act of arranging will highlight those ideas that work without shining too bright a spotlight on those that don't. A formal outline is not always necessary, but a group usually needs a tighter, more detailed organizational plan than does an individual. (See "Outlining" in Part V, Handbook.)

Do not be in a hurry at this stage (or any other stage) to reach agreement. Collaborative groups should not be afraid of argument and disagreement. Objective discussion about such elements as purpose, content, style, and tone is absolutely necessary if all members of the group are to visualize the report in the same way. A failure to get a true consensus on how the report is to meet its purpose and how it should be written can lead to serious difficulties later in the process.

While in the planning stage, a group should take three other steps that can save a lot of hassle and bother later on.

First, they should agree on as many format features as possible, such as spacing, typefaces, table and graph design, and the form of headings and footnotes. Part III, Document Design, will help you with this step.

Second, the group should set deadlines for completed work and stick to them. The deadlines should allow ample time for the revising stage and for the delays that seem inevitable in writing projects.

Third, the group should choose a coordinator from among themselves. The group should give the coordinator the authority to enforce deadlines, call meetings, and otherwise shepherd the group through the collaborative process. Unless the coordinator abuses his or her authority, the group should give the coordinator full cooperation.

When the planning is finished, you may want to take one more step. Collaborative writing, like individual writing, can profit from networking with individuals or groups outside your immediate working group. You may want to seek comments about your content and organizational plan from people with particular knowledge of the subject area. If you're writing in a large organization, it might pay to seek advice from people senior to you who may see political implications your group has overlooked. In writing instructions, you would be wise to discuss your plan with several members of the group to be instructed. Be ready to go back to the drawing board if your networking reveals serious flaws in your plan.

Drafting

In the actual drafting of a document, a group can choose one of several possible approaches.

Dividing the Work

For lengthy documents, perhaps the most common procedure is to divide the drafting among the group. Each member of the group takes responsibility for a segment of the organizational plan and writes a draft based upon the group plan. It's always possible, even likely, that each writer will alter the plan to some degree. If the alterations are slight enough that they do not cause major problems for group members working on other segments of the plan, such alterations are appropriate. However, if such changes will cause problems for others, the people affected should be consulted.

Allow generous deadlines when you divide the work. Even when a group has agreed on the design features, there will be many stylistic differences in the first drafts. A group that divides the work must be prepared to spend a good deal of time revising and polishing to get a final product in which all the segments fit together smoothly.

Drafting in Collaboration

In a second method of collaboration, a group may want to draft the document together, rather than dividing up the work. Word processing, in particular, makes such close collaboration possible. Two or three people sitting before a keyboard and a screen will find that they can write together. Generally, one person will control the keyboard, but all collaborators can read the screen and provide immediate feedback as changes are made to the document. Although such close collaboration is possible, it is a method seldom used in the workplace, probably because it is time consuming and therefore costly. Its use is most often reserved for short, important documents where the writers must weigh every word and nuance.

One Person Doing the Drafting

The third method is to have one person draft the entire document. This produces a uniformity of style but has the obvious disadvantage in the classroom that not everyone will get needed writing experience. An alternative approach is to divide the work but then appoint a lead writer to put the segments together, blending the parts into a stylistic whole. The group may even give the lead writer the authority to make editorial decisions in cases where the group cannot reach agreement on its own. In large organizations you will find all these methods or combinations of them in use.

Revising and Editing

Collaboration works particularly well in revising and editing. People working in a group frequently will see problems in a draft, and solutions to those problems, that a person working alone will not see.

Revising

In revising, concern yourself primarily with content, organization, style, and tone. Be concerned with how well a draft fits its purpose. When the group can work together in the same location, everyone should have a copy of the draft, either on paper or on the computer screen. Comments about the draft should be both criterion-based and reader-based.[2]

CRITERION-BASED COMMENTS   Criterion-based comments measure the draft against some standard. For example, the sentences may violate stylistic standards by being too long or by containing pretentious language. (See Chapter 5, "Achieving a Readable Style.") Perhaps in classifying information, the writer has not followed good classification procedures. (See Chapter 6, "Arrangement Strategies.") The group should hold the draft to strict standards of ethics and accuracy. Whatever the problem may be, approach it in a positive manner. Say something like "The content in this sentence is good. It says what needs to be said, but maybe it would work better if we divided it into two sentences. A 60-word sentence may be more than our audience can handle."

READER-BASED COMMENTS   Reader-based comments are simply your reaction as a reader to what is before you. Compliment the draft whenever you can: "This is good. You really helped me understand this point." Or you can express something that troubles you: "This paragraph has good factual content, but perhaps it could explain the implications of the facts more clearly. At this point, I'm asking what does it all mean. Can we provide an answer to the 'so-what' question here?"

WORD PROCESSING   Word processing offers an attractive technique for revising, particularly when geography or conflicting schedules keep group members apart. Each member can do a draft on a disk and then send a copy of the disk to one or more co-authors. The co-author can make suggested revisions on the disk and send it back to the original author. The revisions should be highlighted in some way, perhaps with asterisks or brackets; many word processors include a redlining feature for this very purpose. If a printer is available, a redlining program such as CompareRite or DocuComp may also be used. The original author can react to the changes in a way he or she thinks appropriate. Collaborators can use electronic mail in a similar way. If the collaborators can get together, they can slip the disk into the word processor and work on it side by side.

COMMENTS FROM OUTSIDE THE GROUP   As with the organizational plan, you should consider seeking comments on your drafts from people outside the group. People senior to you in your organization can help you to ensure that the tone and content of your work reflect the values and attitudes of the organization.

PROBLEMS IN THE GROUP   Although it is effective, collaborative revision can cause problems in the group. We all get attached to what we write. Criticism of our work can sting as much as adverse comments about our personality or habits. Therefore, all members of the group should be particularly careful at this stage. Support other members of the group with compliments whenever possible. Try to begin any discussion by saying something good about a draft. As in discussing the plan, keep comments objective and not personal. Be positive rather than negative. Show how a suggested change will make the segment you are discussing stronger—for instance, by making it fit audience and purpose better.

If you are the writer whose work is being discussed, be open to criticism. Do not take criticism personally. Be ready to support your position, but also be ready to listen to opposing arguments. Really *listen*. Remember that the group is working toward a common goal—a successful document. You don't have to be a pushover for the opinions of others, but be open enough to recognize when the comments you hear are accurate and valid. If you are convinced that revision is necessary, make the changes gracefully and move on to the next point. If you react angrily and defensively to criticism, you poison the well. Other group members will feel unable to work with you and may find it necessary to isolate you and work around you. Harmony in a group is important to its success. Debate is appropriate and necessary, but all discussions should be kept as friendly and positive as possible.

Know when to quit revising. Experienced writers maintain that all writing is subject to infinite improvement. However, none of us have infinity in which to do our work. When the group agrees that the document satisfies the situation and purpose for which it is being written, it's time to move on to editing.

Editing

Make editing a separate process from revision. In editing, your major concerns are format and standard usage. Editing is more easily accomplished by a group than is revision. Whether a sentence is too long may be debatable. If a subject and verb are not in agreement, that's a fact. Use the Handbook (Part V) of this text to help you to find and correct errors. Final editing should also include making the format consistent throughout the document. This is a particularly important step when the work of drafting has been divided among the group. Even if the group agrees beforehand about format, inconsistencies will crop up. Be alert for them. All the equal headings should look alike. Margins and spacing should be consistent. Footnotes should all be in the same style, and so forth. See Part III, Document Design, for help in this important area.

The final product should be seamless. That is, no one should be able to tell where Mary's work leaves off and John's begins. To help you reach such a goal, we provide you with some principles of conferencing.

Collaboration in the Workplace

The collaboration process we have described in this chapter, or one very much like it, is the one you will probably use in a classroom setting. It is also the one you are likely to use in the workplace when a group voluntarily comes together to produce a piece of work. As such, it is a fairly democratic process. However, in the workplace, management may assign a collaborative task. In such cases the process may differ significantly from the voluntary collaborative method we have described.

In an assigned collaboration, people may be placed in the group because they can provide technical knowledge and assistance the group needs to carry out its assignment. For example, within a provincial department of transportation, a group might be assigned to produce an environmental impact statement in preparation for building a new highway. The group might include a wildlife biologist, a civil engineer, a social scientist, and an archaeologist. Furthermore, a professional writer may be assigned to the group to help with the composing process, from planning to editing.

Rather than the group's choosing a leader or a coordinator, management may assign someone to be the leader. Good leadership encourages democratic process and collaboration, and enables people to do what they do best. However, there are times in the workplace when an assigned leader may be arbitrary, for example, about work assignments and deadlines.

Finally, in the workplace, there is often a prescribed process for reviewing the collaborative results. This process may involve senior executives and people with special knowledge, such as lawyers and accountants. The reviewers may demand changes in the document. The group may have some right of appeal, but, in general, the wishes of the review panel are likely to prevail.

Collaboration on the Internet

One important tool for collaboration in the workplace is the Internet, specifically e-mail, FTP (File Transfer Protocol), and synchronous discussions. Using the Internet, group members can work together on a project from remote locations. For example, consider the group working to produce the environmental impact statement for the department of transportation. The biologist might be on part-time loan to the project from the department of parks and wildlife. The civil engineer might be located at the highway construction site. The social scientist and archaeologist could be affiliated with two different universities in two different cities. The professional writer might be located at the department of transportation. Without the Internet to bring these five people together, collaboration on the environmental impact statement would be inefficient, impractical, or impossible.

E-Mail

The group just described might initiate collaborative work on their project by creating a distribution list for e-mail. Each member of the group could then mail a message to a common e-mail address, and all the members of the group would receive a copy of the message. That is, instead of mailing several e-mail messages, a group member would only have to mail one—a considerable reduction in time and effort. In addition, all members of the group would know that they were all getting the same message, leading to feelings of equality and trust among the group members.

A group leader could use such a distribution list to mail messages about scheduling, deadlines, funding, or other information that might affect the operations of the group. Group members could also use the list to exchange research findings, ask questions, or discuss issues that arise during the project.

Individual e-mail could also assist in other phases of the group's collaboration. For example, in drafting the environmental impact statement, the professional writer might have specific questions for the civil engineer. In reviewing the writer's draft, the civil engineer might identify several necessary corrections and e-mail the writer only with that information.

For both individual e-mail and its distribution list, the group would want to use e-mail software that allows users to attach files to their e-mail messages. Such software compresses a file, translates it to binary code, and transmits it over the Internet, complete with all original formatting, graphics, and special characters. When the e-mail message is received, the attached file is displayed on the recipient's computer screen, ready to be accessed by appropriate software. If all group members have compatible systems, it's easy to circulate drafts for review, editing, and revision.

For example, the professional writer could e-mail a message to the group's distribution list and attach a draft of the environmental impact statement for members to review. The e-mail message might identify specific passages that the writer would like the reviewers to pay attention to. Or, the writer might list a series of questions about the document for each reviewer to address.

The members of the group would receive a copy of the e-mail message and the attached file. Each would review the draft, make corrections, and individually e-mail the writer, attaching the revised document to his or her e-mail message. (For more information about e-mail, see Chapter 7, "Electronic Communication.")

FTP Sites

FTP (File Transfer Protocol) sites allow you to upload files from your computer to a remote computer or to download files from a remote computer to your computer. FTP is thus a potential tool for collaboration because it creates a common electronic work site. That is, instead of continually e-mailing information to the group and attaching a copy of a document to your e-mail message, you could upload a copy of a file to the group's designated FTP site and allow each member of the group to download a copy at his or her convenience.

The five people working on the environmental impact study, for example, could house at their FTP site a schedule listing the tasks assigned to each member of the group. As each member completed a designated task, he or she would download a copy of the schedule, note the completion of the task, upload the revised schedule, and discard the previous schedule. Using FTP, the group could also make drafts of documents available for review. Each member of the group could download a copy of the document, make the necessary corrections, and upload the revised version—and all without e-mailing a single message. (For more information about FTP, see Chapter 7, "Electronic Communication.")

Synchronous Discussions

Synchronous discussions can be useful to a group at several points in the collaborative process. Unlike e-mail, synchronous communication is almost simultaneous, with the participants gathered together in real time in a virtual meeting room. Such discussions are often called MUDs (multiple user dimension, dialogue, domain, or dungeon) or MOOs (multiple user domain object-oriented). A number of sites are available on the Internet for synchronous discussions. (For more information about synchronous discussions, see Chapter 7, "Electronic Communication.")

Consider again the group asked to write the environmental impact statement. As soon as this group is assigned to the project, members could meet each other in a synchronous discussion for planning. Group members could introduce themselves, discuss purpose and audience, brainstorm regarding topics to cover, consider guidelines for organization and style, divide the project, and establish a schedule.

Once the project has started, group members might meet periodically in a synchronous discussion to monitor their progress, discuss problems and solutions, and offer each other support. Together they might also compose brief sections of the document that require careful wording or especially sensitive treatment.

They might also use synchronous discussions to conduct a joint review of a draft of the document. That is, instead of each member of the group responding individually to a draft, the entire group would meet at the same time to make corrections and suggestions for revision. Such joint reviews are often helpful, especially if individual reviews yield contradictory suggestions. In a joint review, members have the opportunity to negotiate their differences of opinion and reinforce each other's comments. To arrange a joint review, the professional writer could e-mail a message to the group's distribution list, specifying the subject of the synchronous discussion and attaching a copy of the draft for members to examine before the review.

Synchronous discussions are also valuable at the end of a project. A final meeting allows the group to examine its operations, congratulate itself on its successes, identify its mistakes, and evaluate the collaborative experience.

Like all conferences, synchronous discussions require appropriate collaborative behaviours to be successful. Many of the suggestions in the next section can be applied in electronic meetings as well as in face-to-face situations.

Group Conferences

Collaborative writing is valuable as a means of writing and learning to write. In a school setting, collaborative writing is doubly valuable because it also gives you experience in group conferencing. You will find group conferencing skills necessary in the workplace. Most organizations use the group conference for training, problem solving, and other tasks. In this section we briefly describe good conference behaviour and summarize the useful roles participants can play. You'll find these principles useful in any conference and certainly in collaborative writing.

Conference Behaviour

A good group conference is a pleasure to observe. A bad conference distresses participants and observers alike. In a bad group conference, the climate is defensive. Group members feel insecure, constantly fearing a personal attack and preparing to defend themselves. The leader of a bad conference can't talk without pontificating: Advice is given as though from on high. The group punishes members who deviate from the majority will. As a result, ideas offered are tired and trite. Creative ideas are rejected. People compete for status and control, and they consider the rejection of their ideas a personal insult. They attack those who reject their contributions. Everyone goes on the defensive, and energy that should be focused on the group's task flows needlessly in endless debate. As a rule, the leader ends up dictating the solutions, perhaps what was wanted all along.

In a good group conference, the climate is permissive and supportive. Members truly listen to one another. People assert their own ideas, but they do not censure the opinions of others. The general attitude is, "We have a task to do; let's get on with it." Members reward each other with compliments for good ideas and do not reject ideas because they are new and strange. When members do reject an idea, they do it gently with no hint of a personal attack on its originator. People feel free to operate in such a climate. They come forward with more and better ideas. They drop the defensive postures that waste so much energy and put the energy instead into the group's task.

How do members of a group arrive at such a supportive climate? To simplify things, we present a list of **dos** and **don'ts**. Our principles cannot guarantee a good conference, but if they are followed they can help contribute to a successful outcome.

Dos

- Do be considerate of others. Stimulate people to act rather than pressure them.
- Do be loyal to the conference leader without saying yes to everything. Do assert yourself when you have a contribution to make or when you disagree.
- Do support the other members of the group with compliments and friendliness.
- Do be aware that other people have feelings. Remember that participants with hurt feelings will drag their feet or actively disrupt a conference.
- Do have empathy for others in the group. See their point of view. Do not assume you know what they are saying or are going to say. Really listen and hear what they are saying.
- Do conclude contributions you make to a group by inviting criticism of them. Detach yourself from your ideas and see them objectively as you hope others will. Be ready to criticize your own ideas.
- Do understand that communication often breaks down. Do not be shocked when you are misunderstood or when you misunderstand others.
- Do feel free to disagree with the ideas of other group members, but never attack people personally for their ideas.
- Do remember that most ideas that are not obvious seem strange at first, yet they may be the best ideas.

Don'ts

- Don't try to monopolize or dominate a conference. The confident person feels secure and is willing to listen to the ideas of others. Confident people are not afraid to adopt the ideas of others in preference to their own, giving full credit when they do so.
- Don't continually play the expert. You will annoy other participants with constant advice and criticism based upon your expertise.
- Don't pressure people to accept your views.
- Don't make people pay for past mistakes with continuing punishment. Instead, change the situation to prevent future mistakes.
- Don't let personal arguments foul a meeting. Stop arguments before they reach the personal stage by rephrasing them in an objective way.

Perhaps the rule "Do unto others as you would have them do unto you" best summarizes all these rules. When you speak you want to be listened to. Listen to others.

Group Roles

You can play many roles in a group conference. Sometimes you bring new ideas before the group and urge their acceptance. Perhaps at other times you serve as information giver and at still others as harmonizer, resolving differences and smoothing ruffled egos. We describe these useful roles that you as a conference leader or member can play. We purposely do not distinguish between leader and member roles. In a well-run conference, an observer would have difficulty knowing who the leader is. We divide the roles into two groups: **task roles**, which move the group toward the accomplishment of its task; and **group maintenance roles**, which maintain the group in a harmonious working condition.

TASK ROLES   When you play a task role, you help the group accomplish its set task. Some people play one or two of these roles almost exclusively, but most people slide easily in and out of most of them.

- **Initiators** are the idea-givers, the starters. They move the group toward its task, perhaps by proposing or defining the task or by suggesting a solution to a problem or a way of arriving at the solution.
- **Information seekers** see where needed facts are thin or missing. They solicit the group for facts relevant to the task at hand.
- **Information givers** provide data and evidence relevant to the task. They may do so on their own or in response to the information seekers.
- **Opinion seekers** canvas group members for their beliefs and opinions concerning a problem. They might encourage the group to state the value judgments that underlie a particular proposal.
- **Opinion givers** volunteer their beliefs, judgments, and opinions to the group or respond readily to the opinion seekers. They help set the criteria for a problem solution.
- **Clarifiers** act when they see the group is confused about a member's contribution. They attempt to clear away the confusion by restating the contribution or by supplying additional relevant information, opinion, or interpretation.
- **Elaborators** further develop the contributions of others. They give examples, analogies, and additional information. They might carry a proposed solution to a problem into the future and speculate about how it would work.
- **Summarizers** draw together the ideas, opinions, and facts of the group into a coherent whole. They may state the criteria that a group has set or the solution to the problem agreed upon. Often, after a summary, they may call for the group to move on to the next phase of work.

GROUP MAINTENANCE ROLES When you play a group maintenance role, you help to build and maintain the supportive group climate. Some people are so task oriented that they ignore the feelings of others as they push forward to complete the task. Without the proper climate in a group, the members will often fail to complete their task.

- **Encouragers** respond warmly to the contributions of others. They express appreciation for ideas and reward participants by complimenting them. They go out of their way to encourage and reward the reticent members of the group when they do contribute.
- **Feeling expressers** sound out the group for its feelings. They sense when some members of the group are unhappy and get their feelings out in the open. They may do so by expressing the unhappiness as their own and thus encourage the others to come into the discussion.
- **Harmonizers** step between warring members of the group. They smooth ruffled egos and attempt to lift conflicts from the personality level and objectify them. With a neutral digression, they may lead the group away from conflict long enough for tempers to cool, allowing people to see the conflict objectively.
- **Compromisers** voluntarily withdraw their ideas or solutions in order to maintain group harmony. They freely admit error. With such actions, they build a climate in which participants do not think their status is riding on their every contribution.
- **Gatekeepers** are alert for blocked-out members of the group. They subtly swing the discussion away from the forceful members to the quiet ones and give them a chance to contribute.

Planning and Revision Checklists

The following questions are a summary of the key points in this chapter, and they provide a checklist for composing collaboratively. To be most effective, the questions in this checklist should be combined with the checklist questions following Chapter 2, "Composing." To help you use the two checklists together, we have combined Chapter 2 questions with the key questions from this list and printed them at the back of this book.

Planning

- Is the group using appropriate checklists to guide discussion?
- Has the group appointed a recorder to capture the group's ideas during the planning process?
- When planning is completed, does the group have an organizational plan sufficiently complete to serve as a basis for evaluation?
- How will the group approach the drafting stage?
  By dividing the work among different writers?
  By writing together as a group?
  By assigning the work to one person?

continued >>

- Has the group agreed on format elements such as spacing, typography, table and graph design, headings, and documentation?
- Has the group set deadlines for the work to be completed?
- If the group is using electronic communication, has the group agreed on a site and conventions for exchanging information?
- Should the group appoint a coordinator for the project?
- Are there people you should share your draft with? Supervisors? Peers? Members of the target audience?

Revision

- Are format elements such as headings, margins, spacing, typefaces, and documentation consistent throughout the document?
- Does the group have criteria by which to measure the effectiveness of the draft?
- Is the document accurate and ethical?
- Do people phrase their criticisms in an objective, positive way, avoiding personal and negative comments?
- Are the writers open to criticism of their work?
- Is the climate in the group supportive and permissive? Do members of the group play group maintenance roles as well as task roles, encouraging one another to express their opinions?

 ## Weblinks

Society for Technical Communication
www.stc.org

Strategies for Peer-Reviewing and Team Writing
www.io.com/~hcexres/tcm1693/acchtml/team.html

How to Create the Ideal Brainstorming Session
www.speaking.com/articles/articles,v/vangundyarticle1.html

Exercises

By following the techniques outlined in this chapter, groups could do most of the writing exercises in this book as collaborative exercises. For a warm–up exercise in working collaboratively, work through the following problem:

> **An executive in a client company has requested a definition of a technical term used in a document prepared by your consulting firm.**

a) Divide into groups of three to five people. Consider each group to be a small consulting firm.

CHAPTER 3 WRITING COLLABORATIVELY   49

b) As a group, decide what term you will be defining, then plan, draft, revise, and edit an extended definition (see Chapter 6, "Arrangement Strategies") in a memo format (see Chapter 11, "Correspondence") for the client.

c) Following the completion of the memo, critique your group's performance. Before beginning the critique, appoint a recorder to summarize the critique.

- How well did the members operate as a group?
- What methods did the group use to work together to analyse purpose and audience and to discover its material?
- What technique did the group use to draft its memo?
- Was the group successful in maintaining harmony while carrying out its task?
- What trouble spots emerged?
- What conclusions did the group reach that will help future collaborative efforts?

d) Have the recorders summarize the groups' performances for the class. Using the summaries as a starting point, hold a class discussion on collaborative writing.

WRITING FOR YOUR READERS

Point of View

Lay People
Executives
Experts
Technicians

Providing Needed Background

Defining Terms
Explaining Concepts

Helping Readers Through Your Report

Be Directive
Provide an Appropriate Context
Organize Around Audience Reading Habits

Style

Plain Language
Human Interest
Technical Shorthand
Qualifications

Graphics

Discourse Communities

The Combined Audience

Illustrative Example
Other Situations

International Readers

Cultural Differences
Dealing with Cultural Differences

In Chapter 2, "Composing," we tell you how and why to analyse your readers. In this chapter we provide you with some ways to use that analysis to plan strategies for communicating successfully with your readers. Consider what their point of view is: What will be their concerns and interests when they read what you write? What do your readers already know or not know? Are they highly knowledgeable in your subject matter or not? Do they already have a good grasp of the technical vocabulary and concepts you will use or not?

What are their reading habits? When you have answers to such questions, you will be better prepared to consider matters such as these:

- Satisfying your readers' points of view
- Providing needed background
- Helping readers through your document
- Choosing an effective style
- Choosing appropriate graphics
- Adapting to discourse communities
- Writing for combined audiences

Point of View

One of the most important audience characteristics is their point of view. Why are they reading your document? What is their purpose? What are their expectations? Using point of view as your criterion, you can break audiences down into four convenient categories: lay people, executives, experts, and technicians. Do understand, though, that these categories, while a convenient starting point, are something of a fiction. As you will see as you read the chapter, some executives are close to being lay people, others closer to experts, and so forth. But thinking in terms of these four categories will help you analyse any audience.

Lay People

Who are lay people? They are fourth-graders learning how the moon causes solar eclipses. They are the bank clerk reading a Sunday newspaper story about genetic engineering and the biologist reading an article in *Scientific American* titled "The Nature of Metals." In short, we are all lay people when we are outside our own particular fields of specialization.

Most lay people have at least a high school diploma. In 1991, 16.6% of Canadian adults had a university degree—a higher proportion than that of all other OECD countries, with the exception of the United States. Another 15% had a non-university higher education. In percentage of young adults enrolled in university, Canada led the top ten OECD countries.[1] Despite these encouraging statistics, some studies indicate that as many as 2.9 million adult Canadians read at only marginal levels. They have difficulty reading things such as newspapers, bus schedules, and catalogues. Another 4 million cannot cope with complex reading material.[2] Many high school graduates and even university or college graduates have only a smattering of mathematics and science and are a little vague about both subjects.

Although lay people represent a wide range of educational levels, most lay readers have a similar point of view. They read for interest. They read to understand the world in which they live. In these days of environmental concern and consumerism, they may be reading as a prelude to action.

Lay people are generally much more concerned with what things do than how they work. Their interest is personal. What impact will this new development have on them? They are more interested in the fact that wide-spread computer networks may invade their privacy than the fact that computers work on a binary number system. They are more interested in the safety, efficiency, and cost of nuclear waste disposal than in the technical details of such disposal.

Executives

In general, executives are the managers, supervisors, administrators, and decision makers of an organization. Legislators, granting agency reviewers, high school principals, and farmers, as well as chief executive officers, function as executives. Although most executives have university or college degrees and many have technical experience, they represent many disciplines, not necessarily including the one you are writing about. Some executives may have training in management, accounting, a social science, or the humanities, but little or no technical background. What are their concerns and interests?

Executives want to know how technological developments will affect the development of their companies. Although executives resemble lay readers in many ways, there is also a significant difference between them. What lay people read influences their lives and their decisions, but they only occasionally have to act directly upon it. Executives, however, must often make decisions based upon what they read. People and profits figure largely in executive decisions.

Executives must also consider the social, economic, and environmental effects of their decisions upon the community. Aesthetics, public health and safety, and conservation are key factors, and few executives would consider a report complete if it did not deal with them. All this means that executives are usually more interested in the implications of data than in the data themselves.

What questions do executives want you to answer in a report written for them? They want to know how a new process or piece of equipment can be used. What new markets will it open up? What will it cost, and why is the cost justified? What are the alternatives?

Why did you choose the new equipment over the other alternatives? Give some information about the also-rans. Convince the executive that you have explored the problem thoroughly. For all the alternatives, include comments on cost, size of the project, time to completion, future costs in upkeep and replacement, and the effects on productivity, efficiency, and profits. Consider such aspects as new staffing, competition, experimental results, and potential problems. What are the risks involved? What environmental impact will this new development have? Figure 4-1 lists the information executives feel they need in a report.

Experts, in particular, often find writing for executives a difficult task. Experts are often most interested in methodology and theory. As Professor Mary Coney points out, executives are more interested in function. Excerpts from a salmon study done for a northern fisheries department illustrate the frame of mind the expert researcher should have while writing for the

Problems

What is it?
Why undertaken?
Magnitude and importance?
What is being done? By whom?
Approaches used?
Thorough and complete?
Suggested solution? Best? Consider
  others?
What now?
Who does it?
Time factors?

New Projects and Products

Potential?
Risks?
Scope of application?
Commercial implications?
Competition?
Importance to company?
More work to be done? Any problems?
Required labour, facilities, and
  equipment?
Relative importance to other projects
  or products?
Life of project or product line?
Effect on company's technical position?
Priorities required?
Proposed schedule?
Target date?

Tests and Experiments

What tested or investigated?

Why? How?
What did it show?
Better ways?
Conclusions? Recommendations?
Implications to Company?

Materials and Processes

Properties, characteristics,
  capabilities?
Limitations?
Use requirements and environment?
Areas and scope of application?
Cost factors?
Availability and sources?
What else will do it?
Problems in using?
Significance of application to
  company?

**Field Troubles and
Special Design Problems**

Specific equipment involved?
What trouble developed? Any trouble
  history?
How much involved?
Responsibility? Others? Company?
What is needed?
Special requirements and environment?
Who does it? Time factors?
Most practical solution? Recommended
  action?
Suggested product design changes?

Figure 4-1   WHAT MANAGERS WANT TO KNOW

Source: James W. Souther, "What to Report," *IEEE Transactions on Professional Communication* PC-28 (1985): 6.

executive. In the introduction, the researcher poses the questions that will be answered in the report. They are the questions an executive would ask:

> Why have they gone? Can the runs be restored to any significant degree? Is it reasonable to base a large industry on the harvest cycle of a wild resource? What should be done? What should be done now?[3]

The stated purpose of the report further reassures the executive that the researcher is on the right track:

> Our approach has been first to gather and understand as much relevant information as could reasonably be found; and then to organize, interpret, and project toward the goal of defining a conceptual framework for successful [governmental] actions.[4]

Here it is obvious that scientific findings will be wedded to executive needs. Function—successful action—lies at the heart of the report.

Experts

Who are experts? For our purposes we will define **experts** as people with either a master's degree or a doctorate in their fields or a bachelor's degree and years of experience, such as professors, industrial researchers, and engineers who design and build. They know their fields intimately. Experts are very concerned with how and why things work. They want to see the theoretical calculations and the results of basic research. They want your observations, your facts—what you have seen, what you have measured. They expect you to work your way through your data and your interpretation of those data to your conclusions. In reporting such things, be as complete as time, space, and human patience allow. Modern technology and science depend upon many people cooperatively accumulating facts, many of which seem trivial standing alone.

Technicians

Technicians are at the heart of any operation. They are the people who build, maintain, and operate equipment. Technicians' educational credentials vary widely, ranging anywhere from a high school diploma to university degrees. They may have been trained in a vocational school. The high school graduate may have a great deal of on-the-job training and experience. The university graduate may be better educated about theory but have less practical experience.

Because technicians build, maintain, and operate equipment, their major concern is with how-to information. How do I use this word processing program? How do I operate this lathe? How do I replace the fuel pump in this engine? And so forth.

Although technical audiences care more about how-to information and the practical application of a theory than about the theory itself, they will appreciate some theory. How much theory you give, and how complex you make it, depends on their education and their point of view. College- or university-educated technicians, or those with extensive experience, border on being experts, and you can treat them much as you would an expert. Less expert technicians or people operating as technicians in areas outside their major interest require much less theory. For example, a college professor installing a new washer in her kitchen sink faucet is acting as a technician but would probably not desire much background theory about plumbing.

Providing Needed Background

Without sufficient background, readers will not be able to comprehend and absorb your material. For example, most North American readers of this book know enough about baseball to comprehend a sentence such as "Casey hit Cohen's high hard one down the right field line, moving Morrisey from first to third." North American readers have what reading experts call a *schema* upon which to hang the sentence. That is, they can visualize the baseball field. They know that Casey has to be the batter at home plate and Cohen has to be the pitcher. They know where the right field line is and that it is far enough away from third base to allow Morrisey to gain a few steps on the throw from right field. All that is a lot to know, but readers with the appropriate baseball schema can easily organize and integrate the new information in the sentence into their knowledge. Readers without the appropriate schema can make little sense of the sentence and will not absorb the information in it.

Consider the schema your audience possesses. To give any audience the schema they need, you may have to define terms and explain concepts.

Defining Terms

Although we learn our professional language long after we have acquired our common, everyday language, it becomes such a part of our life that we often forget that others don't share it with us. We forget that we possess both a common language that we share with others and a professional language that we share with a much smaller group. In reaching out to your audience, you must remember that you may need to define specialized terms. You are the host when you write. You have invited your readers to come to you. You owe them every courtesy, and defining difficult terms is a courtesy. If you force your readers to the dictionary every fourth line, their interest will soon flag.

Depending upon the needs of the audience, terms can be defined briefly, often by the substitution of more familiar terms, or at greater length. The following definition of *lidar* from a National Museum of Science and Technology *SkyNews* article combines both techniques. To explain how "the world's biggest thermometer" enables atmospheric physicist Robert Sica and other scientists of the University of Western Ontario's Space and Atmospheric Research Group to measure the impact of global warming, the writer has used brief definitions consisting of familiar terms. Notice that in some brief definitions the word defined precedes the familiar form and in others the familiar term precedes the word defined. Notice also that the definition proceeds from familiar things such as *light* and *radar* to the unfamiliar, such as *Raleigh scattering*.

> To do this work, Western has built the world's largest lidar (**l**ight **d**etecting **a**nd **r**anging), a cousin of radar (**ra**dio **d**etecting **a**nd **r**anging). To "see" an object, radar emits a radio signal that reflects off the target and is captured by a receiver. Lidar works in exactly the same way except that invisible light is substituted for the radio signal.
>
> Lidar uses a high-powered green laser as its light source and Western's 2.7-metre liquid-mirror telescope, the largest of its type in Canada, as the receiver. By measuring how laser light scatters off air molecules (called Raleigh scattering), Sica can get temperature readings for the entire middle atmosphere, from 30 to 100 kilometres above the Earth's surface.[5]

Be careful not to distort the true meaning of terms if you substitute more common terms for technical language. One researcher, for example, felt his work was distorted by this lead in a newspaper story:

A research group reported Friday that marijuana causes chimpanzees to overesti-mate the passage of time, and a single dose can keep them befuddled for up to three days.

The researcher commented:

The term "befuddle" was not employed in our scientific report, and the statement in the news article "and a single dose can keep them befuddled for up to three days" is erroneous and misleading. Three days were required to recover normal baseline per-formance following administration of high doses.[6]

Scientists choose words very precisely and for good reason. Although scientific findings must be interpreted for nonscientific readers, to distort or to sensationalize their work is a disservice to them and to the reader.

The need for definition varies from audience to audience. Audiences with a weak schema may need many words defined. Those with a strong schema need few definitions. To define a word that a reader already knows would be a mistake, but scientific and technical vocabularies are constantly growing. If you are using words that you think any audience may not know, even one that shares your professional knowledge, don't hesitate to define. (See Chapter 6, "Arrangement Strategies.")

Explaining Concepts

The scientific world is full of complex concepts that your readers may or may not comprehend. For example, expert geologists understand the concept of plate tectonics. Nongeologists may not; for them, a writer would have to explain that the land masses of our planet float on plates that are slowly but inexorably moving. One plate crushing against another can cause earth-quakes and raise mountains. The subcontinent of India, in crushing against Asia, raised the Himalayan Mountains. Plate action along the west coast of North America causes earthquakes and volcanic activity.

One way to help a reader visualize a concept is through analogy. In analogy you move from the familiar to the unfamiliar. For example, to help readers understand the slowness with which lithospheric plates move (2–3 cm a year), you could tell them that hair grows about five times as fast. For readers who have difficulty grasping the enormity of geologic time compared to a human life span, you can provide an analogy like this one: If the time that the earth has existed is seen as the height of the CN Tower, then the time of human existence would be comparable to a penny on top of the structure.

Analogy can be useful even when writing for the technical audience. Analogy bridges the gap between a reader's general information and the particular object or theory you are trying to explain. An excerpt from a *Bell Laboratories Record* article on waveguides illustrates the principle:

Every electron orbiting about an atomic nucleus gives rise to magnetic fields. In some materials the field comes largely from the motion of the electron around the nucleus, but in ferromagnetic materials it depends more on the spin associated with the elec-tron itself. The spin creates a small magnetic movement that is precisely aligned with the axis of spin (this can be visualized as similar to the alignment of the earth's magnetic field between the north and south poles.)[7]

As with definitions, some audiences need many concepts explained in order to develop the necessary schema; others need few or none explained. Your audience analysis should tell you how much explanation you have to give any audience.

Helping Readers Through Your Report

Readers need help in getting through written reports—even very good readers. The more new information a document provides, the tougher it is for the reader. You can help readers by being directive, by providing an appropriate context for your material, and by organizing around your audience's reading habits.[8]

Be Directive

Direct your readers through your documents. Provide them with a road map by including sufficient introductions, transitions, summaries, and the like. A longer document needs a set of headings consistently applied and probably a table of contents. Design your document so that your reader comes to know where certain information is presented and how it is presented. For example, the planning and revision checklists in this book are all bulleted lists that come just before the Weblinks and exercises at the end of the chapters. After reading a few chapters, you have learned where to look for them.

You will find instruction about designing documents in Chapter 8, "Document Design." In Chapter 9, "Design Elements," you'll find the information you need to prepare introductions, summaries, conclusions, headings, and the like.

Provide an Appropriate Context

Readers don't read words or sentences in isolation. They understand what they are reading by relating the passage to those that have gone before or that come later. That is, they understand what they are reading by putting it in context. Two ways you can help readers put a passage into an appropriate context are by moving from the familiar to the unfamiliar and, particularly in instructions, by providing the reason for an action before describing the action.

In the following example, the writer begins with glacial deposition, a form of deposition familiar to his readers. The writer then uses glacial deposition to help the readers understand beach deposition. In the fourth paragraph the writer uses beach deposition, now familiar to his readers, to introduce river and delta deposition:

> From the nature and distribution of glacial deposits, geologists have formed a picture of what the earth looked like during a glacial event.
>
> In the same manner, geologists have recognized rocks that were once ancient beach deposits because most beaches are composed of well-sorted sand. The action of

waves along the shores of ancient seas washed out the silt and clay and left behind rounded grains of sand, just like those along present shorelines.

Offshore, where the bottom waters are calmer, the finer sediment settles as mud. In a general way, the size of the sediment grains shows the direction of slope in the sea floor, because the sandy sediment will be near the shore and the mud will be offshore. The same principle of sorting also applies to ancient rocks; marine sandstones and conglomerates were formed closer to shore than were the finer textured marine shales and siltstones.

The same concept of sorting can be used with nonmarine formations, such as river and delta deposits.[9]

When reading instructions, readers expect the reason for an action to be given before the action. Because the following passage inverts that order, it frustrates the reader's expectations:

Drag the image of the disk into the trash to eject the disk.

The following is the order the reader expects:

To eject the disk, drag the image of the disk into the trash.

In Chapter 5, "Achieving a Readable Style," we discuss other ways to make a document more readable.

Organize Around Audience Reading Habits

Readability authorities have classified the way people read into five methods:[10]

- **Skimming:** Going through a document very quickly, mainly to get a general idea of its nature and contents
- **Scanning:** Reading rapidly to find specific needed facts or conclusions, such as looking only for financial information in a report
- **Search reading:** Scanning, but slowed down so as to pick up more of the content
- **Receptive reading:** Reading at whatever speed is necessary for high comprehension
- **Critical reading:** Reading to evaluate the document and its contents

Analyse your own reading habits. When you are reading a newspaper, you probably skim, scan, or search. When you find a story that interests you, you switch over to receptive reading. When you have as much information as you need or want from the article, you are likely to scan or search the rest of it quickly to see if you need or want anything else from it. News stories are structured to allow you to do precisely that. They begin with the journalist's *who, what, when, where,* and *why.* The rest of the story provides additional detail. When you have all the detail you want, you can quit reading and still have the gist of the story.

Because writers for popular magazines such as *Canadian Geographic* and *Maclean's* know that people scan the publication looking for articles that interest them, they often include an interest-catching introduction like this one from an article about global warming:

Imagine a world of relentlessly rising temperatures, where farmlands are scorched into desert and inland waters like the Great Lakes shrink in the heat. As global warming intensifies, the polar ice caps dissolve and ocean levels rise by more than 100 feet, swamping low-lying islands and coastal areas. Vancouver, Halifax, New York City, Amsterdam, Shanghai and other port cities are inundated. As the global floodwaters rise, more than a quarter of the world's population is displaced. Take the nightmarish vision a little further and it becomes the weird scenario conjured by Kevin Costner's overbudget movie-in-progress Waterworld—the human race clinging to survival in an oceanic habitat. And so it must all be fiction, right? Not necessarily. Plenty of scientists believe that the growing accumulation of manmade gases in the Earth's atmosphere could someday push temperatures to dangerously high levels and bring cataclysmic changes to the planet. And after a year that has seen unseasonably warm weather in some places, violent flooding in others and an ice shelf crumbling in the Antarctic, some scientists think that fundamental climate change is no longer just a possibility—it might be happening now.[11]

If the writer can grab your interest in the introduction, you are more likely to continue reading.

Professor James Souther, who researched the reading habits of executives, reported that executive reading habits are surprisingly similar.[12] Professor Souther's research seems to indicate that executives most often skim, scan, and search read. They are likely to read receptively or critically only in such sections as introductions, summaries, and conclusions. Professor Souther reports that "All managers said they read the *abstract*; most said they read the *introduction* and *background* sections as well as the sections containing *conclusions* and *recommendations* to gain a better perspective of the material being reported and to find an answer to that all-important question—'What do we do next?'"[13]

Organize your executive reports so that your readers can easily find the sections they want. Be directive, providing good introductions, transitions, headings, and summaries. Executives expect to see conclusions and recommendations early in a report with the justification following. If you feel you must report a large amount of technical data, put the data in an appendix where executives can read them if they want to (or assign experts to read them). Managers seldom read the body and appendices of reports. When they do, it is because, as Professor Souther reports, they are "especially interested ... deeply involved ... forced to read by the urgency of the problem," or "skeptical" of the writer's conclusions.[14] Figure 4-2 illustrates how managers read reports.

When writing for executives, you should give your conclusions and recommendations clearly. In writing a report for an executive, interpret your material and present its implications—don't just give the facts. James Souther points out that in executive reports, the professional judgment of the writer should be the focal point. "True," Professor Souther writes, "it is judgment based on objective study and evaluation of the evidence; but it is judgment nevertheless."[15] The researcher who amasses huge amounts of detail but neglects to state the implications, conclusions, and recommendations that follow from the facts has failed to do the complete job.

People reading in fields where they have expert or technical knowledge have a greater tolerance for data than do people reading as lay people

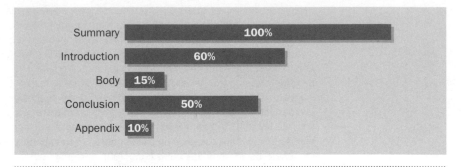

Figure 4-2 HOW MANAGERS READ REPORTS

Source: James W. Souther, "What to Report," *IEEE Transactions on Professional Communication* PC-28 (1985): 6.

or executives, and are more inclined to read receptively. However, because of the enormous amounts of information available in most fields, experts and technicians have also become scanners and search readers. Research indicates that experts review reports quickly to see whether the reports contain needed information. In their review, the experts depend upon, in order of importance, the *summary, conclusions, abstract, title page,* and *introduction.*[16] Therefore, these components must be carefully written in expert reports. As in executive reports, make information accessible through the use of headings.

Technicians scan instruction manuals looking for needed information, rather than reading the manual in sequence. Therefore, manual writers provide directive devices such as tables of contents and headings to allow their readers to read selectively.

Style

Choose a writing style that matches the reading ability and technical knowledge of your audience. For instance, when writing for a nontechnical audience, avoid the more complex sentence structures and technical vocabulary that might be appropriate for an audience that shares your knowledge. Whoever your audience is, you should be no more complicated than necessary.

Plain Language

Use plain language. Some scientific specialties are loaded with mathematics. Others, such as biochemistry, are full of formulas, complicated charts, and diagrams incomprehensible to lay people. Equations, formulas, and diagrams are useful shorthand expressions for experts. They convey information with a precision impossible to obtain in any other way. But what experts sometimes forget are the years they spent learning how to handle such precise tools. The average person, lacking those years of training, often cannot understand them. When you write for people who don't share your knowledge, you must express your ideas in plain language.

In Chapter 5, "Achieving a Readable Style," we discuss how to achieve a style that aids rather than impedes understanding. The example that follows illustrates that style. It is from an Ontario Hydro pamphlet that explains ionizing radiation. To give background information about radiation, the writer uses a vocabulary suited to his audience—lay people with a good general reading level—and well-constructed sentences of a reasonable length. He completes his explanation with examples that supply comparisons familiar to his readers.

All matter on earth—gases, liquids and solids—is composed of invisible building blocks called atoms. There are 92 different naturally occurring types of atoms called elements—from atoms of hydrogen (the lightest) to atoms of uranium (the heaviest). Atoms of different elements can bind together to form substances quite unlike the originals. Two atoms of hydrogen, bound to one atom of oxygen, for example, become a molecule of water.

The atoms of most elements, such as iron, are stable and unchanging over time, but the atoms of some elements—radium, uranium and others—do change. These unstable atoms are radioactive.

While atoms are the building blocks of matter, they are themselves made up of three types of smaller particles—protons, neutrons and electrons—arranged like a miniature solar system. In the centre, or nucleus, are the protons and neutrons. The electrons orbit the nucleus.

This arrangement is well balanced, or stable, in the atoms of most elements. In an unstable atom, however, too much energy is packed in the nucleus. In an attempt to become more stable, an unstable nucleus emits particles and energy until it becomes stable. This process is called radioactive decay, and the emission of particles or energy produces ionizing radiation.

Ionizing radiation is named for its ability to cause a molecule it hits to become electrically charged, or ionized. Living cells may be damaged or killed if they absorb enough ionizing radiation.

Ionizing radiation is emitted mainly in the form of alpha particles, beta particles and/or gamma rays. These different types of radiation have very different properties. For example, alpha particles are large and cannot penetrate even a thin sheet of paper or a few millimetres of air. Beta particles are more penetrating, but can be stopped by several millimetres of plywood or a few metres of air. Gamma rays are very penetrating, but their intensity can be reduced by a metre of concrete or three metres of water.

In addition to nuclear decay, ionizing radiation is produced by X-ray machines and other specialized equipment.[17]

Human Interest

Human interest serves two purposes when you are writing for lay people: It motivates people to read and it seems to help them retain more of what they read.

You often have to motivate lay people to read. Most of us, at any educational level, have an interest in other human beings and in human personalities. Most writers for lay audiences recognize this interest and use it to gain acceptability for their subject matter. For example, an article in *Maclean's* about farm problems will give us statistical information about the number of farmers losing their farms. But the writer of the article knows that many of us do not relate very well to bare, abstract statistics. Therefore, the writer will also usually introduce people into the article. Perhaps Arnie and Olga Hrabluk and their two children, a "typical" farm family living in Alberta, will be described. We'll learn what effect losing their farm has had on their lives. We are interested in learning about what happens to real people, and through such knowledge we can better understand the farm problem.

In the following example, notice how the introduction to an article on why mosquitoes find some Canadians tastier than others uses human drama to capture the reader's interest:

> They stand in the woods clad in coveralls and head nets, sucking mosquitoes off their arms and blowing them into little vials. While most people spend a good portion of their summertime trying to repel the nasty things, at "biting fly centres" the objective is to attract the bloodsuckers.
>
> And with each little red welt, researchers come a bit closer to figuring out why mosquitoes do what they do and to whom—and which repellents are most effective.
>
> Last week, six hungry Guelph grad students, getting $30 for about two hours work, let themselves be fed on by even hungrier mosquitoes, all in the name of science. Working for 16 five-minute sessions, sleeve rolled to the elbow, they suck up the mosquitoes as they land on their arms, then blow them into a vial so they can be counted later. A screen prevents unintentional swallowing.
>
> Entomology graduate student Robbin Lindsay, originally from Winnipeg, lucked out the first day—he was one of the subjects who was treated with repellent and only suffered 28 bites compared with the 550 the untreated guinea pigs received. "I was making fun of them but I'll pay my dues," Mr. Lindsay says. During the six-day trial everyone goes untreated at least twice, "but it's really not that bad. Over the course of the six-day study at the most you'll get 1500 bites. Coming from Winnipeg, you probably get 1500 bites over the course of the summer anyway."
>
> While money is the main motive for signing up to be bitten, Mr. Lindsay says most of the graduate students have an interest in the field and an appreciation of the work being done.
>
> In addition to testing various repellents, University of Guelph researcher Jamie Heal and Dr. Gord Surgeoner hope to test a couple of theories about what characteristics are most attractive to bugs looking for a snack.
>
> If they're right, it's bad news for tall, fidgety people. Mr. Heal says he and Dr. Surgeoner noticed differences in who the bugs eat while doing other repellent experiments. So they decided to try to prove it during this round of repellent testing.
>
> While tall people provide a bigger visual target for the pests, standing head and shoulders above the crowd, they also breathe out more carbon dioxide, which attracts the bugs. People who move around a lot also expel more carbon dioxide and have a higher body temperature, both factors in luring the mini-vampires, Mr. Heal says.[18]

The technique involved in this excerpt is explained by the editor of a science magazine designed for a lay audience:

> We stress readability and the quality and freshness of the writing over content because we think the first imperative is that people actually read the article—not a trivial task when you are trying to interest two million very different people in the complexities of

cosmology or molecular biology. We also think that what most people carry away from a popular magazine article is a rough sense of the subject, not the details. So we emphasize the cultural context, the human impact, the anecdotal example, precisely because they contribute more to that lingering impression and are more important to the lives of our readers than the detailed physics or the viral mechanisms, however scientifically elegant.[19]

In addition to motivating people to read, human interest also seems to improve readers' retention of what they read. In one experiment, *Time-Life* editors were asked to rewrite a passage from a high school history text. They introduced what they called "nuggets" into the passage, that is, anecdotes and stories about historical people. The result: student recall rose from 20% on the original passage to 60% on the rewritten one. Other research indicates that examples, questions, elaborations, and summaries all improve reader recall.[20]

While providing human interest and perhaps even human drama, be careful not to exaggerate scientific achievements. Journalists who write stories about scientific achievements sometimes forget this need for caution, to the dismay of the scientists involved. A newspaper story concerning research on the skin ailment psoriasis carried this headline: "Psoriasis Cure Breakthrough Seen." The lead of the story announced, "Scientists Wednesday announced a breakthrough in treating psoriasis, the skin disease which causes misery for about 6 million Americans." The scientist involved criticized the story, saying that nowhere in the report presented by the scientists was the word *breakthrough* used. He concluded by saying, "The last sentence of our write-up said cure of psoriasis is probably 50 years away. Yet the title of this article you sent says 'Psoriasis Cure Breakthrough Seen.' All I can say is [censored]!"[21]

Technical Shorthand

When you are writing for people who share your technical knowledge, you may use any shorthand methods—such as abbreviations, mathematical equations, chemical formulas, and scientific terms—that you are sure your audience will comprehend. Complicated formulas and equations needed to support the conclusions, but not essential for understanding them, are often placed in an appendix rather than the body of the report.

Where possible, use the standard abbreviations and symbols for your field, as defined by the authorities in that field. Nonstandard symbols should be defined as in this example:

> From Einstein's mass-energy equation, one can write the relations:
>
> $E(Btu) = m (lb) \times 3.9 \times 10$
>
> m being the loss of mass.[22]

The writer does not define *E, Btu*, and *lb* because these are standard symbols and abbreviations for *energy, British thermal units*, and *pounds*. He does define *m* because it is not standard. Writers who do not define nonstandard symbols cannot expect readers to know what they are. In fact, in a few years, returning to their own reports, *they* may not know what the symbols mean. Symbols and abbreviations may be defined as they are used, or if there are many of them, they can be defined in a glossary at the front of the report. (See Chapter 9, "Design Elements.")

Qualifications

Technical reports are, of course, not merely calculations and facts. Technical people as well as executives want your inferences and conclusions. When you draw inferences from your facts and observations, be sure to make no unwarranted leaps. Stay within the bounds of the scientific method. In presenting your conclusions, be careful that your language shows where you are certain and where you are in doubt. In the interests of scientific honesty and caution, most expert discussions and conclusions contain qualifications as well as positive statements. The following excerpt, reporting research to see if time of day affects the adaptive response to exercise, is an example of the balance between positive statements and qualified statements that is typical of scientific style (we have removed the footnotes and have underlined the qualifiers):

> Our data <u>indicate</u> that the training effect is affected by time of day.
>
> The afternoon training was most effective in increasing VO_{2max} and adaptive response of heart rate among the three groups, and also showed an improved blood lactate response to exercise. Although there have been many studies of circadian rhythm or diurnal variations in response to exercise, this is the first report that shows the existence of diurnal variation in the training effect.
>
> <u>It is difficult to explain</u> why afternoon training was most effective because the training effect, represented by an increase in VO_{2max}, is the sum of numerous physiological processes. Diurnal variations in responses to exercise have been identified in measurements of body temperature as it relates to metabolism and in measurements of products of the neurohormonal system such as cortisol, renin, and catecholamine. <u>There is a possibility</u> that these factors together with other unknown factors may play different roles in the diurnal variation of training effects. In addition, our results <u>suggest a possibility</u> that heart rate and blood lactate levels may exhibit different patterns of responses to exercise that depend on the time of day. Most adaptation in heart rate occurred in the afternoon and morning groups, while most adaptation in blood lactate levels occurred in the evening followed by afternoon groups.[23]

Some people object to the amount of qualification in a scientific style. We agree that some writers of scientific reports are too timid in stating their conclusions. Nevertheless, scientists know that certainty in science is a hard-won achievement. They are content with probabilities until thorough experimentation and observation remove all reasonable doubt. Their style reflects their basic caution and honesty.

Graphics

Graphs and tables are essential to most technical reports. Earlier we explained the concept of plate tectonics. To help you visualize that concept, we can provide a visual, as in Figure 4-3, that shows one crust sliding under another.

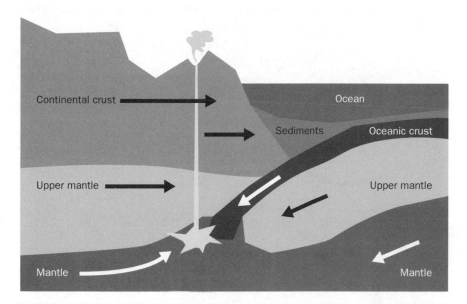

Figure 4-3 CROSS-SECTION OF OCEANIC CRUST SLIDING UNDER CONTINENTAL CRUST
Source: Ontario Ministry of Northern Development and Mines, ROCK ONtario (1994): 11.

SNOW BOX SCORE			
	Average annual snowfall (cm)	*Number of snowy days*	*Total Snowfall (cm) on snowiest day*
Eureka	44	46	15
Resolute	84	82	13
Inuvik	177	99	44
Yellowknife	135	82	28
Baker Lake	100	73	30
Victoria	50	13	53
Regina	116	58	28
Montréal	235	62	41
Halifax	271	64	48
Windsor	117	45	37

Figure 4-4 A SIMPLE TABLE
Source: The Climates of Canada (Ottawa: Ministry of Supply and Services Canada, 1990): 148. Reprinted with the permission of the Minister of Public Works and Government Services Canada, 1998.

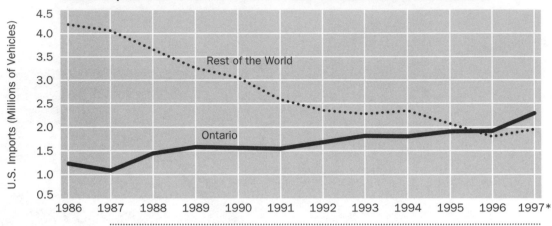

Figure 4-5 A SIMPLE GRAPH

Source: 1997 Ontario Economic Outlook and Fiscal Review (Ministry of Finance, ©
Queen's Printer for Ontario, 1997): 16. Reproduced with permission.

You can use graphics to illustrate concepts and processes, show trends and
relationships, and summarize material. You can use graphics to interest your
readers as well as to inform and explain. You can use bar charts in place of equations to explain mathematical concepts or in place of formulas for chemical
concepts. Or you can combine tables and pictographs that establish facts, formulas, or definitions quickly, clearly, and in a way that interests readers.

Be sure to use graphics suited to your audience. For readers not expert in
reading graphics, use simple tables and graphs, as in Figures 4-4 and 4-5.
For more expert readers of graphics, you can use more complex tables and

Table 2 Characteristics of Engine Operating Pattern								
Name of Pattern	**Operating Time (sec)**	**Equivalent Driving Distance (km)**	**Average Speed (km/h)**	**Ratio of 4 mode (time %)**				**Total Work (kWh)**
				Idling	**Acceleration**	**Cruising**	**Deceleration**	
F20	789	4.726	21.56	34.7	24.9	17.7	22.7	5.79
F40	806	8.870	39.32	13	25.6	38.4	23	8.68
HW1	766	15.290	71.86	2.7	7.8	82	7.5	14.93
High speed Mode	725	Max. Engine Speed 2500rpm	Max. Engine Torque 65kgm	0	0	100	0	19.92

Figure 4-6 A COMPLEX TABLE

Source: Matsuo Odaka and Noriyuki Koike (Ministry of Transport, Japan); Yoshito
Hijikata and Toshihide Miyajima (Hino Motors, Ltd.), "Energy Regeneration of
Heavy Duty Diesel Powered Vehicles," SAE Technical Paper Series # 980891 (SAE
International: Detroit, Michigan: 1998): 16. Reprinted from *Technology for Electric and
Hybrid Vehicles (SP-1331)*. Reproduced with permission © 1998 Society of
Automotive Engineers, Inc.

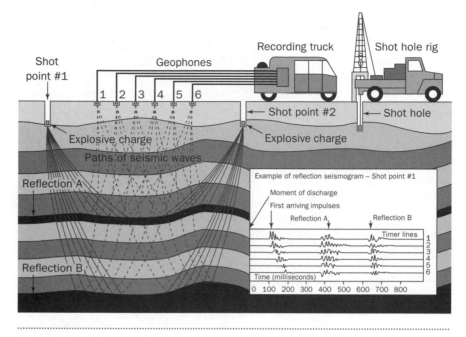

Figure 4-7   A COMPLEX GRAPHIC

Source: The Petroleum Resources Communication Foundation, *Our Petroleum Challenge: The New Era* (Calgary: PRCF): 27.

graphs, as in Figures 4-6 and 4-7. See Chapter 10, "Graphical Elements," for help in choosing and designing graphics suitable to your audience.

Discourse Communities

Discourse communities are communities in which people hold common ideas of what good discourse is. Within a given discourse community, members agree to a large extent about what information is important to them, what style is most acceptable, what lines of argument are most persuasive.[24] The organization for which you work may have a corporate style. As a member of that organization's discourse community, you will be expected to use that style. Various scientific disciplines are discourse communities in themselves. Some are rather plain spoken; others tend toward wordiness and excessive formality. For better or worse, scientists in these disciplines are expected to understand and use the prevailing style.

Most people belong to more than one discourse community. For example, an accountant who works for an insurance company may also in her spare time be the treasurer of her local Big Sisters agency. At the insurance company, she may find it necessary to cultivate a courteous but brisk style. The emphasis in all her reports will be on a straightforward statement of data and the implications of those data. As a volunteer for Big Sisters, she may find it necessary to use a more indirect, less businesslike approach, perhaps more value oriented than money oriented.

In going from business to social agency, the accountant has crossed cultural boundaries. Not surprisingly, cultural boundaries exist between countries and regions of the world. Some of the basic differences in styles of communication among countries and cultures are discussed later in this chapter under International Readers. Should you find yourself writing for readers in a discourse community outside those cultures, you might have to modify our advice.

The Combined Audience

Some writing situations call for you to write to people who clearly belong to one particular audience category. Many more situations do not. Sometimes, one person can have characteristics of several audiences. For instance, someone may be reading about stereo speaker systems that can be installed in his house. He may be a lay person in that he doesn't understand all the electronic jargon. He may be an executive in the sense that he may make a decision about buying such equipment. He may be a technician in that he may install the equipment himself.

Your audience may be a team of executives, experts, and technicians. Most organizational documents have more than one reader. In this age of photocopiers and fax machines, many reports, letters, and memos are copied for people other than the primary reader. Also, reports and correspondence may have a longer life than you anticipate. They go into filing cabinets, where they become a part of organizational history. They may be read years later, perhaps as background to a new development or even as evidence in a trial. Thus, your life is frequently complicated by the need to consider several audiences at once. As in any communication situation, the strategy you choose must suit your purpose, audience, and material.

Illustrative Example

Imagine that you are a computer expert working for a large investment company. You have just completed a study to decide which of two computer systems to install at the company. Let's call them Brand X and Brand Y. The system is to be purchased for the use of the research division of the company. The information systems division (ISD), for which you work, will buy, install, and maintain the system.

You have determined that Brand X, even though it costs slightly more, is the system to buy. You have to write a report stating your conclusions and recommendations and justifying them. You have a combined audience of three people, all of them senior to you:

Eric Galloro. A vice president of the company. The research division is one of his responsibilities. You have heard that his major concern is always cost, and that he doesn't like to read long reports. He is the decision maker in this matter, but he is a team player. He will certainly confer with the other people concerned before making his decision.

Sally Kroger. Head of the ISD. She has a Ph.D. in computer science. She has been with ISD for 10 years and head for the last five. She is a stickler for detail and will want full justification for your conclusions and recommendations. She doesn't mind long reports; she even seems to prefer them.

Colin Lee. Head of the research division. He has been complaining that his staff do not have adequate computer support for their research activities. It is because of his complaints that you conducted your study. He has a master's degree in business administration. You talked to him a good deal when you were assessing the division's computer needs. You know that he uses computers and has a practical interest in them but that he has no interest in computer theory.

How to satisfy this diverse audience? You have stacks of information in front of you: masses of statistics concerning input, output, power, remote consoles, ease of use, available programs, and cost. You have brainstormed a series of pros and cons for each system. The pros and cons are helpful, but they don't lend themselves to a coherent report. Also, they get you into more detail than Eric Galloro or Colin Lee is likely to want.

You analyse the situation. You think about your audience and their true concerns. Eric Galloro will want to be sure that Colin Lee's complaints are taken care of. Also, he will need to be persuaded that the more expensive Brand X is the better choice. Colin Lee's major concern is that his needs will be satisfied. He will not care that the cost is higher for Brand X. Sally Kroger will be interested in cost, but it's not a vital factor for her. She will want to see that Lee's needs are satisfied. She also will be quite interested in a comparison of the maintenance requirements of the two systems.

Now you're getting somewhere. The major concerns for your audience seem to be cost, needs satisfaction, and maintenance. Because Brand X meets the needs of the research division so well and because of its superior maintenance record, you have chosen it over Brand Y despite its higher cost.

The organization of your report begins to fall into place. You decide that your report will have three sections: *cost, needs satisfaction,* and *maintenance.* The cost section can be straightforward and short, probably based largely on some comparison tables. The needs section will show how you assessed the needs of the research division and how Brand X satisfies those needs far better than does Brand Y. You have some good quotes from Colin Lee, which you can include in this section to show that he has been consulted. You remind yourself to keep this section free of computer jargon so that Colin Lee and Eric Galloro can read it.

The maintenance section is of major concern to Sally Kroger and will probably not even be read by Eric Galloro or Colin Lee. It's the section in which you can let yourself go with technical computer language and satisfy Sally's penchant for detail.

When the three sections are complete, you'll top them off with an *executive summary* that states your conclusions and recommendations and succinctly

Reader	Main Concern	Style
Eric Galloro (Decision maker)	Cost	Cost section: straightforward and short, based on comparison tables
Colin Lee (User)	Needs satisfaction	Needs satisfaction section: free of jargon, includes quotes
Sally Kroger (Information systems expert)	Maintenance	Maintenance section: detailed with technical language
Galloro, Lee, Kroger	Satisfying Eric Galloro	Executive summary: conclusions, recommendations, with supporting evidence

Figure 4-8   WRITING FOR A COMBINED AUDIENCE

supports them. (See Chapter 9, "Design Elements.") You suspect that the summary may be the only section Eric Galloro reads, so you remind yourself to make sure that the support for buying the more expensive Brand X is adequate to meet his skepticism. You will also direct your readers through all parts of the report with a good introduction, transitions, and headings.

Step back for a moment and see what you have done. As shown in Figure 4-8, you have considered the major concern of each reader and made sure that you have addressed it. You have satisfied the needs of *the decision maker*, Eric Galloro; *the user*, Colin Lee; and *the expert*, Sally Kroger. Because you know that executives scan reports and read them very selectively, you have organized and will format your report to make scanning easy.

Other Situations

Other situations may be more or less complex than the one we have described for you. For instance, you might need to write a short memo to a primary reader, but you know there will be several secondary readers. To satisfy the primary reader, you would have to adjust the level of technicality to the appropriate level. If the level of technicality is low, you run the risk of boring more technically competent secondary readers, but at least you won't confuse them. If the level of technicality is high, you might have to offer the secondary readers some help in the way of definitions, analogies, and so forth. Often, such help can be kept out of the way of a more technically competent primary reader by putting it in a graphic or an attachment. Because the graphic and attachment stand a little apart from the body of the memo, the primary reader can ignore them.

Sometimes, needed definitions can be placed in footnotes or glossaries where, again, the more expert reader can bypass them. We have much more to say about such matters in Chapters 6, 8, 9, and 10, where we discuss definition, document design, and graphics. Remember that all such devices and techniques are used to satisfy the needs of your readers. Therefore, always begin by considering your audience and consider it at every stage of the writing process, from preliminary research to final formatted document.

International Readers

To be in business in North America is increasingly to be in international business. As Figure 4-9 shows, Canada trades goods all over the world. Although the U.S., Mexico, and Latin America remain major trading partners, trade with Asian countries is increasing rapidly. Canada exports more to Japan than to any European country; more to South Korea than to Germany; and more to China, Hong Kong, and Taiwan than to any European country other than the U.K. and the Netherlands.

What this means for you is that increasingly in considering audience, you may have to consider a foreign audience—an audience that very likely has

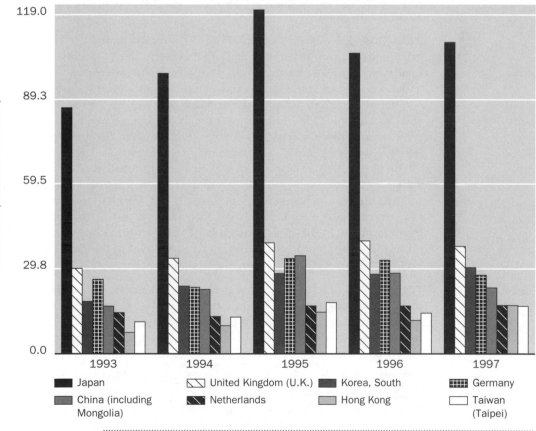

Figure 4-9 CANADIAN EXPORTS OVERSEAS

Source: Industry Canada, *Strategis: Trade Data Online,* http://www.strategis.ic.gc.ca/cgi-bin/tdst-bin/graph.rp, accessed on 15 May 1998. Reproduced with the permission of the Minister of Public Works and Government Services Canada, 1998.

a culture quite different from that of Canada or the United States. You must take these significant cultural differences into account in adapting your writing to your audience. Business people who have not done so have seen sales and opportunities slip away. Be forewarned: If you communicate outside your cultural boundaries, seek advice from experts who understand the cultural differences. To help you understand why such help is necessary, we explain some of the major differences among cultures and then suggest how to deal with them. In our planning and revision checklists at the end of this chapter, we remind you again to take cultural differences into account.

Cultural Differences

Major cultural differences exist in five areas: individualism versus collectivism, time values, business versus personal relationships, power relationships, and relativism.[25] This is not to say that every member of a culture acts like every other member of that culture, but people within a culture tend to act in similar ways.

INDIVIDUALISM VERSUS COLLECTIVISM   Both Canada and the United States prize individualism more than any other country in the world—even more than countries in Western Europe, with which they share many cultural attributes. As a result, individual achievement is highly regarded and rewarded, and independent behaviour is the norm. North Americans tend to be direct and "to the point." We are competitive in work and play, which we often place before family and friends. We are highly analytical and pragmatic. Our self-worth as individuals is bound closely to individual success.

In a collectivistic culture, such as many cultures in Asia, group success and protecting the well-being of the group are more important than individual success. Aggressive, individual behaviour is not tolerated, and group goals take precedence over individual goals. Decisions are made by groups. Promotions are based on seniority and are made from within the ranks of senior group members. In order to keep harmony within the group, people are polite, formal, and indirect, particularly with criticism.

TIME VALUES   The relatively fast pace of North American business practice makes time a highly valued commodity. Workplace values are tied closely to the effective use of time. Using time in nonbusiness pursuits is considered to interfere with efficiency. In many other cultures, time has more complex values and business is conducted in a more expansive fashion.

BUSINESS VERSUS PERSONAL RELATIONSHIPS   In Canada and the United States, it is common for people to keep their business lives separate from their personal lives. Work is in one category, family another. Although this separation seems to be declining to some extent, many business concerns expect workers to put the organization first and the family second.

In many other cultures, business and family are not so compartmentalized. Mexican business people will want to know about your family, your attitudes, and your personal values before they begin to discuss business. Referring to family and recognizing the importance of family is part of their business culture.

POWER RELATIONSHIPS   North American workers accept higher authority and central decision making reluctantly and expect to have some input into decisions. Hierarchies in Canadian and American organizations are flattening out, and organizations are moving toward more participatory management. North American business culture is increasingly informal: Use of first names is common, and even dress is becoming more casual.

In many other cultures, superiors are authoritarian figures; disagreeing with higher authority is unacceptable. Age and seniority are positive factors and major qualifications for leadership. Formality and delicacy in communication are considered extremely important.

RELATIVISM   Many non-Western cultures believe that what is true and valid and what should be done depend on a particular situation. Sensitivity to the elements or layers of a particular circumstance is high and influences reactions and procedural decisions.

In much of Western culture, by contrast, general applicability or universality of rules of behaviour and of correctness is assumed. Rules are often laid down in strictly worded contracts and, once written, govern business and actions.

Dealing with Cultural Differences

Our advice about how to write and speak in this book is predicated on your having an audience that, in general, shares your North American culture. We point out differences between lay people and executives and ways of dealing with them. We advise you to be courteous in correspondence. But for the most part we have set out to teach you the direct, logical, analytical style that is appropriate for a North American audience.

It's a style that calls for such attributes as the following: highlighted main points; conciseness and efficiency; tactfully but squarely stated issues; emphasis on what is done, by whom, and when; logical structure, emphasized by the use of headings and good page design; focus on business not personal issues; and the clear statement of conclusions and recommendations.

It's a style that with some modification will work in much of Western Europe. You would have to understand, for example, that the French like some more formality and ornateness than North Americans but, like us, appreciate logic and the clear statement of conclusions and recommendations. However, in much of Asia, Mexico, and Latin America, it's a style that would be considered direct and brusque to the point of rudeness. Here are a few points to consider when writing for non-Western audiences:

- Be more indirect. Deemphasize the main point or place it at the end of your message.
- Use a formal, even elegant, style.

- Deemphasize structure and the use of headings.
- Recognize that messages may be shared with many others.
- Avoid placing direct blame on any one person or group. Allow readers to save face.
- Discuss business in terms of larger human and organizational concerns.
- Don't rush people to decisions. Allow time for group consensus to build.

For a comparative example of how a letter for a U.S. audience might be modified for a non-Western audience, see pages 289–290 in Chapter 11, "Correspondence."

Planning and Revision Checklists

These questions are a summary of the key points in this chapter, and they provide a checklist for planning and revising any document for your readers.

Planning

- How many readers will you have?
- Is one person (or any one group) your primary reader? Are there secondary readers? **Consider both primary and secondary readers when answering the questions that follow.**
- What is your relationship to the readers?
- What do you hope to accomplish with your document? What is your primary purpose? Secondary? Other?
- Why will the readers read your document? For enjoyment and interest? To learn a skill? To perform a task? To make a decision? To gain knowledge in the subject area? Other?
- What interest, knowledge, and experience do your readers have in the subject of your document? Do they have the necessary schema and background to assimilate your material easily? If not, what can you provide to help them? Explanations? Definitions?

Graphics? Analogies? Examples? Anecdotes?
- What are the readers' attitudes toward your subject matter?
- What are your readers' attitudes toward you?
- If your document includes conclusions and recommendations, how will your readers feel about them? Enthusiastic? Friendly? Hostile? Skeptical? Indifferent?
- Is self-interest involved in the attitudes of your readers? For instance, will they benefit or lose as a result of your document? Will they feel threatened or be made angry by the document?
- If your readers have negative attitudes (hostile, skeptical, indifferent), what can you do to overcome those attitudes? Provide more support? Point out long-term benefits? Soften your language? Make your presentation more interesting?
- Are you writing within a recognizable discourse community, such

continued >>

as a corporation or a professional group? If so, are you familiar and comfortable with the customs and voice of that community? Is there a prevailing style and tone? What arguments are most persuasive? Do you have access to models of similar documents you can use to help you?

• Are you writing across cultural boundaries? Do you need to adjust your tone or style accordingly?

• How are the primary readers likely to read the report? Skim? Scan? Search read? Read for comprehension? Read critically? How will the secondary readers read? Given how your readers will read your document, what can you do to help your readers get the most from it? Will some of the following help: Table of contents? Graphics? Questions? Introductions and transitions? Summaries? Checklists?

• Are you writing to an international audience? Do you need a different tone or style because of this? Consider these questions:

Are your readers individualistic or collectivistic?

Are your readers rank conscious?

What degree of formality will your readers expect?

How do your readers regard time values?

Do your readers see truth as universal or relative?

How sensitive will your readers be to criticism?

How important are family relationships to your readers?

How proficient in English are your readers?

Revision

• Have you written your text at a level appropriate for your readers, both primary and secondary? Do you need more or fewer definitions, examples, descriptions, and explanations? Have you provided analogies and metaphors when they would be useful? Have you moved from the familiar to the unfamiliar?

• Have you met your objectives for each audience addressed?

• Will your readers feel that their objectives have been met?

• Is your purpose clearly stated in your introduction?

• Are your conclusions and recommendations clearly stated? Can your readers easily find them?

• Does your format allow your reader to read selectively? Do your introductions and transitions forecast what is to come?

Have you furnished a table of contents if needed? Do you have enough headings and subheadings to guide your readers? Would review questions, summaries, or checklists be useful?

• Have you furnished good graphic support? Have you helped your reader when possible by using pictures, flowcharts, and diagrams?

• Have you achieved the proper tone? Have you inadvertently said anything rude or misleading? Have you taken cultural differences into account?

• Does your language distort or sensationalize your material in any way?

• Have you international readers? Consider these questions:

Have you been indirect enough?

Have you deemphasized structure and use of headings?

continued >>

Is your style sufficiently formal and respectful?

Have you avoided directly blaming any person or group for perceived difficulties?

Have you addressed human or organizational concerns when appropriate?

Have you avoided a sense of haste?

Is the level of English you have used suitable for your readers?

Weblinks

Plain English Campaign
www.plainenglish.co.uk

Reducing Wordiness
www.leo.stcloud.msus.edu/style/wordiness.html

Cross Cultural Communications for Business and Industry
www.bena.com/ewinters/sect3.html

Exercises

1. Think about some concept in your discipline that you understand thoroughly. Write a letter explaining that concept to someone you know who does not understand it: a good friend, a parent, a sister, or a brother. In your planning, use the checklist provided in this chapter. Include graphics if you think they will help. Your goal is to interest your reader and teach him or her something about a world you understand and enjoy.

2. Select a journal article that discusses some development or concept in your field that may have practical value. For example, it may suggest a new method of producing a product, a new market for an old product, or a service that could be performed for a fee. Imagine an executive who might find a discussion of this concept or development useful. Assume this executive is intelligent and educated but that he or she knows little about the subject matter involved. Write that executive a memorandum in which you explain the concept or development, and fully discuss its implications to the executive's organization. Use graphics if they will help. Use the memorandum format shown in Chapter 11, "Correspondence."

3. Compare and contrast an article or report written for one kind of audience with another written for a different audience—perhaps an article from *Canadian Information Processing* with one from *Computing*

Canada. Get articles on similar subjects and, if possible, in your discipline. Ask and answer some of these questions about the articles:

- What stylistic similarities do you see between the two articles? What dissimilarities? Which article has greater complexity? What indicates this complexity? What is the average sentence length in each article? Paragraph length? Which article defines the most terms?
- What is the author's major concern in each article? How do these concerns contrast?
- What similarities and dissimilarities of format and arrangement do you see?
- Are there differences in the kinds of graphics used in the two articles?
- Which article presents the most detail? Why? What kind of detail is presented in each article?
- How much background information are you given in each article? Does either article refer you to other books or articles?

4. The instructor divides the class into five or six groups. Each group will obtain a book or article on international communication or multicultural relationships, perhaps one of those listed in Appendix B, "A Selected Bibliography." Working in collaboration, each group will write a summary, several pages long, that discusses the main points of the book or article. Using the summaries as a starting point, the groups will participate in a discussion of international communication. At the end of the discussion, each group will turn in its summary to the teacher.

5. Perhaps you are already planning a long paper for your writing course. Using the Planning Checklist in this chapter, write an analysis of the anticipated audience. Prepare your analysis as a memorandum addressed to your instructor. Use the memorandum format shown in Chapter 11, "Correspondence."

ACHIEVING A READABLE STYLE

A readable text is one that an intended reader can comprehend without difficulty. Many things can make a text difficult to read. For example, the content may include unexplained concepts that the reader does not understand. New information may not be explained in terms of material already familiar to the reader. The material may not be arranged or formatted in a way to make it accessible. We cover such aspects of readability elsewhere, notably in Chapter 2, "Composing"; Chapter 4, "Writing for Your Readers"; and Chapter 8, "Document Design." In this chapter, we deal with style elements at the paragraph, sentence, and word level that can make your text clearer and more readable.

Examples of unclear writing style are all too easy to find, even in places where we would hope to find clear, forceful prose. Read the following sentence:

> While determination of specific space needs and access cannot be accomplished until after a programmatic configuration is developed, it is apparent that physical space is excessive and that all appropriate means should be pursued to assure that the entire physical plant is utilized as fully as is feasible.

This murky sentence comes from a report issued by a higher education coordinating board. Actually, it's better than many examples we could show you. Although difficult, the sentence is probably readable. Others are simply indecipherable. When you have finished this chapter, you should be able to analyse a passage like the one just cited and show why it is so unclear. You should also know how to keep your own writing clear, concise, and vigorous. We discuss paragraphs, lists, clear sentence structure, specific words, and pomposity. We have broken our subject into five parts for simplicity's sake, but all the parts are closely related. All have one aim: readability.

If there is a style checker in your word processor, it will incorporate many of the principles we discuss in this chapter. Nevertheless, use it with great care. Style checkers used without understanding the principles involved in good style can be highly misleading. (We discuss style checkers and problems with them more fully in Chapter 2, "Composing.")

The Paragraph

In Chapter 6, we discuss arrangement strategies. These strategies may be used not only to develop reports but also to develop paragraphs within reports. Thus, paragraphs will vary greatly in arrangement and length, depending upon their purpose.

The Central Statement

In technical writing, the **central statement** of a paragraph more often than not appears at the beginning of the paragraph. This placement provides the clarity of statement that good technical writing must have.

In a paragraph aimed at persuasion, however, the central statement may appear at the close, where it provides a suitable climax for the argument. Wherever you place the central statement, you can achieve unity by relating all the other details of the paragraph to the statement, as in this paragraph of inference and speculation:

We have underlined the central statement. The rest of the paragraph elaborates upon the main idea.

> The Rocky Mountains form an effective barrier to the maritime influence of the Pacific Ocean. Cool North Pacific air loses considerable moisture coming over the mountains and is warmed while it descends the eastern slopes of the Rockies and arrives on the rain-shaded Prairies. Still, air of Pacific origin gives rather cloudy, mild, and windy weather to Alberta. Precipitation can be relatively heavy in the foothills and in the Peace River district, where altitude decreases and rain-bearing air masses enter the province freely from the west. However, nowhere is the yearly total precipitation excessive. By way of comparison, Montréal's yearly total of 1070 mm exceeds that of any Alberta station.[1]

Paragraph Length

Examination of well-edited magazines such as *Scientific American* and *Nature Canada* reveals that their paragraphs seldom average more than 100 words in length. Magazine editors know that paragraphs are for the reader. Paragraphing breaks the material into related subdivisions to enhance the reader's understanding. When a paragraph is too long, the central statement, which helps the reader generalize about what she is reading, is often either missing or hidden in the mass of supporting details.

In addition to considering the readers' need for generalized statements to clarify issues, editors also consider the psychological effect of their pages. They know that large blocks of unbroken print have a forbidding appearance that intimidates the reader. If you follow the practice of experienced editors, you will break your paragraphs whenever your presentation definitely takes a new turn. As a general rule, paragraphs in reports and articles should average 100 words or fewer. In letters and memorandums, because of their page layout, you should probably hold average paragraph length to fewer than 60 words.

Transitions

Generally, a paragraph presents a further development in a continuing sequence of thought. In such a paragraph, the opening central statement will be so closely related to the preceding paragraph that it usually provides a sufficient transition. When a major transition between ideas is called for, consider using a short paragraph to guide the reader from one idea to the next.

The following three paragraphs provide an excellent example of paragraph development and transition:

> An important function of lymph flow is to head off infections. At two or three places along its way to the heart, the lymph fluid passes through a node, a bean-sized collection of fibres that filter out micro-organisms so only sterile lymph gets back to the heart.
>
> In an X-ray, lymph nodes show up like beads on a string. The bacteria, viruses and particles of waste matter they collect are attacked by the body's defender cells, which gather in the nodes. These include macrophages, cells that surround and destroy micro-organisms, and lymphocytes, which mount immune responses against the foreign material.
>
> When you have an infection, material will collect in the nodes faster than these defender cells can deal with them, so the node enlarges. If too much material builds up in one node, a node further along the way picks up the excess. That can make for an uncomfortable time, especially when the collection of nodes in the throat—including the tonsils—become increasingly inflamed when a prolific population of virus invaders is being held for destruction by the defending cells.[2]

In the first paragraph, *lymph nodes* is the key term. *Lymph node* or *nodes* appears five times. The first sentence introduces the central theme of the three paragraphs: An important function of the lymph system is to prevent infection. The rest of the paragraph describes nodes within the system.

In the second paragraph, the use of the word nodes creates a transition to the subject of the paragraph: The body's defender cells filter infectious particles in the lymph nodes. The paragraph further develops the central subject of the passage by describing the types of defender cells.

The final paragraph explains how the nodes function as a system—and feel—when the body is fighting off an infection. The transitional element "these defender cells" creates the link with the preceding paragraph. The paragraph closes with a vivid summary image of the viral invaders coralled in the nodes with defender cells armed against them.

The three paragraphs illustrate that you will develop paragraphs coherently when you keep your mind on the central theme. If you do so, the words needed to provide proper transition will come naturally. More often than not, your transitions will be repetitions of key words and phrases, supported by such simple expressions as *also, another, of these four, because of this development, so, but*, and *however*. When you wander away from your central theme, no amount of artificial transition will wrench your writing back into coherence.

Lists and Tables

One of the simplest things you can do to ease the reader's chore is to break down complex statements into lists. Visualize the printed page. When it appears as an unbroken mass of print, it intimidates readers and makes it harder for them to pick out key ideas. Get important ideas out into the open where they stand out. Lists help to clarify introductions and summaries. You may list by (1) starting each separate point on a new line, leaving plenty of white space around it, or (2) using numbers within a line, as we have done here. Examine the following summary from a student paper, first as it might have been written and then as it actually was:

> The exploding wire is a simple-to-perform yet very complex scientific phenomenon. The course of any explosion depends not only on the material and shape of the wire but also on the electrical parameters of the circuit. In an explosion the current builds up and the wire explodes, current flows during the dwell period, and "post-dwell conduction" begins with the reignition caused by impact ionization. These phases may be run together by varying the circuit parameters.

Now, the same summary as a list:

> The exploding wire is a simple-to-perform yet very complex scientific phenomenon. The course of any explosion depends not only on the materials and shape but also on the electrical parameters of the circuit.
>
> An explosion consists primarily of three phases:
>
> 1. The current builds up and the wire explodes.
> 2. Current flows during the dwell period.
> 3. "Postdwell conduction" begins with the reignition caused by impact ionization.
>
> These phases may be run together by varying the circuit parameters.

The first version is clear, but the second version is clearer, and readers can now file the process in their minds as "three phases." They will remember it longer.

Some writers avoid using lists even when they should use them, so we hesitate to suggest any restrictions on the practice. Obviously, there are some subjective limits. Lists break up ideas into easy-to-read, easy-to-understand bits, but too many can make your page look like a grocery list. Also, some journal editors object to lists in which each item starts on a separate line. Such lists take space, and space costs money. Use lists when they clarify your presentation, but use them prudently.

Tables perform a function similar to lists. You can use them to present a good deal of information—particularly statistical information—in a way that is easy for the reader to follow and understand. We discuss tables and their functions in Chapter 10, "Graphical Elements."

Clear Sentence Structure

The basic English sentence structure follows two patterns, *subject-verb-object* (SVO) and *subject-verb-complement* (SVC):

    Canadians(S) love(V) ice cream(O).

    She(S) planned(V) carefully(C).

Around such simple sentences as "Canadians love ice cream," the writer can hang a complex structure of words, phrases, and clauses that modify and extend the basic idea. In this case, the writer actually wrote "Canadians love ice cream, but ice cream is made from whole milk and cream and therefore contains a considerable amount of saturated fat and dietary cholesterol."

In this section on clear sentence structure, we discuss how to extend your sentences without losing clarity. We discuss sentence length, sentence order, sentence complexity and density, active verbs, active and passive voice, and first-person point of view.

Sentence Length

Many authorities have seen sentence length as an indicator of how difficult a sentence is. More recent research has found that although sentence length and word length may be indicators, they are not the primary causes of difficulty in reading sentences. Rather, the true causes may be the use of difficult sentence structures and words unfamiliar to the reader. This position is summed up well in this statement:

    A sentence with 60, 100, or 150 words needs to be shortened; but a sentence with 20 words is not necessarily more understandable than a sentence with 25 words. The incredibly long sentences that are sometimes found in technical, bureaucratic, and legal writing are also sentences that have abstract nouns as subjects, buried actions, unclear focus, and intrusive phrases. These are the problems that must be fixed, whether the sentence has 200 words or 10.

> Similarly, short words are not always easier words. The important point is not that the words be short, but that your readers know the words you are using.[3]

In general we agree with such advice. Sentence density and complexity cause readers more grief than does sentence length alone. Nevertheless, it's probably worth keeping in mind that most professional writers average only slightly more than 20 words per sentence. Their sentences may range from short to fairly long, but, for the most part, they avoid sentences like this one, from a bank:

> You must strike out the language above certifying that you are not subject to backup withholding due to notified payee underreporting if you have been notified that you are subject to backup withholding due to notified payee underreporting, and you have not received a notice from Revenue Canada advising you that backup holding has terminated.

Sentence Order

What is the best way to order a sentence? Is a great deal of variety in sentence structure the mark of a good writer? One study of 20 successful writers, reported in *College English*, found that these experts depended mostly on basic sentence patterns.[4] They wrote 75.5% of their sentences in plain **subject-verb-object (SVO) or subject-verb-complement (SVC)** order, as in these two samples:

> Doppler radar increases capability greatly over conventional radar. (SVO)
>
> Doppler radar can be tuned more rapidly than conventional radar. (SVC)

Another 23% of the time, the professionals began sentences with short **adverbial openers**:

> Like any radar system, Doppler does have problems associated with it.

These adverbial openers are most often simple prepositional phrases or single words such as *however, therefore, nevertheless,* and other conjunctive adverbs. Generally, they provide the reader with a transition between thoughts. Following the opening, the writer usually continues with a basic SVO or SVC sentence.

These basic sentence types—*SVO(C)* or *adverbial + SVO(C)*—were used 98.5% of the time by the professional writers in the study sample. What did the writers do with the remaining 1.5% of their sentences? For 1.2%, they opened the sentence with **verbal clauses** based on participles and infinitives such as "*Breaking* ground for the new church," or "*To see* the new pattern more clearly." The verbal opener was again followed most often with an SVO or SVC sentence, as in this example:

> Looking at it this way, we see the radar set as basically a sophisticated stopwatch that sends out a high-energy electromagnetic pulse and measures the time it takes for part of that energy to be reflected back to the antenna.

Like the adverbial opener, the verbal opener serves most of the time as a transition.

The remaining 0.3% of the sentences (about 1 sentence in 300) were **inverted constructions**, in which the subject is delayed until after the verb, as in this sentence:

> No less important to the radar operator are the problems caused by certain inherent characteristics of radar sets.

What can we conclude from the study? Simply this: professional writers are interested in getting their content across, not in tricky word order. They convey their thoughts in clear sentences unclouded by extra words. You should do the same.

Sentence Complexity and Density

Research indicates that sentences that are too complex in structure or too dense with content are difficult for many readers to understand.[5] Basing our observations on this research, we wish to discuss four particular problem areas: openers in front of the subject, too many words between the subject and the verb, noun strings, and multiple negatives.

OPENERS IN FRONT OF THE SUBJECT   As research indicates, professional writers place an adverbial or verbal opener before their subjects about 25% of the time. When these openers are held to a reasonable length, they create no problems for readers. The problems occur when the writer stretches such openers beyond a reasonable length. What is *reasonable* is somewhat open to question and depends to an extent on the reading ability of the reader. However, most would agree that the 27 words and 5 commas before the subject in the following sentence make the sentence difficult to read:

Opening phrase too dense

> Because of their ready adaptability, ease of machining, and aesthetic qualities that make them suitable for use in landscape structures such as decks, fences, steps, and retaining walls, preservative-treated timbers are increasingly popular for use in landscape construction.

The ideas contained in this sentence become more accessible when spread over two sentences:

Puts central idea before supporting evidence

> Preservative-treated timbers are increasingly popular for use in landscape construction. Their ready adaptability, ease of machining, and aesthetic qualities make them highly suited for use in structures such as decks, fences, steps, and retaining walls.

The second version has the additional advantage of putting the central idea in the sequence before the supporting information.

The conditional sentence is a particularly difficult type of sentence in which the subject is too long delayed. You can recognize the conditional by its *if* beginning:

Subject too long delayed

> If heat (20°-35°C or 68°-95°F optimum), moisture (20%+ moisture content in wood), oxygen, and food (cellulose and wood sugars) are present, spores will germinate and grow.

To clarify such a sentence, move the subject to the front and the conditions to the rear. Consider the use of a list when you have more than two conditions:

List helps to clarify

Spores will germinate and grow when the following elements are present:
- Heat (20°-35°C or 68°-95°F optimum)
- Moisture content (20% + moisture content in wood)
- Oxygen
- Food (cellulose and wood sugars)

WORDS BETWEEN SUBJECT AND VERB   In the following sentence, too many words between the subject and the verb cause difficulty:

Subject and verb too widely separated

Creosote, a brownish-black oil composed of hundreds of organic compounds, usually made by distilling coal tar, but sometimes made from wood or petroleum, has been used extensively in treating poles, piles, cross-ties, and timbers.

The sentence is much easier to read when it is broken into three sentences and first things are put first:

Revised

Creosote has been used extensively in treating poles, piles, cross-ties, and timbers. It is a brownish-black oil composed of hundreds of organic compounds. Creosote is usually made by distilling coal tar, but it can also be made from wood or petroleum.

You might break down the original sentence into only two sentences if you felt your audience could handle denser sentences:

Revised

Creosote, a brownish-black oil composed of hundreds of organic compounds, has been used extensively in treating poles, piles, cross-ties, and timbers. It is usually made by distilling coal tar, but it can also be made from wood or petroleum.

NOUN STRINGS   Noun strings are another way in which writers sometimes complicate and compress their sentences beyond tolerable limits. A noun string is a sequence of nouns that modifies another noun; for example, in the phrase *multichannel microwave radiometer,* the nouns *multichannel* and *microwave* modify *radiometer.* Sometimes the string may also include an adjective, as in *special multichannel microwave radiometer.*

Nothing is grammatically wrong with the use of nouns as modifiers. Such use is an old and perfectly respectable custom in English. Expressions such as *firefighter* and *creamery butter,* in which the modifiers are nouns, go virtually unnoticed. The problem occurs when writers string many nouns together in one sequence or use many noun strings in a passage, as shown in this example:

Seven noun strings in one paragraph is excessive

We must understand who the initiators of water-oriented greenway efforts are before we can understand the basis for community environment decision making processes. State government planning agencies and commissions and designated water quality planning and management agencies have initiated such efforts. They have implemented water resource planning and management studies and have aided volunteer group greenway initiators by providing technical and coordinative assistance.[6]

In many such strings, the reader has great difficulty in sorting out the relationships among the words. In *volunteer group greenway initiators*, does *volunteer* modify *group* or *initiators*? The reader has no way of knowing.

The solution to untangling difficult noun strings is to include relationship clues such as prepositions, relative pronouns, commas, apostrophes, and hyphens. For instance, a hyphen in *volunteer-group* indicates that *volunteer* modifies *group*. The strung-out passage just quoted was much improved by the inclusion of such clues:

Relationship clues help to clarify noun strings

> We must understand who the initiators of efforts to promote water-oriented greenways are before we can understand the process by which a community makes decisions about environmental issues. Planning agencies and commissions of the state government and agencies that have been designated to plan and manage water quality have initiated such efforts. They have implemented studies on planning and managing water resources and have aided volunteer groups that initiate efforts to promote greenways by providing them with technical advice and assistance in coordinating their activities.[7]

The use of noun strings in technical English will no doubt continue. They do have their uses, and technical people are very fond of them. But perhaps it would not be too much to hope that writers would limit their strings to three words or fewer and not use more than one per paragraph.

MULTIPLE NEGATIVES   Writers introduce excessive complexity into their sentences by using multiple negatives. By *multiple negative*, we do not mean the grammatical error of the *double negative*, as in "He does *not* have *none* of them." We are talking about perfectly correct constructions that include two or more negative expressions, such as these:

Negative statements

> We will not go unless the sun is shining.
>
> We will not pay except when the damages exceed $50.
>
> The lever will not function until the power is turned on.

The positive versions of all of these statements are clearer than the negative versions:

Positive statements

> We will go only if the sun is shining.
>
> We will pay only when the damages exceed $50.
>
> The lever functions only when the power is turned on.

Research shows that readers have difficulty sorting out passages that contain multiple negatives. If you doubt the research, try your hand at interpreting this U.S. government regulation (underlining for negatives is ours):

Excessive use of negatives

> § 928.310 Papaya Regulation 10. Order. (a) <u>No</u> handler shall ship any container of papayas (<u>except</u> immature papayas handled pursuant to § 928.152 of this part): (1) During the period January 1 through April 15, 1980, to any destination within the production area <u>unless</u> said papayas grade at least Hawaii No. 1, <u>except</u> that allowable tolerances for defects may total 10 percent. Provided that <u>not</u> more than 5 percent shall be for serious damage, <u>not</u> more than 1 percent for immature fruit, <u>not</u> more than 1 percent for decay: Provided further, that such papayas shall individually weigh <u>not</u> less than 11 ounces each.[8]

Active Verbs

The verb determines the structure of an English sentence. Many sentences in technical writing falter because the finite verb does not comment upon the subject, state a relationship about the subject, or relate an action that the subject performs. Look at the following sentence:

Action in a noun

Sighting of the coast was accomplished by the pilot at 7 A.M.

English verbs can easily be changed into nouns, but sometimes, as we have just seen, the change can lead to a faulty sentence. The writer has put the true action into the subject and subordinated the pilot and the coast as objects of prepositions. The sentence should read:

Action in a verb

At 7 A.M. the pilot saw the coast.

The poor writer can ingeniously bury the action of a sentence almost anywhere. With the common verbs *make, give, get, have*, and *use*, the writer can bury the action late in the sentence in an object:

Action in an object

The manager has the task of ensuring safe conditions on the assembly line.

or

The speaker did not give an adequate explanation of the technique.

Properly revised, the sentences put the action where it belongs, in the verb:

Action in a verb

The manager must ensure safe conditions on the assembly line.

The speaker did not adequately explain the technique.

The poor writer can even bury the action in an adjective:

Action in an adjective

A new discovery produces an excited reaction in a scientist.

Revised:

Action in a verb

A new discovery excites a scientist.

When writing, and particularly when rewriting, you should always ask yourself: "Where's the action?" If the action does not lie in the verb, rewrite the sentence to put it there, as in this sample:

Action in nouns

Music therapy is the scientific application of music to accomplish the restoration, maintenance, and improvement of mental health.

This sentence provides an excellent example of how verbs are frequently turned into nouns by the use of the suffixes *-ion, -ance* (or *-ence*), and *-ment*. If you have sentences full of such suffixes, you may not be writing as actively as you could be. Rewritten to put active ideas into verb forms, the sentence reads this way:

Action in verbs

Music therapy applies music scientifically to restore, maintain, and improve mental health.

The rewritten sentence defines *music therapy* in one-third less language than the first sentence, without any loss of meaning or content.

Active and Passive Voice

We discuss active and passive voice sentences in Chapter 6, but let us quickly explain the concept here. In an active voice sentence, the subject performs the action and the object receives the action, as in "The heart pumps the blood." In a passive voice sentence, the subject *receives* the action, as in "The blood is pumped." If you want to include the doer of the action, you must add this information in a prepositional phrase, as in "The blood is pumped *by the heart.*" We urge you to use the active voice more than the passive. As the *CBE Style Manual* published by the Council of Biology Editors points out, "The active is the natural voice in which people usually speak or write, and its use is less likely to lead to wordiness and ambiguity."[9]

However, you should not ignore the passive altogether. The passive voice is often useful. You can use the passive voice to emphasize the object receiving the action. The passive voice in "Influenza may be caused by any of several viruses" emphasizes *influenza.* The active voice in "Any of several viruses may cause influenza" emphasizes the *viruses.*

Often the agent of action is of no particular importance. When such is the case, the passive voice is appropriate because it allows you to drop the agent altogether:

Appropriate use of passive

Edward Jenner's work on vaccination was published in 1796.

Be aware, however, that inappropriate use of the passive voice can cause you to omit the agent when knowledge of the agent may be vital. Such is often the case in giving instructions:

Poor use of passive

All doors to this building will be locked after 6 P.M.

This sentence may not produce locked doors until it is rewritten in the active voice:

Active voice

The night manager will lock all doors to this building after 6 P.M.

Also, the passive voice can lead to dangling participles, as in this sentence:

Passive with dangling modifier

While conducting these experiments, the chickens were seen to panic every time a hawk flew over.

Chickens conducting experiments? Not really. The active voice straightens out the matter:

Active voice

While conducting these experiments, we saw that the chickens panicked every time a hawk flew over.

(See also "Dangling Modifier," in Part V, Handbook.)

Although the passive voice has its uses, too much of it produces lifeless and wordy writing. Therefore, use it only when it is clearly appropriate.

First-Person Point of View

Once, reports and scientific articles were typically written in the third person— "This investigator has discovered"—rather than first person— "I discovered."

The *CBE Style Manual* labels this practice the "passive of modesty" and urges writers to avoid it.[10] Many other style manuals for scientific journals now recommend the first person and advise against the use of the third person on the grounds that it is wordy and confusing. We agree with this advice.

The judicious use of *I* or *we* in a technical report is entirely appropriate. Incidentally, such usage will seldom lead to a report full of *I's* and *we's*. After all, there are many agents in a technical report other than the writer. In describing an agricultural experiment, for example, researchers will report how *the sun shone, photosynthesis occurred, rain fell, plants drew nutrients from soil*, and *combines harvested*. Only occasionally will researchers need to report their own actions. But when they must, they should be able to avoid such roundabout expressions as "It was observed by this experimenter." Use "I observed" instead. Use "We observed" when there are two or more experimenters.

A Caution About Following Rules

We must caution you before we leave this section on clear sentence structure. We are not urging upon you an oversimplified grade-school style. Mature styles have a degree of complexity to them. As analysis shows, good writers do put information before the subject. Nothing is wrong with putting information between the subject and verb of a sentence. You will find many such sentences in this book. However, you should be aware that research shows that sentences that are too long, too complex, or too dense cause many readers difficulty. Despite increasingly good research into its nature, writing is a craft and not a science. Be guided by the research available, but do not be simplistic in applying it.

Specific Words

The semanticists' abstraction ladder is composed of rungs that ascend from very specific words such as *table* to abstractions such as *furniture, wealth*, and *factor*. The human ability to move up and down this ladder enabled us to develop language, on which all human progress depends. Because we can think in abstract terms, we can call a moving company and tell it to move our furniture. Without abstraction, we would have to bring the movers into our house and point to each object we wanted moved. Like many helpful writing techniques, however, abstraction is a device you should use carefully.

Stay at an appropriate level on the abstraction ladder. Do not say "inclement weather" when you mean "rain." Do not say "overwhelming support" when you mean "62% of the workers supported the plan." Do not settle for "suitable transportation" when you mean "a bus that seats 32 people."

Writing that uses too many abstractions is lazy writing. It relieves writers of the need to observe, to research, and to think. They can speak casually of "factors," and neither they nor their readers really know what they are talking about. Here is an example of such lazy writing.

The writer was setting standards for choosing a desalination plant to be used at an overseas peacekeeping base.

Too abstract

- The cost must not be prohibitive.
- The quantity of water must be sufficient to supply the Base.
- The quality of the water must be high.

The writer here thinks he has said something. He has said little. He has listed slovenly abstractions when, with a little thought and research, he could have listed specific details. He should have said:

Uses specific detail

- The cost should not exceed $1.25 per thousand litres.
- To supply the Base population of 1000, the plant should purify 600 000 litres of water a day. (The Supplies Division sets the standard of 600 litres a day per person).
- The desalinated water should not exceed the national health standard for potable water of 500 parts per million of dissolved solids.

Abstractions are needed for generalizing, but they cannot replace specific words and necessary details. Words mean different things to different people. The higher you go on the abstraction ladder, the truer this is. The abstract words *prohibitive, sufficient*, and *high* could be interpreted in as many different ways as the writer had readers. No one can misinterpret the specific details given in the rewritten sentences.

Abstractions can also burden sentences in another way. Some writers are so used to thinking abstractly that they begin a sentence with an abstraction and *then* follow it with the specific word, usually in a prepositional phrase. They write:

Poor

The problem of producing fresh water became troublesome at the Base.

Instead of

Revised

Producing fresh water became a problem at the Base.

Or

Poor

The circumstances of the manager's disapproval caused the project to be dropped.

Instead of

Revised

The manager's disapproval caused the project to be dropped.

We do not mean to say you should never use high abstractions. A good writer moves freely up and down the abstraction ladder. But when you use words from high on the ladder, use them properly—for generalizing and as a shorthand way of referring to specific details you have already given.

Pomposity

State your meaning as simply and clearly as you can. Do not let the mistaken notion that writing should be more elegant than speech make you sound pompous. Writing *is* different from speech. Writing is more concise, more compressed, and often better organized than speech. But elegance is not a prerequisite for good writing.

A sign at a gas station reads, "No gas will be dispensed while smoking." Would the attendants in that service station speak that way? Of course not. They would say, "Please put out that cigarette" or "No smoking, please." But the sign had to be elegant, and the writer sounds pompous, and illiterate as well.

If you apply what we have already told you about clear sentence structure, you will go a long way toward tearing down the fence of artificiality between you and the reader. We want to touch on just three more points: empty words, elegant variation, and pompous vocabulary.

Empty Words

The easiest way to turn simple, clear prose into elegant nonsense is to throw in empty words, such as these phrases that begin with the impersonal *it*: "It is evident," "It is clear that," or, most miserable of all, "It is interesting to note that." When something is evident, clear, or interesting, readers will discover this for themselves. If something is not evident, clear, or interesting, rewrite it to make it so. When you must use such qualifying phrases, at least shorten them to "evidently," "clearly," and "note that." Avoid constructions like "It was noted by Kowalski." Simply say, "Kowalski noted."

Many empty words are jargon phrases writers throw in by sheer habit. You see them often in business correspondence. A partial list follows:

to the extent that	is already stated
with reference to	in view of
in connection with	inasmuch as
relative to	with your permission
with regard to	hence
with respect to	as a matter of fact

We could go on, but so could you. When such weeds crop up in your writing, pull them out.

Another way to produce empty words is to use an abstract word in tandem with a specific word. This produces such combinations as

20 in number *for* 20

wires of thin size *for* thin wires

red in colour *for* red

When you have expressed something specifically, do not throw in the abstract term for the same word.

Elegant Variation

Elegant variation will also make your writing sound pompous.[11] **Elegant variation** occurs when a writer substitutes one word for another because of an imagined need to avoid repetition. This substitution can lead to two problems: The substituted word may be a pompous one, or the variation may mislead the reader into thinking that some shift in meaning is intended. Both problems are evident in the following example:

Elegant variation

Insect damage to evergreens varies with the condition of the plant, the pest species, and the hexapod population level.

Confusion reigns. The writer has avoided repetition, but the reader may think that the words *insect, pest,* and *hexapod* refer to three different things. Also, *hexapod,* though a perfectly good word, sounds a bit pompous in this context. The writer should have written,

Revised

Insect damage to evergreens varies with the condition of the plant, the insect species, and the insect population level.

Remember also that intelligent repetition provides good transition. Repeating key words reminds the reader that you are still dealing with your central theme (see pages 80–81).

Pompous Vocabulary

Generally speaking, the vocabulary you think in will serve in your writing. Jaw-breaking thesaurus words and words high on the abstraction ladder will not convince readers that you are intellectually superior. Such words will merely convince readers that your writing is hard to read. We are not telling you here that you must forego your hard-won educated vocabulary. If you are writing for readers who understand words such as *extant* or *prototype,* then use them. But use them only if they are appropriate to your discussion. Don't use them to impress people.

Nor are we talking about the specialized words of your professional field. At times these are necessary. Just remember to define them if you feel your reader will not know them. What we are talking about is the desire some writers seem to have to use pompous vocabulary to impress their readers.

The following list is a sampling of heavy words and phrases along with their simpler substitutes.

accordingly: so

acquire: get

activate: begin

along the lines of: like

assist: help

compensation: pay

consequently: so

due to the fact that: because

facilitate: ease, simplify

for the purpose of: for

in accordance with: by, under

in connection with: about

initiate: begin

in order to: to

in the event that: if

in the interests of: for

in this case: here

make application to: apply

nevertheless: but, however

prior to: before

subsequent to: later, after

utilize: use

You would be wise to avoid the word-wasting phrases on this list and other phrases like them. You really don't need to avoid the single words shown, such as *acquire* and *assist*. All are perfectly good words. But to avoid sounding pompous, don't string large clumps of such words together. Be generous in your writing with the simpler substitutes we have listed. If you don't, you are more likely to depress your readers than to impress them. Don't be like the pompous writers who seek to bury you under the many-syllable words they use to express one-syllable ideas, as in this example from a Ministry of Transportation.

Pompous writing

> The purpose of this PPM [Policy and Procedure Memorandum] is to ensure, to the maximum extent practicable, that highway locations and designs reflect and are consistent with provincial and municipal goals and objectives. The rules, policies, and procedures established by this PPM are intended to afford full opportunity for effective public participation in the consideration of highway location and design proposals by highway departments before submission to the Ministry of Transportation for approval. They provide a medium for free and open discussion and are designed to encourage early and amicable resolution of controversial issues that may arise.

We urge you to read as much good writing—both fiction and non-fiction—as time permits. Stop occasionally as you do and study the author's choice of words. You will find most authors to be lovers of the short word. Numerous passages in Shakespeare, for example, are composed almost entirely of one-syllable words.

Good Style in Action

A final example will summarize much that we have said. Insurance policies were verbal bogs for so long that most buyers of insurance gave up on finding one clearly written. However, a committee of industry representatives decided that it was both possible and desirable to simplify the wording of policies. They revised the Ontario Automobile Policy (OAP1), eliminating empty words and using only words familiar to the average reader. In the revision, the writers avoided excessive sentence complexity and used predominantly the active voice and active verbs. They broke long paragraphs into shorter ones. The insurer became *we* and the insured *you*. Definitions were included where needed rather than segregated in a glossary. Multiple negatives were reworded.

The resulting policy is wonderfully clear. Compare a section of the old with the new.[12]

Old:

Passive voice

Average sentence length: 52 words

An 84-word sentence

Termination

11. (1) Subject to section 12 of the *Compulsory Automobile Insurance Act* and sections 237 and 238 of the *Insurance Act*, this contract may be terminated by the insurer giving to the insured fifteen days' notice of termination by registered mail or five days' written notice of termination personally delivered.

    (2) This contract may be terminated by the insured at any time on request.

    (3) Where this contract is terminated by the insurer,

    (a) the insurer shall refund the excess of premium actually paid by the insured over the proportionate premium for the expired time, but in no

Unfamiliar words

Empty words

Dense formatting

event shall the proportionate premium for the expired time be deemed to be less than any minimum retained premium specified; and

(b) the refund shall accompany the notice unless the premium is subject to adjustment or determination as to the amount, in which case the refund shall be made as soon as practicable.

(4) Where this contract is terminated by the insured, the insurer shall refund as soon as practicable the excess of premium actually paid by the insured over the short rate premium for the expired time, but in no event shall the short-rate premium for the expired time be deemed to be less than any minimum retained premium specified.

(5) The fifteen days mentioned in subcondition (1) of this condition begins to run on the day following the receipt of the registered letter at the post office to which it is addressed.

Notice

12. Any written notice to the insurer may be delivered at, or sent by registered mail to, the chief agency or head office of the insurer in the Province. Written notice may be given to the insured named in this contract by letter personally delivered to the insured or by registered mail addressed to the insured at the insured's latest post office address as notified to the insurer. In this condition, the expression "registered" means registered in or outside Canada.

New:

Cancelling Your Insurance

Active voice

Average sentence length: 14 words

Clear, specific language

Well designed format

Short paragraphs

1.7.1 When You Cancel

You may cancel your insurance any time by advising us.

If you cancel, we will calculate the premium you owe on a short rate basis. Short rate means that the premium you owe will include our handling costs. We will refund anything due you as soon as possible.

There may be a minimum premium set out in your Certificate of Automobile Insurance. This will not be refunded.

1.7.2 When We Cancel

Where your policy has been in effect for less than 60 days, we may only terminate your policy for a reason that we have filed with the Ontario Insurance Commission.

Where your policy has been in effect for more than 60 days, we may only terminate your policy for one of the following reasons:

- non-payment of premium,
- you have given false particulars of the automobile,
- you have knowingly misrepresented or failed to disclose information that you were required to provide in the application for automobile insurance, or
- the risk has changed materially.

If we cancel your insurance, we will notify you in writing. We must give you five days notice if we deliver the cancellation in person, or 15 days notice by sending the cancellation by registered mail to your last known address. The 15-day period starts the day after the registered letter reaches the post office that will deliver the letter to you.

Unfamiliar words explained

We will calculate the premium you owe on a proportionate basis. Proportionate means you will pay for the actual number of days you were covered. For example, if half the premium period is over, you will pay half the premium.

There may be a minimum premium shown on your Certificate of Automobile Insurance. This will not be refunded.

If you have paid more than the premium you owe, we will refund the difference when we inform you that we are cancelling your insurance. Your refund may be delayed if the amount of premium you owe is subject to adjustment, or we are waiting for reports in order to determine the premium paid or owing. We will make the refund as soon as possible in that case.

Examples that substitute specific, familiar words for the high abstractions of the original policy are used freely. For instance:

Example

Your car is four years old and is hit on the front left side by an identified but uninsured automobile. The damaged part of the body of your car is repaired. We will pay the cost of the repairs, less the $100 deductible, including new paint for the damaged part of your automobile. If you want the entire car repainted, you will have to pay the cost of painting the rest of the car.

Example

You are involved in an accident for which an uninsured driver is responsible. The minimum liability coverage in the jurisdiction where the accident occurs is $100 000. You suffer losses amounting to $125 000. You recover $50 000 from other insurance coverage. We will pay another $50 000 to bring you up to the limit of the jurisdiction where the accident occurred.

Example

Your car is damaged in a fire. The fire department properly bills you for the cost of putting out the fire. A new transmission must be imported before the car can be repaired. We will pay the fire department's bill, import duties on the replacement part and for the repairs themselves.

Incidentally, there is no fine print in the policy. It is set entirely in 10-point type, a type larger than that used in most newspapers and magazines. Headings and boldface are used freely to draw attention to transitions and important information.

You can clean up your own writing by following the principles discussed in this chapter and demonstrated in the revised insurance policy. Also, if you exercise care, your own manner of speaking can be a good guide in writing. You should not necessarily write the same way you talk. In speech, you may be too casual, even slangy. But the sound of your own voice can still be a good guide. When you write something, read it over; even read it aloud. If you have written something you know you would not say because of its artificiality, rewrite it in a comfortable style. Rewrite so that you can hear the sound of your own voice in it.

Choosing a Style for International Readers

In North America, good technical and business style calls for clarity and succinctness. It's a style that, with some modification, will not offend members of most Western European cultures. However, cultures in which romance languages—such as French, Spanish, and Italian—predominate do prefer a more formal style where conciseness is not an issue.

Asian readers and, to a lesser degree, Mexican and Latin American readers may find the directness of the North American style blunt, even rude. Their style compared with the North American style is more formal, and ideas, particularly dissenting ideas, are presented much more indirectly. In short, the success of any style depends on how readers react to it. We offer our major advice about some of the adjustments you can make on pages 71–74 in Chapter 4, "Writing for Your Readers."

Planning and Revision Checklists

You will find the planning and revision checklists following Chapter 2, "Composing," Chapter 4, "Writing for Your Readers," and at the back of the book valuable in planning and revising any presentation of technical information. The following questions specifically apply to style. They summarize the key points in this chapter and provide a checklist for revising.

Planning

You can revise for good style, but you can't plan for it. Good style comes when you are aware of the need to avoid the things that cause bad style: ponderous paragraphs, overly dense sentences, excessive use of passive voice, pomposity, and the like.

Good style comes when you write to express your thoughts clearly, not to impress your readers. Good style comes when you have revised enough writing that the principles involved are ingrained in your thought process.

Revision

• Do you have a style checker in your word processing software? If so, use it, but exercise the cautions we advocate in Chapter 2, "Composing."
• Are the central thoughts in your paragraphs clearly stated? Do the details in your paragraphs relate to the central thought?

• Have you broken up your paragraphs sufficiently to avoid long, intimidating blocks of print?
• Have you guided your reader through your paragraphs with the repetition of key words and with transition statements?
• Have you used lists or tables when such use would help the reader?

continued >>

- Are your sentences of reasonable length? Have you avoided sentences of 60 to 100 words? Does your average sentence length match that of professional writers—about 20 words?
- Professional writers begin about 75% of their sentences with the subject of the sentence. How does your percentage of subject openers compare to that figure? If your average differs markedly, do you have a good reason for the difference?
- When you use sentence openers before the subject, do they provide good transitions for your readers?
- Have you limited sentence openers before the subject to a reasonable length?
- Have you avoided large blocks of words between your subject and your verb?
- Have you used noun strings to modify other nouns? If so, are you sure your readers will be able to sort out the relationships involved?
- Have you avoided the use of multiple negatives?
- Are your action ideas expressed in active verbs? Have you avoided burying them in nouns and adjectives?
- Have you used active voice and passive voice appropriately? Are there passive voice sentences you should revise to active voice?
- Have you used abstract words when more specific words would be clearer for your readers? Do your abstractions leave unintended interpretations open to the reader? When needed, have you backed up your abstractions with specific detail?
- Have you avoided empty jargon phrases?
- Have you chosen your words to express your thoughts clearly for your intended reader? Have you avoided pompous words and phrases?
- Is your style suitable for international readers?

Weblinks

User Friendly Manuals' Website
www.user-friendly-manuals

Paragraphs and Topic Sentences
www.education.indiana.edu/~istcore/r519/evaluation.html

Audience Awareness
www.english.ttu.edu/courses/1302/Kemp/sp97/help/audience.htm

Exercises

1. **You should now be able to rewrite the example sentence on page 79 in clear, forceful prose. Here it is again; try it.**

   While determination of specific space needs and access cannot be accomplished until after a programmatic configuration is developed, it is apparent that physical space is excessive and that all appropriate means should be pursued to ensure that the entire physical plant is utilized as fully as feasible.

2. Here is the pompous paragraph from page 93. Revise it into good prose:

The purpose of this PPM [Policy and Procedure Memorandum] is to ensure, to the maximum extent practicable, that highway locations and designs reflect and are consistent with provincial and municipal goals and objectives. The rules, policies, and procedures established by this PPM are intended to afford full opportunity for effective public participation in the consideration of highway location and design proposals by highway departments before submission to the Ministry of Transportation for approval. They provide a medium for free and open discussion and are designed to encourage early and amicable resolution of controversial issues that may arise.

3. Following are some expressions that the Council of Biology Editors believes should be rewritten.[13] Using the principles you have learned in this chapter, rewrite them:

- an innumerable number of tiny veins
- as far as our own observations are concerned, they show
- ascertain the location of
- at the present moment
- at this point in time
- bright green in colour
- by means of
- (we) conducted inoculation experiments on
- due to the fact that
- during the time that
- fewer in number
- for the purpose of examining
- for the reason that
- from the standpoint of
- goes under the name of
- if conditions are such that
- in all cases
- in order to
- in the course of
- in the event that
- in the near future
- in the vicinity of
- in view of the fact that
- it is often the case that
- it is possible that the cause is
- it is this that
- it would thus appear that
- large numbers of
- lenticular in character
- masses are of large size
- necessitates the inclusion of

- of such hardness that
- on the basis of
- oval in shape, oval shaped
- plants exhibited good growth
- prior to (in time)
- serves the function of being
- subsequent to
- the fish in question
- the tests have not as yet
- the treatment having been performed
- there can be little doubt that
- throughout the entire area
- throughout the whole of this experiment
- two equal halves
- If we interpret the deposition of chemical signals as initiation of courtship, then initiation of courtship by females is probably the usual case in mammals.
- A direct correlation between serum vitamin B_{12} concentration and mean nerve conduction velocity was seen.
- It is possible that the pattern of herb distribution now found in the Chilean site is a reflection of past disturbances.
- Following termination of exposure to pigeons and resolution of the pulmonary infiltrates, there was a substantial increase in lung volume, some improvement in diffusing capacity, and partial resolution of the hypoxemia.

4. Turn the following sentence into a paragraph of several sentences. See if listing might be a help. Make the central idea of the passage its first sentence.

   If, on the date of opening of bid or evaluation of proposals, the average market price of domestic wool of usable grades is not more than 10 percent above the average of the prices of representative types and grades of domestic wools in the wool category which includes the wool required by the specifications (see (f) below), which prices reflect the current incentive price as established by the Ministry of Agriculture, Food, and Rural Affairs and if reasonable bids or proposals have been received for the advertised quantity offering 100 percent domestic wools, the contract will be awarded for domestically produced articles using 100 percent domestic wools and the procedure set forth in (e) and (f) below will be disregarded.

5. Here are two British samples of bad writing quoted in a British magazine devoted to ridding Great Britain of gobbledygook.[14] Try your hand at improving them.

   - The garden should be rendered commensurate with the visual amenities of the neighbourhood.
   - Should there be any intensification of the activities executed to accomplish your present hobby the matter would have to be reappraised.

6. What follows is a brief article on the healing properties of Aboriginal herbs. The description is intended for an educated lay audience, an audience probably much like you.

Analyse the description using the principles of this chapter:
- paragraph development
- use of lists and tables
- sentence structure
- use of specific words
- pomposity

Consider stylistic elements such as
- transitions;
- paragraph length;
- sentence length, order, density, and complexity;
- active and passive voice.

Using your analysis, decide whether this description succeeds or not. Write a memo to your teacher justifying your decision. (Use the memo format from Chapter 11, "Correspondence.")

The year 1525 must have been a bleak winter. Even the mighty St. Lawrence River was frozen solid. An icy wind howled through the rigging of the ship that had been sent out by the King of France in search of gold. The expedition and even the founding of Canada was in jeopardy: *"la grosse maladie"* had struck. Below deck, at subzero temperatures, the crew groaned even louder than the wind. They knew their certain fate was to perish the same way as a third of their mates had already done—without even the satisfaction of a decent burial in the frost-hard ground.

Jacques Cartier is full of praise in his journals, for the generosity and medical skill of the Native people at the village of Stadacona in those early days. The herbal infusion they offered had a miraculous effect on the crew. Today we know that it was made from the leaves and buds of *Thuja occidentalis*, the yellow or white cedar.

It is not such a miracle when one discovers that cedar is high in vitamins A and C and the *grosse maladie* was likely scurvy. No wonder this was the first Canadian tree to be taken back to France and planted in the Royal Garden at Fontainbleau!

Native Canadians have played an outstanding role in the founding of this nation. Because they had lived on this continent for so many centuries, they were able to come to the aid of afflicted European settlers who recognized only a few of the Canadian medicinal plants. They taught the pioneers how to boil the same cedar leaves on the back burner of the wood stove to protect against influenza during the winter months.

They showed our ancestors how to use the *Trillium erectum* (birth root) as an aid in childbirth. They introduced witch hazel to us—the only shrub in the woods that bears flowers in the autumn after the leaves have fallen off the branches. (And we have found a modern application for this powerful astringent when we soak cotton batting pads in distilled witch hazel from the pharmacy and place them over the closed eyelids of aching, computer-weary eyes.)

During the American invasion of 1812-1814, the Natives, under leaders such as Six Nations chief, Joseph Brant, were instrumental in pushing back enemy lines. While that war was being fought along the Niagara peninsula the Indians taught bewildered homesteaders that nature provided an indigenous garlic (wild leek) which could be combined with sphagnum moss gathered from the marshes and dried in the sun to provide an antiseptic wound dressing. But before you cry "ouch" at the thought of fresh garlic juice hitting a raw wound, remember the alternative: a British army surgeon grinding through the bone of your gangrenous leg!

Another Indian remedy that was very important for the survival of the little colony in British North America in the early years was *Hydrastis canadensis* (goldenseal). This plant contains berberine which is a bitter alkaloid with antibacterial and antiprotozoal effects down to dilutions of 1:6000.

According to Simon Mills, past-president of the National Institute of Medical Herbalists in Great Britain, it appears to exert an astringent effect on the mucous membranes throughout the interior of the body.

During the pioneer period in Eastern Canada, goldenseal was used as a tonic remedy assisting digestion and liver function as well as a local application to infected wounds and ulcers and inflamed skin conditions.

By 1905, 150 tonnes of goldenseal were collected in a single year from the wild. Native herbalist, Janice Longboat of the Six Nations reserve at Oshwekan, Ontario, recalls her grandmother (who was also a herbalist), pointing out a dump truck full of the root being taken away from the reserve. Non-Native wild-crafters were greedy. Unlike their Native teachers, they failed to provide for next year's crop. Today this plant is virtually extinct in the wild.

The British Herbal Pharmacopoeia indicates a rather low dose for this powerful plant: the dried rhizome 0.5-l.0 g three times daily or 0.3-l.0 ml tincture. However, many herbalists use no more than five millilitres a week. Happily, goldenseal remains on the market in Canada, in keeping with the recommendations of the Expert Advisory Committee on Herbs and Botanical Preparations. It must not, however, be used in pregnancy or hypertension.

The impact of Canada's Native peoples on herbal medicine was not confined only to North America. Native remedies made their way to Europe during the 19th century. Early members of the National Institute of Medical Herbalists in Great Britain (which had already been established by 1864), were able to incorporate North American remedies into their repertoire. Today, over one third of the medicinal plants listed in the *British Herbal Pharmacopoeia* are indigenous Canadian plants.

The list is long: black cohosh (*Cimicifuga racemosa*) is still used for arthritis and whooping cough; blue cohosh (*Caulophyllum thalictroides*) is sometimes taken for painful menstrual periods; wild ginger became popular among the pioneers as a substitute for imported *Zingiber officinalis* (imported ginger root), to warm up the body after a chill and to ease indigestion after a heavy meal.

Bayberry bark (*Myrica cerifera*) is still used as an astringent for sore throats and diarrhea. Squaw Vine (*Mitchella repends*) was one of the Native remedies used to facilitate parturition in childbirth. And we haven't even mentioned echinacea, lobelia or ginseng.

We have only just begun to realize the importance of Native North American medicine. It is to be hoped that we will not eliminate more indigenous species before they can be methodically and scientifically explored.[15]

7. **Write a short report, or revise one you did earlier, using the stylistic principles of this chapter.**

PART II

TECHNIQUES

Part II builds on the basic concepts of Part I, emphasizing the need to consider audience and purpose with every writing technique you use. Chapter 6 describes and demonstrates techniques for informing, describing, defining, and arguing. These apply to most forms of technical writing, including the instructions, proposals, and feasibility reports discussed in Part IV. Chapter 7 describes the role that new channels of communication—such as e-mail, electronic discussion lists, synchronous discussions groups, FTP (file transfer protocol) sites, and World Wide Web sites—play in the workplace. This chapter details the limitations as well as the virtues of each medium to help you make informed decisions about which is most effective for a specific communication task.

ARRANGEMENT STRATEGIES

Following the principles of situational and audience analysis, as explained in Chapters 2 and 4, should lead you to an arrangement strategy that fits your purpose and your audience. Nevertheless, being aware of the full array of arrangement strategies available to you can be useful at both the discovery and the arranging stage of composing. Therefore, this chapter is a review of those strategies that have stood the test of time: chronological arrangement, topical arrangement, exemplification, analogy, classification and division, definition, mechanism and process description, and argument.

You can use any of these strategies as an overall arranging principle for an entire report. But you will also use them as subordinate methods of development within a larger framework. For example, within a paper arranged topically you might have paragraphs or small sections based upon chronology, exemplification, classification, and so forth. The multiple strategies can be mutually supportive and not in conflict with one another.

Chronological Arrangement

When you need to relate a series of events for your reader, arranging the events chronologically—that is, by time—is a natural way to proceed. In your chronological narrative, keep your readers informed as to where they are in the sequence of events. In the example that follows, we have printed in boldface type the phrases the authors use to orient their readers. The excerpt is from *Canada's Nuclear Fuel Industry: An Overview*, a background paper produced by the Science and Technology Division of the Library of Parliament's Research Branch. In it, the author describes the beginning of the Canadian uranium industry. The narrative provides a historical overview that helps the reader understand the discussion that follows. Chronological narratives are often used in this way in technical writing.

> Canada was among the first countries to mine and process uranium-bearing ores. Such ores contain trace amounts of radium, which was in great demand for medical treatment and for use by research laboratories **in the early part of the century**. At the height of the demand, radium sold for the equivalent of several million dollars an ounce. Uranium, which had only limited uses, primarily in the ceramics industry, was essentially a by-product of radium production.
>
> **In 1930**, one of the world's richest uranium deposits was discovered by Gilbert LaBine on the shore of Great Bear Lake in the Northwest Territories. The deposit was developed for its radium content by Eldorado Gold Mines Limited, a company formed **several years earlier** by Gilbert and his brother Charles to develop a gold claim in Manitoba.
>
> Concentrate from the mine at Great Bear Lake was shipped across Canada to a refinery built in Port Hope, Ontario, where the radium and uranium were extracted. **At the time**, the Port Hope refinery may have been the largest of its kind in the world. It was the only one in North America, and one of only two in the world that could refine uranium. Canada and Eldorado were thus in a unique position **at the outset of the Second World War** when uranium was needed for the Manhattan project.
>
> **In the spring of 1941**, the U.S. placed an initial order for refined uranium oxide with Eldorado and, **by the end of that year**, U.S. contracts for uranium had committed Eldorado's entire production **until almost the end of 1945**. Eldorado already had a stockpile of several hundred tonnes of uranium concentrates accumulated on the site of its Port Hope refinery. In addition, Eldorado also processed African uranium ore from the Belgian Congo which the U.S. had purchased from the Belgian company, Union Minière. **In 1942**, Eldorado reopened the mine at Great Bear Lake, which had been shut down **in 1940** because of falling demand for radium.
>
> **After the war**, the mine at Great Bear Lake continued to operate **until 1960**, when the deposit was finally exhausted. **By this time**, Canada had a thriving uranium mining industry with mines at Beaverlodge, north of Lake Athabasca; in the Elliot Lake area of Ontario; and at Bancroft, Ontario. The boom that had been created by the nuclear weapons industry was about to end, however. **In 1959**, the U.S. Atomic Energy Commission announced that it would not exercise its options to purchase additional Canadian uranium and **thereafter** the industry went into a decline. Its bare survival of the ensuing slump was thanks in large measure to a Canadian government stockpiling program. It would not be **until 1986** that production matched the level achieved in **1960**.[1]

Because the arrangement of your material follows the sequence of the events you relate, arrangement is not difficult when you use chronological order. Choosing the level of detail you need may be a problem. Obviously, the narrator describing the beginning of the Canadian uranium industry could have used more or less detail than was used. If your purpose is to give a broad overview for a lay or executive audience, limit the amount of detail. On the other hand, if you have an expert audience who will wish to analyse carefully the sequence you describe, you will need to provide considerable detail.

Topical Arrangement

Technical writing projects often begin with a topic, such as "Christmas tree farming." One way to deal with such topics is to look for subtopics under the major topic. These should serve as umbrella statements beneath which you can gather smaller sub-subtopics and related facts. In the case of the Christmas tree topic, the subtopics might very well be "production" and "marketing." "Production" could be broken down further into "planting," "maintaining," and "harvesting." "Marketing" could be broken down into "retail," "wholesale," and "cut-your-own." With some thought, you can break most topics down into umbrella-sized subtopics.

While you are settling upon the topic and subtopics for your paper, you should also be aware of the need to limit the topic. Students, in particular, often hesitate to limit their topic sufficiently. They fear, perhaps, that if they limit their material too severely they will not be able to write essays of a sufficient length. But you will find it easier to write a coherent, full essay of any length if you *limit the scope of your topic.* With your scope limited and your purpose and audience clearly defined, you can fill your paper with specific facts and examples. When your scope is broad and your purpose and audience vague, you must deal in abstract generalizations.

Suppose you wish to deal with the subject of robotics in about a thousand words. If you keep the purpose simply as "explaining robotics," what can you say in a thousand words? Probably just a few generalizations about the theory, history, and applications of robotics.

But suppose you define your purpose and audience in relation to your subject matter. Perhaps your audience is a group of executives who may have an interest in the use of robotics in their industries. You know that their major interest in robotics will be in application, not in history or theory. You limit yourself, therefore, to application. You refine your purpose. You decide you want to give them some idea of the scope of robotics. To do so, you reach into your knowledge of robotics and choose several applications that can serve as illustrative examples.

You decide to focus on the use of robotics in the following three tasks:

- installing windows in automobiles as the automobiles pass on an assembly line
- arc welding in an airplane plant
- mounting chips in a computer factory

Using these three applications as your topics, you can illustrate a wide range of current robotics practices. Within a few minutes, you can limit your topic to a manageable size and make a good start on arrangement.

Exemplification

Technical writing sometimes consists largely of a series of generalizations supported by examples. The writer makes statements, such as these about factors in global warming:

> Earth is getting warmer and the weather more variable. And contrary to conventional wisdom, it's not just humans who are to blame.

Having made such a generalization, the writer must now support it:

> Previously unsuspected natural phenomena may be deeply influencing our weather.
>
> - It's known that ash spewed into the atmosphere by volcanoes, such as Mount St. Helens and Mount Pinatubo, drops temperatures and changes weather patterns. A new theory suggests that volcanoes and earthquakes under the sea, which drive Pacific Ocean currents, may be even more important.
> - Researchers are also discovering that clouds and sunspots are greater climate factors than previously suspected.
> - Jet streams, the high-altitude rivers of air that can change normal movements of moisture and pool hotter or cooler masses of air over continents, may have an effect on warming.[2]

There are two common ways to use examples. One way is to give one or more extended, well-developed examples, as we did above. The other way is to give a series of short examples that you do not develop in detail, as in the following paragraph:

> Vocabularies differ in richness, in their insistence on making distinctions, or in their refusal to note them. English, for instance, is very poor in demonstratives: "this" for something near, and "that" for something far. The Inuit, however, and the Slave Indians of the Mackenzie River, have up to thirty different words expressing specific locations, such as "that in there," "that right up there," and "that-unseen." The theory is that words that accurately pinpoint places are especially useful to people in hunting cultures.[3]

Like almost everything else in writing, the use of examples calls for judgment on your part. Use too few examples and your writing will lack interest and credibility. Use too many examples and your key generalizations will be lost in excessive detail.

Analogy

Analogies are comparisons: They compare the unfamiliar to the familiar in order to make the unfamiliar more understandable for the reader. You should use short, simple analogies, particularly when you are writing for lay people. For example, many people have difficulty in understanding the immense power released by nuclear reactions. A completely technical explanation of $E = mc^2$ probably would not help them very much. But suppose you tell them that if 500 kilograms of matter—a package of butter, for instance—could be converted directly to energy in a nuclear reaction, it would produce enough electrical power to supply Canada and the United States for thirty-two hours (that is, more than eleven billion kilowatt hours). Such a statement reduces $E = mc^2$ to an understandable idea.

Scientists recognize the need for analogy when called upon to explain difficult concepts. To explain to lay readers the enormity of the project to catalogue (within two decades) all of human DNA, Dr. David Suzuki chose this method:

> What is the magnitude of the challenge? The human genome is about three billion bases long—printed out, it would fill two and a half New York phone books. If all DNA molecules in a single human cell were stretched out end to end, with no magnification, they would measure 2.7 metres! (Incidentally, we are made up of some 100 trillion cells, each with 2.7 metres of DNA. That's enough DNA in one person to stretch to the moon and back a million times!)[4]

A writer introducing the geology of Ontario to his lay readers used a familiar measure of time to express the immense age of the Earth relative to humankind:

> If we could cram the Earth's entire past into twelve hours, we would have a very amazing day. Imagine that the Earth was formed at noon, and midnight marks where we are today. For the first few hours, things are very quiet. In fact, it isn't until almost 4 p.m. that the land that will be Ontario appears. Life as we know it didn't make an appearance until the last half hour before midnight. The modern mammals, birds and insects flourish. A mere half-second before midnight, humans arrive on the scene.[5]

Analogies serve particularly well in definitions or descriptions. If, after describing a diode, you tell a lay audience that it is similar to a water faucet in that you can use it to control the flow of electrons or shut them off completely, you make the concept more understandable. Throughout your writing, use analogy freely. It is one of your best bridges to the uninformed reader.

Classification and Division

Classification and division, like chronological and topical arrangements, are useful devices for bringing order to any complex body of material. You may understand classification and division more readily if we explain them in terms of the *abstraction ladder*. We borrow this device from semanticists—people who make a scientific study of words. We will construct our ladder by beginning with a very abstract word on top and working down the ladder to end with a specific term.

While looking at Figure 6-1, keep one important distinction in mind: even "John Smith's kitchen table" is not the table itself. As soon as we use a word for an object, the abstraction process begins. Beneath the word is the

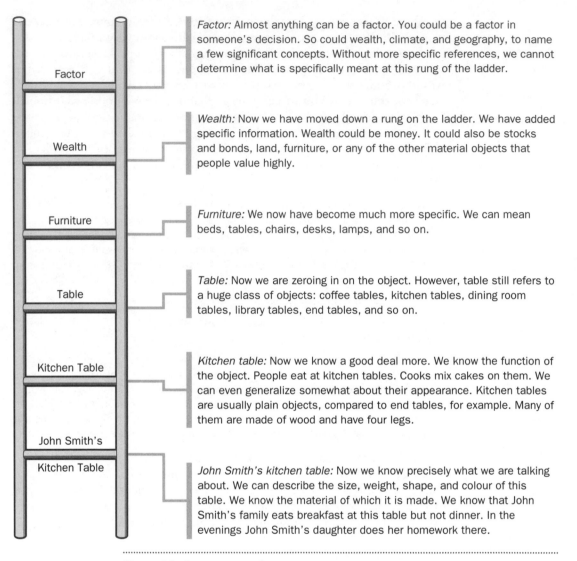

Figure 6-1 ABSTRACTION LADDER

table *we see* and beneath that is the table *itself*, consisting of paint, wood, and hardware that consist of molecules that consist of atoms and space.

In classification, you move *up* the abstraction ladder, seeking higher abstractions under which to group many separate items. In division, you move *down* the abstraction ladder, breaking down higher abstractions into the separate items contained within them. We will illustrate classification first.

Suppose for the moment that you are a dietitian. You are given a long list of foods found in a Canadian home and asked to comment on the value of each. You are to give such information as calorie count, carbohydrate count, mineral content, fat content, vitamin content, and so forth. The list is as follows: onions, apples, steak, green beans, oranges, cheese, lamb chops, milk, granola, lemons, bread, butter, hamburger, muffins, and carrots.

If you try to comment on each item in turn as it appears on the list, you will write a chaotic essay. You will repeat yourself far too often. Many of the things you will say about milk will be the same things you say about cheese. To avoid this repetition and chaos you need to classify the list, to move up the abstraction ladder, seeking groups that look like the following:

Food

Vegetables	Dairy	Cereals
Onions	Milk	Granola
Green beans	Cheese	Bread
Carrots	Butter	Muffins
Meat	**Fruit**	
Steak	Apples	
Lamb chops	Oranges	
Hamburger	Lemons	

By following this procedure, you can use the similarities and dissimilarities of the different foods to aid your organization rather than have them disrupt it.

In division, you move down the abstraction ladder. Suppose your problem is now the reverse of the foregoing. You are a dietitian and someone asks you to list examples of foods that a healthy diet should contain. In this case, you start with the abstraction *food*. You decide to divide this abstraction into smaller divisions such as vegetables, fruit, meat, cereals, and dairy. You then subdivide these into typical examples, such as cheese, milk, and butter for dairy. Obviously, the outline you could construct here might look precisely like the one already shown. But in classification we arrived at the outline from the bottom up; in division, from the top down. Figure 6-2 shows the Food Guide Rainbow, an excellent example of classification and division in action.

Very definite rules apply in using classification and division:

- **Keep all headings equal.** In the preceding example, you would not have headings of "Meat," "Dairy," "Fruit," "Cereals," and "Green Vegetables." "Green Vegetables" would not take in a whole class of food as the other headings do. Under the heading of "Vegetables," however, you could have subheadings of "Green Vegetables" and "Yellow Vegetables."
- **Apply one rule of classification or division at a time.** In the preceding example, the classification is done by food types. You would not in the same classification include headings *equal* to those of the food types for such subjects as "Mineral Content" or "Vitamin Content." You could, however, include such subheadings under the food types.
- **Make each division or classification large enough to include a significant number of items.** In the preceding example, you could have many equal major headings such as "Green Vegetables," "Yellow

 Health and Welfare Canada   Santé et Bien-être social Canada

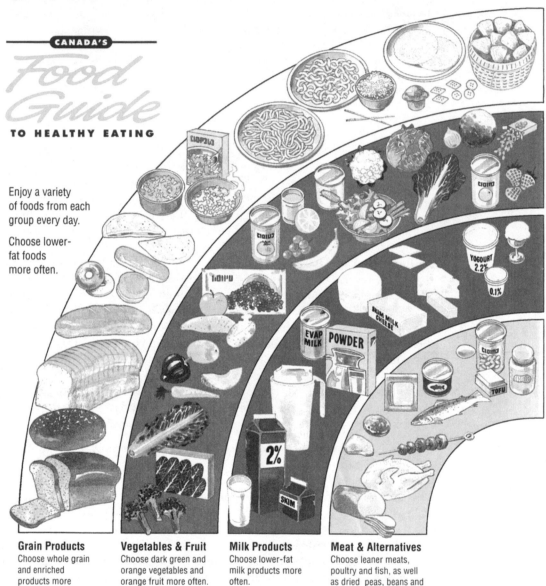

Enjoy a variety of foods from each group every day.

Choose lower-fat foods more often.

Grain Products
Choose whole grain and enriched products more often.

Vegetables & Fruit
Choose dark green and orange vegetables and orange fruit more often.

Milk Products
Choose lower-fat milk products more often.

Meat & Alternatives
Choose leaner meats, poultry and fish, as well as dried peas, beans and lentils more often.

Figure 6-2 CANADA'S FOOD GUIDE RAINBOW: AN EXAMPLE OF CLASSIFICATION

Source: Health and Welfare Canada, *Canada's Food Guide to Healthy Eating* (Minister of Supply and Services Canada, 1992): 12.

Vegetables," "Beef Products," "Lamb Products," "Cheese Products," and so forth. In doing so, however, you would have overclassified or over-divided your subject. Some of the classifications would have included only one item.

- **Avoid overlapping classifications and divisions as much as possible.** In the preceding example, if you had chosen a classification that included "Fruits" and "Desserts," you would have created a problem for yourself. The listed fruits would have to go in both categories. You cannot always avoid overlap, but keep it to a minimum.

As long as writers observe the rules, they are free to classify and divide their material in any way that suits their purposes. An accountant who wishes to analyse the money flow for construction of a province's highways might choose to classify them by source of funding: federal, provincial, municipal. An engineer concerned with construction techniques might choose to classify the same group of roads by surface: concrete, macadam, asphalt, gravel.

In a government publication on production for commercial plants, the authors chose to classify pests that affect nursery stock by this method:

Insect and mite pests may best be considered according to the manner in which they feed and the damage they cause. The following broad groupings have been selected: defoliators, sucking insects, borers, and gall makers.[6]

The publication then proceeds to describe the feeding and damage patterns of the pests under the broad groupings. The authors chose this method of classification because, as they put it, "Controlling pests depends on being able to identify the pest and knowing how and when to best deal with it. Often the damage is so characteristic that the causal agent may be identified without actually seeing the pest at work. Indeed, some pests are so tiny they can't be seen by the unaided eye and others remain concealed within the tissues of the plant." Obviously, species of insects and mites can be classified in many ways. Classifying by manner of feeding and the type of damage caused was the best way to serve the booklet's purpose and the needs of the audience.

Definition

Everyone with a trade or a profession has a specialized vocabulary to suit that occupation. Plumbers know the difference between a *globe valve* and a *gate valve*. Electrical engineers talk easily about *gamma rays* and *microelectronics*. Statisticians understand the mysteries of *chi-square tests* and *one-way analyses of variance*. In fact, learning a new vocabulary is a major part of learning any trade or profession. Unfortunately, as you grow accustomed to using your specialized vocabulary, you may forget that others don't share your knowl-edge—your language may be incomprehensible to them. The first principle in understanding definition is to realize that you will have to do it frequently. You should define any term you think is not in your reader's normal vocabulary. The less expert your audience is, the more you will have to define. Sometimes, when you use a new specialized term, or an old term in a new way, you will even need to define for your fellow specialists.

Definitions range in length from a single word to long essays or even books. Sometimes, but not usually, a **synonym** inserted into your sentence will do, as in this example:

> The oil sump, that is, the oil reservoir, is located in the lower portion of the engine crankcase.

Synonym definition serves only when a common interchangeable word exists for the technical term you wish to use.

Sentence Definitions

Most often you will want to use at least a one-sentence definition containing the elements of a **logical definition**:

> term = genus or class + differentia

Although you may not have heard of the elements of a logical definition, you have been giving and hearing definitions cast in the logical pattern most of your life. In the logical definition, you state that something is a member of some genus or class and then specify the differences that distinguish this thing from other members of the class.

TERM	=	GENUS OR CLASS	+	DIFFERENTIA
An ohmmeter	is	an indicating instrument		that directly measures the resistance of an electrical circuit.
A legume	is	a fruit		formed from a single carpel, splitting along the dorsal and the ventral sutures, and usually containing a row of seeds borne on the inner side of the ventral suture.

The second of these two definitions, particularly, points out a pitfall you must avoid. This definition of a legume would satisfy only someone who was already fairly expert in botany. Lay people would be no farther ahead than before, because terms such as *carpel, ventral suture*, and so forth are not familiar to them. When writing for nonexperts, you may wish to settle for a definition less precise but more understandable:

> A legume is a fruit formed of an easily split pod that contains a row of seeds, such as a pea pod.

Here you have stayed with plain language and given an easily recognized example. Both of these definitions of a legume are good. The one you would choose depends on your audience.

Extended Definitions

To make sure you are understood, you will often want to extend a definition beyond a single sentence. The most common techniques for extending a definition are description, example, and analogy. However, any of the arrangement techniques—chronology, topical order, classification, and division—may be used. The following definition, again from *Chamber's*, goes beyond the logical definition to give a description:

> **anemometer.** An instrument for measuring the velocity of the wind. A common type consists of four hemispherical cups carried at the ends of four radial arms pivoted so as to be capable of rotation in a horizontal plane, the speed of rotation being indicated on a dial calibrated to read wind velocity directly.

In our lay definition of legume an example was given: "such as a pea pod." Often analogy is valuable:

> A voltmeter is an indicating instrument for measuring electrical potential. It may be compared to a pressure gauge used in a pipe to measure water pressure.

The following definition of a tornado is a good example of an extended definition intended for an intelligent lay audience. In it, the writer makes extensive use of both process and mechanism descriptions. Notice, also, that the writer defines other terms needed in understanding tornadoes:

> A tornado is a rare weather event. When one occurs, it can be destructive and life threatening.

Sentence definition

> Sometimes called a twister, a tornado is a violently whirling wind which appears as a funnel-shaped cloud hanging from the base of a dark, threatening thunderstorm cloud. Dust and debris, often mixed with mud and water, can be seen carried from the ground to the funnel.

Defines related terms

> Several tornadoes or funnels may occur simultaneously, or re-develop one after another. Hail, very heavy rain, strong gusty winds and frequent lightning often occur nearby. A tornado can be an isolated incident, or consist of several tornadoes spawned by a series of cumulonimbus clouds over several hours. (A "cumulonimbus" is a type of cloud which produces thunderstorms). In an exceptional case, over 125 tornadoes occurred on April 3 and 4, 1974 in an area extending from the Gulf of Mexico to southern Ontario. On May 31, 1985, tornadoes are known to have struck the Great Lakes region. Nine of these were recorded in southern Ontario.

Describes process

> Experience has shown that tornadoes are produced during intense "severe thunderstorms" when certain meteorological conditions are present. In Ontario, these conditions can occur in the spring and summer months when a low pressure system is approaching the area from the southwest and intensifying at the same time. Another cooler and drier air mass is usually present, to the north and west of this air mass. Through a complex evolution of events, the atmosphere becomes favourable for the growth of very large cumulonimbus clouds. Some of these can produce severe thunderstorms that have the potential to spawn tornadoes.

> Weather forecasters are on the alert for these conditions to develop. They examine weather charts and reports, satellite and radar images to detect as early as possible the factors and conditions which may lead to the development of severe thunderstorms.

Waterspouts are often described as tornadoes over water. Although their physical appearance and characteristics are similar, waterspouts form over water bodies and cannot be sustained over land. Tornadoes develop over land and generally weaken when they pass over water.

The meteorological conditions leading to the formation of waterspouts are different from those associated with tornadoes. During cool days in summer and fall, thunderstorm clouds can develop over a warm water surface such as the lower Great Lakes. Although these clouds do not generally develop to the intense tornado-bearing cumulonimbus cloud, they can produce waterspouts. The waterspouts themselves usually last for a few minutes and do not grow or persist to the extent of tornadoes. Although waterspouts can be damaging, especially to small boats, they are less dangerous than tornadoes.

Describes mechanism

The tornado appears first as a cone-shaped funnel cloud at the base of the dark cumulonimbus cloud. Typically, the tip of the funnel then extends or elongates downwards. As the whirling winds reach the ground, a cloud of debris becomes noticeable and the tornado is fully formed. The tornado moves along a slightly curved path, following the movement of the parent cloud. In most cases, it travels towards a direction between northeast and southeast. The forward motion of the tornado ranges from slow-moving to speeds near 100 km/hour. It can be quite erratic and [travel] along a somewhat zig-zag path. During its travel, the tornado funnel may retract to the cloud base and then lower to the ground again for repeated "touchdowns". The tornado changes its size, shape and path during its lifetime. A weakening tornado may develop a rope-like funnel, become contorted and finally invisible, as the funnel retracts to the cloud base.

From start to finish, most tornadoes last for a matter of minutes, causing damage on a path of less than one kilometre in length and a width of less than 100 metres. However, in an extreme case, a tornado can remain on the ground for over one hour, causing damage along a 100-kilometre path, 500 metres wide.[7]

As this writer has done, extend your definition as far as is needed to ensure the level of reader understanding desired.

Placement of Definitions

You have several options for placement of definitions within your reports: (1) within the text itself, (2) in footnotes or endnotes, (3) in a glossary at the beginning or end of the paper, and (4) in an appendix. Which method you use depends upon the audience and the length of the definition.

WITHIN THE TEXT   If the definition is short—a sentence or two—or if you feel most of your audience needs the definition, place it in the text with the word defined. Most often, the definition is placed after the word defined, as in this example from an Ontario Ministry of Northern Development and Mines publication:

The most common type of sediments deposited in a lake by a glacier is called a **rhythmite**, from the word rhythm. This describes their unique annual repeating pattern. The sediments are found in pairs of layers. There is a bottom layer of sandy silt covered by a top layer of fine clay. The sandy silt accumulated during the summer melting season. The fine-grained clay settled on the lake bottom in winter.[8]

Sometimes, the definition is slipped in smoothly before the word is used—a technique that helps break down the reader's resistance to the unfamiliar term. The following definition is a good example of the technique:

> If the temperature of a gas is raised high enough, the atoms in the gas will collide with sufficient energy to remove their electrons. This will result in a high-temperature medium consisting of positively charged ions and negatively charged electrons, whose overall electrical charge is still neutral. This swirling cloud of charged particles is called a **plasma**.[9]

When you are using key terms that must be understood before the reader can grasp your subject, define them in your introduction.

IN FOOTNOTES AND ENDNOTES   If your definition is longer than a sentence or two, and your audience is a mixed one—part expert and part lay—you may want to put your definition in a footnote at the bottom of the page or an endnote at the end of your report. A lengthy definition placed in the text could distract the expert who does not need it.

IN A GLOSSARY   If you have many short definitions to give and if you have reason to believe that most members of your audience will not read your report straight through, place your definitions in a glossary. (See Figure 6–3 and Figure 9–9, page 212.) When you use a glossary, be sure to draw your readers' attention to it, both in the table of contents and early in the discussion.

IN AN APPENDIX   If you need one or more lengthy extended definitions (say, more than 200 words each) for some but not all members of your audience, place them in an appendix. (See Chapter 9, pages 224–225.) At the point in your text where readers may need them, be sure to explain where they are.

Description

In technical writing, you will chiefly have to describe three things: places, mechanisms, and processes. After explaining the use of visual language in description, we deal with mechanism and process descriptions.

Visual Language

The following description by Roberta Bondar of the auroras seen from space shows how a combination of analogy, imagery, and definition can help readers visualize—and understand—a phenomenon outside their realm of experience.

> For those who have not experienced either the aurora borealis in the Northern Hemisphere or the aurora australis in the Southern Hemisphere, it is hard to imagine the way this light expands outward from the atmosphere into space. It is an incredible sight. The shimmering fingers and curtains of light are the result of the solar wind—an excitation of the Earth's atmospheres near the poles by radiation from the sun. As the solar wind courses through the geomagnetic field and upper atmosphere, electrical energy is generated, driving ionized gas particles into dense gases below. This produces a light show without

Terms printed in boldface

Grammatically parallel sentence fragments used for definition (see "Parallelism" in Part V, Handbook)

When needed, definitions are extended in complete sentences

GLOSSARY

Annelids—Worm-like animals having a segmented body with a distinct head and appendages.

Bedrock—Solid rock underlying vegetation, soil or loose surface material.

Bilateral symmetry—Exists when an organism or its parts can be divided into right and left halves so that one half is the mirror image of the other.

Brachiopods—Organisms with an external shell consisting of two dissimilar curved plates or valves. Each valve is bilaterally symmetrical. Also known as "Lamp Shells."

Bryozoans—A colony of animals usually encrusting sea weeds, shells, and bottom rocks. May also occur as globular or irregular masses or as fan-shaped or branched stems. Also known as sea mats, sea mosses, or moss animals.

Cambrian—The span of geologic time and corresponding rocks from about 570 to 500 million years ago; named after Cambria, the Roman name for Wales where rocks of this age were first studied.

Cephalopods—Free swimming marine moluscs characterized by well-developed head, foot, mouth, eyes, and tentacles; commonly living in the outermost chamber of a multichambered straight or coiled shell.

Chitinophosphatic—Composed of chitin, a resistant organic compound and/or calcium phosphates. Chitin is a skeletal forming material in some animals e.g. trilobites.

Class—A grouping comprising one or more smaller subgroupings of organism called *orders*.

Clastic—Containing fragments (clasts) of pre-existing rocks. cf. detrital.

Correlation—The determination of the position or place of a geologic formation or phenomenon in space or time with respect to a similar formation of phenomenon from another area.

Crinoids—Marine animals resembling flowers. They possess a system of roots, a long beaded stem, a cup-shaped head containing soft parts, and five branched arms extending outwards from the head. Also known as sea lilies.

Dendritic—A branching pattern, as that of a deciduous tree.

Detrital—Formed from loose rock materials (detritus) moved from their place of origin. cf. clastic.

Devonian—The span of geologic time and corresponding rocks from about 400 to about 360 million years ago; named after Devonshire country, England, where rocks of this age were first studied.

Dolostone—A variety of limestone consisting mainly of the mineral Dolomite $CaMg(CO_3)_2$.

Figure 6-3 DEFINITIONS IN A GLOSSARY

Source: Harish M. Verma, *Geology and Fossils, Craigleith Area* (Ontario Ministry of Natural Resources, 1979): 55.

sound, which with its lines, loops, closed circles, patches and vertical pencils of light can use up many magazines of film. Most auroras emanate a greenish-white glow, the colour given off by ionized oxygen. In the Northern Hemisphere in the heart of winter, observers on the ground may see a vertical curtain varying in length and intensity, like a supernatural pipe organ. Or they may see streams of fluorescent-green light particles that drift in the night sky in swirls and flowing lines like sand washed ashore at the edge of an ocean. We have never created fireworks the equal of an aurora.[10]

We visualize things in essentially five ways—by shape, size, colour, texture, and position. In addition, comparison of the unfamiliar with the familiar through analogy is a powerful visualization tool.

SHAPE   You can describe the shape of things with terms such as cubical, cylindrical, circular, convex, concave, square, trapezoidal, or rectangular. You can use simple analogies such as C-shaped, L-shaped, Y-shaped, cigar-shaped, corkscrew, or star-shaped. You can describe things as threadlike or pencil-like or as sawtoothed or football-shaped.

SIZE   You can give physical dimensions for size, but you can also compare objects to coins, paper clips, books, and football fields.

COLOUR   You can use familiar colours such as red and yellow and also, with some care, such descriptive terms as *pastel, luminous, dark, drab*, and *brilliant*.

TEXTURE   You have many words and comparisons at your disposal for texture, such as *pebbly, embossed, pitted, coarse, fleshy, honeycombed, glazed, sandpaperlike, mirrorlike*, and *waxen*.

POSITION   You have *opposite, parallel, corresponding, identical, front, behind, above, below, right, left, north, south*, and so forth to indicate position.

ANALOGY   The use of analogy will aid your audience in visualizing the thing described. In the following example, Spar Aerospace's Shuttle Remote Manipulator System (SRMS)—itself "an analogue of the human arm"—is described with an extended organic analogy which helps the reader visualize the integrity of the design.

> What emerged was an analogue of the human arm, with nerves of copper wiring, bones of graphite fibre and electric motors in place of muscles. Like its human counterpart, it has various rotating joints, two at the shoulder, one at the elbow and three at the wrist.
>
> At fifteen metres in length, and weighing less than 480 kilograms, the Canadarm can lift up to 30 000 kilograms, or the mass of a fully loaded bus, using less electricity than a tea kettle. The arm is controlled by its brain, a sophisticated computer. It has been designed such that it can work both manually with astronauts using hand controls to operate it, or automatically. Its hand is a wire-snare device designed to fit over a special prong or grapple fixture attached to a satellite.[11]

Mechanism Description

The physical description of some mechanism is perhaps the most common kind of technical description. It is a commonplace procedure with little mystery attached to it.

The purpose of a mechanism description is to make the reader *see* the object and understand its function. A good mechanism description should do the following:

- Describe the overall appearance of the mechanism, the material with which it is made, and its function.
- Divide the mechanism into its component parts (for example, a plumber's snake consists of a cable, boring head, and crank).
- Describe the appearance of the parts, give their functions, and show how they work together.
- Give only relevant information. For example, in a description of a plumber's snake, colour would not be mentioned because it is of no consequence.
- Use figurative language—*springlike* and *football-shaped*—and comparisons to familiar objects to clarify and shorten the description.

In the following discussion, we tell you how to plan a mechanism description and provide several typical examples.

PLANNING   There is no formula for writing mechanism descriptions, although most do include certain common elements. You must use your judgment, weighing such matters as purpose and audience. As you plan your mechanism description, you'll need to answer questions like the ones in the planning and revision checklists for mechanism description (page 138). The answers to these questions will largely determine how you arrange your description and the details and so-whats you provide your readers.

EXAMPLES OF MECHANISM DESCRIPTIONS   In Figure 6-4, our annotations draw your attention to the various features of a mechanism description as exemplified in the descriptive overview of the Shuttle Remote Manipulator System (Canadarm). Figure 6-5 is one of several graphics that accompany the robot's description. As demonstrated in Figure 6-5, such graphics are frequently annotated. Parts may be "cut away" to show the interior of the mechanism described, or separated, like the arm booms in this graphic.

Professionals often describe mechanisms for reasons of technology transfer. *Technology transfer* is a rather fancy term for a common but important part of technical and scientific life. Technical people exchange concepts through their technical journals. Sometimes the transfer is from one discipline to another. Very often the concept described concerns a mechanism. Figure 6-6 reproduces a mechanism description as it appeared in a publication devoted to technology transfer. Like most such descriptions, it uses a graphic to reduce the need for extensive written description of its physical characteristics. The reason for and implications— the "so-whats"—of the characteristics and facts described are made clear. In fact, the author's initial paragraph provides a context for understanding the value of the innovative AC device in maintaining fuel channels in nuclear reactors. As is done in most mechanism descriptions, the author divides the mechanism into its parts and gives details of the design features.

Description of function and performance

Since its maiden voyage aboard U.S. Space Shuttle Columbia in 1981, the Shuttle Remote Manipulator System (SRMS), known as Canadarm, has demonstrated its reliability, usefulness, and versatility and has provided strong, yet precise and delicate handling of its payloads. Canadarm uses an end effector with specially designed grapple fixtures to place payloads in orbit.

History of project

The first Canadarm—designed, developed and built by Spar, under contract to the National Research Council of Canada, now the Canadian Space Agency—was a gift from Canada to NASA's Space Shuttle Program. Subsequently, NASA ordered follow-on production units which have resulted in over $400 million in export sales for Canada.

Planned and unplanned applications

Canadarm has performed flawlessly on countless missions: placing satellites into their proper orbit and retrieving malfunctioning ones for repair. Perhaps its most notable mission to date was the 1993 repair of the Hubble Space Telescope.

Canadarm was used as a mobile work platform for astronauts during numerous space walks required to repair the faulty telescope. Canadarm played a critical role during the entire mission—retrieving the satellite, placing it in the cargo bay for repairs, acting as a platform for the astronauts, and then re-deploying it.

Unplanned exercises for Canadarm have included knocking a block of ice from a clogged wastewater vent that might have endangered the shuttle upon re-entry, pushing a faulty antenna into place, and successfully activating a satellite (using a swatter made from briefing covers) that failed to go into proper orbit.

Manoeuvrability

- Capable of accurately manoeuvring payloads of 30 000 kgs (in the weightlessness of space).
- The shoulder joint has two degrees of freedom, the elbow joint has one degree of freedom, and the wrist joint has up to three degrees of freedom.

Productivity

The Canadarm can be operated under astronaut control or automatically (using pre-programmed trajectories to complete specific manoeuvres for the arm).

Reliability

The Canadarm has proven its reliability by successfully completing all of its missions.

Technical data

Technical Details

The Canadarm comprises an upper and lower arm boom, an end effector, and a control centre where the translational and rotational hand controllers direct the movement of the arm.

Use of list for ease of reference

Length: 15.2 m (50 ft)

Diameter: 38 cm (25 in)

Weight on Earth: 410 kg (905 lbs)

Speed of Movement: Unloaded 60 cm/sec (2 ft/sec); Loaded 6 cm/sec (2.4 in/sec)

Upper & Lower: Arm Boom: Carbon Composite Material

Wrist Joint: The degrees of movement (pitch/yaw/roll)

Elbow Joint: One degree of movement (pitch)

Shoulder Joint: Two degrees of movement (pitch/yaw)

Translation Hand Controller: Controls the left, right, up, down, forward, and backward movements of the arm

Rotational Hand Controller: Controls the pitch, roll, and yaw of the arm.

....

Figure 6-4 MECHANISM DESCRIPTION OF CANADARM

Source: Spar Aerospace Limited, *Spar Space Systems Data Sheet* (Brampton, Ont., 1995).

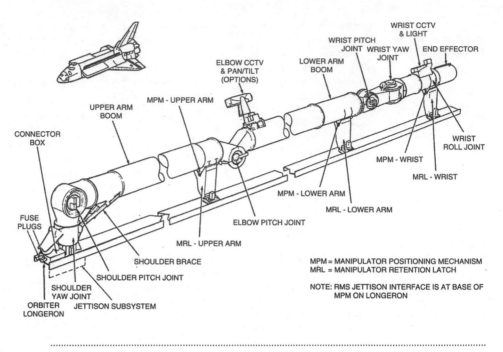

Figure 6-5   GRAPHIC FOR CANADARM

Source: Spar Aerospace Limited, *Spar Space Systems Data Sheet* (Brampton, Ont., 1995).

Process Description

Process description is probably the chief use of chronological order in technical writing. By **process** we mean a sequence of events that progresses from a beginning to an end and results in a change or a product. The process may be humanly controlled, such as the manufacture of an automobile, or it may be natural, such as the metamorphosis of a caterpillar to a butterfly.

Process descriptions are written in one of two ways:

- *For the doer*—to provide instructions for performing the process
- *For the interested observer*—to provide an understanding of the process

A cake recipe is a good example of instructions for performing a process. You are told when to add the milk to the flour, when to reserve the whites of the eggs for later use. You are instructed to grease the pan *before* you pour the batter in, and so forth. Writing good instructions is a major application of technical writing, and we have devoted all of Chapter 15 to it. In this chapter we explain only the second type, which is aimed at providing an understanding of the process.

VERB TENSE, MOOD, AND VOICE   In writing process description, it's important to make the correct choice between present and past tense and to decide which voice and mood to use.

Reprinted from *Ontario Hydro Research Review*

The Application of Electromagnetic Techniques to Fuel Channel Technology   *M. Cenanovic*

Context of need for mechanism "so-whats"

As nuclear reactors age, their need for service and repair increases. Innovative electromagnetic techniques that offer the potential of automation have important advantages over conventional techniques: process times and radiation exposure can be minimized and process reliability can be maximized. Ontario Hydro Research Division's electromagnetic laboratory anticipated these needs and pioneered the use of electromagnetic processes and systems for reactor rehabilitation—in particular, for fuel channels. Two innovative applications of these electromagnetic techniques are spacer location and repositioning (SLAR) and rolled joint separation.

Spacer Location and Repositioning Application

Function of mechanism

When it was established that in some of Ontario Hydro's operating reactors many gartersprings (spacers) were no longer in their correct positions, it became apparent that reactor life could be limited by contact of pressure tube to calandria tube, which resulted in blister formation. To prevent blister formation, an innovative AC device was developed to reposition the gartersprings without any harmful effects on fuel channel integrity [1].

Since the only possible access was to be from inside the pressure tube, the need to create some sort of coupling between the gartersprings and a device that could exert force on the gartersprings was established. When electromagnetic forces are used, two fundamental difficulties in achieving significant interaction with the gartersprings arise: (1) the electromagnetic shielding of the gartersprings by the pressure tube and (2) the unfavourable electromagnetic characteristics of the material of the gartersprings, which has low electrical conductivity, is nonmagnetic, and is similar to the material of which pressure tubes are made.

Parts of mechanism

The principal feature of the AC device developed (Figure 1) is its efficient conversion of magnetic energy, which is transmitted through the conductive wall of the pressure tube, into continuous mechanical movement of

the gartersprings. The governing principle of the AC device is the creation of a travelling magnetic field in a fashion similar to that of a linear induction motor (LIM), where the gartersprings acts as the rotor. A three-phase, low-power electrical excitation at low frequency achieved this desired result. Thus, two fundamental difficulties were overcome simultaneously, and significant electromagnetic interaction with the gartersprings was achieved.

So-whats

The device was demonstrated in-reactor, and a modification of the device is now being used successfully in the latest version of the SLAR tool, which consists of a free-end LIM and a centre LIM. The centre LIM was designed for central mounting on the Mark III SLAR tool. This tool can reposition fuel channel gartersprings in reactor channels with up to 100 000 hours of creep deformation resulting from full-power operation. The free-end LIM is used only for repositioning purposes, whereas the centre LIM serves two purposes: it exerts electromagnetic repositioning force on the spacer, and it provides the SLAR tool with strong support for the full bending load imposed by the pressure tube bending mechanism. This results in significant savings to Ontario Hydro and other CANDU reactor owners because of extended reliable reactor life.

References

1. Cenanovic MB, Mauriera H. The AC device for repositioning of gartersprings in CANDU reactors. *Nucl J. Can.* December 1987; 1:355-358.

2. Pritchard DF, Cenanovic MB. Pickering large scale fuel channel replacement separation of pressure tube rolled joints by rapid induction heat. *Canadian Nuclear Society, proc of 6th Ann Conf*, Ottawa, Canada, June 3-4, 1985.

3. Cenanovic MB, Ng MKC, Malkiewicz TA, Lee JT. Rolled joint separation by shock heating. *Canadian Nuclear Society, Proc of CANDU Maintenance Conf*, Toronto, Canada, November 22-24, 1987.

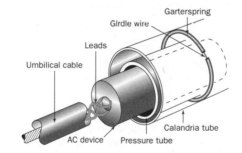

Figure 1   AC device in the fuel channel arrangement.

Figure 6-6   TECHNOLOGY–TRANSFER MECHANISM DESCRIPTION

Source: M. Cenanovic, "The Application of Electromagnetic Techniques to Fuel Channel Technology," *Ontario Hydro Research Review* 8 (August 1993): 56-57.

Processes that are ongoing are usually described in the present tense, as if each step were unfolding before the reader's eyes (we have set the verbs in boldface):

Present tense

Blood from the body **enters** the upper chamber, the atrium, on the right side of the heart and **flows** from there into the lower chamber, the ventricle. The ventricle **pumps** the blood under low pressure into the lungs, where it **releases** carbon dioxide and **picks up** oxygen.

The rationale for the use of present tense is that the process is an ongoing and continuing process—the heart's pumping of blood. Therefore, it is described as going on as you are observing it.

However, processes that occurred in the past and are completed are described in the past tense. A major use of past tense in process description is found in empirical research reports where the procedures the researcher followed are described in past tense (verbs in boldface):

Past tense

During the excavation delay we **accomplished** two tasks. First, we **installed** a temporary intake structure and **tested** the system's efficiency. Second, we **designed, built,** and **installed** a new turbine and generator.

In writing instructions, you will commonly use the active voice and imperative mood. In following your instructions, it is the reader who is the doer. With its implied *you*, the imperative voice directly addresses the reader:

Imperative mood

Clean the threads on the new section of pipe. **Add** pipe thread compound to the outside threads.

But in the process description for understanding, where the reader is not the doer, the use of imperative mood would be inappropriate and even misleading. In writing a process for understanding, therefore, you will ordinarily use the indicative mood in both active and passive voice:

Active voice
Passive voice

The size of the cover opening **controls** the rate of evaporation.

The rate of evaporation **is controlled by** the size of the cover opening.

In active voice, the subject does the action. In passive voice, the subject receives the action. The passive voice emphasizes the receiver of the action while deemphasizing or removing completely the doer of the action. (Incidentally, as the preceding examples illustrate, neither doer nor receiver has to be a human being or even an animate object.) When the doer is unimportant or not known, you should choose passive voice. Conversely, when the doer is known and important, you should choose the active voice. Because the active is often the simpler, more direct statement of an idea, choose passive voice only when it is clearly indicated. We have more to say on this subject on pages 87-89.

EXAMPLES OF PROCESS DESCRIPTION   As with all technical writing, you can write process descriptions for varied audiences. In the following excerpt, the writer describes how geologists determine the ages of igneous rocks. The intended audience is an educated lay person. The writer uses present tense throughout and predominantly the active voice.

Overview of process

How do geologists determine the ages of rocks? Like detectives, they look for clues to the events taking place when the rock was formed. If the rock is igneous in origin (i.e., formed by cooling from a molten state either deep inside or on the surface of the earth) the clue to its age is provided by radioactive elements (like uranium and thorium) that were incorporated in the rock in minute quantities at the time of its formation. In the early 1900s it was discovered that radioactive elements, from the moment they come into existence, spontaneously break down to form other lighter elements some of which may be radioactive and also suffer the same fate.

Description of process

This process of spontaneous disintegration, called radioactive decay, continues until a stable, nonradioactive element is formed that does not decay any further. For example, uranium-238 (one variety of uranium found in nature), eventually transforms into lead-206, a nonradioactive element. A convenient way of visualizing the transformation or decay process is to consider how much time is taken by one half of the original radioactive element to change to a nonradioactive element. This time is called the half life period and is different for different radioactive elements. In the case of uranium-238, the half life is 4,510 million years. In other words, if we start with one gram of uranium-238, one-half gram will change to lead-206 in 4,510 million years. The other one-half gram will still be uranium-238. In another 4,510 million years, one-half of one-half (one-fourth) of the original uranium-238 will be converted to lead-206, so that, after 9,020 million years, the sample will contain one-fourth gram of uranium-238 and three-fourth gram of lead-206.

Let us turn the situation around. If, today, we found a one gram sample of uranium-lead mixture which, upon analysis, revealed a composition of one-half gram U-238 and one-half gram Pb-206, we would conclude that the sample had originated 4,510 million years ago, at which time all of it was U-238. Thus, by analyzing for the amount of a radioactive element present in a rock, and comparing this to the amount of nonradioactive decay products, the period of decay can be determined. This provides an absolute age, in years, for the rock. ... [A]t the end of four half lives one-sixteenth of the original radioactive element is left, the remainder having decayed. In theory a given amount of radioactive element never completely decays. At any one time, it will always have one-half left to decay.[12]

In writing process descriptions designed to provide understanding, you'll find that extensive detail is not always necessary or even desirable. As in mechanism description, the amount of detail given relates to the technical knowledge and interest of your readers. When the *Vancouver Sun* publishes an article about open–heart surgery, its readers do not expect complete details on how such an operation is performed. Rather, they expect their curiosity to be satisfied in a general way. The author of the description of the radioactive decay process used a level of detail he felt would satisfy his audience—general readers with an interest in the geology and fossils of the Ontario Craigleith area.

Figure 6-7 shows a process description written for an executive audience. It deals with shipworms, marine organisms that attack wood immersed in salt water. As with description written for a lay audience, the writer chooses her level of detail carefully. As you read it, notice that no attempt is made to give full information about the shipworm, as an entomologist might desire. We don't learn, for example, how the shipworm reproduces, nor do we even learn very clearly what it looks like. For the intended readers of the letter, such information is not needed. They need to know what is presented—the

Marine Consultants
42 Acadian Avenue
Dartmouth, NS
B4L 1T3

(902) 481–4247
Fax (902) 481–4251

17 July 1999

Mr. Avery Brandisi
Chief Executive Officer
Maritime Transport Inc.
963 Shaunslieve Drive
Halifax, NS B6K 4P7

Dear Mr. Brandisi:

We have as you requested examined the condition of the pilings that support the Maritime Transport east pier. The pilings show only minor shipworm damage. However, because of the high probability that your pilings will suffer further shipworm damage if not protected, we recommend that you take action as soon as possible.

Shipworms are mollusks that bore into submerged wood and do extensive damage to it. The shipworms, so-called because when fully grown they resemble worms, begin life as small organisms looking for a place to lodge. When a shipworm comes to rest on wood, it changes into a worm-like animal with a pair of shells on its head. Using these shells, the shipworm bores its way into the wood. As the head bores in, the end of the worm-like body remains at the entrance hole. The shipworm lives on the wood borings and the organisms in the sea water it passes through itself.

Although shipworms may reach lengths up to one metre, the entrance hole remains the same size. Thus, the wood can be completely honeycombed with shipworms and except for small entrance holes look perfectly sound. This is what can happen to your pilings if they are not properly treated.

Ironically, your firm and many other waterside businesses in Halifax harbour are victims of the progress made in cleansing the water in the harbour. When the harbour was heavily polluted, it would not support most marine animals, including shipworms. In the now relatively clear water of the harbour, shipworms have returned and are causing major damage that will take millions of dollars to repair.

Either sheathing or chemical treatment would offer your pilings a good measure of protection. If you like, we can help you choose the best treatment and recommend reputable contractors to do the work.

Sincerely,

Mary Chen

Mary Chen
Consulting Entomologist

Figure 6-7 EXECUTIVE PROCESS DESCRIPTION

process by which the shipworm lodges on the wood and how it bores into it. They need to know that the damage done by shipworms is largely invisible from the exterior of the wood. Finally, they need to know that they must take action and what that action has to be.

Empirical research reports are written for experts. The section in the report that describes the *methods* used by the researcher is a process description. Because the research has been completed by the time it is reported, methods sections are written in past tense, usually in a mixture of active and passive voice. Writers of such reports include enough detail about the procedure so that readers as expert as themselves could duplicate the research. Because of that requirement, the level of detail in an expert report is normally much higher than in a lay or executive report. The writer, having an expert audience, uses technical language freely. The following excerpt is the methods section from a report on research that evaluated consumers' understanding and use of fat and cholesterol information on food labels.

METHODS

Sample

A mall intercept was the method chosen to gather data from the quota sample. An experienced market research company was commissioned to carry out the interviews of 149 consumers who were the main grocery shoppers for their households, in the representative cities of London (n=74) and Toronto (n=75). Sampling quotas were set for age, sex and education to match the national survey. The quotas for age were 40%: 18 to 24 years, 60%: 35 to 70 years; for sex: 80% women, 20% men; and for education: 60% high school or less, 40% post secondary in some form. The interviews, conducted according to the method described by Cowan, took an average of 18 minutes.

Questionnaire

The study objectives and the data collection instrument were developed under the guidance of an advisory group with representatives from government, the food industry and universities. A 31-item questionnaire was developed using a combination of closed-ended, Likert scale and open-ended questions. Questions focused on the claim statements "low fat", "reduced in fat", "low in saturated fat", "no cholesterol", "fat free" and "light", which have very specific meanings associated with the regulated wording, and the terms "non-hydrogenated", "polyunsaturates, monounsaturates and saturates", and "% butter/milk fat" (B.F./M.F.). A reference question on the importance of reducing dietary fat was included for comparison of nutrition awareness with other recent studies.

Two product comparison tests were included. One test asked consumers to evaluate the fat content of three samples of margarine. All margarines had a nutrition panel and contained the same amount of fat, but claims and prominence given to descriptive information about fat and cholesterol varied on the packages.

The second test focused on the hydrogenation of the margarines. The only product labelled "non-hydrogenated" was shown to respondents who were first asked to interpret the term, and then to indicate if the other samples of margarines were "non-hydrogenated".

Demographic data were gathered on respondents' household income, size and composition.

Data Analysis

The data were analyzed using the computer software package STAS (Megatab Logiciel Inc., Montreal). The confidence level for the total sample is ±8% for values in the 50% range. Statistical accuracy improves to ±4% as answers approach 5% or 95% values. Significant differences between demographic subgroups were assigned at a 95% confidence level.[13]

PLANNING   As with mechanism descriptions, there are no easy formulas to follow in writing process descriptions. You must exercise a good deal of judgment in the matter. As in all writing, you must decide what your audience needs to know to satisfy its purpose and yours. However, the process description checklists should provide guidance to aid you in exercising your judgment (and revising globally).

Argument

Whenever you are exercising your professional judgment and expressing an opinion, you will need the tools and techniques of argument. In a business setting, you would argue for your recommendations and your decisions. As a scientist, you would argue in the discussion section of a research report to support the conclusions you have reached. Argument is indispensable for the technical person.

You must present your argument in a persuasive way. The use of *induction, deduction*, and *comparison* is necessary in argument. *Toulmin logic*, named for its creator, Steven Toulmin, is a good technique for discovering an argument and presenting it. We cover all these points in this chapter.

Convincing Argument

In argument, you deal with opinions that lie somewhere on a continuum between verifiable fact and pure subjectivity. Verifiable fact does not require argument. If someone says a room is 9 metres long and you disagree, you don't need an argument, you need a tape measure. Pure subjectivity cannot be argued. If someone hates the taste of spinach, you will not convince him or her otherwise with argument. The opinions dealt with in argument may be called propositions, premises, claims, conclusions, theses, or hypotheses, but under any name they remain opinions. Your purpose in **argument** is to convince your audience of the probability that the opinions you are advancing are correct.

Typically, an argument supports one main opinion, often called the **major proposition**. In turn, the major proposition is supported by a series of minor propositions. **Minor propositions**, like major propositions, are opinions, but generally they are nearer on the continuum to verifiable fact. Finally, the minor propositions are supported by verifiable facts and frequently by statements from recognized authorities.

To understand how you might construct such an argument, imagine for the moment that you are the waste management expert in an environmental consulting firm. Land developers constructing a new housing subdivision called Hawk Estates have turned to your firm for advice. Hawk Estates, like many new subdivisions, is being built close to a city, Champlain, but not in the city. The problem at issue is whether Hawk Estates should build its own sewage disposal plant or tap into the sewage system of Champlain. (The developers have already ruled out individual septic tanks because Hawk Estates is built on nonabsorbent clay soil.) Champlain will allow the tap-in. You have investigated the situation, thought about it a good deal, and have decided that the tap-in is the most desirable alternative. The land developers are not convinced. It is their money, so you must write a report to convince them.

MAJOR PROPOSITION In developing your argument, it helps to use a chart such as the one illustrated in Figure 6-8. The chart enables you to clearly separate and organize your major proposition, minor propositions, and evidence. First you must state your major proposition: "Hawk Estates should tap in to the sewage system of the city of Champlain."

MINOR PROPOSITIONS AND EVIDENCE Now you must support your major proposition. Your first and most relevant minor proposition is that Champlain's sewage system can handle Hawk Estates' waste. Questions of cost, convenience, and so forth would be irrelevant if Champlain could not furnish adequate support. As you did with your major proposition, you begin this section of the report with your minor proposition. To support this proposition, you give the estimated amount of waste that will be produced by Hawk Estates, followed by a statement from the Champlain city engineer that the city system can handle this amount of waste.

The minor proposition that states "the overall cost to Hawk Estates taxpayers will be only slightly more if they are tapped into the city rather than having their own plant" is a difficult one. It's actually a rebuttal of your argument, but you must deal with it for several reasons.

First and foremost, you must be ethical and honest with the developers. Second, it would be poor strategy not to be. If they find that you have withheld information from them, they will doubt your credibility. You decide to put this proposition second in your argument. In that way, you can begin and end with your strongest propositions, a wise strategy. To support this proposition you would list the initial cost of the plant versus the cost of the tap-in. You would further state the yearly fee charged by the city versus the yearly cost of running the plant. You might anticipate the opposing argument that the plant will save the homeowners money. You could break down the cost per individual homeowner, perhaps showing that the tap-in would cost an average homeowner only an additional 10 dollars a year, a fairly nominal amount.

Your final minor proposition is that the proposed plant, a sewage lagoon, will represent a nuisance to the homeowners of Hawk Estates. Because the cost for the tap-in is admittedly higher, your argument will probably swing on this minor proposition. State freely that well-maintained sewage lagoons do not smell particularly, but then point out that authorities state that sewage

MAJOR PROPOSITION	MINOR PROPOSITION	EVIDENCE
	Colorful Springs can handle Hawk Estates sewage.	• Estimate of waste from Hawk Estates. • City engineer's statement that Colorful Springs can handle estimated waste.
Hawk Estates should tap into sewage system of Colorful Springs.	Overall cost to Hawk Estates taxpayers only slightly higher if tapped into Colorful Springs.	• Initial cost of plant vs. cost of tap-in. • Yearly fee charged by Colorful Springs vs. operating cost of sewage lagoon. • Cost per individual tax payer.
	Proposed plant, a sewage lagoon, will be a nuisance to home owners.	• Well maintained lagoons Okay. • Lagoons hard to maintain, often smell bad, experts say. • Lagoon has to be located upwind of development.

Figure 6-8 ARGUMENT ARRANGEMENT CHART

lagoons are difficult to maintain. Furthermore, if not maintained to the highest standards, sewage lagoons emit an unpleasant odour. To clinch your argument, you show that the only piece of land in Hawk Estates large enough to handle a sewage lagoon is upwind of the majority of houses during prevailing winds. With the tap-in, all wastes are carried away from Hawk Estates and will cause no odour or unsightliness.

ORGANIZATION When you draft your argument, you can follow the organization shown on the chart, adding details as needed to make a persuasive case. Although your major proposition is actually the recommendation that your argument leads to, you present it first, so that your audience will know where you are heading. In executive reports, which this one is, major conclusions and recommendations are often presented first, as we point out in Chapter 4, "Writing for Your Readers."

When you sum up your argument, draw attention once again to your key points. Point out that in cost and the ability to handle the produced wastes, the proposed plant and the tap-in are essentially equal. However, the plant will probably become an undesirable nuisance to Hawk Estates. Therefore, you recommend that the builder choose the tap-in.

Throughout any argument you appeal to reason. In most technical writing situations, an appeal to emotion will make your case immediately suspect. Never use sarcasm in an argument. You never know whose toes you are stepping on or how you will be understood. Support your case with simply stated, verifiable facts and statements from recognized authorities. In our example, a statement from potential buyers that "sewage lagoons smell bad" would not be adequate. A statement to the same effect from a recognized engineering authority would be acceptable and valid.

Induction and Deduction

Much of your thought, whether you are casually chatting with friends or are on your most logical and formal behaviour, consists of induction and deduction. In this section we cover induction and deduction and discuss some of the fallacies you'll want to avoid in using them.

INDUCTION   Induction is a movement from particular facts to general conclusions. It's a method of discovering and testing the inferences you can draw from your information. Induction is the chief way we have of establishing causality, that A caused B. The inductive process consists of looking at a set of facts, making an educated guess to explain the facts, and investigating to see whether the guess fits the facts. The educated guess is called a *hypothesis*. No matter how well constructed your hypothesis is, remember it is only a guess. Be ready to discard it in an instant if it doesn't fit your facts.

The whole process of gathering evidence, making hypotheses, and testing hypotheses against the evidence is the scientific method at work. Looking for **similarities** and **differences** is the major tool in testing hypotheses. Examining similarities and differences in the population has led medical authorities, including Health Canada, to declare that cigarette smoking is hazardous to your health. They looked at the population and saw a difference: There are those who smoke and those who don't. Within these two groups, they looked for similarities. Smokers had in common a high incidence of respiratory problems, including emphysema and lung cancer. Nonsmokers had in common a low incidence of such problems. The higher incidence of such problems in the smoking group when compared to the nonsmoking group was a significant difference.

Whenever you argue inductively to support a hypothesis, you must accept the possibility that new evidence may prove you wrong. Nevertheless, far more judgments and decisions are made on inductive arguments than on direct evidence. Well-constructed inductive arguments are powerful. Yes,

Health Canada officials could possibly be proven wrong, but more and more people are not betting their lives on it.

In the following example, the author argues inductively for the proposition that life does not exist on Mars. The argument is supported by a series of conclusions based upon evidence gathered by the Viking spacecraft.

Major proposition

The primary objective of Viking was to determine whether life exists on Mars. The evidence provided by Viking indicates clearly that it does not.

Three of Viking's scientific instruments were capable of detecting life on Mars:

Capability of cameras

Conclusion

Paragraph explaining function and capability of GCMS and presenting conclusion about its findings

Function of biology instrument

Capability of biology instruments

Appeal to authority

Evidence for presence of oxidants

Conclusion

- The lander cameras could have photographed living creatures large enough to be seen with the human eye and could have detected growth changes in organisms such as lichens. The cameras found nothing that could be interpreted as living.
- The gas chromatograph/mass spectrometer (GCMS) could have found organic molecules in the soil. Organic compounds combine carbon, hydrogen, nitrogen, and oxygen and are present in all living matter on Earth. The GCMS searched for heavy organic molecules, those that contain complex combinations of carbon and oxygen and are either precursors of life or its remains. To the surprise of almost every Viking scientist, the GCMS, which easily finds organic matter in the most barren Earth soils, found no trace of any in the Martian samples.
- The Viking biology instrument was the primary life-detection instrument. A one-cubic-foot box, crammed with the most sophisticated scientific hardware ever built, it contained three tiny instruments that searched the Martian soil for evidence of metabolic processes like those used by bacteria, green plants, and animals on Earth.

The three biology instruments worked flawlessly. All showed unusual activity in the Martian soil, activity that mimicked life. But biologists needed time to understand the strange chemistry of the soil. Today, according to most scientists who worked on the data, it is clear that the chemical reactions were not caused by living things.

Furthermore, the immediate release of oxygen when the soil contacted water vapor in the instrument, and the lack of organic compounds in the soil, indicate that oxidants are present in the soil and in the atmosphere. Oxidants—such as peroxides and superoxides—are oxygen-bearing compounds that break down organic matter and living tissue. Therefore, even if organic compounds were present on Mars, they would be quickly destroyed.

Analysis of the atmosphere and soil of Mars indicated that all the elements essential to life on Earth—carbon, nitrogen, hydrogen, oxygen, and phosphorus—are present on Mars. Liquid water is also considered an absolute requirement for life. Viking found ample evidence of water in two of its three phases—vapor and ice—and evidence for large amounts of permafrost. But it is impossible for water to exist in its liquid state on Mars.

Restatement of major proposition

Possibility for future research

The conditions now known to exist on Mars and just beneath the surface of Mars do not allow carbon-based organisms to exist and function. The biologists add that the case for life sometime in Mars' distant past is still open.[14]

This passage shows well the characteristics of an inductive argument. The argument begins with the major proposition. The major proposition is then supported by a series of conclusions that are in turn supported by evidence. Remember, whatever the terminology used—conclusion, proposition, thesis, and so forth—generalizations based upon particulars are opinions, nothing more and nothing less. The frequent statements concerning the capabilities of the equipment are intended to strengthen the argument by showing that high-quality equipment was used. The references to the scientists who worked on the Viking project are appeals to authority. A closing qualification leaves open the possibility that life existed on Mars in the past.

DEDUCTION Deductive reasoning is another way to deal with evidence. While in inductive reasoning you move from the particular to the general, in **deductive reasoning** you move from the general to the particular. You start with some general principle, apply it to a fact, and draw a conclusion concerning the fact. Although you will seldom use the form of a syllogism in writing, we can best illustrate deductive reasoning with a **syllogism**:

1. All professional golfers are good athletes.
2. Sonja is a professional golfer.
3. Therefore, Sonja is a good athlete.

In expressing deductive reasoning, we seldom use the form of the syllogism. Rather, we present the relationship in abbreviated form. We may say, for instance, "Because Sonja was a professional golfer, I knew she was a good athlete." Or "The substance is lead. It will melt at 327.4° C."

Although induction is the more common organizing technique in argument, deduction is sometimes used, as in this example:

Methanogens, like other primitive bacteria, are anaerobic: They live only in areas protected from oxygen. This makes sense, since there was virtually no oxygen in the atmosphere when bacteria first evolved. But once bacteria developed chlorophyll a, the pigment of green plants, they began to use carbon dioxide and water for photosynthesis and produced oxygen as a waste product. When massive colonies of these photosynthetic bacteria developed, they pumped large amounts of oxygen into the atmosphere. Oxygen is a powerful reactive gas, and most early bacteria were not equipped to survive with it. Some bacterial species that were adapted to the new gas, including the oxygen producers themselves, continued to thrive. Others presumably evolved special metabolisms to protect them from oxygen, found anaerobic environments, or disappeared.[15]

Presented formally, the syllogism in this paragraph would go something like this:

1. Methanogens cannot live in oxygen.
2. Oxygen was introduced into the methanogens' environment.
3. Therefore, methanogens either evolved special metabolisms to protect them from oxygen, found anaerobic environments, or disappeared.

LOGICAL FALLACIES Many traps exist in induction and deduction for the unwary writer. When you fall into one of these traps, you have committed what logicians call a **fallacy**. Avoid a rush to either conclusion or judgment. Take your time. Don't draw inferences from insufficient evidence. Don't assume that just because one event follows another, the first caused the second—a fallacy that logicians call *post hoc, ergo propter hoc* (that is, *after this, therefore, because of this*). You need other evidence in addition to the time factor to establish a causal relationship.

For example, in the sixteenth century, tobacco smoking was introduced into Europe. Since that time, the average European's life span has increased severalfold. It would be a fine example of a *post hoc* fallacy to infer that smoking caused the increased life span, which in fact probably stems from improvements in housing, sanitation, nutrition, and medical care.

Another common error is applying a syllogism backwards. The following syllogism is valid:

1. All dogs are mammals.
2. Jock is a dog.
3. Therefore, Jock is a mammal.

But if you reverse statements (2) and (3) you have an invalid syllogism:

1. All dogs are mammals.
2. Jock is a mammal.
3. Therefore, Jock is a dog.

Jock could be a cat, a whale, a Canadian, or any other mammal. You can often find flaws in your own reasoning or that of others if you break the thought process down into the three parts of a syllogism.

Comparison

In business and technical situations, you frequently have to choose between two or more **alternatives**. When such is the case, the method of investigating the alternatives will usually involve comparing the alternatives one with another. (Contrast is implied in comparison.) To be meaningful, the comparisons should be made by using standards, or **criteria**. Perhaps you have bought a car recently. When you did, you had your choice of many alternatives. In reaching your decisions, you undoubtedly compared cars using criteria such as price, comfort, appearance, gas mileage, and so forth. Perhaps you even went so far as to rank the criteria in order of importance, for example, giving price the highest priority and appearance the lowest. The more conscientiously you applied your criteria, the more successful your final choice may have been.

After you bought your car, no one asked you to make a report to justify your decision. However, in business it's common practice for someone to be given the task of choosing among alternatives. The task involves a report that makes and justifies the decision or recommendation. When such is the case, a comparison arrangement is a good choice. You can arrange comparison arguments by **alternatives** or by **criteria**.

ALTERNATIVES Assume you work for a health organization and that you are comparing two alternative contact lenses: daily wear and extended wear. Your criteria are cost, ease of use, and risk of infection. After the necessary explanations of the lenses and the criteria, you might organize your material this way:

• **Daily wear**   • **Extended wear**
  Cost   Cost
  Ease of use   Ease of use
  Risk of infection   Risk of infection

In this arrangement, you take one alternative at a time and run each through the criteria. This arrangement has the advantage of giving you the whole picture for each alternative as you discuss it. The emphasis is on the alternatives.

CRITERIA   In another possible arrangement, you discuss each criterion in terms of each alternative:

- **Cost**
  Daily wear
  Extended wear

- **Ease of use**
  Daily wear
  Extended wear

- **Risk of Infection**
  Daily wear
  Extended wear

The arrangement by criteria has the advantage of sharper comparison. It also has an advantage for readers who read selectively. Not every reader will have equal interest in all parts of a report. For example, an executive reading this report might be most interested in cost, a consumer in ease of use, an optometrist in risk of infection.

Toulmin Logic

When you construct an argument, it can be difficult to see the flaws in it. When you expose the same argument to your friends, even in casual conversation, they will be more objective and can often spot the flaws you have overlooked. **Toulmin logic** provides a way of checking your own arguments for those flaws.[16]

DISCOVERING FLAWS IN ARGUMENT   Because Toulmin logic is a way of raising questions readers may ask, its use will make your arguments more reader oriented. Toulmin logic comprises five major components:

1. Claim   The major proposition or conclusion of the argument
2. Grounds   The evidence upon which the claim rests—facts, experimental research data, statements from authorities, and so forth
3. Warrant   Evidence that justifies the grounds and makes them relevant to the claim
4. Backing   Further evidence for accepting the warrant
5. Rebuttal Counterarguments; exceptions to the claim, warrant, or backing; or reasons for not accepting them

Arguments are rather complex chains of reasoning in which you have to argue not only for your claim but for the grounds upon which the claim is based. Toulmin logic helps you to construct the chain.

As an example, let's consider the hypothesis that animals can reason:

Claim
Grounds

Animals are capable of formulating behaviour based on conscious thought.

Some animals experience perceptual consciousness, involving memory and sense perceptions. Others exhibit reflective consciousness, i.e., an awareness of their thoughts

Warrant

separate from the objects they are directed towards. The "Clever Hans" incident, which exposed as fraudulent a horse's apparent mathematical skills, has trapped scientists for generations in a dogmatic dismissal of the possibility that animals experience conscious thought. In fact, consciousness is a universal trait in the animal kingdom, according to scientist Donald Griffin.

Biologist James Gould's studies of the honey bee for over a decade have documented behaviour that can be taken as evidence of thinking. In one experiment, bees trained to come to a feeding station were captured on their way from the hive, carried in the dark to another area of their range, and released. They circled and quickly flew off to where they were headed when captured, even when the station was hidden behind trees. This behaviour of the bees—assessing where they were, remembering where they wanted to go, and planning a route—is usually taken as evidence of thinking.

Warrant

In another experiment, Gould moved the feeding station at regular intervals. During the first several moves, the bees looked for the station at its old site, but they quickly learned to anticipate the new location. If the trainer was slow in moving the station, the bees would fly ahead, waiting at the spot where it was about to be placed. Apparent from this behaviour is the ability to form mental maps and plans.

Warrant

Researcher Bernd Heinrich devised an experiment to test animal thinking by presenting animals with a completely new situation and observing how they solved it. Heinrich raised five ravens from the time they were nestlings and presented them with a problem. Meat was tied to a string and hung from a perch so the birds could not reach it. Frustrated for six hours, one raven finally sat on the perch and pulled the string up section by section with its beak, holding it with his foot until the meat was within reach. Three of the other four birds subsequently learned how to pull up the meat, all in slightly different ways. One never figured it out. Gould views Heinrich's experiment as yielding impressive evidence that the birds appeared to solve the problem through "cognitive trial and error."

Up to this point, the argument that animals have cognitive qualities comparable to humans seems to be going well. But, if you dig further, you will find rebuttals.

Rebuttal

McMaster University psychology professor Bennet Galef argues that the well-known flexibility in the behaviour of animals does not imply consciousness. Human thoughts and feelings are difficult to study in a scientific way and the same applies to animals. There is no objective evidence to support the view that because animals have representations they have human-like thoughts and feelings.

Rebuttal

Hank Davis, a University of Guelph animal behaviour scientist, argues that if psychologists don't know what role conscious thought plays in human behaviour, then questions of whether animals can think and whether such thought is necessary for them to behave are intrinsically problematic.

Rebuttal

John Alcock, an Arizona State University biologist, claims, like Galef, that the extreme views on animal thinking suffer from problems of testability. He explains that developing "a hypothesis on mental processes that can be rejected by carefully collected evidence—the essence of science—is something, to the best of my knowledge, that hasn't been done for the very good reason that it is so difficult to figure out how to do it."[17]

And so on. Digging for evidence on animals' capability for conscious thought reveals a sharp division, with reputable scientists coming down on both sides of the question. The claim has to be qualified, perhaps something like this: "Some scientific studies show evidence of mental processes in animals that we equate with human cognition, but because of difficulties inherent in the science of such studies, they have not convinced all scientists of animal consciousness." Applying Toulmin logic has resulted in a weaker claim, but it is a claim that can be supported with the existing evidence.

ARRANGING ARGUMENTS FOR READERS Toulmin logic can help you arrange your argument as well as discover it. Though you would not want to follow Toulmin logic in a mechanical way, thinking in terms of claim, grounds, warrant, backing, rebuttal, and qualifier can help you to be sure you have covered everything that needs to be covered. Obviously, claim and grounds must always be presented. In most business situations, as we have pointed out, the claim is likely to be presented first, particularly in executive reports. However, in a situation where the readers might be hostile to the claim, it might be preferable to reverse the order. If the grounds are strong enough, they may sway the readers to your side before they even see the claim. On the other hand, if a hostile audience sees the claim first they may not pay enough attention to the grounds to be convinced.

Rebuttals should always be considered and, if serious, should be included in your presentation. You have an ethical responsibility to be honest with your readers. Furthermore, if your readers think of rebuttals that you do not deal with, it will damage your credibility. If you can counter the rebuttals successfully, perhaps by attacking their warrant or backing, your claim can stand. If you cannot counter them, you will have to qualify your claim.

How deeply you go into warrants and backing depends upon your readers. If your readers are not likely to realize what your warrant is (for example, "Respected scientists agree with this hypothesis"), then you had better include the warrant. If your readers will be likely to disagree with your warrant or discount its validity, then you had better include the backing. All in all, Toulmin logic can be a considerable help in discovering and arranging an argument. It is also extremely useful in analysing the soundness of other people's arguments.

Planning and Revision Checklists

You will find the planning and revision checklists that follow Chapter 2, "Composing," and Chapter 4, "Writing for Your Readers," valuable in planning and revising any presentation of technical information. The following checklists specifically apply to organizational strategies. As well as aiding in planning and revision, they summarize the key points in this chapter.

Chronological Arrangement

Planning

- Do you have a reason to narrate a series of events? Historical overview? Background information? Drama and human interest for a lay audience? Forecast of future events?
- What are the key events in the series?
- In what order do the key events occur?
- Do you know or can you find out an accurate timing of the events?
- How much detail does your audience need or want?

Revision

- Is your sequence of events in proper order?
- Are all your time references accurate?
- Have you provided sufficient guidance within your narrative so that your readers always know where they are in the sequence?
- Is your level of detail appropriate to your purpose and the purpose and needs of your audience?

Topical Arrangement

Planning

- What is your major topic?
- What is your purpose?
- What is your audience's interest in your topic? How do their interest and purpose relate to your purpose?
- Given your purpose and your audience's purpose, how can you limit your topic? What subtopics are appropriate to your purpose and your audience's purpose? Can you divide your subtopics further?

Revision

- Do your topics and subtopics meet your purpose and your audience's purpose and interests?
- Did you limit your subject sufficiently so that you can provide specific facts and examples?
- Do you have headings? Do your headings accurately reflect how your readers will approach your subject matter?

Exemplification

Planning

- Do your generalizations need the support of examples?

- Do you have or can you get examples that will lend interest and credibility to your document?

continued >>

Revision
- Have you left any generalizations unsupported? If so, have you missed a chance to interest and convince your readers?

- Have you provided sufficient examples to give interest and credibility to your material?

Analogy

Planning
- What is your audience's level of understanding of your subject matter?
- Would the use of analogy provide your readers with a better understanding of your subject matter?
- Are there things familiar to your readers that you can compare to the unfamiliar

concept—for example, water pressure to voltage?

Revision
- Have you provided analogies wherever they will help reader understanding?
- Do your analogies really work? Are the things compared truly comparable?

Classification and Division

Planning
- Where is your subject matter on the abstraction ladder? Are you moving up the ladder, seeking higher abstractions under which you can group your subject matter (classification)? Are you moving down the ladder, breaking your abstractions down into more specific items (division)?
- What is your purpose in discussing your subject matter?
- What is your audience's purpose and relationship to your subject matter?
- What classification or division will best meet your purpose and your audience's needs?

Revision
- Are all the parts of your classification equal?
- Have you applied one rule of classification and division at a time?
- Is each classification or division large enough to include a significant number of items?
- Have you avoided overlapping classifications and divisions?
- Does your classification or division meet your purpose and your audience's needs?

Definition

Planning
- Do your readers share the vocabulary you are using in your report? Or do you need to make a list of the words you need to define?
- Do any of the words on your list have readily available synonyms known to your readers?

- Which words will require sentence definitions? Which words are so important to your purpose that they need extended definitions?
- How will you extend your definition? Description? Example? Analogy? Chronology? Topical order? Classification? Division? Graphics? Are there words

continued >>

within your definition that you need to define?

- Does everyone in your audience need your definitions? How long are your definitions? How many definitions do you have?
- Where can you best put your definitions? Within the text? In footnotes? In a glossary? In an appendix?

Revision

- In your sentence definitions, have you put your term into its class accurately? Have you specified enough differences so that your readers can distinguish your term from other terms in the same class?
- Will your readers understand all the terms you have used in your definitions?
- Have you used analogy and graphics to help your readers? If not, should you?
- Does the placement of your definitions suit the needs of your audience and the nature of the definitions?

Mechanism Description

Planning

- What is the purpose of the description?
- Why will the intended reader read the description?
- What are the purpose and function of the mechanism?
- How can the mechanism be divided?
- What are the purpose and function of the parts?
- How do the parts work together?
- How can the parts be divided? Is it necessary to do so?
- What are the purpose and function of the subparts?
- Which of the following are important for understanding the mechanism and its parts and subparts: Construction? Materials? Appearance? Size? Shape? Colour? Texture? Position?

- Are there any so-whats that you need to express explicitly for the reader?
- Would the use of graphics aid the reader?
- Would analogies clarify the description for the reader?

Revision

- Does your description fulfill your purpose?
- Does the level of detail in your description suit the needs and interests of your readers?
- Have you made the function of the mechanism clear?
- Have you divided the mechanism sufficiently?
- Do your descriptive language and analogies clarify the description?
- Have you clearly stated your so-whats?
- Have you provided enough graphic support? Are your graphics sufficiently annotated?

Process Description

Planning

- What is the purpose of the description?
- Why will the reader read the description?
- What is the reader's level of experience and knowledge regarding the process?

- What is the purpose of the process?
- Who or what performs the process?
- What are the major steps of the process?
- Are there graphics and analogies that would help the reader?

continued >>

Revision
- Does your description fulfill your purpose?
- Does your description suit the needs and interests of your readers?
- Have you chosen the correct tense—either past or present?
- Have you chosen either active or passive voice appropriately?
- Are the major steps of the process clear?
- Have you provided enough graphic support? Are your graphics sufficiently annotated?

Argument

Planning
- What is your claim, that is, the major proposition or conclusion of your argument?
- What are your grounds? What is the evidence upon which your claim rests—facts, experimental research data, statements from authorities, and so forth?
- Do you need a warrant that justifies your grounds and makes them relevant?
- Do you need further backing for your grounds and warrant?
- Are there rebuttals—counterarguments; exceptions to the claim, warrant, or backing; or reasons for not accepting them? Can you rebut the rebuttals? If not, should you qualify your claim? Will you present your argument unethically if you do not state the rebuttals and deal with them honestly?
- Are you choosing among alternatives? If so, what are they?
- What are the criteria for evaluating the alternatives?
- Is your audience likely to be neutral, friendly, or hostile to your claim? If your audience is hostile, should you consider putting your claim last rather than first?

Revision
- Is your claim clearly stated?
- Do you have sufficient grounds to support your claim?
- If needed, have you provided a warrant and backing for your grounds?
- Does any of your evidence cast doubt on your claim? Have you considered all serious rebuttals?
- Have you dealt responsibly and ethically with any rebuttals?
- Have you remained fair and objective in your argument?
- Have you presented evidence for causality beyond the fact that one event follows another?
- If you have used deductive reasoning, can you state your argument in a syllogism? Does the syllogism demonstrate that you have reasoned in a valid way?
- Is your argument arranged so that it can be read selectively by readers with different interests?

Weblinks

Persuasive Communications: Using You-Attitude and Reader Benefit
www.wuacc.edu:80/services/zzcwwctr/you-attitude.txt

Strategies for Writing Persuasive Letters
www.wuacc.edu:80/services/zzcwwctr/persuasive-ltrs.wm.txt

Persuasive Writing
www.mes.umn.edu/~hoefer/web/perwrite.htm

Exercises

1. Write an informative memo to an executive. Base the arrangement of the memo on one of the techniques described in this chapter. Accompany your memo with a short explanation of why you chose the arrangement technique you did. Your explanation must show how your purpose and your reader's purpose and interests led to your choice. For instruction on the format of memos, see Chapter 11, "Correspondence."

2. Write a chronological narrative of several paragraphs that is intended to serve as a historical overview. Choose as a subject for your narrative some significant event in your professional field. Accompany your narrative with a description of your audience and an explanation of how their purpose and yours led to the level of detail you use in your narrative.

3. Write an extended analogy of several paragraphs that will make some complicated concept in your discipline comprehensible to a grade four student.

4. Write an extended definition of some term in your academic discipline. Use a graphic if it will aid the reader. In a paragraph separate from your definition, explain for your instructor your purpose and audience.

5. Choose three common household tools such as a can opener, vegetable scraper, pressure cooker, screwdriver, carpenter's level, or saw. For each tool, write a one-paragraph description.

6. Write two versions of a process description intended to provide an understanding of a process. The first version is for a lay audience whose interest will be chiefly curiosity. The second version is for an expert or executive audience that has a professional need for the knowledge. The process might be humanly controlled, such as buying and selling stocks, writing computer programs, fighting forest fires, giving cobalt treatments, or creating legislation. It could be the manufacture of some product—paint, plywood, digital watches, maple syrup, fertilizer, extruded plastic. Or you might choose to write about a natural process—thunderstorm development, capillary action, digestion, tree growth, electron flow, hiccupping, the rising of bread dough. In a separate paragraph accompanying each version, explain for your instructor how your situational analysis guided your strategy.

7. Write a description of a mechanism that has moving parts, such as an internal combustion engine. You may choose either a manufactured mechanism—such as a farm implement, electric motor, or seismograph—or a natural mechanism, such as a human organ, an insect, or a geyser. Consider your readers to have a professional interest in the mechanism. They use it or work with it in some way. You may include a graphic as a part of your description. In a paragraph separate from your description, explain for your instructor your purpose and audience.

8. Write a memo to an executive that recommends the purchase of some product or service the executive needs to conduct his or her business. Your memo should establish criteria and justify the choice of the product or service you recommend against other possible choices. See Chapter 11 for information on memo format.

9. Your new boss on your first job knows how important it is for the organization to stay aware of trends that may affect the organization. He or she asks you to explore such a trend. The possibilities are limitless, but you may wish to explore some trend in your own field. For example, are you in computer science? Then you might be interested in the latest trends in artificial intelligence. Are you in forestry? Are there trends in the uses and kinds of wood products? Develop a claim about the trend; for example, "If trend A continues, surely B will result" or "Trend A will have great significance for X industry." Support your claim with a well-developed argument that demonstrates your ability to use induction, deduction, and Toulmin logic. Write your argument as a memorandum to your boss. See Chapter 11 for information on memo format.

10. You are a member of a consulting firm. Your firm has been called in to help a professional organization deal with a question of major importance to the members of the organization. For example, nurses have an interest in whether nurses should be allowed to prescribe medication and therapy. You will probably be most successful in this exercise if you deal with organizations and questions relevant to your major. Investigate the question and prepare a short report for the executive board of the organization. Your report should support some claim; for example, nurses should be allowed to prescribe medication and therapy. Use Toulmin logic in discovering and presenting your argument. That is, be aware of the need to provide grounds, warrants, backings, and qualifiers. Anticipate rebuttals and deal with them ethically and responsibly. Use Part III, Document Design, to help you format your report.

ELECTRONIC COMMUNICATION

Today, virtually every business handles at least a portion of its communications through e-mail, and millions of organizations have created Web sites. Business cards and commercial advertising, for example, often carry a company's e-mail and World Wide Web addresses. The effective technical communicator today must be skilled not only in the creation of paper documents but also in the writing, revising, editing, and designing of electronic messages.

In his book *Being Digital* (1995), Nicholas Negroponte describes how technology has changed the communication process from an exchange of *atoms* to an exchange of *bits*—that is, instead of communicating by shipping pieces of paper across cities, countries, continents, and oceans (using considerable human and energy resources in the process), we're now communicating with higher efficiency by transferring digital code from computer to computer. The cost and speed are virtually identical whether the message travels across the room or across the world.

This chapter is designed to equip you with the abilities you will need to function effectively in the era of electronic communication. It addresses the on-the-job applications of e-mail, electronic discussion lists, synchronous discussion groups, FTP (file transfer protocol) sites, and World Wide Web sites. (For information on citing such sources, see pages 509–511.)

E-Mail

Electronic mail, or e-mail, is correspondence over a computer network, delivering a message from the writer's computer to the reader's computer. The network might operate only within a specific organization (i.e., a local area network or intranet) for correspondence internal to the organization, or it might be external (i.e., the Internet) for correspondence across or among organizations.

Advantages and Disadvantages of E-Mail

E-mail is rapidly replacing a substantial portion of traditional paper correspondence. The reasons for this change are the higher speed and lower cost of e-mail.

First, e-mail is faster than conventional mail. E-mail allows you to mail your message instantaneously without the need of moving paper around. Your message goes directly from your computer to your reader's computer within minutes instead of one or more days. And you could receive the answer to your letter just as quickly. Potentially, e-mail has the immediacy of oral conversation.

Second, e-mail is a less expensive medium for correspondence: It eliminates the costs of paper, print cartridges, envelopes, and postage, as well as the costs associated with the distribution, filing, and storage of paper correspondence. E-mail messages are composed, distributed, received, filed, and stored through your computer. For a typical organization, the savings are substantial. For example, the rising costs of paper and postage are minimized, and fewer file folders and file cabinets are required for sorting and storing correspondence.

E-mail communication, however, has its risks. In the rapid exchange of ideas that e-mail encourages, you might fail to be as careful in choosing your words and phrases as you ordinarily would be. You might write something that isn't quite what you intended, leading to a message that is incorrect, ambiguous, or impolite. Such a message could damage your credibility and your relationship with your audience. E-mail might be as immediate as oral conversation, but your readers can't hear your voice or see your face; they have only your written words with which to judge the accuracy, civility, and sincerity of your message.

In addition, because e-mail is a newer medium of communication, existing as bits instead of as atoms, people often think of it as less important or official. Keep in mind, however, that e-mail is written communication—it has the potential permanence and legal significance of paper correspondence. E-mail requires thoughtful composing, editing, and proofreading.

Finally, though e-mail is *potentially* as fast as oral conversation, it isn't *necessarily* as fast. For example, you might mail your message today, but that doesn't require your readers to read or reply to your message today—it could be tomorrow, next week, next month, or never. You should learn to expect variable speeds for replies to your e-mail.

E-Mail Versus Other Media

How do you decide when to use e-mail, when to write a letter or memo, when to fax, or when to pick up the telephone or even speak face-to-face?

First, consider the conventions of your organization. Has it established policies or traditions regarding communication media? Is news of the organization distributed by e-mail? Are changes of company policy announced by memo? Are complaints or suggestions written in letters? Are promotions and demotions always discussed face-to-face?

Second, consider the ethics of using each communication medium relative to your purpose and audience. For example, do you think it would be ethical to notify employees of their termination by e-mail? By memo? By telephone?

Third, consider the relative efficiency or practicality of each communication medium.

FACE-TO-FACE MEETINGS   Speak face-to-face to emphasize the importance or urgency of your message and to personalize the communication. A face-to-face conversation offers the greatest opportunity to establish a close human relationship: Both parties see each other, offer greetings, and occupy the same time and space. A full exchange of verbal and visual information is possible, and participants are able to ask and answer questions. Because no written record of the conversation is generated, you might choose to verify specific details of your conversation by e-mail, a fax, a memo, or a letter, as appropriate.

TELEPHONE   If a face-to face conversation is impractical or if you already have established a close human relationship, use the telephone to emphasize the importance or urgency of your communication. Telephone conversations offer a limited opportunity to personalize the communication because only the voices of the individuals are available (unless the call allows video as well as audio transmission). You do, however, retain the ability to ask and answer questions. Again, however, neither caller receives a written copy of the information communicated, so to verify the details of your telephone conversation, follow up with e-mail, a fax, a memo, or a letter, as appropriate.

LETTERS AND MEMOS   Compose letters and memos to address subjects of sufficient importance to justify the extra time, effort, and cost involved in preparing and transmitting a paper version of your message. That is, a letter or memo requires paper, ink, envelope, and your attention to the printing process, and once printed, the letter or memo must be delivered to its recipient. It passes through your organization's internal mail delivery system: It is picked up, sorted, and distributed—a labour-intensive process. If the recipient is outside your organization, postage will add again to the cost of your message.

FAX   Choose fax communication to establish a written record on subjects of importance and urgency or to transmit graphic images quickly. With a fax, you take a message composed on your computer in bits, transfer it to paper, convert it back into bits in order to send it over the telephone lines, and transfer it once more to paper at the receiver's fax machine. This process isn't especially efficient, but it does offer your reader a rapid copy of your message or image.

E-MAIL Consider e-mail to exchange messages on day-to-day business and subjects of limited importance. Typical e-mail messages are brief, but most systems will also allow you to attach a file to your e-mail message—like sending a cover letter with a report attached to it. Special software compresses the file and translates it to binary code for transmission. Your reader will require similar software to reverse the process and access the file.

E-Mail Etiquette

Because e-mail has characteristics of both oral and written communication and of both informal and formal communication, writers adopt a variety of styles for their e-mail messages. (See Chapter 11, "Correspondence," for detailed descriptions of the conventions for correspondence.) Although e-mail has the structure of a memo (with its designations of From, To, and Subject), it is usually written as a business or personal letter, with a salutation at the beginning of the message and the writer's "signature" at the end.

If your relationship with the reader is strictly professional, you might compose e-mail as though it were a business letter, starting with a greeting such as "Dear Dr. Smith" or "Dr. Smith" and closing with "Sincerely" and your e-mail signature (i.e., name, title, and e-mail address). If your relationship is both professional and personal (e.g., if you've previously talked face-to-face or by telephone), you might adopt a friendlier greeting such as "Dear Bill" or "Bill," omit the "Sincerely," and close with your e-mail signature. Or if your message is strictly business, you might omit the salutation altogether and proceed directly to the point of your message.

Whichever opening or closing you choose, consider also the etiquette of your e-mail message.

1. **Be polite.** Never e-mail when you're feeling irritated or discouraged; you might write something that you'll later regret. Consider also your reader's feelings, and be sensitive to the power of the written word: Without the cushion of your smile or the delicacy of your voice, your words might be perceived as insulting or offensive. To minimize misunderstandings, especially avoid satiric, ironic, or sarcastic comments. If you believe your words might be misinterpreted, you might incorporate emoticons to signal your attitude—for example, :-) for a smile, ;-) for a wink, or :-(for a frown. Keep in mind, however, that emoticons are often perceived as frivolous or trivial and could diminish the professional quality of your e-mail message.
2. **Never write a message that you wouldn't want others to see.** Your reader could always copy and distribute your message to others without your permission. Your message could also be monitored by your organization (remember that your e-mail messages

are the property of the organization that provides you with e-mail access). In addition, like the paper correspondence of your organization, your e-mail messages could be subject to subpoena and legal review.

3. **Respect the privacy of e-mail messages.** Never copy and distribute a writer's message to others without that writer's permission. The writer might have intended his or her message to remain confidential.

4. **Keep your messages brief.** Don't ask your reader to scroll through paragraphs of unnecessary information to locate the news of your message. If you are replying to a previous message, copy only the pertinent passages of the original message.

5. **Answer your e-mail promptly, especially requests for information.** Your reader may be unable to take action or make a decision until he or she receives your reply.

6. **Keep your paragraphs short.** Short paragraphs simplify reading and organize your message visually, without adding to the bit size of your message. A space between two paragraphs uses as much machine memory as a space between two sentences.

7. **Edit and proofread carefully.** Although typographical errors are characteristic of e-mail messages because of the rapid exchange of information that e-mail allows, such errors could diminish your credibility and distract from your message. Audience analysis is important here: Some readers will tolerate such errors, but others won't. If your relationship with your audience is solely professional, apply strict standards to your grammar, spelling, and punctuation.

Electronic Discussion Lists

Electronic discussion lists are groups of people with a common interest or affiliation, such as employees of a company or members of a professional association, who communicate with one another by e-mail. In electronic discussion groups, a writer mails a message to a common e-mail address, and all subscribers to the list receive a copy of that message.

Lists are either open or closed. In open lists, membership is unrestricted—all requests to subscribe are automatically approved. In closed lists, membership is restricted to a specified group of people—the manager of the list individually approves each request to subscribe.

Ordinarily, you subscribe by mailing a subscribe message (e.g., subscribe [list name] [your first name] [your last name]) to the listserver or listprocessor that operates the list. Once subscribed, you receive a message that welcomes you to the list and explains basic commands, such as how to mail messages to the list and how to unsubscribe from the list.

Lists are either monitored or unmonitored. In a monitored list, all messages mailed to the list are initially reviewed by the list manager. Acting as the list's editor, or moderator, the manager will either accept a message for publication on the list or intercept a message that seems repetitious of previous messages, irrelevant to the list, or otherwise of little merit. In unmonitored lists, all messages are mailed directly to the list without filtering or editing by the list manager.

Using Discussion Lists on the Job

Electronic discussion lists will support your communication with colleagues both inside and outside your organization. Inside your organization, for example, electronic discussion lists allow you to collaborate with all contributors to a project, regardless of their geographical location or when they might be available for discussion. You can easily exchange ideas and arrive at decisions without meeting face-to-face. Or your organization might sponsor a list for all its engineers, to encourage consistent engineering practices across the organization. Similarly, technical writers on a discussion list might address issues of writing style to arrive at a uniform style for all company publications.

Outside your organization, your professional association might sponsor a discussion list, allowing you to solicit or offer advice regarding new research findings, innovative techniques, state-of-the art equipment, and up-to-date information sources. Like reading a professional journal or attending a professional conference, subscribing to such a list will help you stay current in your discipline and be a valuable member of your organization. Such discussion lists also make it easy for you to establish a professional reputation and a network of support outside your organization.

Discussion List Etiquette

All of the principles of e-mail etiquette apply to electronic discussion lists. In addition, consider the following guidelines:

1. **Once you join a list, observe the discussion for a while before you start to contribute to it.** Remember that you're joining a conversation that is already in progress. It's polite to listen for a while before speaking yourself. By briefly "lurking" in this way, you will develop a clearer understanding of the purpose of the list, the nature and style of messages on the list, and the appropriate way to ask and answer questions.

2. **If the list offers archives of previous messages or FAQs (Frequently Asked Questions), review this material.** It will familiarize you with the major topics of conversation and keep you from raising a subject or asking a question that has already been discussed thoroughly.

3. **Don't engage in "flaming" on the list.** Deliberately provocative and insulting comments disrupt the collaborative community that the list is designed to establish. If you consider a message to the list genuinely offensive, e-mail privately to either the contributor of the message or the manager of the list.

4. **Don't write to the list to correct a contributor's spelling or grammatical errors.** Some readers will consider such a message insulting to the individual you corrected and distracting from the important business of the list. If you consider it necessary to correct a contributor's spelling or grammatical errors, e-mail privately to the contributor.

5. **If you decide to quit a list, remember to mail your unsubscribe command to the listserver or listprocessor address that you used to subscribe.** This address usually starts with either a listserv@ or a listproc@ designation. Never mail your unsubscribe command to the list's address.

Synchronous Discussion Groups

Both e-mail and electronic discussion lists are examples of asynchronous communication. You might write your message today, but it could be tomorrow or later before the recipient reads it and replies. In synchronous communication, however, the exchange of messages is almost simultaneous. Instead of being separated in time, the participants are gathered in real time in a virtual meeting room. As we mention in Chapter 3, such groups are usually called MUDs (multiple user dimension, dialogue, domain, or dungeon) or MOOs (multiple user domain object-oriented).

Discussion space

Bill has connected.
Paolo has connected.
Laura asks, "Are we all here?"
Tamika says, "I think this is everybody except Jiong. He told me he'd be a few minutes late. And I'll have to leave soon. I'm sorry. I have a meeting with a client to review billing records. It's going to be ugly."
Bill smiles sympathetically.
Laura says, "Okay, let's get started. I talked to Tom yesterday and he'd like us to move all of our software documentation online. The cost of paper is killing us."
Tamika asks, "How soon?"
Paolo asks, "Could we complete our current projects and switch all new projects to online?"
Laura says, "Starting today."
Jiong has connected.
Bill says, "But I'm almost finished with the manual for 6.0. If I have to adapt it for online, it could delay product release by two to four weeks."
Jiong says, "Hi, everybody. Sorry I'm late."
Tamika [to Laura]: I'll have to e-mail you later.
Tamika has disconnected.

Message space

Figure 7-1 SYNCHRONOUS DISCUSSION SCREEN

In a synchronous discussion, the screen has a scrolling discussion space and a message space (see Figure 7-1). The discussion space displays the ongoing conversation of the group and notes whenever a participant enters or exits the meeting room. This space is visible to all participants. The message space is visible only to you. Here you compose your contribution to the conversation.

Synchronous discussions are often disjointed because all participants sit at their individual computers unaware of what others are writing until the messages appear in the discussion space. Moreover, all participants can contribute to the conversation at the same time. That is, while you're reading a message, composing a reply, and transmitting that reply, other participants may be doing likewise. By the time your message appears in the discussion space for others to read, the question you're answering or the idea you're responding to has scrolled on. Other participants may have already answered the question, said what you were thinking, shifted the conversation in a different direction, or changed the subject entirely.

In addition, the transmission lag (from the mailing of your message to the display of your message) could be considerable, depending on the number and quality of links (e.g., modems, leased lines, satellite uplinks) between your computer and the computer that serves the discussion group. The more links or the lower their quality, the more likely are overloads, crashes, detours, and delays. If the server is heavily loaded, it could also be slow to process your message. Adjusting to the lags in a synchronous discussion requires a little patience and practice.

In synchronous discussions, however, you never have to wait for others to stop speaking before you contribute your ideas to the conversation; no participant has to worry about being interrupted or interrupting others. Each participant also has a chance to revise and edit his or her message before contributing it, so the discussion can be more deliberative. And, whereas a face-to-face meeting or a conference call can lose a participant's good idea in the shuffle of competing voices, synchronous discussions generate a written record, making the contributions of all participants available for later review.

Using Synchronous Discussions on the Job

If face-to-face meetings are impractical because colleagues work at different times or in different locations, meeting in a synchronous discussion could be a satisfactory alternative. Or face-to-face meetings might be possible, but unproductive: The physical location might be uncomfortable or inconvenient, leaving participants inattentive or easily distracted. One or two individuals with loud voices or assertive personalities might dominate the conversation, deliberately or unintentionally intimidating others. Some individuals might be quiet in face-to-face meetings and hesitant to contribute their ideas. In synchronous discussion groups, such problems are avoided. Each participant contributes from the comfort and convenience of his or her office, and each participant's contribution is equally visible to the group.

Inside your organization, for example, synchronous discussions could easily support a collaborative project. Because all contributors are generating messages at the same time, synchronous discussions are especially appropriate for creative exploration of a subject. For example, meeting in a MOO, a group of engineers can develop criteria for judging the safety or efficiency of a product or procedure. Business executives can direct a brainstorming session for a sales promotion or advertising campaign. A team of scientists might devise a list of possible solutions for a problem in the chemical composition of a new plastic. Or computer programmers might consider options for the design of a software application.

Synchronous discussions also allow group members to get to know one another better and build trust. Socializing in a MUD or a MOO gives colleagues the opportunity to discover their similarities, share their knowledge, explore their mutual interests, and recognize their differences.

Outside your organization, synchronous discussion groups are also important. Your professional association might sponsor a continuous or periodic MUD or MOO, offering you a vehicle to exchange research findings, challenge conventional thinking, socialize with colleagues, and explore the possibilities of your profession. Participating in such discussion groups will help you meet the people in your profession, keep up-to-date in your field, and remain a valuable member of your organization. If you participate regularly in such synchronous discussion groups, you will also build a professional reputation and a network of support outside your organization.

Synchronous Discussion Etiquette

The principles of e-mail etiquette apply also to synchronous discussion groups. In addition, consider the following guidelines.

1. **Don't monopolize the conversation.** Gauge the frequency with which other participants are contributing messages and do likewise. Other participants may not type as well as you do or have as much experience with synchronous discussions. In addition, other participants may be experiencing a long transmission lag time. Give your colleagues time to compose and convey their ideas.

2. **Pay attention to other contributors, especially those just entering the conversation.** Acknowledge and reply to their messages. Nobody likes to be ignored. New participants often need to be encouraged and will appreciate your consideration and support.

3. **Keep your participation interactive by switching often from writing to reading and vice versa.** Keep in mind that the other participants can't see you and so must gauge your involvement in the conversation by the frequency of your messages. If you stop to write long messages or to read for a long period of time, the other participants will wonder why you have disappeared from the conversation. If you write long messages, you will also force the other participants to disappear from the conversation while they read what you've written. Sooner or later they will start skimming or ignoring your long messages.

FTP Sites

FTP (file transfer protocol) sites are important locations on the Internet for the distribution of information. FTP allows you to upload files from your computer to a remote computer or to download files from a remote computer to your computer. FTP allows you to transmit information as bits instead of as atoms, easily, quickly, and inexpensively. The computer that you upload to or download from is the FTP server.

Using FTP Sites on the Job

On the job, FTP can serve a variety of purposes. For example, with FTP you can create a common electronic work site for all the people working on a proposal, user's manual, or recommendation report. Instead of continually making and distributing paper copies of the draft, or sending e-mail to each member of the team and attaching a copy of the file to your e-mail message, you can upload a copy of the file to your company's FTP site and allow each team member to download a copy as necessary, at his or her convenience.

Or suppose you have files for your customers to review, such as online software documentation, new product specifications, or updates and corrections to earlier publications. Instead of printing and mailing all that information to all of your customers (at a considerable cost to your company), you can upload the information to your company's FTP site and allow customers to download only those files that meet their needs and interests.

In addition, through FTP you can obtain files necessary to your work on a project, downloading information or applications from a remote site. For example, if you're investigating copyright issues, you can search the Internet for sites housing judicial decisions or records of legislative hearings and then download the pertinent files. Or, if you're thinking of buying a new graphics or animation program, you can visit the manufacturer's FTP site and download a demonstration copy to assist you in your decision making.

Accessing FTP Sites

There are two types of FTP sites: standard FTP and anonymous FTP. With standard FTP, you must provide a designated user name and password in order to obtain access to the FTP server for uploading or downloading files. Such sites are established for the exchange of information within a specific group of users.

Anonymous FTP sites are available to the wider public. All users are invited to visit the site, but access is ordinarily limited to the downloading of files— that is, you can get files off the anonymous FTP server, but you can't put your files on it. Typically, your user name is "anonymous" and your password is either "guest" or your e-mail address. The majority of anonymous FTP sites, however, are accessible through the World Wide Web without a user name or password.

Most FTP sites offer a directory, index, or ReadMe file that describes each of the files available, including its size. This file is a good place to start your visit to that FTP site.

FTP Etiquette

Uploading or downloading files is a strain on the remote computer offering the FTP service, slowing access for the routine users of that server. Such servers often house traffic from e-mail lists, synchronous discussion groups, and World Wide Web sites. Whenever possible, use the FTP site before or after business hours and transfer only a couple of files at a time. Choose files carefully, and consider their size. Larger files require longer transmission times. Keep in mind that anonymous FTP sites are public, sometimes serving thousands of users. Avoid tying up such sites during business hours with a thoughtless request for numerous large files.

World Wide Web Sites

The World Wide Web is a collection of interconnected documents stored on computers all over the world. World Wide Web documents are hypertextual: Highlighted words or images in each document are links to other documents in the collection. World Wide Web documents are also multimedia, capable of incorporating animation and sound, as well as text and graphics.

You navigate the World Wide Web by using browsing software (e.g., Netscape Navigator or MicroSoft Internet Explorer) and clicking on the pertinent links in each document. Each computer offering World Wide Web documents also has a special address to which you can link directly. This address is called the URL (Uniform Resource Locator). Figure 7-2 identifies the parts of a typical URL.

Using the World Wide Web on the Job

The World Wide Web offers a variety of resources that can make you more productive and efficient on the job. Thousands of individuals, corporations, nonprofit organizations, educational institutions, and government agencies have established World Wide Web sites, collectively offering millions of pages of information.

For example, if your organization uses Federal Express to ship its packages, you can go to the Federal Express site to track a package and find out the precise time your package arrived at its destination and who signed for it. You can visit the sites of major newspapers such as the *New York Times*, the *Globe and Mail*, the *Financial Post,* and the *Guardian Weekly* for news stories pertinent to your organization. You can check your suppliers' sites to investigate or purchase goods and services for your organization. You might visit the site of your professional association to obtain a membership application, news of the discipline, or information on ethical practices in your profession. You might go to the sites of government agencies—such as the Natural

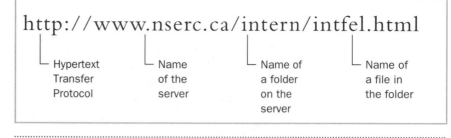

Figure 7-2 PARTS OF A URL

Sciences and Engineering Research Council of Canada (NSERC) and Environment Canada—to find out about recent and pending regulations or research. You can also explore the sites of your chief competitors to examine the specifications for their newest products or to see their latest advertising promotions.

In addition, the World Wide Web allows you to distribute information quickly and easily. For example, you might develop a site that functions like a billboard, promoting your organization's image as well as its goods and services. Or you can create a site that functions like a catalogue, with pages that identify your company's products and permit customers to make purchases by credit card. You can also create a site that functions like a technical manual, offering instructions on how to assemble, maintain, or service your company's products. To such sites you might add links that allow your customers to e-mail their questions or complaints to you.

The World Wide Web's multimedia capability gives you the power to make such billboards, catalogues, and manuals dynamic and interactive. For example, you can use sound and animation at your site to let your customers see and hear your products in operation. You might speak directly to your customers through a brief audio–video clip, directing their attention to your newest product, highlighting special items, or personally guaranteeing their satisfaction. You could use animated illustrations to demonstrate difficult or dangerous procedures, minimizing the potential ambiguity of words and static diagrams. The possibilities are almost unlimited.

Navigating the World Wide Web

With thousands of sites and millions of pages, the World Wide Web is the biggest library of information resources available. But how do you know what's out there? And how do you find what you're looking for? To help you navigate the World Wide Web, a variety of search engines are available, such as AltaVista, Excite, InfoSeek, Lycos, Magellan, and Yahoo. A search engine is a research service that scours the Internet (including FTP sites and World Wide Web pages) looking for files with key words pertinent to your subject.

A simple search looks only for the presence of key words (e.g., *ethics*). A focused search looks for the presence or absence of specific combinations of key words, using plus signs and minus signs as prefixes. For example, a search for *technical communication ethics* asks for all files containing at least one of the three words: *technical, communication,* or *ethics*. A search for *+technical +communication +ethics* narrows the focus to only those files containing all three words. A search for *−technical +communication +ethics* asks for all files containing both *communication* and *ethics* but not the word *technical*.

Each service is a little different—more or less comprehensive, more or less specialized. You might wish to try several search engines to see which directs you most quickly to the most appropriate sources for your subject or field.

Also available are metasearch engines such as MetaCrawler and SavvySearch. A metasearch service will submit your key words to several search engines simultaneously, thus offering you a kind of one-stop shopping in your research process.

Keep in mind, however, that a visit to the World Wide Web can be a little confusing and intimidating. There is so much information available to you and it is so easy to jump from site to site and link to link that you might lose track of the pages you have already visited. Here are several tips to keep you from losing your way.

1. **Check the GO menu item.** The GO menu item of your browsing software shows the footprints of your search: It lists all the pages you have visited since you left your home page. Choosing a page from the GO list will immediately take you back to that page.

2. **Use the BACK and FORWARD buttons.** Once you leave your home page, your browsing software activates a BACK button that will take you back to pages you have already visited. Once you back up, the FORWARD button is activated—it allows you to reverse direction and proceed to the last new page you visited. The BACK and FORWARD buttons allow you to retrace your steps. If you noticed useful information on a previous page but didn't note the specific page, using the BACK and FORWARD buttons will help you look for it.

3. **Use the BOOKMARK or FAVOURITES function.** When you find a page that you think will be particularly useful to you, especially a page that you might wish to visit often, use the BOOKMARK or FAVOURITES function to note the location of that page. This menu item lists all the pages that have been so noted. Choosing a page from the BOOKMARK or FAVOURITES list will take you immediately to that location on the World Wide Web.

4. **Open multiple windows.** Using multiple windows allows you to keep a page of information readily available while you continue browsing for additional information.

Also keep in mind that almost anyone can put almost anything on the World Wide Web. As you navigate from site to site, consider carefully the source of the information you discover. If you question the accuracy of information at a site, investigate:

- Is it possible to verify the information using traditional resources?
- Who operates the site? What is the professional reputation of this organization or individual?
- Does the site display the e-mail address of the organization or individual? If so, write to it with your comments and questions.

Creating a World Wide Web Site

To create a Web site, you will need access to a computer that has a direct Internet connection, the server software necessary to establish a World Wide Web service, and the space available for storage of World Wide Web pages. A variety of Internet service providers offer access to such World Wide Web servers.

You will also need authoring software. World Wide Web pages are written using HyperText Markup Language (HTML), a special coding that identifies the elements of each page, such as titles, headings, lists, and block quotations. You can do the HTML coding yourself, or you can save time with authoring software (e.g., Microsoft FrontPage or Netscape Composer). Such programs apply HTML to your word-processed files by translating your designated formatting features to HTML tags. Even if you have authoring software, however, you should still know the basics of HTML: This knowledge will help you to interpret the coding of pages you would like to imitate and permit you to do a little quick editing of your pages whenever necessary.

In creating your site, consider the following guidelines:

1. **Explore and experiment.** Navigate the World Wide Web for a while, locating pages you would like to imitate or designs you would like to adapt for your site. The almost unlimited variety of sites offers a good stimulus for your creativity.
2. **Strive for a consistent design for all the pages at your site.** A consistent design will make your site more memorable, and it will help visitors to recognize when they have entered and when they have exited your site.
3. **Make your site inviting but simple.** Don't litter your pages with decorative graphics. Focus your reader's attention on information instead of ornamentation.
4. **Focus your efforts on the home page.** This is where visitors will usually enter your site. Make this page especially inviting and easy to navigate. Include links to all the other pages of your site. If your home page is unattractive or confusing, this is where visitors will also exit your site.
5. **Be sensitive to the cultural differences of your international audience.** Keep in mind that the World Wide Web is worldwide. Avoid idioms, slang, and biased language (see pages 71–74).
6. **Give your visitors opportunities to interact with your pages.** Remember that a World Wide Web site is a dynamic medium, intrinsically different from the static paper page. Visitors don't want

simply to read or to view your World Wide Web pages. They want to interact—to click on links and audio or video clips. They want to do things over the World Wide Web, such as order merchandise, download software, make reservations, or complete applications.

In designing your pages, keep in mind the following common practices. (Also see Chapter 8, "Document Design," for general guidelines on design.)

1. **Make it as easy as possible for visitors to navigate your pages with a minimum of scrolling.** If, for instance, a page happens to be fairly long, you might want to display a menu of links at the top and bottom of the page.

2. **Avoid excessive links in the running text.** Each link in the running text is a distraction from your message, requiring readers to make a choice—exit the page or continue reading. Notice how in Figure 7-3, internal and external links are clearly divided and listed at the bottom of the page. The running text itself contains only two links.

3. **Include identifying information on each page.** At the bottom of every page, place a copyright notice, the date of the latest revision, and your e-mail address (as shown at the bottom of the NSERC page in Figure 7-3). Visitors to your site will want to know whom to credit as the source of the information, how up-to-date the information is, and whom to contact with questions or comments.

4. **Choose a light, solid colour for the background of your pages, such as a light gray, green, or blue.** Text displayed on dark or patterned backgrounds can be attention getting, but it is also more difficult to read. Remember that the background is just that—background. If it's a distraction, it's ineffective and inefficient. Try to focus your reader's attention instead on the foreground—the text of your pages.

5. **Adjust the length of your pages to your information.** Ordinarily, pages on the World Wide Web are relatively short. Each contains approximately one to three screens of information. If the material on a page is a long list, however, readers might prefer to scroll through the multiple screens of information and avoid the loading time that always accompanies a change of pages.

6. **Keep illustrations small.** Large illustrations are impressive, but often they take a long time to load. For indifferent visitors and people with slower machines, that long load time could be annoying. Instead, include only a thumbnail-size illustration that interested visitors can click on in order to load the larger version.

7. **Restrict animation to video or audio–video clips that the visitor specifically clicks on to view**. Continuous motion (e.g., a blinking word) is a highly distracting element, which reduces the reader's ability to pay attention to the other information on the page. The ability to animate your page doesn't always make animation a good idea.

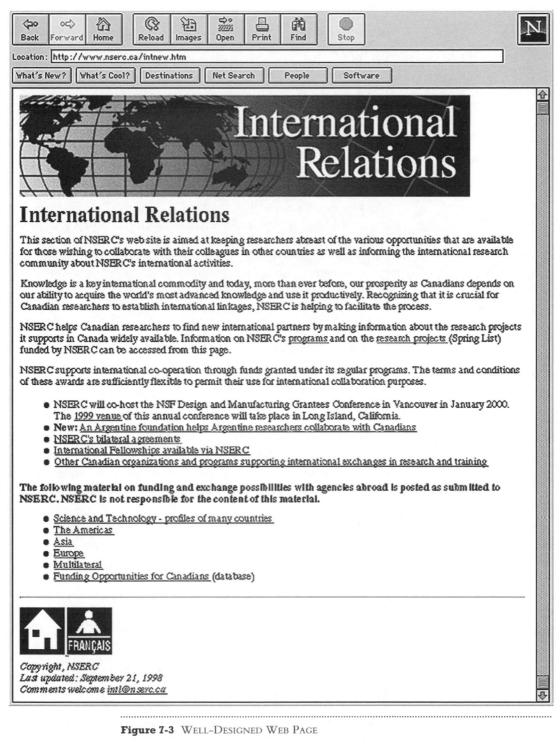

International Relations

This section of NSERC's web site is aimed at keeping researchers abreast of the various opportunities that are available for those wishing to collaborate with their colleagues in other countries as well as informing the international research community about NSERC's international activities.

Knowledge is a key international commodity and today, more than ever before, our prosperity as Canadians depends on our ability to acquire the world's most advanced knowledge and use it productively. Recognizing that it is crucial for Canadian researchers to establish international linkages, NSERC is helping to facilitate the process.

NSERC helps Canadian researchers to find new international partners by making information about the research projects it supports in Canada widely available. Information on NSERC's programs and on the research projects (Spring List) funded by NSERC can be accessed from this page.

NSERC supports international co-operation through funds granted under its regular programs. The terms and conditions of these awards are sufficiently flexible to permit their use for international collaboration purposes.

- NSERC will co-host the NSF Design and Manufacturing Grantees Conference in Vancouver in January 2000. The 1999 venue of this annual conference will take place in Long Island, California.
- New: An Argentine foundation helps Argentine researchers collaborate with Canadians
- NSERC's bilateral agreements
- International Fellowships available via NSERC
- Other Canadian organizations and programs supporting international exchanges in research and training

The following material on funding and exchange possibilities with agencies abroad is posted as submitted to NSERC. NSERC is not responsible for the content of this material.

- Science and Technology - profiles of many countries
- The Americas
- Asia
- Europe
- Multilateral
- Funding Opportunities for Canadians (database)

Copyright, NSERC
Last updated: September 21, 1998
Comments welcome intl@nserc.ca

Figure 7-3 WELL-DESIGNED WEB PAGE

Source: Natural Sciences and Engineering Research Council of Canada, http://nserc.ca/intnew.htm, accessed on 30 May 1998.

8. **Use only two levels of headings.** On a scrolling page, readers often have difficulty keeping track of the organization and hierarchy of information.

9. **Minimize your use of italics.** Italics are difficult to read on the screen.

10. **Use bold type selectively and consistently.** Bold type is attention getting and identifies information of special importance, but it loses its power of emphasis if you use it excessively or arbitrarily.

11. **Edit and proofread carefully.** Errors in grammar and punctuation are distracting, and they jeopardize the credibility of your site.

12. **Check the design of your site using a variety of computers and monitors.** A page that looks good on your monitor or loads quickly on your computer might be distorted on a different monitor or load slowly on a different computer. In designing your pages, therefore, consider the likely visitors to your site. What kind of computer equipment will they have? Should you design your pages for viewing on high-speed computers and 21-inch monitors or on slower machines and smaller screens?

13. **Check the design of your pages using variations of typography.** Visitors to your site have some control over how your pages will look on their screen. Specifically, visitors can decide the following for themselves:
    - Colour of the links
    - Underlining of the links
    - Colour of the type
    - Size of the type
    - Typeface

Check the design of your pages using variations of these five elements to determine whether your site still looks inviting and navigable. A change of typeface, for example, from Times to Helvetica could distort the display of a list or paragraph.

Once you have designed your site, you still have to maintain it. Remember the following guidelines.

1. **Register your site with a variety of search engines.** Registering your site will make it easy for people to locate your site and see the information and services you have to offer. You can register your site by visiting the home page of a search engine and filling out a brief form with your e-mail address, the URL, and a description of your site. The search engine will then scour the files at your site and add the keywords it finds there to its database. You can also register by using a submission service such as World Wide Web Broadcaster; you fill out a single form, and the service automatically registers your site with a number of search engines.

2. **Keep updating your pages.** Give visitors to your site a reason to return regularly. Offer new information and new opportunities to interact with your pages.

3. **Periodically check all of your internal and external links to see that each is still active.** (Internal links connect to other pages of your site; external links connect to pages at other sites.) Dead links annoy your visitors and jeopardize the efficiency and credibility of your site. Ordinarily, internal links break accidentally because you have made a mistake in the HTML coding while updating or editing your pages. External links break if the creator of a World Wide Web site closes or changes its address (usually because the person or organization changes its Internet access provider). A variety of software applications are available to check links.

4. **Avoid changing the address of your site.** Changing your address will cause dead links at all the other sites with links to your pages. In addition, earlier visitors to your site who noted your location will be left with the wrong address. If you must change your address, notify visitors to your existing site of the coming change as soon as possible. Include on the existing site a link to your new site, and keep the existing site open for at least one month while you direct visitors to your new address. E-mail your new address to appropriate discussion lists, and register your new address with appropriate search engines.

Planning and Revision Checklists

You will find the Planning and Revision Checklists that follow Chapter 2, "Composing," and Chapter 4, "Writing for Your Readers," valuable in planning and revising any presentation of technical information. The following questions specifically apply to electronic communication. They summarize the key points in this chapter and provide a checklist for planning and revising.

E-Mail

Planning
- Is e-mail the appropriate way to communicate this message? Or would it be more effective if it were presented face-to-face? By telephone? By fax? In a letter or memo?
- What are the topic and purpose of your message?
- Who is your reader? Do you know each other personally as well as professionally?
- How formal or informal should you be in addressing your reader and discussing your topic?
- Do you have the reader's correct e-mail address?

Revision
- Is your e-mail message polite and professional?
- Have you avoided comments that might be misunderstood or misinterpreted?
- Will you be embarrassed if other people besides the intended reader see this message?
- Is your message brief?
- Are the paragraphs short?
- Have you proofread carefully for typographical errors?

continued >>

World Wide Web Sites

Planning

• What is your purpose in creating a World Wide Web site?
• Who are the likely visitors to your site?
• What kinds of information will you offer at your site?
• How can you make your site interactive?
• How many different pages of information will you create at your site? How will you link these pages?
• What links will you include to other World Wide Web sites?

Revision

• Do all the pages at your site have a consistent design?

• Are the pages inviting? Easy to navigate? Easy to read?
• Are illustrations, video, audio, and animation integrated effectively?
• Have you included a complete menu of links at the top and bottom of every page?
• Does each page carry a copyright notice, date of latest revision, and your e-mail address?
• Have you been sensitive to cultural differences among the likely visitors to your site?
• Have you proofread carefully for typographical errors?
• Have you registered your site with a variety of search engines?

Weblinks

A Beginner's Guide to Effective Email
www.webfoot.com/advice/estyle.html?Author

Electronic Mail Etiquette
www.stcloudstate.edu/~isedu/etiquette.html

HTML Resource Website
www.3.org/MarkUp/MarkUp.html

Exercises

1. Using e-mail, interview three professionals from three different organizations in your field. Compare and contrast their answers to the following questions:
   • How much e-mail do you receive and send daily?
   • How much time do you spend reading and responding to your e-mail?
   • Do you subscribe to electronic discussion lists? If so, how do such lists contribute to your job?

- Do you participate in synchronous discussions on the job? If so, how often? What is the purpose of such discussions?
- What do you like and dislike about e-mail communication?

Examine their replies carefully. How would you characterize the style of each of their e-mail messages? Is it polite and professional? Is it formal or informal? Write a brief report that summarizes the findings of your research.

2. Join a discussion list that is pertinent to your major. For a full week, review the messages mailed to this list. How active is the list? What are the subjects discussed? How many people participate in the discussion? Are participants cooperative and supportive? Do you consider the list a useful source of information? Why or why not?

3. Visit the World Wide Web site of a major employer in your field. Analyse the effectiveness of the site. What is its purpose? Who are likely visitors to this site? Is the site designed appropriately? Why or why not? Write a brief report of your analysis.

4. Visit a search engine of your choosing. Investigate one of the following topics:
   - +e-mail –etiquette +ethics
   - +MOO +FAQ
   - +FTP –anonymous
   - +HTML +multimedia +interactive

How many sources of information does the search engine locate for you? Examine at least five of these sources. What does each source add to your understanding of electronic communication?

PART III

DOCUMENT DESIGN

Part III deals with document design and graphics. Good design—creating a format that helps readers to find information and to read selectively—is vitally important in technical writing. Chapter 8 deals primarily with the format and appearance of the document. Chapter 9 tells you how to construct all those elements that full reports need, such as covers, tables of contents, introductions, discussions, and summaries. Chapter 10 tells you how to use tables, graphs, drawings, and photographs to inform your reader about concepts, processes, trends, relationships, and objects. Technical writing is marked by a wide use of graphics.

DOCUMENT DESIGN

CHAPTER 8

As you have seen in the previous chapters, effective writing requires a number of composing strategies, based on your audience's needs. But effective writing is more than *writing*, more than just words on the page or computer screen, more than correct sentences arranged in logical paragraphs. To be effective, your document must also work visually.

With the ever-increasing capabilities of software to change the appearance of text, to incorporate graphics with text, even to include animation and sound with text, you have many choices in how your document will look on paper or online. This chapter will help you make wise choices for designing both paper and online documents.[1]

Understanding the Basics
of Document Design

Readers judge your work from the presentation as well as from the content of the document and the style of your writing. In fact, a reader's first impression comes from the appearance of your work, not from what it says. A negative first impression may be difficult to overcome. A positive first impression may add to the persuasiveness of your position or convince your readers to put a little more effort into finding what they need and understanding what they find.

Good design also does more than simply make your paper document, computer screen, or World Wide Web page visually attractive. The layout and headings may actually help or hinder the reader. Look at Figures 8-1 and 8-2. Which would you rather receive if you were the reader? The page in Figure 8-2 invites reading and use because it's broken into manageable chunks. The headings, list, and table all help the reader to quickly see the structure of the writer's points and to grasp the important information.

These five principles will help you plan your document's visual design:

- Know what decisions you can make.
- Choose a design that fits your situation.
- Plan your design from the beginning.
- Reveal your design to your readers.
- Keep your design consistent.

Know What Decisions You Can Make

Many companies have a standard format for reports, letters, or proposals. Many journals have standard formats that all manuscripts must follow. Companies have also been developing standards and style sheets for online documents and World Wide Web sites. Before you develop your document, find out what format requirements are already in place. Don't change formats arbitrarily, just to be different. If you think the format you are being asked to use doesn't work well for your audience and your content, find out who makes decisions on format and present a case for the changes that you want.

You may also be limited by the software that is available, by the budget you will have for printing and binding, by the disk space you are allotted for an online document, or by the capabilities of your audience's computer screens. Find out about constraints like these. Look for ways to change these constraints, but if changes cannot be made, do the best you can within them. You can produce a document that is visually effective even with the most basic word processing program, as in Figure 8-2.

Choose a Design That Fits Your Situation

Don't make your document any more complex than the situation requires. You don't need a table of contents or a glossary for reports that are under five

-- 3 --

With the substantial growth in computing in the College of Engineering during the past decade, the issue of linking the departments through a computer network has become critical. The network must satisfy a number of criteria to meet the needs of all of the engineering departments. We first state these criteria and then discuss them individually in detail.

To adequately serve both faculty and student needs in the present environment, the network must be able to handle the number of computers currently in use. In addition, the system must be able to expand and link in additional computers as the number of computers increases over the next few years. The different types of computers that the departments presently possess must all be linkable to the network, and the types of computers that are scheduled for purchase must also be able to be connected to the network. The network should permit the transfer of files in both text and binary form in order to facilitate student access to files and collaborative exchange among faculty and research associates. The network must also have adequate bandwidth in order to handle the expected traffic. Finally, the network must permit both students and faculty to link to the existing national networks.

Each department currently has both computer laboratories for students and computers that are associated with faculty research projects. The various departments possess different numbers of computers. The Aeronautical Engineering Department at present has 27 computers, while Civil Engineering has 12. The Electrical Engineering Department has the most in the College with 46. Mechanical has 22, and Nuclear Engineering, the smallest department in the College, presently has 7. This means that the entire College presently has 114 computers that will need to be networked.

In order to meet their different needs, each department has focused on the purchasing of computers with differing strengths. The computers provide for faculty and advanced students to program in a variety of languages including Pascal, C, and Fortran.

The page with just text looks dense and uninviting.

Readers can't tell at a glance what the text is about.

Figure 8-1 AN EXAMPLE OF POOR FORMATTING

With the substantial growth in computing in the College of Engineering during the past decade, the issue of linking the departments through a computer network has become critical. The network must satisfy a number of criteria to meet the needs of all of the engineering departments. We first list these criteria and then discuss them individually in detail.

Large headings make the topics and structure obvious.

A bulleted list makes the points more memorable.

Each item in the list becomes the heading for a subsection.

The subsection headings are also bold but smaller than the main section heading.

The shorter line length makes the text easier to read and makes the headings stand out.

The numbers are much clearer in a table.

What must the network do?

To serve both faculty and students, the network must be able to

- handle the number of computers currently in use
- link different types of computers
- expand as the number of computers increases
- link to the national networks
- transfer and store both text and binary files

The network must also have adequate bandwidth in order to handle the expected traffic.

Handling the number of computers currently in use

Each department has both computer laboratories for students and computers that are associated with faculty research projects. The following table shows the number of computers in each department at the end of the last fiscal year.

Aeronautical Engineering	27
Civil Engineering	12
Electrical Engineering	46
Mechanical Engineering	22
Nuclear Engineering	7
Total	114

Linking different types of computers

In order to meet their different needs, each department has focused its purchasing on machines with different strengths. The computers

The footer on every page reminds readers of the overall topic.

Figure 8-2 THE PAGE FROM FIGURE 8-1, REFORMATTED

Drawing Product Help

To draw a box:

Decide where to put one corner of the box and move the mouse so that the cursor is in that position on the screen. Press and hold the left mouse button, sliding the mouse along the diagonal of the box, that will appear on the screen as you move the mouse. When the box is the desired size, release the mouse button.

Figure 8-3 INSTRUCTIONS IN PARAGRAPH STYLE ARE DIFFICULT TO FOLLOW, BOTH ONLINE AND ON PAPER

Drawing Product Help

To draw a box:

1. Decide where to put one corner of the box.

2. Move the mouse so that the cursor is in that position on the screen.

3. Press and hold the left mouse button, sliding the mouse along the diagonal of the box.

   The box appears as you move the mouse.

4. When the box is the size you want, release the mouse button.

Figure 8-4 INSTRUCTIONS IN LIST FORM ARE EASIER TO FOLLOW

---

pages. Add appendix material only if it is necessary and will be useful for your readers.

You'll impress readers most by providing just the information they need in a way that makes it easy for them to find and understand it. Many people read technical and business documents selectively. They scan the document, looking for sections that are relevant to their needs. They try to grasp the main points quickly because they are busy and have far too much to read.[2]

Similarly, users working with a computer program are not likely to read the entire user's manual. They go to the manual or to online help when they have a specific problem or need instructions for a specific task. They want to get to the right page or screen immediately. They want the instructions to stand out on the page or screen. Look at Figures 8–3 and 8–4. The numbered steps in Figure 8–4 are easier to read and follow than the prose paragraph in Figure 8–3.

Plan Your Design from the Beginning

Think about how you will arrange and present your information as you plan the document. Ask basic questions like these:

- How will people use the document? Will most people read it from beginning to end? Will they want to skim it and grab the main points without reading more? Will they want to jump to a specific topic? Even if they read the document through once, will they want to come back later and find a specific point quickly?
- Will most people see this document on paper or on a computer screen?
- Will you be able to include graphics easily? Will you be able to use colour?
- What type of print document are you creating? (Other chapters in this book give you specific ideas for preparing letters and memos, instructions, proposals, and different types of reports.)
- What type of online document are you creating? There are many types of online documents, including e-mail messages, online résumés, online help that comes with a product, World Wide Web pages, online forms, and computer presentations.[3] (For more about e-mail, World Wide Web pages, and other forms of online communication, see Chapter 7. For more about print and online résumés, see Chapter 12. For more about designing visuals to accompany oral presentations, see Chapter 17.)

As you answer these questions, think about these points: If people will skim and scan your document, the table of contents and page layout can help them find information quickly. (The rest of this chapter includes techniques for developing effective designs to help people find what they need.) If the document is going to be read on a computer screen, you may have both more constraints and more opportunities than if the document were printed on paper. We read more slowly from the computer screen than from paper,[4] so limiting the amount of information and leaving blank space between paragraphs or list items is crucial in an online document. Graphics and colour may be easier and less expensive to include in an online document than in a paper document.

Reveal Your Design to Your Readers

Seeing the text is the first step in reading a document. Research on how people read and process information shows that readers have to understand how the material is organized before they can make sense of it.[5] Headings reveal the organization of your document so that readers can see what you are writing even before they try to grasp your message on the sentence level. A few well-placed and well-written headings that show the structure and logic of the discussion can help readers, even in a memo. Longer reports definitely need headings and a table of contents that lists the headings. In online documents—such as help systems and World Wide Web pages—a contents list leads to pages whose titles are like the headings in paper documents. You'll learn more about how to write and design effective headings later in this chapter.

Keep Your Design Consistent

Consistency in design is essential to easy reading. When you have considered your audiences, the content you have to deliver, and the ways that people will read and use your document, you can develop a page layout (a design) that will work well for your situation. Once you have the page layout planned, don't change it for arbitrary reasons. In this book, you know when you are beginning a new chapter, when you are at a new section, and when you are at another part of the same section, because the headings at each level are consistent throughout the book. Look again at Figure 8-2. Is it obvious where the major section starts? Is it obvious that there are two parallel subsections?

To help yourself maintain consistency as you create a document, you can use templates, or style sheets, in your word processing program. Most programs let you design each element of a document and then set the design as a repeatable style. The style includes the type size; the typeface, or font; placement of an element on the page; whether the text has a border (also called a line or a rule) over or under it; whether the text or headings are bold or italic; the amount of space that comes before and after a heading; the style of the text that follows each kind of heading; and so forth. If you decide you want to change what all the level 2 headings look like, you can do so easily if you are using a style sheet: Just change the definition of the style, and all the headings in that style will be changed automatically.

Another part of planning in order to keep your design consistent is thinking about the types of information that you have. Once you have a list of the types of information, you can plan a design that shows the same type of information in the same way throughout the document.

To see what inconsistent format can do, compare Figure 8-8, which illustrates major violations of principles for good formatting, with Figure 8-9, which incorporates the guidelines in this chapter.

Designing Effective Pages and Screens

Visually effective pages and computer screens are inviting. They are designed on a grid, so readers know where to look for information. They have space inside the text, around the graphics, and in the margins, so they look open and information is easy to locate. The line length and margins help people read easily. You can use the following six suggestions to help you develop visually effective pages and screens:[6]

- Design on a grid.
- Leave ample margins.
- Use blank space to group information.
- Set the spacing for easy reading.
- Use a medium line length.
- Use a ragged right margin.

Design on a Grid

Pages and screens that look overly busy are difficult to read and use. One way to keep them from looking busy is to design on a grid. A grid is a pattern of vertical and horizontal lines on a page or screen that marks places for different types of information. In document design, the vertical lines are usually the most important elements of the grid. Figure 8-5 shows you several possible grids for different types of documents.

To set up a grid, first list all the types of information that you have. Include the headers or footers (the information that comes at the top or the bottom of print pages); all the levels of headings that you will be using; the types of text, such as regular prose paragraphs, as well as examples and indented quotes if you'll be using them; and the different types of graphics that you'll have. Then draw several sketches on paper of ways to combine these types of information on a page or screen. As you do that, line up the elements so that you have relatively few straight lines going down the page.

Figure 8-2 is set up on a grid with three starting points for the information. The headings are at the left margin. The text is in block paragraphs indented an inch (2.5 cm) from where the headings start. The bulleted list and the left column of the table start at the same place on the page, an inch in from the text. (You don't have to make each indent an inch—two or three characters or half an inch [1.25 cm] also works well.)

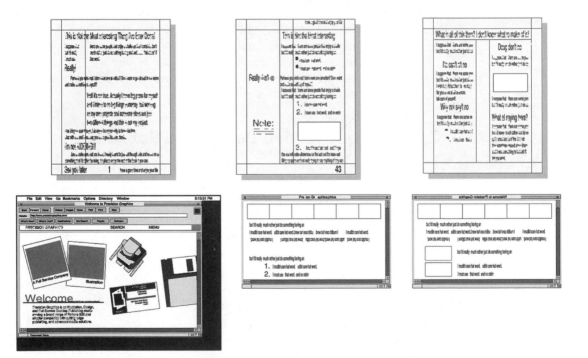

Figure 8-5 A FEW OF MANY POSSIBLE GRIDS FOR PRINT AND ONLINE DOCUMENTS

Lost in (Disk) Space

Disk is cheap, until you add up all the hidden costs. Most of the 14,000 users of hopper, for example, have a disk quota of 5 megabytes. If everyone happened to reach this quota on the same day, we'd need 70,000 megabytes (about 70 gigabytes) of disk space. (Of course we can do with far less because individual disk usage fluctuates quite a bit.)

The hidden cost is in your time and frustration. If you hit your personal quota, at a minimum you'll find it disruptive (you won't be able to do any work); in the worst case, you could even lose some of your data.

To avoid these scenarios, you need to know how to find out what your quota is, how to determine how much disk space you're currently using (that is, how close you are to reaching your quota), how to remove unneeded disk files, and how to compress little-used disks files so they take up less space.

What is My Disk Quota?

To determine your quota, type the quota command like so:

```
quota
```

Here's some sample output

```
Disk quotas for user jdoe (uid 983):
Filesystem  blocks quota  limit grace files quota limit grace
/home/h3a     36  5120 7168        11    0    0
```

We're interested in the 'quota' column just to the right of the 'blocks' column. This person has a quota of 5,120 kilobytes.

How Much Disk Space Am I Using?

To find out how much disk space you're using for all your files right now, type

```
du -ks
```

This shows you the amount of disk space, in kilobytes, taken up by all your files (including all the files in any subdirectories you may have).

Compare the amount you're using with your quota. If you're at about 80 or 90% of your quota, it's time to take action.

How Do I Remove Unneeded Files?

The easiest way to free up disk space is to delete files you no longer need. To delete a file named 'myfile', you would type

```
rm myfile
```

But if you have a lot of files (and particularly if you have lots of subdirectories), you may want to find your biggest unneeded files and just delete those. To find your biggest files, type

```
du -ka | sort -rn | more
```

(The '|' is the pipe symbol and is typically found a few keys to the right of the letter 'P'.)

This displays the sizes of all your files in order from largest to smallest, with the sizes shown in kilobytes. But be careful here. Interspersed with your files will be one line for each of your subdirectories. (You probably don't want to delete whole subdirectories.)

If you can find a few very large files that you no longer need, just remove them and your work is done. But only delete files that you recognize. Some applications (like tin and pine) create auxiliary files that are needed by that application. In general, if you didn't create the file, don't delete it unless you understand the application and you're sure the application will not need the file again.

By the way, files named 'core' are typically not needed. Remove them with the rm command.

How Do I Compress Little-used Files?

In between all the unneeded files and the files you consider crucial, there's often a middle ground: files that you

might need some day, but you're not sure. If these files are large and if you don't use them very often, you can compress them so they'll use less disk space. Then, when you need one of them back, you can simply uncompress it.

To compress a file named 'myfile', type

```
compress myfile
```

This creates a compressed copy of myfile in a file named myfile.Z and deletes myfile. This only takes a few seconds and will typically reduce a file's size quite a bit, particularly for ASCII text files. Binary files (e.g., 'a.out' files) typically don't compress very well, if at all. In fact, if the compress command detects that compression will not save you any disk space it tells you so and aborts.

There are ways of working with files while they're compressed, but most often you'll simply uncompress the files as you need them.

For example, to uncompress 'myfile.Z', you'd type

```
uncompress myfile.Z
```

This restores the file 'myfile' to its original state.

What If I Need Help?

For help with any of the above commands you can view the online manual page. For example, to learn more about the quota command, type

```
man quota
```

This will display a brief description of the command and its options (switches), as well as provide one or more examples.

For more help, students can contact the Advisor in room W71, extension 6840. Faculty and staff can call the CCS Help Desk at extension 6806.

Figure 8-6 THREE EQUAL COLUMNS

Source: "Computing and Communications Services," *CCS Newsletter* (Winter 1998): 7.

The main heading is in the left column. The heavy rule (line) over the words also shows that it is a main heading.

The section level heading is in the right column. The rule (line) over the heading draws the reader's eyes down into the section.

The three instructions linked to the graphic give an overview of the method for using the program.

Each section includes only a small amount of text. Busy users can read what they need easily.

4   INTRODUCTION

Visio basics

Before you start working in Visio, it's helpful to understand the basics of drawing in Visio and how Visio differs from other drawing programs you might have used. The big difference is this: you can create drawings without having to draw.

Drag and drop drawing

Pointer tool

The easiest way to create a drawing in Visio is by dragging shapes from a *stencil* to a drawing page. This method is called drag and drop drawing.

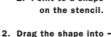

1. **Point to a shape on the stencil.**

2. **Drag the shape into the drawing window.**

3. **Drop an instance on the page.**

Stencils are collections of *master shapes*. When you open a stencil, you see its *master shape icons* on a green background. When you open the drawing window, you see the drawing page—which looks like a piece of paper—on a blue background. You drag a master shape from the stencil to the drawing page and drop an *instance* of the master shape into your drawing.

Figure 8-7 TWO UNEQUAL COLUMNS
Source: Visio Corporation, *Visio 3.0, Using Visio.* Used with permission.

Indenting lists, tables, examples, and other special features of your page or screen makes them easy to find. However, don't make different indents for each type of information. In Figure 8-2, for instance, the bulleted list and the table use the same vertical grid line. If you have too many different features starting at too many places across the page, the page will look confusing instead of inviting.

Figures 8-6 and 8-7 show you other examples of grids. Figure 8-6 is a page from a fact sheet that uses a three-column grid. Figure 8-7 is a page from a computer manual. It uses a two-column grid. The left column is narrow and is used for headings and notes. The right column, with the text and graphic, takes up about two-thirds of the page. On this introductory page, the writer put the instructions in the left column, linked to the graphic. On the later, regular instruction pages, the instructions are in numbered lists with graphics under the relevant instruction. The manual has a very consistent and attractive layout.

Don't mix different grids on the same page. In fact, try to keep the same grid for all the pages that contain the same type of information.[7]

Leave Ample Margins

Look at Figure 8-8. Do you want to read it? Too little space makes the page look dense and uninviting. Now look at Figure 8-9. Wouldn't you rather read this version? Blank space (often called *white space* on paper) makes the page look inviting and makes information easier to find and read.

You can incorporate blank space into documents in several ways. One place for blank space is at the margins—the space around the edges of the paper, computer screen, or window on the computer screen. If your document will be read on paper, also think about how it will be bound. If you are putting your work in a binder, be sure to leave room for the binding. Don't punch holes through the text. Think about whether a reader will want to punch holes in a copy later or put the work in a binder. Figure 8-10 shows these guidelines for margins on a standard 8-by-11-inch page:

top margin	1 inch (2.5 cm)
bottom margin	1 inch (2.5 cm)
left margin	1 inch (2.5 cm), if material is not being bound
	2 inches (5 cm), if material is being bound
right margin	1 inch (2.5 cm)

If you are going to photocopy on both the front and back of the page, leave space for the binding in the left margin of odd-numbered pages and in the right margin of even-numbered pages. Some word processing programs let you set the margins so that they alternate for right-hand (odd-numbered) pages and left-hand (even-numbered) pages. If you cannot set alternating margins, set both the right and the left margin at about 1½ inches to allow for binding two-sided copies.

Use Blank Space to Group Information

Don't think of blank space as wasted or empty space. Space is a critical element in the layout, for both paper and screens. Look at how all the examples

Long lines and the uninterrupted flow of text obscure the new procedures.

TO: All Department Heads

SUBJECT: New Copy Procedures

    A recent study of our copy centre request procedures indicates that we are not fulfilling copy requests as efficiently as possible. A number of problems surfaced in the survey. First, many requests, particularly large orders, are submitted before the copy centre opens. Others are submitted after the copy centre closes. As a result, the copy centre has an enormous backlog of copy orders to fill before it can begin copy orders submitted after 8:30 A.M., when the centre officially opens. This backlog may throw the centre two or three hours behind schedule. All copy requests throughout the day then require over two hours to complete. By 2:00 P.M., any copy requests submitted may not be filled that day. If large orders arrive unexpectedly even a routine copy request may take two days to complete.

    To remedy the situation, we will change to the following copy request procedure beginning Monday, February 3. The copy centre will close at 3:00 every afternoon. Two work-study employees will work at the centre from 3:00 until 5:00 to complete all orders by 4:00. If you submit copy requests by 3:00, the centre will have them ready by 4:00. In short, all requests will be filled the day they are submitted. However, do not leave copy requests after 3:00, as these will not be processed until the following day. However, we guarantee that if you leave your request for copies with us between 8:30 and 3:00, you will have them that day.

    Requests for copies of large orders—over 100 copies of one item, single/multiple copies of any document over 25 pages, or front/back photocopying of one item up to 50 copies—will require that a notice be given the copy centre one day in advance. That way, the centre can prepare for your copy request and be sure to have it ready for you. Copies of the request form are attached. Please complete one of these and send it to Lynda Haynes at the copy centre so that she can schedule all big jobs. If you submit a big copy request without having completed the form, your request will be completed after other requests are complete.

    Allow plenty of time for routine jobs—at least two hours, and three if possible. Beginning February 3, give all copy requests to the receptionists at your office number. Be sure you attach complete instructions. Give your name, your phone number, and your office number. State the number of copies required and any special instructions. Specify staples or clips, colour paper, and collation on multi-page copies.

    Pick-up procedures also change February 3. All copy jobs, after they are complete, will be placed in each department's mail box. No copies will be left outside the copy centre after closing time. No copies will be left with the receptionist. Large orders that will not fit mail boxes will be delivered to your office.

    If you have questions about this new procedure, please contact Lynda Haynes at 2257.

Figure 8-8 MEMO THAT VIOLATES FORMAT GUIDELINES

in this chapter use space, and note all the ways that the more visually effective examples use space well. The space in the margins is important, but it's not enough. Graphic designers call margins *passive space* because margins only define the block of the page or screen that readers should look at. Graphic designers know that *active space* inside the text is really what makes the difference in an effective layout.

TO: All Department Heads   DATE: January 27, 1999

FROM: Lynda Haynes

SUBJECT: **New Procedures for Ordering Copies from the Copy Centre**

                EFFECTIVE DATE: MONDAY, FEBRUARY 3, 1999

To handle orders more quickly and efficiently, the Copy Centre is changing its procedures. Please inform everyone in your department and ask them to follow these new procedures.

The information is in the order in which users need it.

Deciding If You Have a Large Order or a Routine Request

First, you must decide if you have a large order or a routine request. A large order is
- more than 100 copies of any item
- more than 50 copies of any item to be copied two-sided (front/back)
- single or multiple copies of any document over 25 pages

Following the Procedures for a Large Order

The page with lots of white space is easier to read.

1. Fill out one of the attached Request for Copying a Large Order forms.
2. Send the completed form to Lynda Haynes at the Copy Centre at least **one day in advance** of the day you need the copying done.

   That way, Lynda can schedule big jobs and you will avoid delays in getting your copying completed.

Following the Procedures for a Routine Request

The headings in bold break the text into meaningful sections.

1. Attach complete instructions to your request. Include
   - your name, phone number, and office number
   - the number of copies you need
   - for multiple-page copies: instructions on collating and staples or clips
   - any special instructions, such as paper colour
2. Give all copy requests to the Copy Centre receptionists.
3. Allow 2 to 3 hours for your order to be filled.

NOTE:
Routine requests left between 8:30 AM and 3:00 PM will be processed by 4:00 PM on the same day.

The Copy Centre will close at 3:00 PM. Orders left after that time will be processed the next day.

Getting Your Copies

Copies will be delivered to your department's mailbox. If the order is too large for your mailbox, it will be delivered to your office.

If You Have Questions . . .   Contact Lynda Haynes at ext. 2257.

Figure 8-9 A REVISION OF FIGURE 8-8

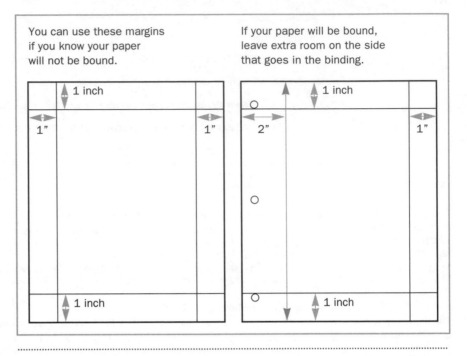

You can use these margins if you know your paper will not be bound.

If your paper will be bound, leave extra room on the side that goes in the binding.

1 inch

1"   1"

1 inch

1 inch

2"   1"

1 inch

Figure 8-10 Page Layouts Showing Margins for 8½-by-11-Inch Paper. (Some people prefer a larger, 1½-inch margin at the bottom of the page.)

If you are developing material to be viewed online (as in an online document, a help system, or a World Wide Web page), you may not be able to control how wide a screen or window the reader will use. If you can control the margins, try to leave at least a little room on either side if your document is going to be viewed across the entire screen. However, many online documents are viewed in windows that are smaller than a full screen. These usually don't include space in the margins because the lines of text would then be extremely short.

For online documents, passive margin space is not as critical as it is on paper. However, active space inside the text is even more critical in online documents than it is on paper. Most online documents are not read continuously; rather, users consult them in an effort to quickly locate and act on information. Space helps users locate information quickly, helps them keep their place, and gives them smaller, more manageable "chunks" to deal with.

Here are several techniques to get space onto your pages and screens:

- Use headings frequently. Put them above the text or to the left of the text and put space before them.
- Use bulleted lists for three or more parallel points. Use numbered lists for steps in instructions. Lists are often indented inside the text, and each item may be separated from the others by a blank space.
- Use pictures, tables, and other graphics, both because they provide relief from paragraphs of text and because they make points visually obvious that would take many words to explain. (See Chapter 10, "Graphical Elements.")

- Separate paragraphs with an extra blank line, or indent the first line of each paragraph. In online documents, make your paragraphs even shorter than you would in paper documents so that there is space even in a small window. Online, one instruction or one short sentence may make an appropriate paragraph. Look again at Figures 8-3 and 8-4. The space is an active design element that makes the instructions in Figure 8-4 much easier to follow than the instructions in Figure 8-3.

Set the Spacing for Easy Reading

It's common in paper documents such as letters and memos to use single spacing, unless the document is very short. When you use single spacing, put an extra line between paragraphs.

Drafts are usually double spaced to give writers and editors more room in which to write their corrections and notes. When you use double spacing in drafts, you have to have some way to show where new paragraphs begin. Indent the first line of each paragraph or add an extra line between paragraphs. Even final reports are often done in double spacing or space-and-a-half.

For documents that will be read on the computer screen, set the spacing so each line can be read easily but so there is more space between paragraphs than between lines within the paragraph. Double spacing is not usually used for continuous text on the screen because a typical screen holds only about one-third of what a paper page holds.

Use a Medium Line Length

Long lines of uninterrupted text are tiring to read. Moreover, readers are likely to lose their place in moving from the right margin of a long line back to the left margin of the next line. Very short lines are also difficult to read. They make the text appear choppy, and readers may have trouble keeping the sense of what they are reading. Figure 8-11 illustrates the problems with both very long and very short lines of text.

The number of characters that fits in a certain amount of space depends in part on the size and style of type that you are using. (See the section on

---

Long lines of type are difficult for many people to read. Readers may find it difficult to get back to the correct place at the left margin. The smaller the type, the harder it is for most people to read long lines of type.

Very short lines
take up too
much space
and make
comprehension
difficult.

Figure 8-11 VERY LONG LINES AND VERY SHORT LINES ARE HARD TO READ

Choosing Readable Type in this chapter for more on this subject.) If you have one column of text on paper or in a full-width computer screen, try to keep the lines of text to about 50 to 70 characters, or about 12 to 15 words. That's what this book does.

In a format with two equal columns, keep each column to about 35 characters, or about 5 words. If your online document comes up in a window on the computer, you will, of necessity, use short lines. Set the default line length so that a typical short instruction fits well on one line.

Use a Ragged Right Margin

Since you first began writing by hand on ruled notebook paper and then once you began typing, you have been accustomed to having a firm left margin in your documents. The first line of a paragraph of text either starts at that left margin (called *block style*) or is indented two or five spaces (called *indented style*). This book uses indented style for paragraphs. Many letters and memos today use block style. Figure 8-1 is an example of the indented style for paragraphs. Figure 8-2 is in block style. In both styles, all the lines after the first one in a paragraph start at the same firm left margin.

Although text is almost always lined up on the left margin, it is not always also lined up evenly on the right margin. The text of this book is even on both the left and the right. Most of the examples in the figures in this chapter are even on the left but not on the right. The technique of making all the text align exactly on the right margin is called *justifying the text*. When the text is lined up on the left but is not justified on the right, we say it has a *ragged right margin*.

Be careful if you decide to justify type on the right margin. Some word processing programs create unsightly gaps in justified type that make the text very difficult to read. Research shows that regular spacing eases the reading process. If all the extra space needed to fill out a line of text is put between just two of the words, the words will not be evenly spaced across the line. Readers' eyes tend to focus on the large space between words rather than on the words themselves.[8]

Even if your computer can microjustify—divide extra space evenly across the line so that you can hardly tell there is any—think about the purpose and audience for your work. Justified type gives a document a formal tone. Unjustified (ragged right) type gives a document a more friendly, personal tone. Many journals have changed from justified type to ragged right because ragged right is more readable and because they want to look modern. Readers like unjustified text.[9] Poor readers have more difficulty reading justified text.[10] Online documents almost always have ragged right margins, both because reading from the screen is more difficult than reading from paper and because writers want to make their online documents look modern and friendly.

Choosing Readable Type

Today's technology gives you many choices for the shape of the letters, numbers, and other characters in your text. These different shapes are called *type, typefaces*, or *fonts*. Companies, or groups within companies, often have style guidelines that tell you what fonts to use for official reports, letters, manuals, and online documents. If you aren't in one of those companies, or if you are writing a document that is not covered by the style guidelines, you are likely to have to make decisions about what to use.

These six suggestions will help you choose type that is easy to read:

- Choose a legible type size.
- Choose a typeface (font) that is appropriate for the situation.
- Use special typefaces sparingly.
- Use highlighting effectively.
- Use a mixture of cases, not all capitals.
- Use colour carefully.

Choose a Legible Type Size

Type is measured in points. A point is 1/72 of an inch, so a letter in 36-point type is about half an inch high. On a computer, you have a wide choice of point sizes, from very small to very large, as you can see in Figure 8-12.

Research conducted before word processing was commonplace suggested that 8- to 10-point type was best, but that was for typeset documents like this book that are printed at very high resolution. Most documents today are printed on desktop printers at a resolution of only 300 or 600 dots per inch (2.5 cm). At that resolution, 8-point, even 10-point type, is difficult to read.

For most word-processed documents, you will find that 12-point type works well for the regular text. You may want to use 10-point or 11-point type for headers, footers, and footnotes. You can then use larger sizes for titles and headings, but don't make them so large that they destroy the balance of the page. (The section on designing useful headings has more on type size for headings. Also, Figure 8-21 on page 189 shows an example of a page with good choices of type size as well as style and placement for headings.)

This is 8-point type.
This is 10-point type.
This is 12-point type.
This is 14-point type.
This is 18-point type.
This is 24-point type.
This is 36-point type.

Figure 8-12 TYPE COMES IN DIFFERENT SIZES

Times New Roman	The quick brown fox jumped over the lazy dog.
Century Schoolbook	The quick brown fox jumped over the lazy dog.
Arial	The quick brown fox jumped over the lazy dog.
Courier New	The quick brown fox jumped over the lazy dog.

Figure 8-13 The Same Text in the Same Point Size but in Different Fonts Takes Up Different Amounts of Space on the Page

In some online situations, such as e-mail, you may not have a choice of what type size or font to use. In writing other online documents, such as a help file, make sure the type is large enough to be read by most users at the distance they sit from their monitors and with the monitors they use. Both on paper and online, experiment with different fonts in different sizes to see what is most readable with the technology that you have—and, for online, with the technology that most of your readers have.

The shape and spacing of the letters also affect how much room the font takes up on a page or screen and how readable it is. Type in one font may look much tighter and smaller than type in the same point size in another font because of the way the letters are shaped and how they are spaced when typed next to each other. Figure 8-13 shows you four fonts, all in 13-point type.

Choose a Typeface (Font) That Is Appropriate for the Situation

There are thousands of type fonts, and you may have a wide selection to choose from with your technology. Type fonts can be divided into two main groups: *serif type*, which has extenders on the letters, and *sans serif type*, which does not have extenders. Figure 8-14 shows you the difference between serif and sans serif type. Many computer programs give you a choice of several different serif and sans serif fonts. Figure 8-15 shows you examples of some of those choices from one program.

Serifs draw the reader's eye across the page, so most books and other long paper documents are printed with serif type. Sans serif type works well in

Figure 8-14 Type Comes in Two Major Styles: Serif and Sans Serif (Without Serifs)

Serif Typefaces	Sans Serif Typefaces
Times	Helvetica
Palatino	Futura Light
Garamond	Franklin Gothic
Schoolbook	Helvetica Narrow
Courier	OCRA

Figure 8-15 SOME TRADITIONAL AND NEW TYPEFACES (FONTS) AVAILABLE ON THE MACINTOSH COMPUTER

brochures and other short documents. Sans serif type also works well for visuals with oral presentations because viewers are at a distance from the words, and they're reading single lines at a time. (See Chapter 17, "Oral Reports," for more on presentations.)

Experts are still discussing whether serif or sans serif type is better for online documents. Many writers prefer sans serif typefaces for their online documents because, with the poor resolution of many screens, serifs can make individual letters more difficult to read. Also, sans serif type, like ragged right margins, gives a document a more modern look. Figures 8-3 and 8-4 show text in 12-point sans serif type.

In general, once you decide on a font for your document, use that font throughout the document. An exception to that rule is that even if you are using a serif font for the text, sans serif works well in tables, figure captions, and the legends with your graphs. You can also switch to a sans serif font for the headings and headers or footers. The instruction manual in Figure 8-7 uses serif type for the text and sans serif type for the numbered marginal instructions.

Use Special Typefaces Sparingly

Some computers offer unusual typefaces. These typefaces are not generally appropriate for technical reports or for online documentation. They are not as readable as the typefaces in Figure 8-15.

Use Highlighting Effectively

There are many ways to highlight material—to draw the reader's attention to parts of your document that you want to emphasize. We have already discussed two ways: changing the size of the type to indicate a heading and using space to set off specific elements such as headings, lists, and tables. You have several other choices for highlighting:

boldface

italics

<u>underlining</u>

changing the colour

> Placing information in a box

Setting rules above and below the material. This is often used for cautions or warnings.

As you design your documents and decide on highlighting techniques, keep these four points in mind:

- Don't use too many techniques.
- Be consistent in the way you use each technique.
- Match the highlighting to the importance of the information.
- Don't use any technique for more than a short sentence.

DON'T USE TOO MANY TECHNIQUES   Highlighting calls attention to specific elements in the text. If you use too many different kinds of highlighting or use one kind too often, you dilute the effect.

BE CONSISTENT IN THE WAY YOU USE EACH TECHNIQUE   Highlighting helps readers quickly grasp different elements in the text. Once you choose a technique for highlighting a particular kind of information, use that technique consistently for that kind of information. If you use italics for specially defined words, do so throughout. If you decide to set off cautions and warnings with rules above and below the text, use that technique for all cautions and warnings and don't use it for anything else.

MATCH THE HIGHLIGHTING TO THE IMPORTANCE OF THE INFORMATION
Type that is set **boldface** stands out more on a page than *italics*. Both stand out more than <u>underlining</u>. Boxes make what is boxed clearly separate from the text, so they are useful for examples, as in many of the figures in this chapter. As you plan highlighting, be sure to match your highlighting to your readers' expectations. For example, in print, readers expect to see book titles in *italics*. If you don't have italics, readers expect to see book titles <u>underlined</u>. Readers who have seen many computer manuals and engineering handbooks expect to see warnings and cautions set apart from the rest of the text.

DON'T USE ANY TECHNIQUE FOR MORE THAN A SHORT SENTENCE   Whole paragraphs underlined, set in boldface or italics, or printed in a different colour are difficult to read. Instead of enticing readers to pay attention to the material, long sections in highlighting turn readers away.

Figure 8-16 is a memo that uses too much underlining in an attempt to emphasize the major points. Despite the underlining, it does not invite reading. Figure 8-17 shows how white space, underlined headings, and a judicious use of bold in the text make the memo more inviting and easier to read and, especially, make the major points more obvious.

Use a Mixture of Cases, Not All Capitals

Don't use all capitals for text. A sentence in all capitals takes about 13% more time to read than a sentence typed in the regular uppercase and lowercase

TO: Michael Morfea   DATE: May 2, 1999

FROM: Melina Katsikis

SUBJECT: Short Course Request from Ocean Drilling

Because I will be away on a three-week teaching assignment, I would appreciate your handling the following request, which came in just as I was preparing to leave today.

Randy Allen, Director of the offshore drilling research team would like a short course in writing offshore safety inspection reports. He would like the short course taught from 2-4 P.M. Monday-Friday afternoons, beginning week after next. The class must be scheduled then, as the team leaves the following week for their next research cruise.

The drilling research team spends two weeks each month on cruise. After they return, they have one week to complete their reports before briefing begins for the next research expedition. Because of the short season and their rigid schedule, they cannot attend our regularly scheduled writing classes.

Allen says that the cultural and educational backgrounds of the team are varied. Three of the ten regular researchers are native Europeans who attended only European universities. Of the remaining seven, three have Canadian degrees, and four attended school in American universities. As a result of their varied educational backgrounds, their reports lack uniform handling of English and organization. All the researchers have expressed interest in having a short review of standard English usage so that their reports to management will be more uniform.

Sarah Kelley says she can develop a class for the drilling team. We have materials on reports, style, and standard usage in the files. She can work with Ocean Drilling to determine the best report structure and develop a plan. These items can be easily collected and placed in binders. We also have summary sheets on each topic that will be good reference aids when the researchers write their reports following their cruise.

Sarah will contact you Monday morning. If her proposal meets with your approval, please give Randy Allen a call, at extension 721, before noon. He has a staff meeting scheduled at 1:30 and would like to announce the short course then. In fact, if the course cannot be scheduled this month, it cannot be taught for six months because of off-season cruise schedules. Allen wants this course before the team begins a series of four reports during the off-season.

Please arrange a time for Sarah to meet with Randy so they can go over several previous reports. Sarah wants to be sure that what she covers in the course is what they need.

If you need to talk to me about this request, I will be staying at the Victoria Hotel in Charlottetown.

Figure 8-16 MEMORANDUM WITH OVERUSE OF UNDERLINING AND LACK OF HEADINGS

letters that we expect.[11] All capitals slows down reading because we use the shapes of letters to help us read, and the shapes disappear with all capitals.

A sentence in all capitals also takes up about 30% more space than the same sentence in lowercase letters. Mixed case is especially important online because space is always at a premium on screen and because text is harder to read on the screen. In addition, if you use all capitals in e-mail, readers think you're shouting at them.

TO: Michael Morfea   DATE: May 2, 1999

FROM: Melina Katsikis

SUBJECT: Request from Offshore Drilling Team for a Special Short Course

ACTION REQUIRED: **By Monday noon, May 6**

     Because I will be away on a three-week teaching assignment, I would appreciate your handling the following request, which came in just as I was preparing to leave today.

How About Offshore Drilling Want?

     Randy Allen, Director of the offshore drilling research team, would like a short course in offshore safety inspection reports. He would like the short course taught from 2-4 P.M. Monday-Friday afternoons, beginning week after next. The class must be scheduled then, as the team leaves the following week for their next research cruise.

Why Do They Want a Specialized Short Course?

     The drilling research team spends two weeks each month on cruise. After they return, they have one week to complete their reports before briefing begins for the next research expedition. Because of the short season and their rigid schedule, they cannot attend our regularly scheduled writing classes.

     Allen says that the cultural and educational backgrounds of the team are varied. Three of the ten regular researchers are native Europeans who attended only European universities. Of the remaining seven, three have Canadian degrees, and four attended school in American universities. As a result of their varied educational backgrounds, their reports lack uniform handling of English and report organization. Allen says that all the researchers have expressed interest in having a short review of standard English usage so that their reports to management will be more uniform.

How Can We Handle Their Request?

     Sarah Kelley says she can develop a class for the drilling team. We have materials on reports, style, and standard usage in the files. She can work with Ocean Drilling to determine the best report structure and develop a plan. These items can be easily collected and placed in binders. We also have summary sheets on each topic that will be good reference aids when the researchers write their reports following their cruise.

What Needs to Be Done Immediately?

     Sarah will contact you Monday morning. If you approve her teaching the class, please give Randy Allen a call, at extension 721, **before noon. He has a staff meeting scheduled at 1:30 and would like to announce the short course then. In fact, if the course cannot be scheduled this month, it cannot be taught for six months because of off-season cruise schedules. Allen wants this course before the team begins a series of four reports during the off-season.**

     Please arrange a time for Sarah to meet with Allen so they can go over several previous reports. Sarah wants to be sure that what she covers in the course is what they need.

Figure 8-17 MEMO REDESIGNED WITH QUESTIONS AS HEADINGS

Use Colour Carefully

On paper, avoid printing the text in colour. Black ink on white paper provides the best contrast, and high contrast between paper and ink is necessary for easy reading. Coloured paper may be a better choice if it enhances the effectiveness of your document. For example, some companies use light gray, cream, or light blue paper for major reports and proposals. Some companies use paper of one colour for the main body of the report and another colour for the appendices. Some use coloured sheets as dividers between sections of reports. If you use coloured paper, choose a very light shade to keep the contrast between ink and paper high.

You may be able to print a document in more than one colour. If so, use colour judiciously. Colour works well in headings and in visuals such as graphs, charts, and pictures, but it doesn't work well for text on paper.

When planning to use colour in a printed report or other document, think about what may happen to the document in the future. If it is likely to be photocopied, make sure that colour is not the only indicator of any particular feature, because the colour will be lost in photocopying. Also, remember that some people are colourblind: They cannot distinguish certain colours.

There is often an added cost to printing paper documents in colour. Online, colour is free, but don't go overboard using a rainbow of colours. Also, keeping a high contrast between the text and the background is important on screen as well as on paper. For example, a solid light blue makes a good background colour for the screen, but blue is not a good colour for text because our eyes don't focus well on blue letters.[12] Don't create artistic backgrounds that make the text difficult to see. You want readers to pay attention to your words and pictures, not to the background. (See Chapter 7, "Electronic Communication," for guidelines on developing World Wide Web pages.)

The golden rule for all aspects of document design, both on paper and on screen, is to make the page or screen look clear, uncluttered, and consistent. Keep it simple.

Helping Readers Locate Information

To help your readers find what they need and understand your document, you have to plan a useful structure for the document (organize it well), and you have to show that structure to the readers (design it well). In the previous sections of this chapter, we showed you how to use page layout and fonts to make your document clear and easy to use. In this section, we show you how to give readers clues to the document's overall structure.

As we pointed out earlier in the chapter, most people read technical and business documents selectively, both in print and online. With a print document, readers may glance over the table of contents to see what the document is about and then pick and choose the sections to read by looking for headings that match their needs and interests. They may skim through the pages, stopping when a heading or example or graphic strikes them as relevant or important. They may need to go back to the document later to check specific facts, and they'll want to find the relevant pages quickly.

Readers seldom work through an online document from beginning to end. They *use* an online document or help system or World Wide Web site rather than *read* it. They jump from the contents page (which corresponds to the table of contents of a paper document) or from the search function (which corresponds to an index) directly to a topic that interests them. To help readers (users) find what they need quickly, you have to arrange your document well and then give them clues to your arrangement.

Following are three ways to help your readers find information easily:

- Write useful headings.
- Design useful headings.
- Use page numbers and headers or footers in print documents.

Write Useful Headings

Headings are the short lines—the titles—that you put above each section and subsection of your document. Even short documents, such as memos, instructions, and letters, can benefit from headings. Compare Figure 8-16 with Figure 8-17 to see how useful headings can be, even in a short memo.

In longer documents, headings are essential to break the text into manageable pieces. Furthermore, in longer documents, the first few levels of headings become the table of contents. Online documents, such as help systems and World Wide Web pages, use headings too. Those headings may become a contents page in a help system or online document, or they may be the home page or top of the page of a World Wide Web site. Each heading becomes a link to the relevant section so that a user can click on the heading and jump directly to that section.

Headings are the road map to your document. For a print document, the headings come from your outline, although you usually don't use Roman numerals or letters in headings. If you are creating an online document, you should first develop an outline for it, too, and think carefully about the headings. These five suggestions will help you write useful headings:

- Make the headings meaningful.
- Use questions, verb phrases, and sentences instead of only nouns.
- Use standard key words if readers expect them.
- Make the headings at a given level parallel.
- Make sure the headings match the table of contents.

MAKE THE HEADINGS MEANINGFUL   Generic headings such as *Part I* or *Section 2* give no clues about the content of your work. Make your headings tell your story. Readers should be able to read only your headings, without any of your text, and understand the overall content as well as the structure (the arrangement) of your document.

USE QUESTIONS, VERB PHRASES, AND SENTENCES INSTEAD OF ONLY NOUNS
The best way to write headings is to put yourself in your readers' place. Will readers come to your document with questions? Then questions will make

good headings. Will they come wanting instructions for doing tasks? Then verb phrases that match the actions they need to take will make good headings. Will they come seeking knowledge about a situation? Then statements of fact about that situation will make good headings. Figure 8-18 shows how effective it can be to use questions, verb phrases, and statements as headings.

To see headings like these in actual documents, look back at figures that appeared earlier in this chapter. Figure 8-2 shows two levels of headings on the same page. You see a question at the first level and two verb phrases at the second level. If you had more of this proposal to look at, you would see other questions as first-level headings.

USE STANDARD KEY WORDS IF READERS EXPECT THEM   You may be working on a document for which readers expect to see a certain set of headings in a certain order, as in a standard proposal format. In that case, you should organize your material in the order and with the headings that your readers expect. Figure 8-19 shows the headings you might use in a standard proposal format.

Questions are useful as headings in a brochure.

    What does the gypsy moth look like?
    How can we protect trees from gypsy moths?
    How often should we spray?

Verb phrases are useful in instruction manuals.

Verb phrases can be gerunds, like these:
    Adding a graphic
    Selecting the data
    Selecting the type of graph to use
    Adding a title

Verb phrases can be imperatives, like these:
    Make your attendance policy clear.
    Explain your grading policy.
    Announce your office hours.
    Supply names of texts to be purchased.
    Go over assignments and their due dates.

Short sentences are useful in memos and reports.

    Our workload has doubled in the past year.
    We are also being asked to do new tasks.
    We have logged 560 hours of overtime this year.

Figure 8-18 DIFFERENT STRUCTURES YOU CAN USE FOR EFFECTIVE HEADINGS

Project Summary	Facilities and Equipment
Project Description	Personnel
Rationale and Significance	Budget
Plan of Work	

Figure 8-19 KEY WORDS AS HEADINGS IN A PROPOSAL

However, be wary of using single nouns or strings of nouns as headings in most documents. Headings that are only nouns may be ambiguous, overly technical, or too general. Research shows that people have a great deal of difficulty predicting what information comes under noun headings.[13]

MAKE THE HEADINGS AT A GIVEN LEVEL PARALLEL Like list items, headings at any given level in a document should be parallel. (See Parallelism in Part V, Handbook.) Parallelism is a very powerful tool in writing. See for yourself the difference parallelism makes by comparing the two sets of headings in Figure 8-20.

MAKE SURE THE HEADINGS MATCH THE TABLE OF CONTENTS To check how well your headings tell your story and to check how well you've maintained parallel structure in headings, use your word processing program to create an outline view, or a table of contents, for your draft document in print or online. Both in print and online, the headings become the table of contents. In a print document, readers can use the table of contents to turn to a particular section. They know they're in the right place if the heading for that section matches the wording in the table of contents. The same is even more true online, where readers almost always move by jumping directly from a heading in the contents to a screen of information. If the

Nonparallel Headings	**Parallel Headings**
Graph Modifications	Modifying a graph
Data selection updating	Changing the data
To add or delete columns	Adding or deleting columns
How to change colour or patterns	Changing the colours or patterns
Titles and legends can be included	Adding titles and legends

Figure 8-20 HEADINGS THAT USE THE SAME SENTENCE STRUCTURE—PARALLEL HEADINGS—ARE EASIER FOR USERS TO FOLLOW

heading (the title) on the screen they come to doesn't match the heading that they clicked on in the contents, they may be confused and unsure whether they are where they thought they were going.

Design Useful Headings

Headings do more than outline your document. They also help readers find specific parts quickly, and they show the relationship among the parts. To help readers, headings have to be easily distinguished from the text and each level of heading has to be easily distinguished from all the other levels. Figure 8–21 is a good example of a print document with four levels of headings. You can

---

Controlling Soil-Borne Pathogens in Tree Nurseries

Types of Soil-Borne Pathogens and Their Effects on Trees

Simply stated, the effects of soil-borne pathogens ....

....

The soil-borne fungi

At one time, it was thought that the soil-borne fungi ....

....

Basiodiomycetes. The basiodiomycetes are a class of fungi whose species ....

Phycomycetes. The class phycomycetes is a very diversified type of fungus. It is the ....

The plant parasitic nematodes

Nematodes are small, unsegmented ....

....

Treatments and Controls for Soil-Borne Pathogens

....

....

....

Figure 8-21 FOUR LEVELS OF HEADINGS IN A REPORT

see how the writer uses boldface to distinguish all headings from the text and then uses type size, capitalization, and placement on the page to distinguish each level of heading from the other levels. Of course, for all headings at any given level, the type size, capitalization, and placement are the same. In this case, each level 2 heading is in 14-point boldface, on a line by itself, with major words capitalized. Each level 2 heading starts at the left heading margin, which is further left than the left text margin.

These eight suggestions will help you design useful headings:

- Limit the number of heading levels.
- Create a pattern for the headings and stick to it.
- Match size to importance.
- Keep all headings at one level the same.
- Put more space before a heading than after it.
- Keep each heading with the section that it covers.
- Use headings frequently.
- Consider using numbers with your headings.

LIMIT THE NUMBER OF HEADING LEVELS Student papers and technical documents that are meant to be read on paper shouldn't need more than four levels of headings. If you have more than four levels, consider dividing the

You can change type size

This Is the Title
This Is the Second Level of Heading
This Is the Third Level of Heading

You can change placement on the page or screen

This Is the Title

This Is the Second Level of Heading

This Is the Third Level of Heading

You can change the way the headings are capitalized

THIS IS THE TITLE

This Is the Second Level of Heading

This is the third level of heading

You can put rules under or over the headings

This Is the Title
_____

This Is the Second Level of Heading

Figure 8-22 FOUR WAYS TO SHOW LEVELS OF HEADINGS

material into two chapters. Online documents shouldn't need more than two levels of headings because readers see much less at one time online than in a paper document.

CREATE A PATTERN FOR THE HEADINGS AND STICK TO IT   Although your choices depend in part on the technology you are using, you almost certainly have several options for showing levels of headings.[14] Figure 8-22 illustrates a variety of ways to show different levels of headings. You can combine these to create the pattern for your headings. For example, you can change size, placement, *and* capitalization to show the different levels of headings. You can have rules with one or two of your levels of headings. Look again at Figure 8-21 to see how the writer has combined size and placement to create a pattern in which the level of each heading is obvious.

MATCH SIZE TO IMPORTANCE   Changing the type size is one way to indicate levels of headings. If you use different type sizes, make sure that you match the size to the level of importance. If the headings are different sizes, readers expect first-level headings to be larger than second-level headings, second-level headings to be larger than third-level headings, and so on. The lower-level headings can be the same size as the text, but no level of heading should be smaller than the text. That would violate readers' expectations. If you use different type sizes for different heading levels, don't make the differences too great.

KEEP ALL HEADINGS AT ONE LEVEL THE SAME   Readers bring expectations to documents based on past experience. They also develop expectations from what they see on paper or on the screen. Once they "see" your document—that is, once they understand your structure and the way you are using headings—they expect to be able to use that pattern to understand the entire document. So, be consistent in the way you use headings throughout the document.

PUT MORE SPACE BEFORE A HEADING THAN AFTER IT   Headings announce the topic that is coming next in your document. Therefore, you want the heading to lead the reader's eye down the page or screen into the text that follows. One way to do that is to have more space, on the page or screen, before the heading than after it, as in Figures 8-2 and 8-9.

If you are going to use a rule with the heading, consider putting it *above* the heading rather than below it. A rule above the heading creates a "chunk" that includes both the heading and the text that it covers. A rule above the heading also draws the reader's eye down into the text that follows instead of up and away from that text. See Figure 8-7 for an example.

KEEP EACH HEADING WITH THE SECTION THAT IT COVERS   Don't leave a heading at the bottom of a page when the text appears on the next page. Make sure you have at least two lines of the first paragraph on the page with the heading. In some cases, you may want each topic to be on a separate page so that the heading and all the text of a topic appear together. The formal reports in Chapter 14 illustrate effective ways of breaking pages.

Most word processing programs have functions that help you keep headings from being stranded at the bottom of a page and that allow you to set up your document so that all headings of a certain level start on a new page.

USE HEADINGS FREQUENTLY   Frequent headings break up the monotony of text on the page or screen. They also help readers who are skimming to grasp the main points of the document quickly. In a short brochure, you might want a heading on every paragraph or every panel. In a report, you probably want a heading for every subsection, which might cover two or three paragraphs. In general, in print, you want to have clues to the text's arrangement on every page; online, you should have a heading on every screen or window. On a World Wide Web page, you want to keep each topic short and give each topic a heading.

CONSIDER NUMBERS WITH YOUR HEADINGS   In many companies and agencies, the standard for organizing reports and manuals is to include a numbering system with the headings. The two most commonly used systems are

- The traditional outline system
- The multiple-decimal system

Figure 8-23 shows the two systems.

The rationale for these systems is that you can refer to a section elsewhere in the report by its number. The numbering systems, however, have several disadvantages. In both these systems, if you want to add or remove a section, you have to renumber at least part of the report. Unless your software does this for you automatically, renumbering is tedious and highly susceptible to error. Also, many readers find it difficult to follow these numbering systems, especially if you use more than three levels. The multiple-decimal system is particularly difficult for most people to use. For example, if you see a heading marked 1.1.1.1 (and some government reports can be found that go to a fifth level, 1.1.1.1.1), you will likely have a difficult time remembering what the main division 1.0 actually was.

In short, clear headings are more useful than numbers. If you are not required to use a numbering system, we suggest that you not institute one. However, many government agencies and many companies, especially those that prepare documents for the government, require one of these numbering systems. Therefore, it pays to be familiar with them.

If you use a numbering system with your headings, you must also put the numbers before the entries in your table of contents.

Use Page Numbers and Headers or Footers in Print Documents

In addition to clearly worded and visually accessible headings, you can use other devices to make your content and organization clear in printed documents. Two good ways are to number each page and to include running headers or footers.

Traditional outline system

TITLE

I.   FIRST-LEVEL HEADING

    A.   Second-Level Heading

        1.   Third-level heading

        2.   Third-level heading

    B.   Second-level heading

II.   FIRST-LEVEL HEADING

    A.   Second-Level Heading

        1.   Third-level heading

        2.   Third-level heading

    B.   Second-Level Heading

Multiple-decimal system

TITLE

1.0   FIRST-LEVEL HEADING

    1.1   Second-Level Heading

        1.1.1   Third-level heading

        1.1.2   Third-level heading

    1.2   Second-Level Heading

2.0   FIRST-LEVEL HEADING

    2.1   Second-Level Heading

        2.1.1   Third-level heading

        2.1.2   Third-level heading

    2.2   Second-Level Heading

Figure 8-23 TWO TYPES OF NUMBERING SYSTEMS

NUMBER THE PAGES You have been numbering the pages of essays, research papers, and book reports for years, but you may not have considered the importance of page numbering as a document design tool. Page numbers help readers keep track of where they are and provide easy reference points for talking about a printed document. Always number the pages of your drafts and final documents that people are going to read on paper.

Note that if the document is going to be used online, page numbers aren't usually helpful. In most online documents, readers can skip around in the document, jumping from one topic to another in any order. One place where page numbers are useful online, however, is in a set of visuals for an oral presentation. These may be created with software and projected directly from the computer or printed on transparencies and shown on an overhead projector (see Chapter 17, "Oral Reports"). To help your audience know where you and they are in the presentation, you may want to number your slides. You may want to let the audience know how many slides there are with a notation like this:

Slide 1 of 10

Short manuscripts and reports that have little prefatory material almost always use Arabic numerals (1, 2, 3), like the page numbers in this book. The commonly accepted convention is to centre the page number below the text, near the bottom of the page, or to put it in the upper right-hand corner. Always leave at least one double space between the text and the page number. Put the page number in the same place on each page. Page numbers at the bottom of the page often have a hyphen on each side, like this:

– 17 –

As reports grow longer and more complicated, the page-numbering system also may need to be more complex. If you have a preface or other material that comes before the main part of the report, it is customary to use small Roman numerals (i, ii, iii) for that material and then to change to Arabic numerals for the body of the report. The opening pages of this book use Roman numerals, and the balance use Arabic numerals.

In a report, the introduction may be part of the prefatory material or the main body. The title page doesn't show the number but is counted as the first page. The page following the title page is number 2 or ii.

When numbering the pages, you have to know whether the document is going to be printed or photocopied on one side of the paper or two. If both sides of the paper will have printing on them, you may have to number some otherwise blank pages in word processing files. New chapters usually start on a right-hand page—that is, on the front side of a page that is photocopied on both sides. The right-hand page always has an odd number. If the last page of your first chapter is page 9, for example, and your document will be photocopied double-sided, you have to include an otherwise blank page 10 so that the first page of your second chapter will be a right-hand page (in this case, page 11) when the document is printed, copied, and bound.

The body of a report is usually paginated continuously, from page 1 to the last page. For the appendices, you may continue the same series of numbers, or you may change to a letter-plus-number system. In that system, the pages in Appendix A are numbered A-1, A-2, and so on. The pages in Appendix B are numbered B-1, B-2, and so forth. If your report is part of a series, or if your company has a standard report format, you will need to make your page numbering match that of the series or standard.

Numbering appendices with the letter-plus-number system has several advantages:

- It separates the appendices from the body. Readers can tell how long the body of the report is and how long each appendix is.
- It clearly shows that a page is part of an appendix and which appendix it belongs to. It makes pages in the appendices easier to locate.

- It allows the appendices to be printed separately from the body of the report. Sometimes the appendices are ready before the body of the report has been completed, and being able to print the appendices first may save time and help you meet a deadline.
- It allows the pagination of either an appendix or the body to be changed without requiring changes in the other parts.

INCLUDE HEADERS OR FOOTERS In long paper documents, it helps readers if you give them information about the document at the top or bottom of the page. If the information is at the top of the page, it is a **header**. This book uses headers printed in 8½-point type to help you find chapters quickly as you look through the pages. If the information is at the bottom of the page, it is a **footer**. The document in Figure 8-2 uses a footer.

A typical header for a report would show the author's name, the title of the report, and the date. It might look like this:

Jane Fernstein

Feasibility Study

June 1997

A typical header for a letter would show the name of the person receiving the letter, the page number, and the date. It might look like this:

Dr. Jieru Chen   -2-   June 16, 1997

The header does not appear on the title page of the report or on the first page of a letter. Most word processing programs allow you to set up your file so that the header starts on the second page.

Online documents should also have indicators that tell people both what document they are in and what part of the document they are looking at.

Planning and Revision Checklists

You will find the Planning and Revision Checklists that follow Chapter 2, "Composing," and Chapter 4, "Writing for Your Readers," valuable in planning and revising any presentation of technical information. The following questions specifically apply to document design. They summarize the key points in this chapter and provide a checklist for planning and revising.

General Questions

Planning
- Have you planned the format?
- Have you considered how people will use your document?
- Have you checked on the software and hardware that you will use to prepare both drafts and final copy? (Do you know what options are available to you?)

continued >>

- Have you found out whether you are expected to follow a standard format or style sheet?
- Have you thought about all the features (headings, pictures, tables) that you will have, and have you planned a page or screen design that works well with those features?
- Have you thought about how you will make the arrangement obvious to your readers? (What will you do to make it easy for people to read selectively in your document?)

Revision
- Is your document clean, neat, and attractive?
- Is your text easy to read?
- Will your readers be able to find a particular section easily?
- If your document is supposed to conform to a standard, does it?

Questions About Setting Up a Useful Format

Planning
- Have you set the margins so that there is enough white space around the page, including space for binding, if necessary?
- Have you set the line length and line spacing for easy reading?
- Have you decided how you are going to show where a new paragraph begins?
- Have you decided whether to use a justified or ragged right margin?
- Have you planned which features to surround with extra white space, such as lists, tables, graphics, and examples?

Revision
- Have you left adequate margins? Have you left room for binding?
- Are the lines about 50 to 70 characters long? If you are using two columns, are the lines about 35 characters long in each column?
- Is the spacing between the lines and paragraphs consistent and appropriate?
- Can the reader tell easily where sections and paragraphs begin?
- Have you left the right margin ragged? If not, look over the paper to be sure that the justification has not made overly tight lines or left rivers of white space.
- Have you used the white space to help the reader find information?
- Have you put white space around examples, warnings, pictures, and other special elements?
- Have you used lists for steps in procedures, options, and conditions?

Questions About Making the Text Readable

Planning
- Have you selected a type size and typeface that will make the document easy to read?
- Have you planned for highlighting? Have you decided which elements need to be highlighted and what type of highlighting to use for each?
- Do you know whether you can use colour? If you can, have you planned what colour to use and where to use it in the document?

Revision
- Is the text type large enough to be read easily?

continued >>

- Have you been consistent in using one typeface?
- Have you used uppercase and lowercase letters for the text and for most levels of headings?

- Have you used highlighting functionally? Is the highlighting consistent? Does the highlighting make important elements stand out?

Questions About Making Information Easy to Locate

Planning

- Have you planned your headings? Have you decided how many levels of headings you will need? Have you decided on the format for each level of heading?
- Will the format make it easy for readers to tell the difference between headings and text? Will the format make it easy for readers to tell one level of heading from another?
- Have you decided where to put the page numbers and what format to use?
- Have you decided on headers or footers (information at the top or bottom of each page)?
- Have you found out whether you are expected to use a numbering system? If you are, have you found out what system to use and what parts of the document to include?

Revision

- Have you checked the headings? Are the headings informative? Unambiguous? Consistent? Parallel?
- Will readers get an overall picture of the document by reading the headings?
- Is the hierarchy of the headings obvious?
- Can readers tell at a glance what is heading and what is text?
- If readers want to find a particular section quickly, will the size and placement of the headings help them?
- Have you checked the page breaks to be sure that you do not have a heading by itself at the bottom of a page?
- Are the pages of a paper document numbered?
- Are there appropriate headers or footers?
- If you are using a numbering system, is it consistent and correct?

 ## Weblinks

Communications Arts Magazine
www.commarts.com

Design in Motion
www.itp.tsoa.nyu.edu/~review/current/focus/Roxby1.intro.html

Ideabook
www.ideabook.com/design.htm

Exercises

1. Assume that the memo below was sent to instructors at your university. The memo announces that they have been selected to use the

experimental teaching evaluation forms that the university wants to evaluate. The main part of the memo, paragraph 2, provides instructions on how to give the evaluations. The teachers who receive this memo are not expecting to receive it and are totally unfamiliar with the new teaching evaluation, a copy of which is attached to the memo. Reformat the memo to help them administer the evaluation correctly and let them know what they should do after they give the evaluation.

DATE: November 11, 1999

FROM: Karen Jones
                   Associate Director of Testing

TO: Faculty

As you know, the university has made every effort to see that teaching evaluations, which are given once a year, are as accurate a reflection as possible of the effectiveness of your teaching. We know that this goal is your desire. To help us better achieve this goal, we are launching a pilot program to test a new kind of evaluation. You were one of 50 faculty who agreed to test the new evaluation system. Because you are getting this memorandum, you are one of the faculty chosen for the trial evaluations. After you receive your scores, we will send you a response form to allow you to express your views on the evaluation. We will then set up an interview with you so that we can more fully discuss your views of the accuracy of the results and changes you think should be made.

When you receive the questionnaire, a copy of it is attached, we want you to do a number of things. Please announce that the questionnaire will be given and urge students to attend class that day. If some students are absent the day you give the questionnaire, give those students a questionnaire the next class period. For the trial questionnaire, it is imperative that every student in the trial sections complete a questionnaire. Have someone else administer the questionnaire— either a colleague or your departmental assistant. Be sure you are not present while the students are completing the questionnaire. Have the person who is monitoring the questionnaire collect all of them and place them back in the envelope. These should be sealed in front of the students. The person monitoring the questionnaire should return these to the testing office (104 Banting) immediately after the test. The tests should be left at the test desk, which is the first desk on the right after you enter the office. Give the test to the administrative assistant in charge of the trial test evaluation. Her name is Carol Cornish. She will be there from 8-11 and 1-4 every class day during the test week, which will be the first week in December (December 2-6). Sign the sheet to indicate that you have returned your trial test. You will receive your printout by the last week in November (November 25-29). When you receive your printout, it will include a date that tells you when we will want to talk to you further. The response card, indicating your feelings about the accuracy of the trial evaluation, should be completed and returned immediately.

If you have any questions, please call Luisa Cordeiro at ext. 9912.

2. **Revise the memorandum that follows, which is to be sent to plant engineering managers, so that it clearly explains the company's policy for paying for continuing education courses.**

TO: Plant Engineering Managers   DATE: September 1, 1999

FROM: Hamish McKay
              District Superintendent

SUBJECT: Company Education Policy

Here is the company's policy on education, which many of you have asked about. Please keep it for your files for reference.

Policy 44.7. Advanced Education and Training. This policy applies to all employees except technicians and maintenance personnel. In order to encourage management personnel to achieve increasing professional competence in their disciplines and to enhance advancement potential, personnel who register for credit at the undergraduate or graduate level in accredited institutions will be reimbursed for tuition costs, registration fees, required textbooks, lab equipment, and other required materials upon completion of these courses. Certification that the specific course(s) will enhance the employee's professional growth must be provided by the employee's direct supervisor and countersigned by the supervisor's superior, unless the employee's supervisor holds the rank of vice president. Successful completion, defined as a grade of B or higher, must be attained in any course before the employee can apply for compensation. Costs of travel to the institution and costs of nonrequired materials such as paper, photocopies, and clerical help will not be reimbursed nor submitted to the company clerical staff. Submission to the Training Division of all receipts for all expenses, approval of the direct supervisor that the course fills the requirements of this policy, and documentation of successful completion are required before reimbursement will be permitted by the Training Division. Supervisors may allow release time for their employees to enroll in credit courses when work schedules permit. Release time is encouraged only when scheduled meetings of extremely important courses occur during regular working hours. If possible and necessary, personnel may be required to make up working time outside normal working hours. If the credit course can be taken outside the individual's normal working hours, no release time will normally be allowed. To receive reimbursement, staff should submit Training Division Form 6161 to the Training Division in accordance with the instructions on that form.

3. Have you recently seen a document that you found difficult to read or follow because it was not designed according to the guidelines in this chapter? Write a brief report to the company or agency that put out the document. Give specific recommendations for changing the design. Support your recommendations.

4. Revise an earlier writing assignment, using the design guidelines you have learned in this chapter.

5. When university or college students receive a package of forms about financial aid, they also get a page of information about the financial aid program. Here are the headings from one province's version of this information page:

   The Financial Aid Program
   Eligibility
   Deferments

> Terms and Conditions
> Loan Institutions
> Eligible Institutions
> Liability for Repayment
> Application Process

Are these headings meaningful to you? Are they in the most logical order? Plan an information page that would be more useful to you. Write a set of headings that you would like to see on the information page. (Hints for this exercise: If you would ask questions, write the headings as questions. Don't just translate the nouns in this example into other words. Think about the content and arrangement that you, as the reader, would want to see.)

6. Prepare a tentative table of contents for your final report. Show the sentence style that you will use for each level of heading. Show the typography that you will use for each level of heading. Check your table of contents for parallelism.

7. Plan the page layout for your final report. Will you use a header or a footer? Where will you put the page numbers? Will you use a numbering system? If so, which one will you use? Prepare one or more sample pages using the word processor and printer that you will be using for the report. The pages do not have to have real text on them. For example, you can type, "Level One Heading," and "This is what the text will look like." The pages should indicate the margins, line length, spacing, type choices, and so on. Show all the levels of headings that you are planning to use. Also show how you will handle graphics with the text.

8. Find an online document, help system, or World Wide Web site from which you can print a few screens of information. Critique the organization and design of the information. What about it works well, based on the principles in this chapter? What about it does not work well?

DESIGN ELEMENTS OF REPORTS

Chapter 8, "Document Design," discussed strategies for achieving good design. In this chapter, we discuss how to design the component elements of reports. We divide these elements into three groups: prefatory elements, main elements, and appendices.

Our approach to format in this chapter is descriptive, not prescriptive; that is, we describe some of the more conventional practices found in technical reporting, while at the same time acknowledging that many universities, colleges, companies, and journals call for practices different from the ones we describe. Therefore, we do not recommend that you follow at all times the practices in this chapter. If you are a student, however, your instructor may insist that you follow this chapter fairly closely, in the interests of class uniformity.

Prefatory Elements

Prefatory elements help your readers to get into your report. The letter of transmittal or preface may be the readers' first introduction to the report. The table of contents reveals the structure of your report. In the glossary, readers will find the definitions of terms that may be new to them. All the prefatory elements discussed in this section contribute to the success of your report.

Letter of Transmittal and Preface

We have placed the letter of transmittal and preface together because they are often quite similar in content. They usually differ in format and intended audience only. You will use the letter of transmittal when the audience is a single person or a single group. Many of your reports as a student will include a letter of transmittal to your professor, usually placed just before or after your title page. When on the job, you may handle the letter differently. Often, it is mailed before the report, as a notice that the report is coming, or it may be mailed at the same time as the report but under separate cover.

Generally, you will use the preface for a more general audience when you may not know specifically who will be reading your report. The preface or letter of transmittal introduces the reader to the report. It should be fairly brief. Always include the following basic elements:

- Statement of transmittal or submittal (included in the letter of transmittal only)
- Statement of authorization or occasion for report
- Statement of subject and purpose

Additionally, you may include some of the following elements:

- Acknowledgments
- Distribution list (list of those receiving the report—used in the letter of transmittal but not in the preface)
- Features of the report that may be of special interest or significance
- List of existing or future reports on the same subject
- Background material
- Summary of the report
- Special problems (including reasons for objectives not met)
- Financial implications
- Conclusions and recommendations

How many of the secondary elements you include depends upon the structure of your report. If your report's introduction or discussion includes background information, there may be no point in including such material in the preface or letter of transmittal. See Figures 9-1 and 9-2 for a sample letter of transmittal and a sample preface.

If the report is to remain within an organization, the letter of transmittal will become a memorandum of transmittal. This changes nothing but the format. See Chapter 11, "Correspondence," for letter and memorandum formats.

Cover

A report's cover serves three purposes. The first two are functional and the third aesthetic and psychological.

First, covers protect pages during handling and storage. Pages wrinkle, become soiled and damaged, and may eventually be lost if they are not protected by covers. Second, because they are what readers first see as they pick up a report, covers are the appropriate place to display identifying

Centre and South Hastings Recycling Board

270 West Street, Trenton, Ontario K8V 2N3
(613) 555-6266, fax (613) 555-6850

April 17, 1999

Mr. Bob Breeze
Ministry of Environment and Energy
7th Floor, 40 St. Clair Ave. West
Toronto, Ontario M4V 1M2

Dear Mr. Breeze:

Re: Blue Box 2000: Empty Aerosol and Paint Can Project

Statement of transmittal, subject, authorization

Attached is a copy of the final report "Blue Box 2000: Empty Aerosol and Paint Can Project" which has been approved by both the Centre & South Hastings Recycling Board and a multi-stakeholder Steering Committee which was set up to oversee the project. The Steering Committee included representatives from the Ministry of Environment and Energy (MOEE), the Ministry of Labour (MOL), the Canadian Aerosol Information Bureau (CAIB), the Canadian Paint and Coatings Association (CPCA), the local fire department, the contractor (HGC Management) and the Recycling Board.

Conclusions

The report finds that empty aerosols and empty paint cans can be recycled without problems and at no extra cost. There have been no incidents at any stage of the operation—from the curb to marketing the material. Other findings are summarized on page 4 of the report.

Copies of this report will be distributed to members of the AMRC and OMMRI. Please let me know how many copies will be required by your Ministry.

I trust this is the information you require.

Yours truly,

Jill Dunkley

Recycling Coordinator

Distribution list

cc: Rick Harris, MOEE (Kingston)
   Nav Dhaliwal, MOEE (Waste Reduction Branch)
   Chuck Beach (CAIB)
   Joe Hruska (OMMRI)
   Linda Varangu (AMRC)

Figure 9-1 LETTER OF TRANSMITTAL
Source: City of Orillia.

Subject and purpose

Guidelines for usage

Future needs

PREFACE

The intention of this manual is to keep those who are involved with erosion and sediment control in provincial agencies, municipalities, conservation groups, and private industries informed of the most up-to-date strategies and practices. The practice of erosion and sediment control has been rapidly evolving over the past decade. This manual draws from the experience of the past and surveys current planning approaches and management practices.

While erosion and sediment control should be addressed in the context of watershed or subwatershed planning processes, this training manual was developed specifically for on-site management techniques only. It should be stressed, however, that site-specific conditions require flexibility.

As new control or preventive technologies emerge that can be shown to produce the desired results, they should be given an opportunity for implementation. There is a need for innovative designers to develop better designs and for reviewing agencies to encourage innovation by showing flexibility in applying agency criteria.

Figure 9-2 PREFACE

Source: James Li (Ryerson Polytechnic University), *Erosion and Sediment Control Training Manual* (Ontario Ministry of the Environment, Spring 1998): iv. © Queen's Printer for Ontario. Reproduced with permission.

SELECTED CHARACTERISTICS OF THE PEOPLES OF THE COMMONWEALTH OF INDEPENDENT STATES

by

Anne K. Chimato

Geography 334   July 27, 1999

Figure 9-3 STUDENT LABEL

information such as the report title, the company or agency by or for which the report was prepared, and security notices if the report contains proprietary or classified information. Incidentally, students should not print this sort of information directly on the cover. An alternative is to put the information onto gummed labels readily obtainable at the campus bookstore, and then fasten the labels to the cover. A student label might look like the one in Figure 9-3.

Finally, covers bestow dignity, authority, and attractiveness. They bind a bundle of manuscript pages into a finished work that looks and feels like a report and has some of the characteristics of a printed and bound book.

Suitable covers need not be expensive and sometimes should not be. Students, particularly, should avoid being pretentious. All three purposes may be served by covers of plastic or light cardboard, perhaps of 30- or 40-pound substance. Students can buy such covers in a variety of sizes, colours, and finishes.

While you are formatting your report, remember that when you fasten it into its cover, about one inch (2.5 cm) of the left margin will be lost. If you want a standard margin, you must leave two inches (5 cm) on your paper. Readers grow irritated when they must exert brute force to bend open the covers to see the full page of text.

Title Page

Like report covers, title pages perform several functions. They dignify the reports they preface, of course, but far more important, they provide identifying information and help to orient the report users to their reading tasks.

To give dignity, a title page must be attractive and well designed. Symmetry, balance, and neatness are important. The most important items should be boldly printed; items of lesser importance should be subordinated. These objectives are sometimes at war with the objective of giving the report users all the data they may want to see at once. Here, we have listed in fairly random order the items that sometimes appear on title pages. A student paper, of course, would not require all or even most of these items. The first four listed are usually sufficient for simple title pages.

- Name of the company (or student) preparing the report
- Name of the company (or instructor and course) for which the report was prepared
- Title and sometimes subtitle of the report
- Date of submission or publication of the report
- Code number of the report
- Contract numbers under which the work was done
- List of contributors to the report (minor authors)
- Name and signature of the authorizing officer
- Company or agency logo and other decorative matter
- Proprietary and security notices
- Abstract
- Library identification number
- Reproduction restrictions
- Distribution list (A list of those receiving the report. If the letter of transmittal does not contain this information, the title page should.)

Of course, placing all of these items on a single page would guarantee a cluttered appearance. Include what you must, but not more.

Word processing allows report writers to use different type sizes and styles on a title page to indicate what is important and what is subordinate. Use this capability discreetly. Don't turn your title page (or any other part of your report) into a jumble of different typefaces. Generally, different type sizes and the use of boldface and plain style will suffice. Figure 9-4 illustrates a title page.

Pay particular attention to the wording of your title. Titles should be brief but descriptive and specific. The reader should know from the title what the report is about. A title such as "Effects of Incubation Temperatures on Sexual Differentiation in Turtles: A Geographic Comparison" is illustrative. From it, you know specifically the research being reported. To see how effectively this title works, leave portions of it out, and see how quickly your understanding of what the article contains changes. For example, "Sexual Differentiation in Turtles" would suggest a much more comprehensive report than does the actual title. A title such as "Effects of Incubation Temperatures" could as well

---

Final Report of the Committee on Word Processing Alternatives for the Oxford Insurance Company

Prepared for
Dennis Colcombet
Vice President for Information Services

Committee Members
Betty Robinett, Chair
Terry Collins
Ann Duin
Donald Ross

10 December 1999

Distribution List
Ann Bailly, Office Manager
Vickie Mikelonis, Computer Technician
Arthur Walzer, Purchasing Officer

Figure 9-4 TITLE PAGE

be about chickens as turtles. On the other hand, adding the words "An Investigation into" to the beginning of the title would add nothing useful. The test of whether a title is too long or too short isn't in the number of words it contains but what happens if words are deleted or added. Keep your titles as brief as possible, but make sure they do the job.

Table of Contents

A table of contents (TOC) performs at least three major functions. Its most obvious function is to indicate the page on which discussion of each major topic begins; that is, it serves the reader as a locating device. Less obviously, a TOC forecasts the extent and nature of the topical coverage and suggests the logic of the arrangement and the relationship of the parts. In the prewriting stage, provisional drafts of the TOC enable the author to "think on paper"; they act as outlines to guide the composition.

A system of numbers, letters, type styles, indentations, and other mechanical aids has to be selected so that the TOC will perform its intended functions. Figure 9-5 shows a TOC suitable for student reports. We

Make all major headings distinctive. All capitals or boldface are good choices.

Line up all numbers, arabic and roman, on right-hand digits.

Show hierarchy with indentation. If you have used a numbering system in the report, repeat it in table of contents.

In subheadings, capitalize first and last words and all principal words.

CONTENTS

Page

ii

Figure 9-5 TABLE OF CONTENTS FROM A STUDENT REPORT

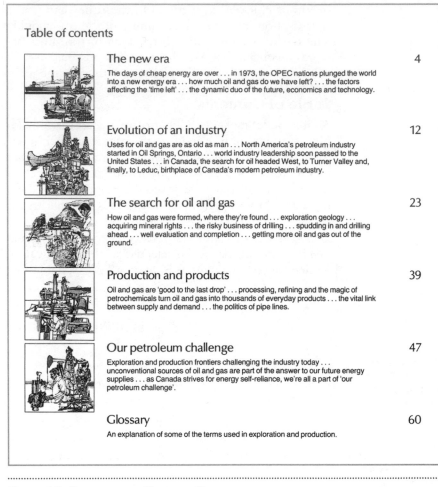

Table of contents

The new era 4

The days of cheap energy are over . . . in 1973, the OPEC nations plunged the world into a new energy era . . . how much oil and gas do we have left? . . . the factors affecting the 'time left' . . . the dynamic duo of the future, economics and technology.

Evolution of an industry 12

Uses for oil and gas are as old as man . . . North America's petroleum industry started in Oil Springs, Ontario . . . world industry leadership soon passed to the United States . . . in Canada, the search for oil headed West, to Turner Valley and, finally, to Leduc, birthplace of Canada's modern petroleum industry.

The search for oil and gas 23

How oil and gas were formed, where they're found . . . exploration geology . . . acquiring mineral rights . . . the risky business of drilling . . . spudding in and drilling ahead . . . well evaluation and completion . . . getting more oil and gas out of the ground.

Production and products 39

Oil and gas are 'good to the last drop' . . . processing, refining and the magic of petrochemicals turn oil and gas into thousands of everyday products . . . the vital link between supply and demand . . . the politics of pipe lines.

Our petroleum challenge 47

Exploration and production frontiers challenging the industry today . . . unconventional sources of oil and gas are part of the answer to our future energy supplies . . . as Canada strives for energy self-reliance, we're all a part of 'our petroleum challenge'.

Glossary 60

An explanation of some of the terms used in exploration and production.

Figure 9-6   PROFESSIONAL TABLE OF CONTENTS

Source: The Petroleum Resources Communication Foundation, *Our Petroleum Challenge: The New Era* (Calgary: PRCF): 3.

have annotated the figure to draw your attention to a few key points. However, the annotations are suggestions only. There are many acceptable variations in TOCs. For example, the leader dots in Figure 9-5 are used to carry the reader's eyes from the end of each title to the page number and to tie the page together visually. However, this practice is by no means universal. Some people feel the leader dots clutter the page, and therefore do not use them. If you use a numbering system in your report (see pages 192-195), the TOC should reflect that system.

In Figure 9-6, we reproduce a professionally created and visually interesting TOC. When you design your own TOC, avoid overcrowding. There is seldom justification for going beyond three levels of headings; beyond three levels, users have almost as much trouble locating items in the TOC as they have in locating them by flipping through the report. Be sure that page numbers in your TOC match the page numbers in your final draft. Remember that the wording of the TOC entries and the headings on the text pages must be exactly the same. Every entry in the TOC must also be in the report. However, not every heading in the report needs to be in the TOC. That is, if you have four levels of headings in your report, you might list only the top three levels in your TOC.

List of Illustrations

If a report contains more than a few illustrations, say more than three or four, it is customary to list the illustrations on a separate page or on the TOC page. Illustrations are of two major types: tables and figures. A **table** is any array of data, often numerical, arranged vertically in columns and horizontally in rows, together with the necessary headings and notes. **Figures** include photographs, maps, graphs, organization charts, and flow diagrams—literally any illustration that does not qualify as a table by the preceding definition. (For further details, see Chapter 10, "Graphical Elements.")

If the report contains both tables and figures, it is customary to use the page heading "Illustrations" or "Exhibits" and to list all the figures first and then all the tables. If you have all of one kind of figure in your report, you can use the appropriate term as your heading; for example, "Maps" is used as a heading in Figure 9-7. If you have various kinds of figures, use "Figures" as your heading.

Arabic numerals are used for figures and roman numerals for tables.

When titles run two or more lines, indent all lines after the first.

In titles, capitalize first and last words and all principal words. Do not capitalize articles, prepositions, and coordinating conjunctions unless they are a first or last word.

ILLUSTRATIONS

MAPS   Page

1. European States of the CIS 2

2. Ethnic Divisions of the European States of CIS 7

3. Central Asian States of the CIS 12

4. Ethnic Divisions of the Central Asian States
    of the CIS 16

TABLES

I. Comparison of Selected Characteristics of the
    People of the European States of the CIS....................3

II. Comparison of Selected Characteristics of the
    People of the Central Asian States of the CIS............13

iii

Figure 9-7 LIST OF ILLUSTRATIONS

Illustration titles should be brief, yet as self-explanatory as possible. Avoid a cumbersome expression such as "A Figure Showing Characteristic Thunderstorm Recording." Say simply, "Characteristic Thunderstorm Recording." On the other hand, do not be overly economical and write just "Characteristic" or "A Comparison." At best, such generic titles are only vaguely suggestive.

The simple list in Figure 9-7 should satisfy most needs. Notice in the figure that arabic numerals are used for figures and roman numerals for tables. This practice is common but by no means standard. Make sure that your page numbers are correct and that the titles listed accurately repeat the titles in the report.

Glossary and List of Symbols

Reports dealing with technical and specialized subject matter often include abbreviations, acronyms, symbols, and terms not known to the nonspecialist. Thus, a communication problem arises. Technically trained persons have an unfortunate habit of assuming that what is well known to them is well known to others. This assumption is seldom justified. Terms, symbols, and abbreviations change in meaning with time and context. In one context, CMA may stand for Canadian Manufacturers' Association; in another context, for Canadian Medical Association. The letter K may stand for Kelvin or some mathematical constant. The meaning given to Greek letters may change from one report to the next, even though both were written by the same person.

Furthermore, writers seldom have complete control over who will read their reports. A report intended for an engineering audience may have to be read by managers, legal advisors, or sales representatives. It is wise to play it safe by including a **list of symbols** or a **glossary** or both. Readers who do not need these aids can easily ignore them; those who do need them will be grateful.

The list of symbols is normally a prefatory element. A glossary may be a prefatory element or placed as an appendix at the end of the report. When you first use a symbol found in your list of symbols or a term found in the glossary, tell your reader where to find the list or the glossary. Figure 9-8 illustrates a list of symbols. Figure 9-9 illustrates a glossary.

Abstracts and Summaries

Abstracts and **summaries** are overviews of the facts, results, conclusions, and recommendations of a report. In many formats, such as empirical research reports and feasibility reports, abstracts or summaries will be placed near the front of the report. In that position, they both summarize the report and allow busy readers to decide whether they want to read further. As we pointed out in Chapter 4, "Writing for Your Readers," both executives and experts expect the abstract or summary to come early in the report.

In more discursive reports, such as magazine articles, summaries most often come at the end of the report, where they serve to draw things together for the reader. Many reports, particularly empirical research reports, have an abstract at the beginning and a summary at the end. These facts raise the question of

---

SYMBOLS

A	Mass number
A.W.	Atomic weight
c	Velocity of light (2.998×10^{10} cm/sec)
D	H^2 atom (deuterium)
E	Energy
e-	Electron
e	Electronic charge (1.602×10^{-10} abs. coulomb)
ev	Electron volt
F	Free energy
(g)	Gas phase
H	Heat content
h	Planck's constant (6.624×10^{-27} erg/sec)
I_{sp}	Specific impulse
k	Boltzmann's constant (1.3805×10^{-16} erg/deg)
ln	Natural logarithm

* * * *

α	Alpha particle
γ	Gamma ray
ζ	Bond energy
μ	Micro
ρ	Density

Figure 9-8 LIST OF SYMBOLS

when an overview is an "abstract" and when it is a "summary." In general, these principles hold true:

- Abstracts are placed before technical reports, such as empirical research reports, meant for technical audiences.
- Summaries are placed before business and organizational reports, such as proposals and feasibility reports. When the audience is primarily an executive audience, the summary will be known as an executive summary.
- An overview placed at the end of a report will probably be called a summary.

Because abstracts and executive summaries always appear as prefatory elements, we discuss them in this section. We discuss other types of summaries and conclusions and recommendations on pages 219-224, where we discuss how to end a report.

Use parallel sentence fragments for glossary definitions. (See "Parallelism" section in Handbook.)

Use complete sentences to add information to definition.

GLOSSARY

Btu	the amount of heat required to raise the temperature of one pound of water one degree Fahrenheit.
degree day	a temperature standard around which temperature variations are measured.
design temperature	the maximum reasonable temperature expected during the heating or cooling season. Design calculations are based upon this number.
heat transmission coefficient	the quantity of heat in Btu transmitted per hour through one square foot of a building surface.
infiltration	the air leaking into a building from cracks around doors and windows.
sensible heat	heat that the human body can sense.
thermal conductivity	the quantity of heat in Btu transmitted by conduction per hour through one square foot of a homogeneous material for each degree Fahrenheit difference between the surfaces of the material.
thermal resistance	the reciprocal of thermal conductivity.

vii

Figure 9-9 GLOSSARY

ABSTRACTS   Discussed here are abstract style and two kinds of abstracts: **informative** and **descriptive**.

Never use "I" statements in either kind of abstract. Report your information impersonally, as though it were written by someone else. The informative abstract in Figure 9-10 shows the style. This is not an arbitrary principle. If you publish your report, your abstract will probably be reprinted in an abstracting journal, where the use of "I" is inappropriate. Also, many companies, in the interest of good intracompany communication, publish the abstracts of all company research reports. The restriction on the use of "I" makes the use of passive voice common in abstracts. Because your full report contains complete documentation, you need not footnote or otherwise document the information in abstracts.

Figure 9-10 illustrates an **informative abstract**. Informative abstracts are most often intended for an expert audience; therefore, their authors can use the technical language of the field freely. Like most informative abstracts, the one in Figure 9-10 summarizes three major elements of the full report:

- The objectives of the research or the report
- The methodology used in the research
- The findings of the report, including the results, conclusions and recommendations

Most professional journals or societies publish stylebooks that include specifications about how to write an abstract. Many journals, because of high publication costs, will set an arbitrary limit of 200 words for abstracts. Because abstract writing uses many of the same techniques as summary writing, you might want to read what we say about summaries on pages 219–224.

The main purpose of the **descriptive abstract** is to help busy readers decide whether they need or want the information in the report enough to read it entirely. The descriptive abstract merely tells what the full report contains. Unlike the informative abstract, it cannot serve as a substitute for the report itself. Many reports contain descriptive abstracts, and many abstracting journals print them. The following example is typical of the content and style of a descriptive abstract:

> The management of the process by which technical documents are produced usually proceeds according to one of two models, the "division of labour" model or the "integrated team" model. This article reports on a survey that suggests the prevalence of each model and that gives insights into how the choice of a management model affects the practice of technical communication and the attitudes of technical communicators.[1]

ABSTRACT

Research objectives

Methodology

Findings

This study investigated the role of signaling in helping good readers comprehend expository text. As the existing literature on signaling, reviewed in the last issue of the <u>Journal</u>, pointed to deficiencies in previous studies' methodologies, one goal of this study was to refine prose research methods. Two passages were designed in one of eight signaled versions each. The design was constructed to assess the individual and combined effect of headings, previews, and logical connectives. The study also assessed the effect of passage length, familiarity, and difficulty. The results showed that signals do improve a reader's comprehension, particularly comprehension two weeks after the reading of a passage and comprehension of subordinate and superordinate inferential information. This study supports the hypothesis that signals can influence retention of text-based information, particularly with long, unfamiliar, or difficult passages.

Figure 9-10 INFORMATIVE ABSTRACT

Source: Jan H. Spyridakis, "Signaling Effect: Increased Content Retention and New Answers—Part II," *Journal of Technical Writing and Communication* 19 (1989): 395.

SUMMARY

Problem definition

The University is steadily falling behind in the faculty and student use of computers. Our existing computer labs have insufficient numbers of computers, and those we do have are badly dated. We have faculty who are capable of designing computer programs for instructional use but who are reluctant to do so because their students do not have access to computers. Too many graduates are leaving the University as computer illiterates.

Information Resources has considered three solutions to the problem:

Alternatives considered

1. Require all incoming students to buy a microcomputer at an approximate cost of $1500 each. At an interest rate of 8%, students could repay the University for their computers in 16 quarterly payments of $108.31 each.

2. Provide those students and faculty who want them with microcomputers through the University bookstore at deep discounts. Purchasers would arrange their own financing if needed.

3. Upgrade the University computer labs by providing $1 million over the next fiscal year to provide microcomputers, printers, software, and new furniture. Student computer lab fees of $25 per quarter will pay the cost of material and employees to run the labs.

Recommendation

Effect of recommendation

We recommend both alternatives 2 and 3. We reject alternative 1 on the grounds that we must not put educational costs out of reach for our students. Solutions 2 and 3 would make enough computers available for the immediate future to encourage their use by both students and faculty.

Figure 9-11   EXECUTIVE SUMMARY

The descriptive abstract discusses the *report*, not the subject. After reading this abstract, you know that this article "gives insights into how the choice of a management model affects the practice of technical communication and the attitudes of technical communicators," but you must read the article to gain the insights. Whether a report is 10 or 1000 pages long, a descriptive abstract can cover the material in less than 10 lines.

EXECUTIVE SUMMARY   Placed at the front of a report, the **executive summary** ensures that the points of the report important to an executive audience are immediately accessible. To that end, it is written in a nontechnical language suited to an executive audience. Seldom more than one page long, double spaced, it emphasizes the material that executives need in their decision-making process. It need not summarize all the sections of the report. For example, writing for a combined audience of scientists and executives, a writer might include a theory section in a report. The executive summary might skip this section altogether or treat it very briefly.

In their decision making, executives weigh things such as markets, risks, rewards, costs, and people. If your report recommends buying new equipment, they want to be assured that you have examined all reasonable alternatives and considered cost, productivity, efficiency, profits, and staffing. If you are reporting research, executives take your methodology for granted. They care very little for the physics, chemistry, or sociology behind a development. What they want to know are your results and the implications of those results for the organization.

For a list of the questions that executives ask in different situations and that, therefore, an executive summary should answer, see Figure 4-1, p.53. Before writing an executive summary, look at that figure and read pages 52-54, where we discuss the reading habits of executives. The annotated executive summary in Figure 9-11 illustrates the technique and the major parts of an executive summary.

Place an executive summary immediately before the introduction and label it "Summary" or "Executive Summary." In short reports and memorandum reports, the executive summary often replaces the introduction and is followed immediately by the major discussion.

Main Elements

The body of a report contains detailed information and interpretation. The body needs to be introduced and, normally, finished off with an ending of some sort that may include a summary, conclusions, recommendations, or simply a graceful exit from the report. We discuss all these elements in this section.

Introduction

A good introduction forecasts what is to follow in the rest of the report. It directs the reader's mind to the subject and purpose. It sets limits on the scope of the subject matter and reveals the plan of development of the report. Early in your paper, you also give any needed theoretical or historical background; this is sometimes included as part of the introduction.

SUBJECT   Never begin an introduction with a superfluous statement. The writer who is doing a paper on read-only memory in computers and begins with the statement "The study of computers is a vital and interesting one" has wasted the readers' time and probably annoyed them as well. Announce your specific subject as early as possible in the introduction, preferably in the very first sentence. The sentence "This paper will discuss several of the more significant applications of the exploding wire phenomenon to modern science" may not be very subtle, but it gets the job done. The reader knows what the subject is. Often, in conjunction with the statement of your subject, you will also need to define some important terms that may be unfamiliar to your readers. For example, the student who wrote the foregoing sentence followed it with these two:

> A study of the exploding wire phenomenon is a study of the body of knowledge and inquiry around the explosion of fine metal wires by a sudden and large pulse of current.

> The explosion is accompanied by physical manifestations in the form of a loud noise, shock waves, intense light for a short period, and high temperatures.

In three sentences the writer announced the subject and defined it. The paper is well under way.

Sometimes, particularly if you are writing for nonspecialists, you may introduce your subject with an interest-catcher. The following example introduces a discussion of Canada's petroleum industry.

> In 1930, the Canadian humourist and economist Stephen Leacock wrote: "In our day, the true distinction between humanity and all the rest of the animate kingdom is that man is the animal that uses oil."

> Like other industrialized nations in the world, Canada relies upon oil as its primary energy source. Natural gas, Canada's emerging energy giant, is also coming into its own as a major source of energy. At present providing about 65% of our energy needs, the two are Canada's most important sources of energy. They will continue to be for years to come.

> They are the reason for the existence of one of Canada's most vital industries, the petroleum industry, whose activities are closely woven into the social, economic and political fibre of our country, and make the lead stories in our news media.[2]

Or you may simply extract a particularly interesting fact from the main body of your paper. For example,

> Last year, the Transportation Safety Board attributed 13 aircraft accidents to clear air turbulence. What is known about this unseen menace that can cripple an aircraft, perhaps fatally, almost without warning?

In this example, the writer catches your interest by citing the accident rate caused by clear air turbulence and nails the subject down with a rhetorical question in the second sentence. Interest-catching introductions are used in brochures, advertisements, and magazine and newspaper articles. You will rarely see an interest-catching introduction in business reports or professional journals. If you do, it will usually be a short one.

PURPOSE   Your statement of purpose tells the reader *why* you are writing about the subject you have announced. By so doing, you also answer the reader's question "Should I read this paper or not?" For example, a position paper on the public health issues surrounding an oil company's application to drill at certain specific sites begins as follows:

> This brief presents the position prepared by the Riverton Health Services, operating arm of the Riverton Board of Health, with respect to Canadian Exploration Petroleum's well license application numbers...

Readers who have no reason to be interested in such a discussion will know there is no purpose in reading further.

Another way to understand the purpose statement is to realize that it often deals with the *significance* of the subject. Writers for the Calgary-based Petroleum Resources Communication Foundation described the scope of the Foundation in order to introduce the purpose of their publication:

The Foundation was established in 1975 for the sole purpose of communicating with the public about Canada's petroleum industry. Its communication programs are based on information and facts about exploration, production, transportation and hundreds of other activities and functions related to crude oil and natural gas in Canada. Its members, more than 110 companies and professional societies involved in all facets of the industry, believe that communication with the public is as important as any other job they do.

With this information booklet, as with all its communication projects, the Foundation hopes to increase the knowledge Canadians have of the petroleum industry and create a better understanding of the role it has in Canada today.

Much could be written about the events and activities, people and places which can only be briefly referred to here. It is hoped, however, that this booklet arouses your curiosity about this exciting, challenging industry. It is your invitation to take up "Our Petroleum Challenge."[3]

SCOPE   The statement of scope further qualifies the subject. It announces how broad the treatment of the subject will be. Often it indicates the level of competence expected in the reader for whom the paper is designed. For example, a student who wrote, "In this report I explain the application of superconductivity in electric power systems in a manner suitable for under-graduate students" declared his scope as well as his purpose. He is limiting the scope to superconductivity in electric power systems and stating that his target audience is not composed of high school students or graduate physicists but of undergraduate university students.

PLAN OF DEVELOPMENT   In a plan of development, you forecast your report's organization and content. The principle of psychological reinforcement is at work here. If you tell your readers what you are going to cover, they will be more ready to comprehend as they read along. The following, taken from the introduction to a paper on enriching flour with iron, is a good example of a plan of development:

This study presents a basic introduction to three major areas of concern about iron enrichment: (1) which form of iron is most suitable; (2) potential health risks from overdoses of iron, such as cardiovascular disease, hemochromatosis, and the masking of certain disorders; and (3) ignorance of the definitions, extent, and causes of iron deficiency.

You need not think of the announcement of subject, purpose, scope, and plan of development as four separate steps. Often, subject and purpose or scope and plan of development can be combined. In a short paper, two or three sentences might cover all four points, as in this example from a booklet on Ontario's Air Quality Index:

That's why we created this booklet. It explains the AQI system and how it works, and gives a handy chart that outlines the AQI rating system. It also defines the pollutants we measure, what effects they can have on people, animals and plants, and what precautions should be taken when the AQI readings reach various levels.

Finally, we list the phone numbers you'll need to get more information for you and your audiences—24 hours a day. We hope you will use them and contact us to present an accurate picture of Ontario's environment. Because that's why we're here…so we can all get a better understanding of the air we breathe.[4]

Also, introductions to specialized reports may have peculiarities of their own. These will be discussed in Part IV, Applications.

THEORETICAL OR HISTORICAL BACKGROUND   When the theoretical or historical background is not too lengthy, you can incorporate it into your introduction. In the following excellent introduction, the writer begins with background, makes his subject and purpose clear, and closes with a paragraph that states his scope and plan of development:

In recent years, two questions have received a good deal of attention in the field of business and technical writing, or professional communication, as I will call it. One question is old and one new, but both are closely related—at least to professional communication teachers and researchers who are trained in the profession of literary criticism. The first question is as old as technical and business writing courses, dating back to the 1910s: To what extent, if any, should business and technical writing courses serve the pragmatic needs of business and industry, and to what extent, if any, should those courses teach the concerns of literary studies? The second question is relatively new, but it has received a great deal of attention in recent years: What is the responsibility, if any, of the instructor of these courses to teach ethics? The two questions are related in complex ways because, for some teachers in the field of professional communication, putting business and technical writing courses at the service of business and industry is viewed as ethically suspect, and there have been a number of articles recently that argue or suggest that business and technical writing courses for students majoring in science, technology, and business should ask those students to critique the ethical basis of science, business, and industry from what is essentially the perspective of literary studies, as we shall see.

Let me say from the outset that I believe that all teachers—and all professions and all institutions and indeed all human beings—have a responsibility to promote ethical behavior. So, too, every profession, institution, and human being ought to engage in critical reflection at times. The question is not whether teachers, courses, disciplines, professions, and institutions should promote ethical behavior but how, when, and for what purposes they should be promoted. These are far more complex questions, and they cannot be answered without instructors considering their methods, timing, and motives for raising ethical issues. In this article, I want to point out some potential difficulties—which are essentially ethical difficulties—in literature-trained faculty teaching ethics in professional communication courses, and I will warn against a too-hasty—uncritical, if you will—pursuit of certain kinds of critical reflection as a goal of these courses.

First, I will examine the historical and an institutional context of my two central questions and look at two recent answers to them. Then I will turn to an obscure chapter in the history of business and technical communication—the teaching of "engineering publicity" at Massachusetts Institute of Technology (MIT) in the early 1920s—to see the unusual answer of one institution to these questions at a crucial point in its history. Finally, I will suggest why I believe that answer is worth serious consideration by those of us involved in writing instruction and curricular planning for students who will enter business and professional communities, both outside and within academia (for we must remember that academics—even those in literary studies—are professionals as well).[5]

If the background material is extensive, however, it more properly becomes part of the body of your paper.

Discussion

The discussion will be the longest section of your report. Your purpose and your content will largely determine the form of this section. Therefore, we can prescribe no set form for it. In presenting and discussing your information, you will use one or more of the techniques described in Part II, Techniques, or the special techniques described in Part IV, Applications. In addition to your text, you will probably also use headings (see pages 186–192) and visual aids such as graphs, tables, and illustrations.

When thinking about your discussion, remember that almost every technical report answers a question or questions: What is the best method of desalination to create a water supply for an overseas peacekeeping mission? How are substances created in a cell's cytoplasm carried through a cell's membranes? What is the nature of life on the ocean floor? How does single parenthood affect the children in the family? Ask and answer the reporter's old standbys: Who? What? When? Where? Why? How? Use the always important "so-what?" to explore the implications of your information. However you approach your discussion, project yourself into the minds of your readers. What questions do they need answered to understand your discussion? What details do they need to follow your argument? You will find that you must walk a narrow line between too little detail and too much.

Too little detail is really not measured in bulk but in missing links in your chain of discussion. You must supply enough detail to lead the reader up to your level of competence. You are most likely to leave out crucial details at some basic point that, because of your familiarity with the subject, you assume to be common knowledge. If in doubt about the reader's competence at any point, take the time to define and explain.

Many reasons exist for too much detail, and almost all stem from writers' inability to edit their own work. When you realize that something is irrelevant to your discussion, discard it. It hurts, but the best writers will often throw away thousands of words, representing hours or even days of work.

You must always ask yourself questions like these: Does this information have significance, directly or indirectly, for the subject I am explaining or for the question I am answering? Does the information move the discussion forward? Does it enhance the credibility of the report? Does it support my conclusions? If you don't have a yes answer to one or more of these questions, the information has no place in the report, no matter how many hours of research it cost you.

Ending

Depending upon what sort of paper you have written, your ending can be a summary, a set of conclusions, a set of recommendations, or a graceful exit from the paper. Frequently, you'll need some combination of these. We'll look at the four endings and at some of the possible combinations.

It's also possible in reports written with executives as the primary audience that the "ending" may actually be placed at the front of the report. Remember the audience analysis research we discussed in Chapter 4, "Writing for Your Readers." It indicates that executives are more interested in summaries, conclusions, and recommendations than they are in the details of a report. Thus, many writers in business and government move these elements to the front of their reports. They may be presented in separate sections labelled "Summary," "Conclusions," and "Recommendations" or combined into an executive summary (see pages 214–215). In either case, the body of the report may be labelled "Discussion" or even "Annexes."

SUMMARY   Many technical papers are not argumentative. They simply present a body of information that the reader needs or will find interesting. Frequently, such papers end with summaries. In a summary, you condense for your readers what you have just told them in the discussion. Good summaries are difficult to write. At one extreme, they may lack adequate information; at the other, they may be too detailed. In the summary you must pare down to material essential to your purpose. This can be a slippery business.

Suppose your purpose is to explore the knowledge about the way the human digestive system absorbs iron from food. In your discussion you describe an experiment conducted with Venezuelan workers that followed isotopically labelled iron through their digestive systems. To enhance the credibility of the information presented, you include some details about the experiment. You report the conclusion that vegetarian diets decreased iron absorption.

How much of this should you put in your summary? Given your purpose, the location and methodology of the experiment would not be suitable material for the summary. You would simply report that in one experiment vegetarian diets have been shown to decrease iron absorption.

In general, each major point of the discussion should be covered in the summary. Sometimes you may wish to number the points for clarity. The following, from a paper of about 2500 words, is an excellent summary:

> The exploding wire is a simple-to-perform yet very complex scientific phenomenon. The course of any explosion depends not only on the material and shape of the wire but also on the electrical parameters of the circuit. An explosion consists primarily of three phases:
>
> 1. The current builds up and the wire explodes.
> 2. Current flows during the dwell period.
> 3. "Post-dwell conduction" begins with the reignition caused by impact ionization.
>
> These phases may be run together by varying the circuit parameters.
>
> The exploding wire has found many uses: it is a tool in performing other research, a source of light and heat for practical scientific application, and a source of shock waves for industrial use.

Summaries should be concise, and they should introduce no material that has not been covered in the report. Read your discussion over, noting your main generalizations and your topic sentences. Blend these together into a paragraph or two. Sometimes you will represent a sentence from the discussion with a sentence in the summary. At other times you will shorten such sentences to phrases or clauses. The last sentence in the example above represents a summary of four sentences from the writer's discussion. The four sentences themselves were the topic sentences from four separate paragraphs.

With a word processor, you might do well to copy the material you are summarizing and then go through it, eliminating unwanted material to make your summary. Such a technique may be easier and more accurate than retyping the material.

CONCLUSIONS Some technical papers work toward a conclusion. They ask a question, such as "Are nuclear power plants safe?," present a set of facts relevant to answering the question, and end by stating a conclusion: "Yes," "No," or sometimes, "Maybe." The entire paper aims squarely at the final conclusion. In such a paper, you argue inductively and deductively. You bring up opposing arguments and show their weak points. At the end of the paper, you must present your conclusions. Conclusions are the inferences drawn from the factual evidence of the report. They are the final link in your chain of reasoning. In simplest terms, the relationship of fact to conclusion goes something like this:

Facts	**Conclusion**
Car A averages 10 litres per 100 kilometres.	On the basis of litres/100km, Car B is preferable.
Car B averages 6.5 litres per 100 kilometres.	

Because we presented a simple case, our conclusion was not difficult to arrive at. But even more complicated problems present the same relationship of fact to inference.

In working your way toward a major conclusion, you ordinarily have to work your way through a series of conclusions. In answering the question of nuclear power plant safety, you would have to answer many subquestions concerning such things as security of the radioactive materials used, adequate control of the nuclear reaction, and safe disposal of nuclear wastes. The answer to each subquestion is a conclusion. You may present these conclusions in the body of the report, but it's usually a good idea to also draw them all together at the end of the report to support the major conclusion. Here, for example, are the conclusions to a report that questioned whether the class of chemicals known as phthalates endangered public health:

> Based on the observations made thus far, there is no evidence of toxicity in humans due to phthalates, either from foods, beverages, or household products as ordinarily consumed or used.

> These observations, coupled with the limited use of phthalate-containing food packaging materials and the low rate of migration of the plasticizers from packaging material to food, support the belief that the present use of phthalates in food packaging represents no hazard to human health.[6]

All the conclusions presented are supported by evidence in the report.

In larger papers or when dealing with a controversial or complex subject, you would be wise to precede your conclusions with a summary of your facts. By doing so, you will reinforce in your reader's mind the strength and organization of your argument. In any event, make sure your conclusions are based firmly upon evidence that has been presented in your report. Few readers of professional reports will take seriously conclusions based upon empty, airy arguments. Conclusions are frequently followed by recommendations.

RECOMMENDATIONS   A conclusion is an inference. A recommendation is the statement that some action should be taken or not taken. The recommendation is based upon the conclusions and is the last step in the process. You conclude that Brand X bread is cheaper per 100 grams than Brand Y and just as nutritious and tasty. Your final conclusion, therefore, is that Brand X is a better buy. Your recommendation is "Buy Brand X."

Many reports, such as feasibility reports, environmental impact statements, and research reports concerning the safety of certain foods or chemicals, are decision reports that end with a recommendation. For example, we are all familiar with the government recommendations that have removed certain artificial sweeteners from the market and placed warnings on cigarette packages. These recommendations were all originally stated at the end of reports looking into these matters.

Recommendations are simply stated. They follow the conclusions, often in a separate section, and look something like this:

Based upon the conclusions reached, we recommend that our company

- Not increase the present level of iron enrichment in our flour.
- Support research into methods of curtailing rancidity in flour containing wheat germ.

Frequently, you may have a major recommendation followed by additional implementing recommendations, as in the following:

Major recommendation

Implementing recommendations

We recommend that the Ministry of Transportation build a new overpass on Highway 7 at a point approximately 10 kilometres east of Highway 50.

- The Ministry's location engineers should begin an immediate investigation to decide the exact location.
- Once the location is pinpointed, the Ministry's right-of-way section should purchase the necessary land for the approaches to the overpass.

You need not support your recommendations when you state them. You should have already done that thoroughly in the report and in the conclusions leading up to the recommendations. It's likely, of course, that a full-scale report will contain a summary, conclusions, and recommendations.

GRACEFUL CLOSE   A short, simple, nonargumentative paper often requires nothing more than a graceful exit. As you would not end a conversation by turning on your heel and stalking off without a "good-bye" or a "see you later" to cover your exit, you do not end a paper without some sort of close. In a short informational paper that has not reached a decision, the facts should be still clear in the readers' minds at the end, and they will not need a summary. One sentence, such as the following, which might end a short speculative paper on superconductivity, will probably suffice:

> Because superconductivity seems to have numerous uses, it cannot fail to receive increasing scientific attention in the years ahead.

Sometimes, even a long, involved paper can profit from a graceful close. In the next example, the author gracefully exits a long, scholarly paper with a reference to other work that supports his own:

> Teachers of professional communication have a unique interdisciplinary perspective and thus a unique responsibility. They can—indeed they must—daily negotiate the distance between "the two cultures." C. P. Snow, who coined the phrase, was both a physicist and a man of letters, and it is salutary to recall that his famous essay (perhaps more often cited than read) is not an ethical indictment of the ethical position of scientific "culture," but just the opposite. Writing to his fellow literati, he says, "the greatest enrichment the scientific culture could give us is . . . a moral one." Snow praises scientific "culture" for its commitment to human improvement manifested in active involvement. Snow takes to task the other culture, the "mainly literary" one, for an ethical complacency "made up of defeat, self-indulgence, and moral vanity," a complacency to which "the scientific culture is almost totally immune." And he concludes, "It is that kind of moral health of the scientists which, in the last few years, the rest of us have needed most; and of which, because the two cultures scarcely touch, we have been most deprived" (414). Both cultures have changed much in the four decades since Snow published his essay, but perhaps each culture still has much to learn from the other, even about ethics.[7]

COMBINATION ENDINGS We have treated summaries, conclusions, and recommendations separately. Indeed, a full-scale report leading to a recommendation will often contain in sequence separate sections labelled "Summary," "Conclusions," and "Recommendations." When such is the case, the summary will often be restricted to a condensation of the factual data offered in the body. The implications of the data will be presented in the conclusions, and the action to be taken in the recommendations.

However, in many reports, the major elements of factual summary, conclusions, and recommendations may be combined. A combination of summary, conclusions, and recommendations placed at the front of a report for a technical audience will probably be labelled an abstract. It will be, in fact, what we describe on pages 212-213 as an informative abstract. The same combination located at the end of a report for any audience would probably be called a summary. A summary written specifically for an executive audience and located at the front of the report will be an executive summary (see pages 214-215).

It's unfortunate that there is a slight confusion of terms when these elements are used in different ways. Don't let the confusion in terminology confuse the essence of what is involved here. In all but the simplest reports, you must draw things together for your readers. You must condense and highlight your significant data and present any conclusions and recommendations you have.

Notice how this conclusion to a forestry research report smoothly combines all these elements:

SUMMARY

Summary of conclusions

Black spruce advance growth is abundant on the wettest, most nutritionally and floristically poor site types. Advance growth is most abundant in the <u>Chamaedaphen</u> operational group, relatively abundant in the <u>Ledum</u> operational group and somewhat less abundant in the Feathermoss-<u>Sphagnum</u> group. However, there is great variability in stocking within operational groups and even within FEC vegetation types. Regression models that employ stand attributes such as basal area, stand composition, and percent cover by alder provide more consistent estimates of advance growth stocking. Most advance growth originates as layers and most has a single upright stem.

Recommendations

Conclusions and management implications

In the absence of better information, a precut stocking to black spruce advance growth of at least 80% is recommended to ensure satisfactory natural regeneration from this source. Harvesting in the winter, minimizing machinery travel over cutovers, careful mechanical felling, off-ground forwarding, and full-tree harvesting are recommended to reduce damage to advance growth during logging operations.[8]

Appendices

Appendices, as the name implies, are materials appended to a report. They may be materials important as background information or needed to lend the report credibility. They will not in most cases be necessary to meet the major purpose of the report or the major needs of the audience. For example, if you are describing research for an executive audience, they will likely be more interested in your results and conclusions than in your research methodology. If your audience consists totally of executives, you might include only a bare-bones discussion of your methodology in your report.

But suppose you have a primary audience of executives and a secondary audience of experts. You could satisfy both audiences by placing a detailed discussion of your methodology in an appendix—out of the executives' way but readily accessible for the experts. Like most decisions in technical writing, what goes into the body of a report, what goes into an appendix, and what is eliminated altogether are determined by your audience and purpose.

During the final stages of arranging your report, determine whether materials such as the following should be placed in appendices:

- Case histories
- Supporting illustrations
- Detailed data
- Transcriptions of dialogue
- Intermediate steps in mathematical computation
- Copies of letters, announcements, and leaflets mentioned in the report
- Samples, exhibits, photographs, and supplementary tables and figures
- Extended analyses
- Lists of personnel
- Suggested collateral reading
- Anything else that is not essential to the sense of the main report

Before you place anything in an appendix, consider the effect on the report. Be certain that shifting an item to an appendix does not undermine your purpose or prevent the reader from understanding major points of the report.

Documentation

When information in a report is taken from previous sources, those sources need to be fully and consistently documented. There is no universal system of documentation. The system used differs from one university or company to another and even from one department to another. Therefore, writers of reports need to be aware of which system of documentation is required or favoured and document their sources accordingly.

The section on Documentation in the Handbook covers the basic principles of three of the most common guides for citation and documentation—those of the Modern Language Association (MLA), the American Psychological Association (APA), and the Chicago Manual of Style.

Planning and Revision Checklists

You will find the planning and revision checklists that follow Chapter 2, "Composing" (pages 31-33 and at the back of the book), and Chapter 4, "Writing for Your Readers" (pages 74-76), valuable in planning and revising any presentation of technical information. The following questions specifically apply to the elements of reports. They summarize the key points in this chapter and provide a checklist for planning and revising.

Planning

- Which does your situation call for, a letter of transmittal or a preface?
- Will you bind your report? If so, remember to leave extra space in the left-hand margin.
- Does your situation call for any information on your title page beyond the basic items: name of author, name of person or organization receiving the report, title of report, and date of submission?
- Have you used a system of headings that must be repeated in your table of contents?
- Have you used a numbering system that must be repeated in your table of contents?

- Do you have enough illustrations to warrant a list of illustrations?
- Have you used symbols, abbreviations, acronyms, and terms that some of your readers will not know? Do you need a list of symbols or a glossary?
- Does your report require an abstract? Should you have an informative or descriptive abstract or both?
- Is your primary audience an executive one? Does the length of your report require an executive summary?
- What will be the major questions in the executives' minds as they read your report? Plan to answer these questions in the executive summary.

continued >>

- Are your subject, purpose, scope, and plan of development clear enough that you can state them in your introduction?
- Do you need an interest-catcher in your introduction?
- Do you need definitions or theoretical or historical background in your introduction?
- What information do your readers really need and want in your discussion? What questions will they have? What details do they want?
- What kind of ending do you need: summary, conclusion, recommendations, graceful exit, or a combination of these?

- Do you have an executive audience? Should your "ending" come at the beginning of the report?
- Do you have material that would be better presented in an appendix rather than in the discussion? Should you leave it out altogether?
- Do you have material you need to document: direct quotes, research data and theories, illustrations?

Revision

- Does your letter of transmittal contain clear statements of transmittal, the occasion for the report, and subject and purpose of the report? Do you need any other elements, such as a distribution list?
- Does your preface contain clear statements of the occasion for the report and the subject and purpose of the report? Do you need any other elements, such as acknowledgments?
- Is your cover suitable for the occasion of the report? Is it labelled with all the necessary elements?
- Is your title page well designed? If you have used word processing, have you kept your design simple? Does your title page contain all the needed elements? Does your title describe your report adequately?
- Have you an effective design for your table of contents? Do the headings in your table of contents match their counterparts in the report exactly? Are the page numbers correct?
- Do you have a simple but clear numbering system for your illustrations? Do the titles in your list of illustrations match exactly the

titles in the report? Are the page numbers correct?
- Do you have a glossary and a list of symbols (if needed)? Have you written your glossary definitions correctly?
- Are your abstracts written in the proper impersonal style? Does your informative abstract cover all the major points of your report? Have you avoided excessive detail? Does your abstract conform to the length requirements set for you?
- Does your executive summary answer the questions your executive audience will have? Have you included clear statements of your conclusions and recommendations? Have you held the length to one double-spaced page?
- Does your introduction clearly forecast your subject, purpose, scope, and plan of development? Does the introduction contain definitions or theoretical or historical background, if they are needed?
- Does your discussion answer all the questions you set out to answer? Does it contain any material irrelevant to your subject and purpose?

continued >>

- Does your ending draw things together for the readers? Does it condense and highlight your significant data? Does it present your conclusions and recommendations? Should the "ending" come at the front of the report?
- Does the appendix material belong in the appendix? If any material in an appendix is a key to a major point, move it to the discussion. If it seems irrelevant to the report, remove it altogether.
- Have you documented everything that needs documenting in your report? Have you documented accurately? Do your notes or citations follow the appropriate format rules?

Weblinks

Citing Information in MLA and APA Format
www.143.110.13.151/depts/LIBRARY/citemast.htm

Memos
www.rpi.edu/dept/llc/writecenter/web/text/memo.html

Technical Reports
www.io.com/~hcexres/tcm1603/acchtml/techreps.html

Exercises

1. Reprinted below is an excerpt from a research report[9] on the reliability of dietary information on the Internet. Some key components of the report have been omitted. Following your instructor's suggestions, imagine that you are the writer of this report and provide some or all of the following elements:

   - Letter of transmittal
   - Informative abstract
   - Introduction
   - Headings
   - Recommendations

The Quality of Dietary Information on the World Wide Web

Karen Davison, BASc, RDN, MSc Candidate, Faculty of Health and Human Sciences, Department of Community Health, Shucai Guan, PhD, Faculty of Natural Resouces and Environmental Studies, University of Northern British Columbia, Prince George, B.C.

The keyword searches in this study were conducted in February 1996 using various search engines available through Netscape Navigator. All sites accessed by the three keyword searches were reviewed by two raters to determine whether the information was consistent with the Canadian Guidelines for Healthy Eating (2) and the Nutrition Recommendations for Canadians (3). In instances where WWW sites were repeated, the particular sites were assessed once. WWW sites that contained no specific dietary recommendations, were under construction or that contained dietary information for specific diseases and disorders were not included.

A literature review was conducted to discover if other measurement tools or definitions for assessing dietary information quality existed. No scales per se could be located; however, one paper provided criteria for what constituted nutrition misinformation. The definition of this term was "erroneous facts or misinterpretation of nutrition and food science"(7). Because this term is broadly defined (8), there would have been considerable difficulty in establishing a clear conception of what constituted adequate quality of dietary information. The provision of national guidelines as a standard allowed for objective assessment of web sites with dietary content.

Because the Internet provides information on a global basis, the authors considered whether international dietary standards should be utilized. Many countries use recommendations developed by two international groups: the Food and Agricultural Organization (FAO) and the World Health Organization (WHO). The FAO/WHO recommendations are considered sufficient for the maintenance of health in nearly all people; however, they are based on slightly different judgement factors (9). For example, the FAO/WHO recommendations take into consideration that worldwide, people are generally smaller and more physically active than the population of Canada. Because the recommendations of different nations do not differ widely (10), it seemed reasonable that applying Canadian standards for this study is unlikely to affect the interpretation of the results. Thus information from web sites with a high proportion of foreign content was considered acceptable unless it directly contradicted the criteria used for this study.

Dietary information could also be located by other keywords such as diabetes, heart disease, pregnancy and cancer or by entering boolean variables (combining terms with "and", "or", etc.). These techniques were not utilized for two reasons. First, the criteria for determining dietary information quality in this study could not be applied to nutrition recommendations made for specific conditions. It is also unlikely that the general healthy population would access these sites or use these techniques to obtain general nutrition advice.

For each keyword search at least 100 titles were provided. Some of these links provided further access to other WWW sites which were also included in this study. Most search engines utilized showed ten titles at one time on the computer screen. Dietary information on the WWW originated from many countries including Canada, Germany, Japan, China, Australia, United States, and Switzerland.

A total of 365 web sites were accessed through various search engines and three keyword searches. Of these, 45.8% (n=167) provided specific dietary recommendations and these originated from Canada and the U.S. Among these North American sites, 76 (45.5%) provided nutrition information that was considered to be inconsistent with Canadian standards. These sites included recommendations in one or more of the following categories: dietary supplements (n=49, 64.5%), herbal remedies (n=44, 57.9%), special preparations for weight control (n=29, 38.2%) and specific diets that suggested the elimination of certain food groups from one's daily intake (n=2,2.6%).

The dietary information of the 167 web sites originated from private vendors (n=69, 41.3%), individual home pages (n=27, 16.2%), health organizations (n=32, 19.2%) and academic institutes (n=39, 23.4%). The number of sites within each of these categories that provided dietary information inconsistent with Canadian standards were 44 sites (57.9%), 31 sites (40.8%), and one site (1.3%) for private vendors, individual home pages, and health organizations, respectively. All of the academic institution web pages provided information that was consistent with Canadian guidelines.

The total number of WWW sites that provided dietary advice per keyword search were 55 (32.9%), 16 (9.6%) and 96 (57.5%) for "diet", "food" and "nutrition" respectively. Of the 167 total web pages providing dietary recommendations, the number of sites within each of the keyword searches that were inconsistent with accepted principles were 25 (15.0%), 11 (6.6%) and 48 (28.7%) for "diet", "food" and "nutrition" respectively. These figures included web sites that were replicated.

Based on the results of this study, it would appear that this form of computer technology can be a potential source of inconsistent dietary information. This poses many difficulties for the nutrition professional.

Readily available dietary information that differs from national guidelines can affect both consumers and health professionals (12-14). In the extreme case, consumers may be led to forego legitimate nutrition care and pursue questionable products or therapies with the potential for nutrient toxicities or deficiencies, or being exposed to toxic components in unsafe products, as well as undesirable nutrient-drug interactions. Such a potential is not unique to the Internet. It also exists in the traditional print media. However, the impact of the Internet is potentially greater because of its reach and the lack of regulation. Depending on the impact that the Internet will have, public opinion based on inconsistent dietary information could affect sound nutrition education and practices as well as public policies, including resource allocation and legislation (12).

The WWW sites reviewed in this particular study included only general dietary information. Nutritional advice for specific diseases was not assessed. One may speculate, however, that web sites containing such recommendations would also be variable in quality as much of the health information on the Internet is not reviewed prior to release, not unlike the wide range of printed materials containing similar information currently available to the general public.

The majority of dietary misinformation in this particular study was accessed through the "nutrition" keyword search. It is likely that consumers wishing to access personal nutrition advice would key in this particular word. Although resources on the WWW are constantly changing, it is highly probable that inconsistent dietary information will continue to be easily accessible.

Because there is no concise definition of what constitutes dietary misinformation (8, 12, 13), advice that differs from national standards may not necessarily be considered as inaccurate. For this review, the Canadian Guidelines for Healthy Eating (2) and Nutrition Recommendations for Canadians (3) were chosen because they are a baseline for general dietary advice utilized by health professionals. The WWW sites in this study that were considered not to be consistent with Canadian dietary guidelines contained recommendations for supplements and herbal remedies as well as the elimination of specific food groups from one's daily intake.

In addition to the challenge of inaccurate or misleading dietary advice easily accessible by the public, as the popularity of the Internet continues to expand and allows for increased global exchange of dietary information, one may question whether national guidelines will serve a useful purpose. Some inconsistencies among national guidelines can be potentially confusing to the general public in the global environment (e.g. the difference in emphasis on dietary cholesterol between American and Canadian guidelines). It may be questioned whether future dietary messages would be more effective if governments work towards establishing common standards.

This study focused on the most popular service of the Internet, the WWW (1, 4-6). Future research in this area could include investigating other search tools and Internet services. In addition, quality of information in other topic areas could be explored.

Based on the results of this research, anyone searching for personal nutrition advice through the "diet", "food" and "nutrition" keyword searches would likely find information consistent with Canadian standards less than 50% of the time based on the total number of web sites providing specific dietary advice. Based on this information, it is evident that consumers should become more aware of how to assess multimedia sources for reliable dietary information.

The challenge of dealing with inconsistent dietary information will persist and continue to interfere with sound nutrition education. Qualified nutrition professionals, however, can help to positively shape the food choices of the general public by disseminating accurate information through the Internet and their interactions with the public. Several books, magazines and journals dealing with the Internet are available at libraries and bookstores. Dietitians new to the Internet could refer to these resources or contact the systems specialist in their work setting for further information about this computer technology.

Computer networks in general and the Internet in particular are likely to play a more important role in many aspects of nutrition in the future. The Internet has been recognized as becoming a critical factor for global health in the next century (15, 16). Conditions such as the proliferation of unreliable health information via the Internet and other media sources, as well as the continuing economic pressure on health resources, could have implications for the quality of health care in the future (17, 18). On a positive note, health professionals who access the Internet may be able to provide more effective client care as vast amounts of accessible and relevant information is readily available to them.

Dietitians who take on the challenge and exploit the Internet's resources can find rewards for themselves and their clients. At the same time, nutrition experts should be aware that the WWW is a potential source of inconsistent dietary information for the general public. This research would appear to indicate that there is a need to develop strategies to address inconsistent nutrition information through this avenue.

Acknowledgements

The authors wish to thank Xiaolong Yang and staff members of the University of British Columbia's Computing and Telecommunications Department who provided assistance with this project.

References

1. Glowniak JV. Medical Resources on the Internet. Ann Intern Med 1995;123:123-131.

2. Health and Welfare Canada. Action Towards Healthy Eating. Canada's Guidelines for Healthy Eating and Recommended Strategies for Implementation. The Report of the Communications/Implementation Committee. Ottawa: Supply and Services Canada, 1990.

3. Health and Welfare Canada Nutrition Recommendations...A Call for Action, Summary Report of the Scientific Review Committee and the Communications/Implementation Committee, Ottawa:Supply and Services Canada, 1989.

4. Schatz BR,Hardin JB.NCSA mosaic and the world wide web: global hypermedia protocols for the Internet. Science 1994; 271:1934-1939.

5. Browne S. The Internet via MOSAIC and World-Wide Web.Emeryville,CA:Ziff-Davis Press, 1994.

6. Tomaiuolo NG. Accessing Nursing Resources on the Internet Computers in Nursing 1995;13(4):159-164.

7. Ashley JM, Harvis WT. Position of The American Dietetic Association: Food and nutrition misinformation. J Am Diet Assoc 1995;95(6);705-707.

8. Roebuck JB, Hunter B. The awareness of health-care quackery as deviant behavior. J Health Soc Behav 1972;13;162-166.

9. Guthrie H, Picciano MF. Human Nutrition. St. Louis, MI: Mosby Publishing, 1995;27.

10. Hamilton-Nunelly EM, Whitney, EN, Sizer-Sienkiewicz F. Nutrition Concepts and Controversies-Fifth Edition. St. Paul's, MA: West Publishing Company, 1991.

11. Rubin A, Babbie E. Research Methods in Social Work, Second Edition, Pacific Grove, CA: Brooks/Cole Publishing Company, 1993.

12. Louis Harris and Associates. Health, Information and the Use of Questionable Treatments: A Study of the American Public. Washington, DC: US Dept. Of Health and Human Services, 1987.

13. Pepper C. Quackery: A $10 Billion Scandal. Washington, DC; US Government Printing Office; 1984.

14. Short SH. Health quackery; our role as professionals. J Am Diet Assoc 1994;94-607-661.

15. LaPorte Re, Akazawa S, Hellmonds P, et al. Global public health and the information superhighway. Br Med J 1994;308;1651-1652.

16. Lacroix EM, Backus JE, Lyon BJ. Service providers and users discover the Internet. Bulletin of the Medical Library Association, 1994; 82(4): 412-418.

17. Rambo N, Fuller S. (1993). From bench to bedside; research and testing of Internet resources and connections in community hospital libraries. Proceedings-the Annual Symposium on Computer Applications in Medical Care 1993:549-53.

18. Lindberg DA, Humphreys BL, Computers in medicine. J Am Med Assoc 995;273(21): 1667-8.

2. Consult the Documentation section in the Handbook (pp. 495–512), then modify the list of references at the end of the report in Exercise 1 in accordance with MLA, APA, or Chicago Manual of Style guidelines.

3. Compile a list of difficult and unusual terms you may have to introduce in the final report of your own selected project. Will you need a glossary? If so, prepare a draft of the glossary.

4. Prepare at least a tentative table of contents for your proposed final report. Use at least two levels of headings.

5. In a published report or textbook, locate as many of the elements discussed in this chapter as possible. What variations and departures do you find?

GRAPHICAL ELEMENTS

In creating technical reports, you have two main ways of communicating information: verbal expression (words) and visual display (pictures). We live in a society that emphasizes visual forms of communication. Movies, advertising, and television are obvious examples, but even familiar forms of verbal communication, such as newspapers and magazines, rely on visual as much as verbal communication. Most report writers soon realize the value of effective visual presentation, as most readers, products of a visual society, quickly tire of writing that relies too heavily on verbal presentation.

Document design and format, discussed in Chapter 8, are the basic tools for making verbal expression easy to see and understand. Then, by knowing how to use the many varieties of graphs, drawings, figures, and tables, you have additional tools for turning words into visual images that help readers understand numbers and concepts quickly and accurately.

As in all aspects of technical writing, you have an ethical responsibility to develop graphics that present an accurate picture of your data. You may want to refer frequently to Chapter 2 to help you remain aware of issues that pertain to the ethical presentation of technical information. After discussing guidelines on choosing the best graphic to present a specific type of concept, we will shift our focus to emphasize accurate graphic development. In learning how to present technical information effectively, you will need to know a few basic rules for developing graphs, drawings, figures, and other visual aids so that these are accurate, easy to see and understand, and appropriate for the document you need to write.

Today, graphics software offers an almost unlimited range of visual display. It is important to be aware of ways that graphics can be used to communicate your message, and to know the basic types of visual presentation available and how to use them effectively. Most graphics programs give you choices for displaying data, but the visual form you choose will be yours. Increasingly powerful graphics software can create artistic but highly distorted visual representations; only you can determine whether your graphic presents your data or concept in an effective, accurate way that enhances your reader's understanding of your message.

Because the focus of this chapter is on graphics, we will present it through both graphics and verbal discussion. We will show you how to use verbal presentation to support visual presentation, but our emphasis will be on showing you an array of graphics—many good ones, some of questionable quality. By the time you complete the exercises in this chapter, you should have a basic understanding of how to use common types of graphics to help your readers visualize data or concepts. We provide guidelines and methods for the following:

- Choosing graphics
- Designing tables
- Designing graphs
- Designing other forms of graphics
- Integrating text and visuals
- Designing graphics for accuracy and effectiveness
- Choosing the best graphic for the information and the audience

Choosing Graphics

Why use graphics? History shows us that ancient peoples used pictures and drawings to communicate long before they developed writing. Art itself exists as a monument to the human tendency to express ideas visually. In spite of the importance of writing in modern cultures, visual ways of expressing information are quicker and more effective than writing for helping readers visualize trends, processes, relationships among steps or parts of processes, and comparisons. Graphics can help you show a reader what information is the most important. Because thinking and reasoning are enhanced if we can *see* the idea or the information being presented, effective graphics can be powerful, persuasive tools for helping readers understand and remember. For example, the drawing in Figure 10-1 comes from an early sixteenth-century medical book. The drawing helps you see how broken limbs were straightened in the early 1500s, even though the process is described in some detail in several pages of

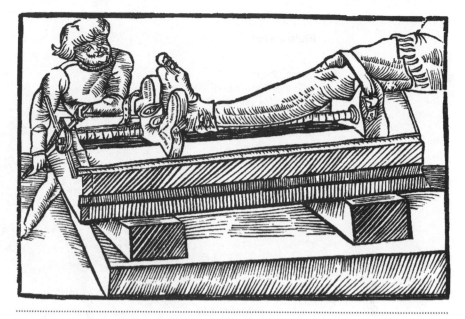

Figure 10-1 HIERONYMUS VON BRAUNSCHWEIG, *EXPERYENCE OF THE WARKE OF SURGERI*, LONDON, 1525.

text. The modern drawing in Figure 10-2 helps you understand the lymph system, "a system of thousands of tiny hearts." The modern drawing works just as effectively as the sixteenth-century drawing to convey its concept.

In planning your report, be aware of ways in which information can best be presented in visual form. As you write and revise, continue to think of ways to make your material more visually accessible. In Chapter 5, we emphasize that style should make your meaning clear to your reader; that is, you want your reader to *see* what you mean. Graphics can also help your reader visualize data, relationships, processes, and concepts. If words will achieve clarity, then graphics may not be necessary. If graphics supported by verbal discussion will aid your reader, then look for ways to visualize your point. As illustrated in Figure 10-2, visuals are an excellent way to make abstract or technical information immediately obvious to readers. Be sure to choose the best visual for the type of information you are trying to convey.

- To help your readers see trends, use graphs, such as bar graphs, line graphs, and surface graphs.
- To summarize information, use bar graphs, line graphs, and surface graphs.
- To help your readers see relationships within quantities of data, use tables.
- To emphasize or reinforce the meaning of data, begin with a table and then use a graph to accentuate the differences suggested by the data.

For example, Figure 10-3 shows you two graphics. The table, as its title indicates, shows readers variations in runoff after rainfall simulation for an

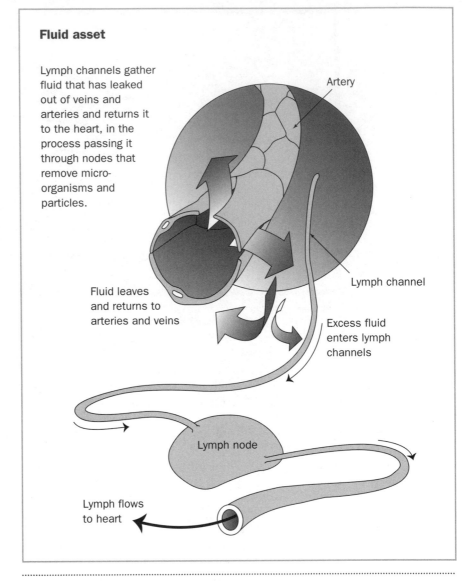

Fluid asset

Lymph channels gather fluid that has leaked out of veins and arteries and returns it to the heart, in the process passing it through nodes that remove micro-organisms and particles.

Artery

Lymph channel

Fluid leaves and returns to arteries and veins

Excess fluid enters lymph channels

Lymph node

Lymph flows to heart

Figure 10-2 DRAWING USED TO VISUALIZE PROCESS HIDDEN FROM NORMAL VIEW
Source: "A Swell System of Tiny Hearts," artist David Alrich, *The Globe and Mail* (28 June, 1995): A11.

Ontario Ministry of Transportation erosion study. The graph allows us to see that variation much more clearly. When you collect data, you will likely need to use a table to arrange it initially. From the table, many graphics programs will allow you to select a more powerful visual way of presenting the data.

 • To help your reader visualize processes, use drawings and flowcharts.

Table 2: Runoff from control, blanket and mulch plots MTO erosion study

Time (min)	Control Sites (mL, average)		Blanket Sites (mL, average)		Mulch Sites (mL, average)		% Reduction from control
	Interval	Cumulative	Interval	Cumulative	Interval	Cumulative	
0	0	0	0	0	0	0	-
2	600	600	315	315	0	0	100
4	2450	3050	1725	2040	1740	1740	29
6	3327	6377	2865	4905	1915	3655	42
8	3867	10243	3715	8620	2365	6020	39
10	4169	14413	4105	12725	2705	8725	35
12	4113	18526	4395	17120	3195	11920	22
14	4223	22749	4525	21645	3585	15505	15
16	4260	27009	4610	26255	3800	19305	11
18	4560	31569	4745	31000	3910	23215	14
20	4460	36029	4820	35820	3960	27175	11
22	4417	40446	5060	40880	3749	30924	15
24	4500	44946	5095	45975	4045	34969	10
26	4597	49543	5240	51215	3690	38659	20
28	4640	54183	5380	56595	4535	43194	2
30	4643	58826	5475	62070	4255	47449	8

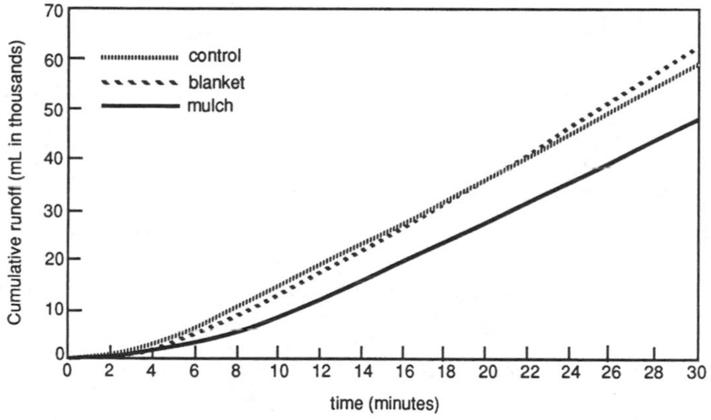

Figure 3/ Runoff from control, blanket and mulch sites (mean values/treatment)

Figure 10-3 TABLE CONVERTED INTO A GRAPH

Source: Ontario Ministry of Transportation, Research and Development Branch, *Quantitative Evaluation of the Effectiveness of Erosion Control Materials* (Toronto, 1990): 10.

Figure 10-4, from a government pamphlet on caulking and weatherstripping, shows the different places air can leak from a home. The representation of the leakage sites helps readers better understand the overall purpose of the publication: saving fuel costs and eliminating cold draughts.

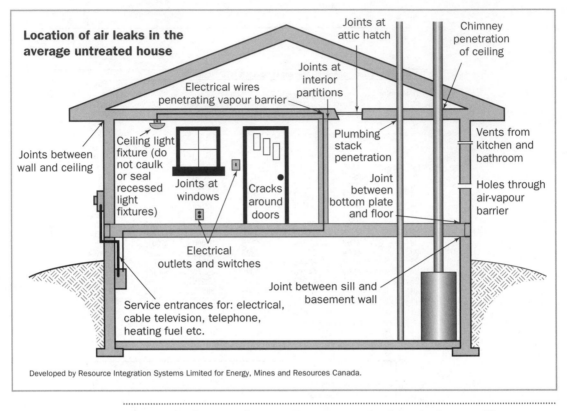

Figure 10-4 Drawing Showing Location of Air Leaks in Average Untreated Home

Source: Ontario Ministry of Environment and Energy, *Where and How to Caulk & Weatherstrip* (Toronto: MEE, n.d.): 3.

- To improve the impact of your message, use photographs and creative graphics.

The map in Figure 10-5, from a government publication entitled *The Climates of Canada*, shows the frequency of tornadoes across the country, providing a visual context for the publication's discussion of tornadoes. In addition, photographs are used to show what a tornado looks like and the kind of damage it can cause (Figures 10-6 and 10-7). Meanwhile, another kind of climatological phenomenon, the greenhouse effect, is represented in the same publication by means of the drawings in Figure 10-8.

- To help simplify concepts, use drawings, flowcharts, diagrams, algorithms, and schematics.
- To present objects, use photographs if you need detail or realism and if cost is not a factor. Use drawings if you want to show your reader only selected features of an object.

Figure 10-9 helps readers see the human genome from four perspectives, including detailed enlargements of specific components.

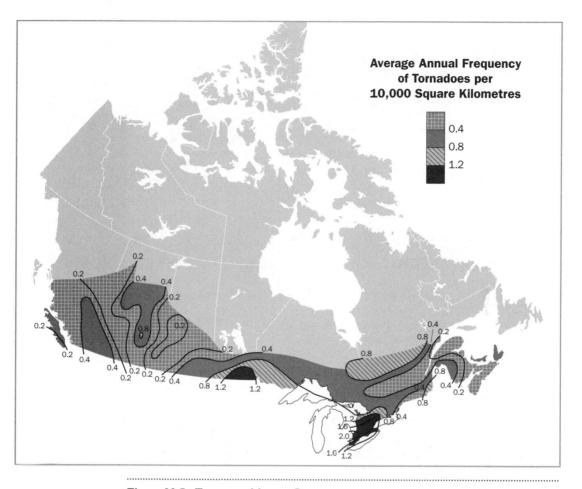

Figure 10-5 Tornado Map of Canada

Source: Environment Canada, *The Climates of Canada*, Ministry of Supply and Services Canada, p.55. Reprinted with permission of the Minister of Public Works and Government Services Canada, 1998.

As each of these graphics illustrates, you have a variety of ways to help your reader see what you mean. In choosing a graphic, always consider your purpose and your reader's profile: the kind of information you need to present, the context in which you are presenting it, and your reader's preferences. Consider graphics when you are planning your document, but continue to look for ways to visualize your point even as you are writing and revising.

In deciding when and how to use graphics as you plan your document, remember these five guidelines:

- Keep your graphic as simple as possible so that your reader has no difficulty understanding the message you wish to convey.
- Place the graphic as close to the point it explains as possible. Announce the graphic (what it is or shows), insert the graphic, then add any verbal explanation your reader will need to fully understand the graphic.

Figure 10-6   THE FUNNEL CLOUD OF A
TORNADO
Source: A/P Wide World Photo

Figure 10-7   THE AFTERMATH OF A TORNADO
Source: Canapress/AP Photo/Schnectady Daily Gazette/
Heather Rohan

WHAT IS THE GREENHOUSE EFFECT?

Sunlight passes through the atmosphere and warms the Earth.

Earth re-radiates infrared heat energy—some escapes to space, but water vapour, dust, carbon dioxide (CO_2) freons, nitrous oxide, methane and other greenhouse gases in the atmosphere absorb and trap most of the heat, returning it to the Earth.

Higher concentrations of greenhouse gases trap more heat; the atmosphere and earth's surface temperatures increase.

Burned forests release excessive CO_2 and other gases to the atmosphere, preventing the earth's infrared (heat) energy from escaping into space thus heating up the Earth even more.

CO_2 and other industrial gases from automobiles and factories remain trapped in the atmosphere where they surround the Earth like a blanket.

Figure 10-8   SERIES OF ILLUSTRATIONS EXPLAINING THE GREENHOUSE EFFECT
Source: Environment Canada, *The Climates of Canada*, Ministry of Supply and Services Canada, p.151.
Reprinted with permission of the Minister of Public Works and Government Services Canada, 1998.

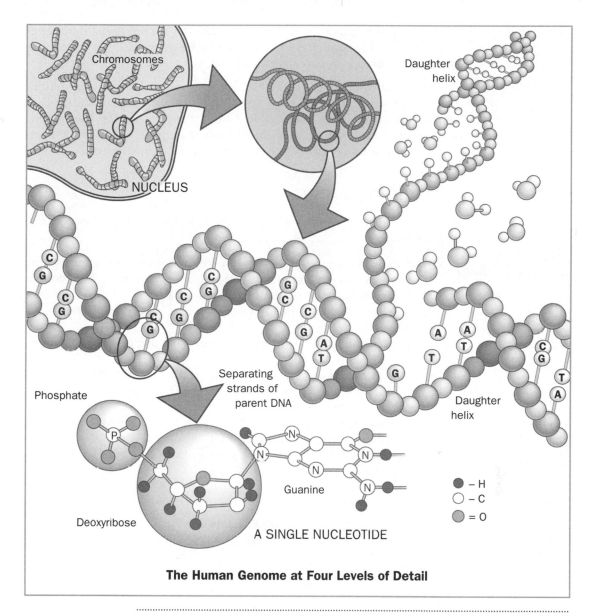

Chromosomes

NUCLEUS

Daughter
helix

Phosphate

Separating
strands of
parent DNA

Daughter
helix

P

Deoxyribose

Guanine

A SINGLE NUCLEOTIDE

● – H
○ – C
● = O

The Human Genome at Four Levels of Detail

Figure 10-9 DIAGRAM SHOWING DETAILS OF A BIOLOGICAL STRUCTURE

Source: Casey, Denise and Dan Jacobsen, "Primer on Molecular Genetics, 1991–1992"
Human Genome Program Report (Washington, DC: Department of Energy). *Diagram*
from http://www.gdb.org/Dan/DOE/.

- Know the expected length of your document. Graphics can extend
  the size of any report and increase reproduction costs.
- Realize that you usually have a *choice* of graphics. If a graphic you decide
  to use initially does not convey your point quickly and accurately, consider other ways of presenting the information visually.

- Computer graphics software makes available an increasing number of graphics. However, the effectiveness of your information in any form is a decision that you, not the computer, must make.

After you make your graphics selection, consult the following guidelines to be sure that the image your graphics program generates is as simple, clear, and effective as possible. As you plan and develop your graphics, you may want to keep the summary chart on pages 266–267 handy, as it provides a quick review of the principles we will present here.

Designing Tables

As you examine the following guidelines for developing tables, refer to Figures 10-10 and 10-11, which illustrate each point:

- Tables need titles. If you use several tables in your report, number the tables. Place the table number and title above the table. Be sure that the title clearly indicates the content of the table.
- If you use a table from another source, give that source beneath the table.
- Every column in a table should have a heading that identifies the information beneath it.
- Headings should be brief. If headings need more explanation, include this information in a footnote beneath the table. Use lowercase letters, numbers, or symbols (e.g., ★, +, or §).
- If possible, box your table.
- Keep tables as simple as possible. Do not include data not relevant to your purpose. Avoid excessive lines or data that give your table a crowded appearance.

TABLE NUMBER TITLE			
Stub Heading[a]	Column Heading[b]	Column Heading	
		Subheading	Subheading
Line Heading Subheading Subheading Line Heading	Individual "cells" for tabulated data		
[a]Footnote [b]Footnote			

Figure 10-10 TABLE WITH FOOTNOTES. NOTICE USE OF LETTERS FOR FOOTNOTES.

Production

	Capacity (million tonnes KCl)	Mine-Site Employees	1993 Production (million tonnes KCl)	1992 Production (million tonnes KCl)
Rocanville	1.901	331	1.242	1.272
Lanigan	3.424	316	.981	1.057
Allan	1.569	297	.577	.658
Cory	1.361	129	.458	.412
Esterhazy[1]	.953	2	.431	.451
New Brunswick	.717	341	.138[2]	na
Patience Lake	1.041	86	.075[2]	na
Total	10.966	1502	3.902	3.850

[1]Production at Esterhazy is mined from PCS reserves by International Minerals and Chemical Corporation (Canada) Limited under a long-term agreement.

[2]Since purchase, October 7, 1993.

Figure 10-11 TABLE WITH FOOTNOTES. NOTICE USE OF NUMBERS FOR FOOTNOTES.

Source: Potash Corporation of Saskatchewan Inc., *1993 Annual Report, Building Global Success* (Saskatoon: Potash Corp., 1993): 12.

- Always alert your readers to graphics that will appear.
- Attempt to place the table at the point in the discussion where it will help your reader. Do not lead readers through a complicated prose explanation and then refer to the graphic that simplifies the explanation. Send them to the graphic immediately, and they can cut back and forth between the prose and the graphic as necessary. For example, we introduced Figures 10-10 and 10-11 before we began using these two examples to help you visualize the verbal guidelines for designing tables.
- Integrate all tables with your verbal discussion. Introduce the table, present it, and then follow the table with appropriate analysis. Any time you refer to a table, use the table number.

Many computer programs will insert tables and other graphics into the text when you instruct them to do so. However, effective integration of the pertinent text with the graphic is your responsibility.

Designing Graphs

Information presented in tables can often be converted into a graph, as we have already shown in Figure 10-3. As you looked at Figure 10-3, your eyes were probably drawn first to the line graph rather than the table because the line graph allowed you to see the relationships among the numbers more quickly

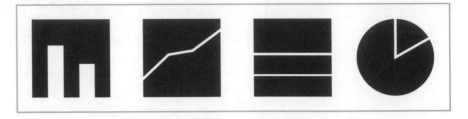

Figure 10-12 THE FOUR BASIC TYPES OF GRAPHS

than the table did. The basic kinds of graphs you can use to visualize data are bar graphs, circle graphs, divided bar graphs, and line graphs. See Figure 10–12 for examples of each of these types of graphs.

Guidelines for graphs are similar to those for tables. Figure 10–13 exemplifies three effectively presented graphs. Examine these three graphs and the discussion that accompanies them as you consider the following guidelines:

- Graphs need clear titles. Number graphs if you include more than one in a report.
- Introduce the graph in the text and discuss its significance. Try to place the graph as close as possible to the discussion to which it relates.
- Make the graph big enough to be legible.
- Avoid placing too much information on a graph. Computer graphics will allow you to pack a tremendous amount of information into

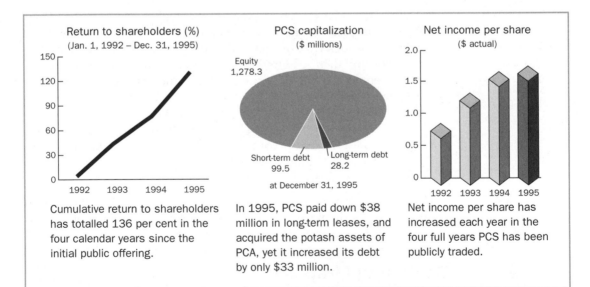

Figure 10-13 REPORT SEGMENT THAT SHOWS INTEGRATION OF THREE GRAPHS

Source: Potash Corporation of Saskatchewan Inc., *1993 Annual Report, Building Global Success* (Saskatoon: Potash Corp., 1993): 3.

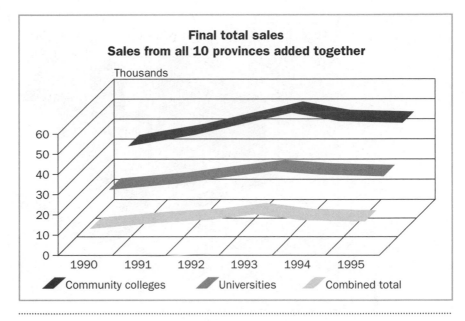

Figure 10-14   THREE-DIMENSIONAL LINE GRAPH WITH SHIFTING DEPTH. THREE-DIMENSIONAL GRAPHS CAN CREATE OPTICAL ILLUSIONS.

a graph. Placing too much information in a graph can reduce reader comprehension. The bar and line graphs in Figure 10-13 present limited information very simply.

- Be sure to label the x-axis and the y-axis on all graphs—what each measures and the units in which each is measured. In Figure 10-13, the identifying information is in the description beneath each graph.
- If you borrow a graph from another source, be sure to acknowledge the source, generally by placing a source note beneath the graph. The examples we use in this chapter follow this guideline.
- Colour can enhance the effect of a graphic, but excessive colour can reduce comprehension and distort information. The use of colour also makes any kind of reproduction—photocopies, transparencies, professional printing—considerably more costly. Two well-chosen colours can add variety and interest to a page.
- Make the graph accurate. Computer graphics allow a tremendous range of special effects. However, artistic graphs are not always either effective or accurate. Three-dimensional graphics are often difficult to interpret. Understanding the relationships of the three lines in Figure 10-14 is difficult because of the 3-D grid, which can create an optical illusion. A simple two-dimensional line graph of the same information would be less artistic but easier to comprehend. The upward slope of the three-dimensional bar graphs in Figures 10-15 and 10-16 makes it difficult for readers to compare the relative heights of the bars.

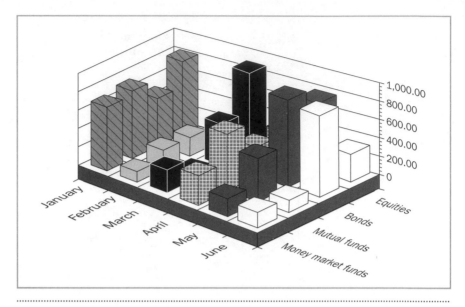

Figure 10-15   THREE-DIMENSIONAL GRAPH. MOST READERS FIND THREE-DIMENSIONAL GRAPHS HARD TO INTERPRET. BECAUSE OF THE UPWARD SLOPE OF THE PLANE, THE RELATIVE HEIGHTS OF THE BARS ARE DIFFICULT TO DETERMINE.

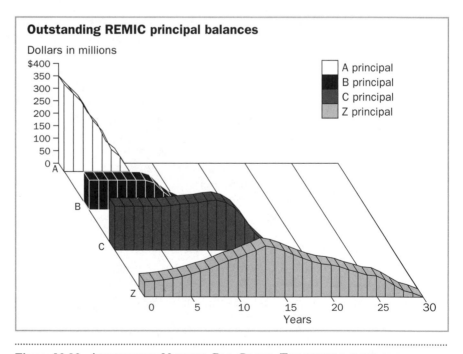

Figure 10-16   ARTISTIC BUT UNCLEAR BAR GRAPH. THE UPWARD SLOPE OF THIS GRAPH MAKES THE HEIGHTS OF THE BARS DIFFICULT TO COMPARE.

Source: Fannie Mae, *Investing in REMIC Securities* (Washington, DC, 1992).

Because of the characteristics of various kinds of graphs, you will need to remember basic guidelines for each.

Bar Graphs

Bar graphs are useful in showing comparisons among quantities of information. Bar graphs may be drawn either vertically (Figure 10-17) or horizontally (Figure 10-18). Page layout—how much space you have—often determines how you decide to draw your bar graph. Bar graphs are used

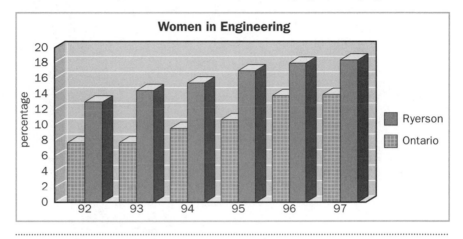

Figure 10-17 CLEARLY PRESENTED COMPARATIVE BAR GRAPH

Source: Prof. Malgorzata Zywno, Dept. of Electrical and Computer Engineering, and Mr. Larry Anta, "Discover Engineering Goes Digital," *CCS Newsletter*, Computing and Communications Services, Ryerson Polytechnical University (Spring 1998): 1. With permission from Ryerson Polytechnical University

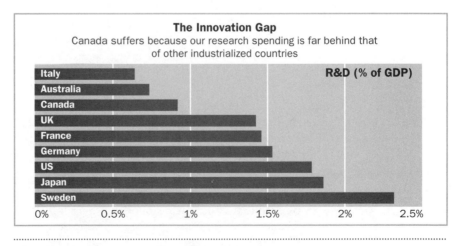

Figure 10-18 HORIZONTAL BAR GRAPH

Source: Canadian Business (June 26/July 10, 1998): 50. Reprinted by permission of Canadian Business Magazine ©1998.

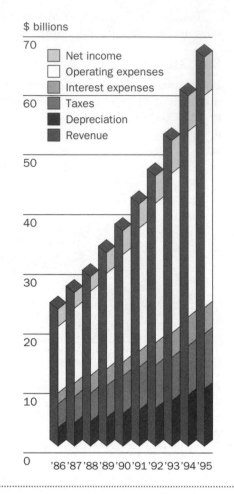

Figure 10-19 THREE-DIMENSIONAL BAR GRAPH WITH EXCESSIVE SEGMENTATION. LACK OF SPACING BETWEEN BARS AND NUMEROUS SEGMENTS MAKE THIS BAR GRAPH TOO DENSE.

frequently in material written for general audiences—newspapers, annual corporate reports, and magazines—but they are useful any time you need to show relationships among fixed quantities of data. Bar graphs are also useful in oral presentations because they quickly reveal comparisons. Examine Figures 10-17 and 10-18, which make very different kinds of comparisons, as you consider the following guidelines:

- Be sure that you clearly label the x-axis and the y-axis on bar graphs. Readers need to know what is being measured.
- If you choose three-dimensional bar graphs, watch for distortion. As we see in Figures 10-15 and 10-16, the upward tilt of the graph makes it difficult to determine the relative heights of the bars presented as blocks.

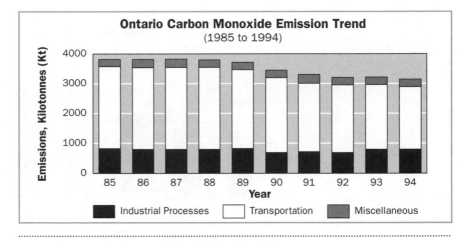

Figure 10-20 DIVIDED BAR GRAPH USING SHADING

Source: Air Quality in Ontario: 1994 Comprehensive Report (Ministry of the Environment and Energy, © Queen's Printer for Ontario, 1995): 26. Reproduced with permission.

- Try to write captions on or near the bars, as shown in Figures 10–17 and 10–18. Avoid complicated legends (or keys) that slow reader comprehension. Legends can be particularly difficult to use with divided bar graphs, such as Figure 10–19. When bars are divided into too

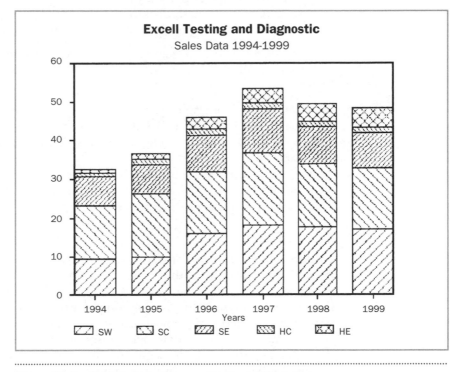

Figure 10-21 DIVIDED BAR GRAPH WITH CROSS HATCHING

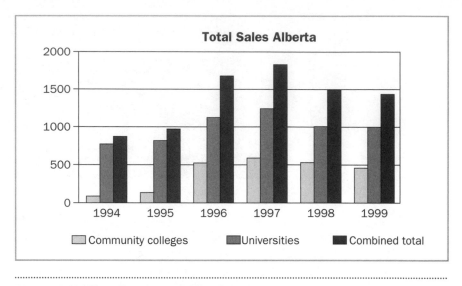

Figure 10-22   Two-Dimensional Bar Graph

many divisions and when the reader must consult a legend to interpret these divisions, the result can be confusion rather than effective
communication.

• For divided bar graphs with extensive divisions, try to use colour or
shading to distinguish divisions, as illustrated in Figure 10-20, rather
than cross-hatching patterns, shown in Figure 10-21.

Three-dimensional bar graphs, such as those in Figures 10-15 and 10-16
are generally not any better than standard two-dimensional ones, such as
Figure 10-22.

• Do not use a bar graph if you will have to use an excessive number of bars,
which can lead to visual clutter. Using three-dimensional bar graphs,
such as those shown in Figure 10-19, will also reduce the number of
bars you can use.
• Allow adequate space between bars. For example, Figures 10-20, 10-21,
and 10-22 are more visually accessible than Figure 10-19 because spacing between bars provides easier viewing.

Circle Graphs

Circle graphs or pie graphs are most often used to portray percentages or proportions. One problem with the pie graph is the limitation on the number
of segments into which the circle can be divided before comprehension of
the relative sizes is reduced. As your computer program builds circle graphs,
watch for the number of segments that you will need. Sometimes shading or
cross hatching can be used to differentiate segments, as in Figure 10-23, so that
the differences between the segments are easier for the reader to see. In
Figure 10-23, the changes in the composition of Alberta's gross domestic

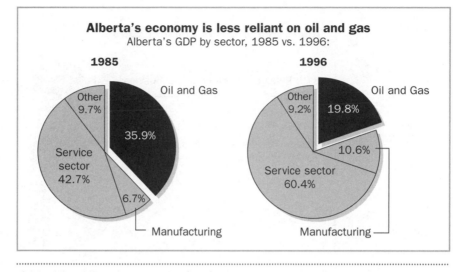

Figure 10-23 COMPARATIVE CIRCLE GRAPHS
Source: Alberta Treasury.

product over about a decade are illustrated by means of two circle graphs. The different shades in each graph denote the various sectors of the province's GDP—service, oil, gas, and manufacturing. This arrangement highlights proportion and allows the reader to see how certain sectors contribute more substantially than others. Similarly, Figure 10-24 reveals the distribution and proportion of sales across a geographic region.

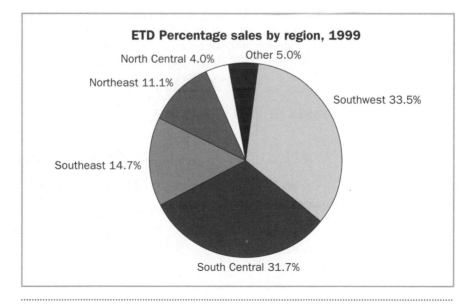

Figure 10-24 BLACK-AND-WHITE SEGMENTED CIRCLE GRAPH

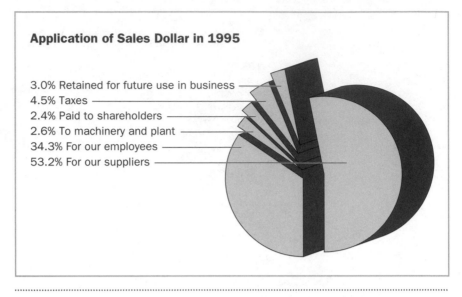

Figure 10-25 THREE-DIMENSIONAL CIRCLE GRAPH (NO DISTORTION)

- Use colour or "texture" (e.g., cross hatching) to enhance the point you are making with your graph. As Figure 10-23 shows, use of the same shades of colour to portray the same information on each circle graph allows easy visual comparison between corresponding segments of the two graphs.
- Watch for distortion when you use three-dimensional circle graphs.

Computer software allows you to draw three-dimensional bar graphs and circle graphs, but you must be sure that the perspective from which the graph is drawn does not distort the proportions. Figure 10-25 illustrates a three-dimensional circle graph that uses shading and three-dimensional

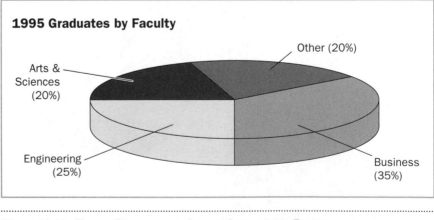

Figure 10-26 THREE-DIMENSIONAL CIRCLE GRAPH WITH DISTORTION

Energy 88¢

Lamps 4¢   Labour 8¢

Figure 10-27 CIRCLE GRAPH PRESENTED AS CANADIAN "LOONY"

Source: Ontario Hydro, *Reduce Your Overheads with Energy Efficient Lighting* (Toronto: Ontario Hydro, n.d.): 2.

presentation effectively. In the circle graph in Figure 10-26, the three-dimensional presentation distorts the size of the segments.

• Clearly label all segments.

Like all graphs, circle graphs must be clearly labelled. Whether identifications are placed inside or outside the circle, figures and identifications should be horizontal, as in Figure 10-27 (a rather ingenious and creative use of a circle), to preserve the comprehension of the graph.

Divided whole bars (as illustrated in Figure 10-28) are gaining in popularity because they are similar to divided bar graphs, as shown in Figures 10-19 through 10-21, which have been used extensively in technical reports for the past two decades.

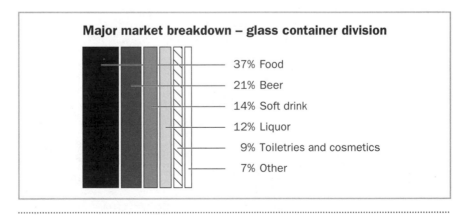

Major market breakdown – glass container division

37% Food
21% Beer
14% Soft drink
12% Liquor
9% Toiletries and cosmetics
7% Other

Figure 10-28 DIVIDED WHOLE BAR GRAPH

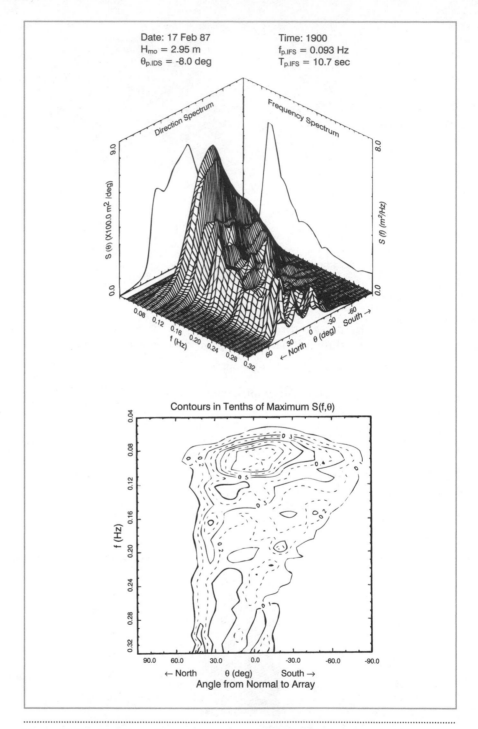

Figure 10-29   CONTOUR GRAPH CONVERTED INTO THREE-DIMENSIONAL GRAPH. THE CONTOUR GRAPH IS NOT NEARLY AS VISUALLY EFFECTIVE AS THE THREE-DIMENSIONAL ONES.

Line Graphs

Line graphs are most often used when more precision is required than bar graphs can show and to reveal changes and trends over time. Often, you will have choices between bar graphs and line graphs, with the information for both coming from a table, as was shown in Figure 10-3.

- Label the x-axis and the y-axis clearly.

Like bar graphs, line graphs must have clearly labelled axes to show what variables you are comparing. The independent variable is placed on the horizontal (x) axis, and the dependent variables are placed on the (y) axis and the (z) axis. In Figure 10-29, note that the two-dimensional contour graph is not nearly as visually effective as the computer-generated three-dimensional version.

- Choose the scale of each axis—x, y, and z—to show the appropriate steepness of the slope of the line.

The major difficulty in designing line graphs lies in choosing the spacing for both axes so that the steepness (slope) of the line accurately measures the actual trend suggested by the data. In Figure 10-30, both graphs depict the same data, but the slope changes drastically because of the different scales used in designing each set of axes. Computer graphics will allow you to adjust the intervals on the x- and the y-axis, but only you can tell whether the slope of your graph shows the trend depicted by your data.

- Avoid placing excessive lines on one graph.

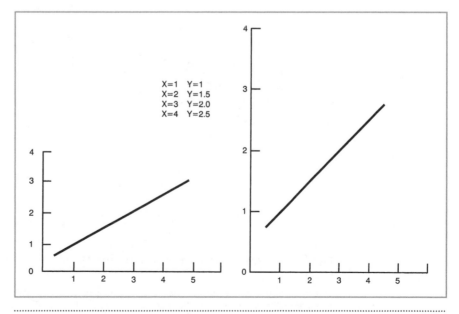

Figure 10-30 EFFECT OF SCALING ON SLOPE. NOTE THAT INCREASING HEIGHT OF POINTS ON THE Y-AXIS INCREASES THE STEEPNESS OF THE LINE.

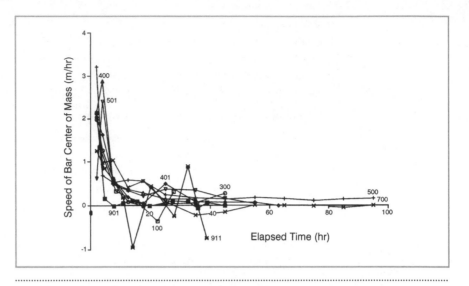

Figure 10-31   LINE GRAPH WITH EXCESSIVE OVERLAPPING LINES. OVERLAPPING LINES CAN REDUCE LEGIBILITY.

Source: Nicholas C. Kraus, Coastal Engineering Research Center, Vicksburg, MS, *Beach Profile Change Measured in the Tank for Large Waves* (Washington, DC: Department of the Army, U.S. Army Corps of Engineers, 1990): 76.

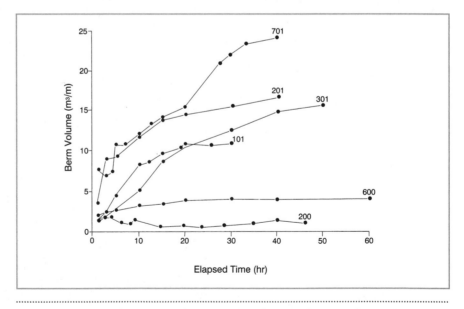

Figure 10-32   LINE GRAPH WITH SIX LINES THAT DO NOT REDUCE COMPREHENSION—MINIMAL OVERLAPPING

Source: Nicholas C. Kraus, Coastal Engineering Research Center, Vicksburg, MS, *Beach Profile Change Measured in the Tank for Large Waves* (Washington, DC: Department of the Army, U.S. Army Corps of Engineers, 1990): 74.

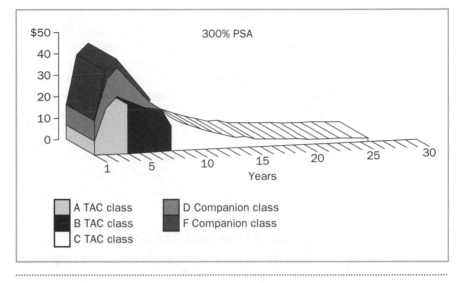

300% PSA

A TAC class   D Companion class
B TAC class   F Companion class
C TAC class

Figure 10-33 STACKED GRAPH. INTERPRETING COMPARATIVE QUANTITIES IS DIFFICULT BECAUSE OF THE 3-D PERSPECTIVE.

Source: Fannie Mae, *Investing in REMIC Securities* (Washington, DC, 1992).

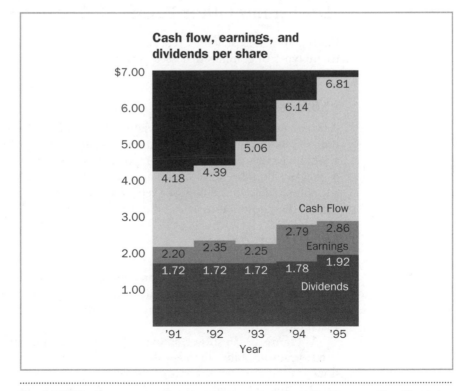

Cash flow, earnings, and dividends per share

Figure 10-34 GRAPH THAT COMBINES FEATURES OF LINE GRAPHS AND BAR GRAPHS

Another issue in designing line graphs concerns the number of lines that may be imposed on one plane. When several lines occur on one graph and then overlap, the graph may become difficult to interpret, as illustrated in Figure 10-31. The number of lines on one axis should generally not exceed three, but the number you can impose will depend on clarity. If lines are spaced apart and do not overlap, you may be able to place more than three on the axis, as is shown in Figure 10-32.

An interesting version of the line graphs is the surface, or stacked graph, which emphasizes the line by shading the area beneath it. Surface graphs can be very artistic, as shown in Figure 10-33, but the quantities they present are often hard to determine. The reader has to interpolate at any point to determine the difference and the amount pictured. In Figure 10-33, the need for the legend or key reduces the visual accessibility of the graph even more.

Combined Line and Bar Graphs

As Figure 10-34 illustrates, you can combine line graphs and bar graphs in the same visual aid, depending on the kind of information you want to display. The step graph shown here combines features of the bar graph, stacked graph, and line graph to compare cash flow, earnings, and dividends per share.

Designing Other Forms of Graphics

Photographs, line drawings, representation drawings, and flowcharts are other useful types of graphics that allow you to help your reader visualize the idea you are presenting.

Photographs

As you have already observed in Figures 10-6 and 10-7, photographs may be used in technical reports to capture important detail, and perhaps to add realism. In accident reports, photographs preserve details that may be essential in determining the cause of the damage or its extent. Because photographs add substantially to the cost of a report and must be of high quality to be effective, the photographs selected must clearly achieve their purpose.

Line Drawings

Line drawings are often preferable to photographs when you want to present only the details of an object or process. Unlike photographs, line drawings allow you to select what you want the reader to see. Cutaway line drawings, such as that in Figure 10-35, an underground hydroelectric generating station, reveal internal structures.

As Figure 10-36 shows, an exploded view of an object—in this case an exterior automobile mirror—allows the reader to see quickly the relationships among the components of the object.

Drawings also enable you to help your reader understand processes. For example, Figure 10-37 uses a line drawing to show the steps in the oil refining process.

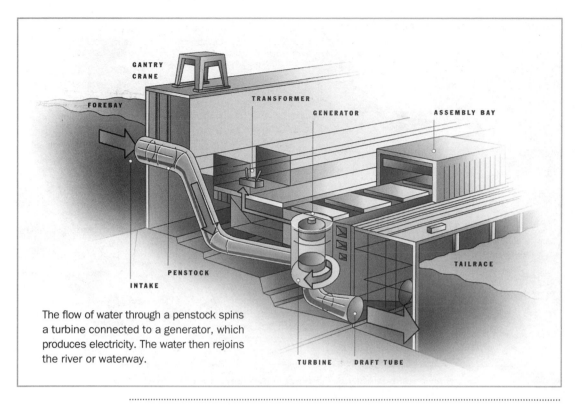

The flow of water through a penstock spins a turbine connected to a generator, which produces electricity. The water then rejoins the river or waterway.

Figure 10-35 CUTAWAY DRAWING

Source: Hydroelectric: Sustaining Nature's Bounty (Ontario Hydro Generation Company.): 7.

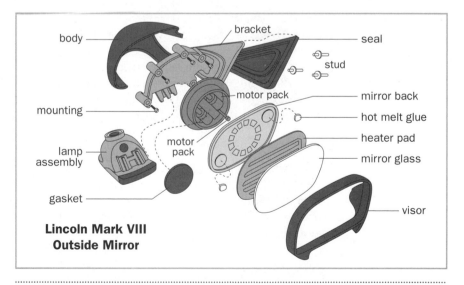

Lincoln Mark VIII Outside Mirror

Figure 10-36 CONSTRUCTION OF LINCOLN MARK VIII LIGHTED OUTSIDE MIRROR

Source: Niall R. Lynam. "Added Feature Automotive Mirrors." SAE Technical Paper Series # 980922. SAE International (Detroit, Michigan: 1998): 193.

Simplified schematic of oil refining process

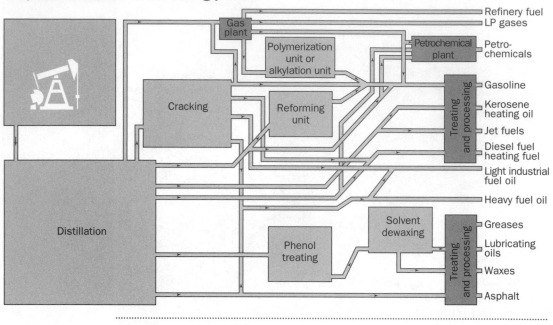

Figure 10-37 DRAWING USED TO SHOW OIL REFINING PROCESS

Source: The Petroleum Resources Communication Foundation, *Our Petroleum Challenge: The New Era* (Calgary: PRCF): 42.

Line drawings can also be used to represent and supplement concepts discussed in the text. For example, a 1995 *Globe and Mail* article raised concerns about the artificial and uncontrolled ecosystem of Lake Ontario. Illustrating the article was a conceptual drawing of Lake Ontario's complicated food web, shown in Figure 10-38 (page 261).

As these drawings illustrate, an important feature of line drawings (as well as all graphics) is effective use of labelling. From the drawing, the labels on various parts, and the title of the drawing, the reader should be able to determine what the drawing means.

Flowcharts

Flowcharts are drawings that show steps in a process. Figure 10-39 (on page 262) shows an algorithm flowchart. These types of charts are often useful for showing steps in an operation or for showing decision-making processes. The chart in Figure 10-39 shows the joint correction method for two robot arms.

Integrating Text and Visuals

Many of the tables, bar graphs, line graphs, and line drawings in this chapter can stand alone. Effective titles and labelling often allow one visual to replace

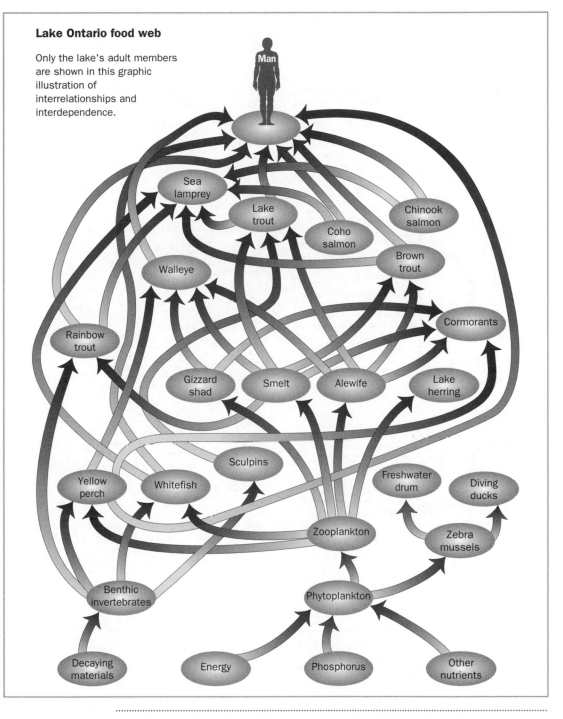

Lake Ontario food web

Only the lake's adult members are shown in this graphic illustration of interrelationships and interdependence.

Figure 10-38 CONCEPTUAL DRAWING OF THE FOOD WEB OF LAKE ONTARIO

Source: Illustration for "A Lake Inhabited by Newcomers," artist Paul Sneath, *The Globe and Mail* (15 July, 1995): D8.

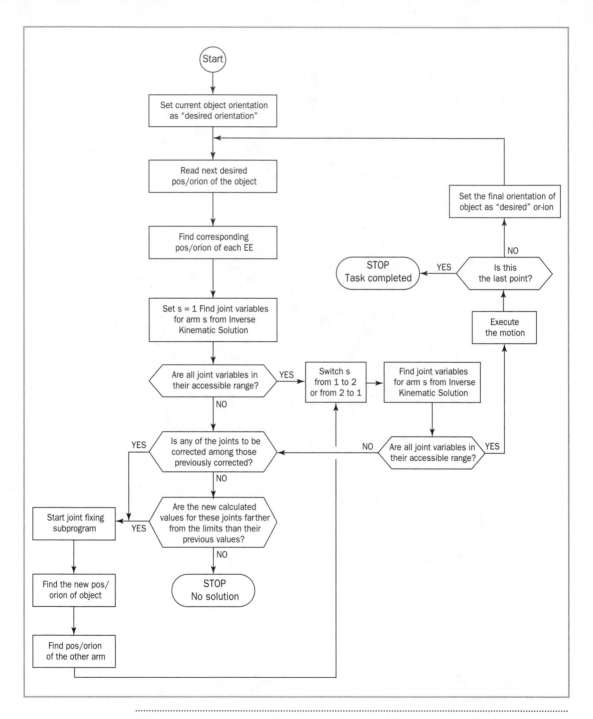

Figure 10-39   Algorithm Flowchart Showing Adjustment of Robot Arms

Source: Ahmad Hemami, "Admissible Path Planning in Coordinated Motion of Two Robot Arms" (presented at the Fifth World Conference on Robotics Research, Cambridge, Massachusetts, September 27-29, 1994). Reprinted with permission of the Society of Manufacturing Engineers.

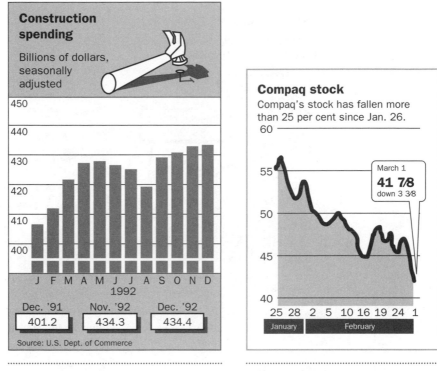

Figure 10-40 Bar Graph with Segment Removed

Figure 10-41 Line Graph with Suppressed Zero to Show Sharp Share Price Drop

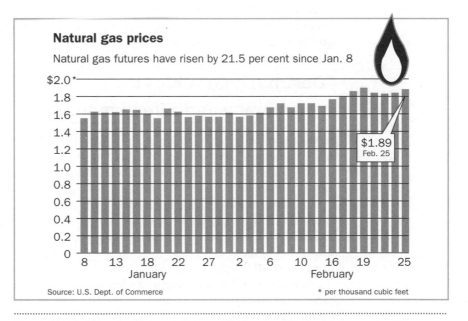

Figure 10-42 Bar Graph with X-Axis Designed to Reflect Accurate Changes in Gas Prices

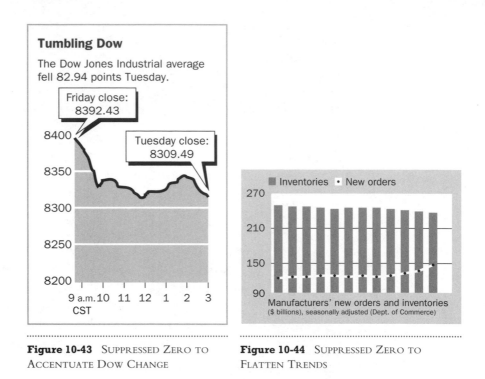

Figure 10-43 SUPPRESSED ZERO TO ACCENTUATE DOW CHANGE

Figure 10-44 SUPPRESSED ZERO TO FLATTEN TRENDS

hundreds of words. In other situations, however, an accompanying verbal discussion helps a reader visualize a highly technical, abstract concept. Thus, an important technique in graphic design is coordination of the verbal and the visual presentation. In this chapter, we want you to be able to see the differences between effective and ineffective graphics. However, we also integrate our examples with written guidelines for their selection and accurate use.

Designing Graphics for
Accuracy and Effectiveness

In the previous sections on tables and graphs, we have briefly alluded to the importance of making graphics accurate as well as effective. The challenge of making your graphics present information accurately requires that you make careful choices as you design your graphics.

Using three-dimensional graphics is not the only way that information can be visually distorted. The scale of the x and y axes can make a significant difference to how your information appears. In designing a graph, you should begin the x and y axes at 0, unless beginning at some other point will not distort information.

In order to reduce the height of a bar or line graph without creating visual distortion, you can remove a portion of the bars, as shown in Figure 10-40, without changing the general trend that the bars indicate.

You avoid distorting the trend of the bar graph by choosing the intervals on the y-axis carefully. For example, examine Figure 10-41, the graph of Compaq Computer Corporation's stock prices for January and February 1993. If you were to redraw the graph to begin the origin at 0, the slope of the line would not change. The slope of the line, indicating the drop from $55 per share to 41 7/8 in one month is represented accurately on the graph. Similarly, Figure 10-42, showing changes in natural gas prices, uses interval differences of $.20, as this is a significant change in price.

However, business publications often distort the intervals on the y-axis to emphasize extreme highs or lows in financial performance. Figure 10-43 graphs sharp declines in the Dow Jones industrial index over a short period—six hours—to convey the writer's view of the severity of this decline. Figure 10-44, with its y-axis scaling of $90-$270 million, is designed to show that inventories have not declined substantially, and new orders have not increased substantially.

In short, how you set up your y-axis will depend on the change you want your graph to show. As a writer, you have an ethical responsibility to present your graphic so that it represents the trend you want to show your reader without misrepresenting the facts.

Choosing the Best Graphic for the Information and the Audience

Much numerical information usually appears in tabular form, generated as computer printouts of raw data. After selecting the data from the printout, you then need to know how to display the information. Sometimes you have choices, as we show in Figure 10-45. To choose the best graphic, use the help we provide:

- As you *plan* your report, consult the planning checklist on pages 267-268.
- As you *generate* your graphics, keep the following summary (pages 266-267) handy to guide you in your choice and development of visuals for accuracy and effectiveness.
- As you *evaluate* your graphics for possible revision, consult the revision checklist on pages 268-269.

Table IV: Testing Time Before Failure

Test no.	RPM	Hours-minutes
1	4,000	4:08
2	5,000	4:02
3	6,000	3:55
4	7,000	3:45
5	8,000	3:26
6	9,000	2:45
7	10,000	1:15

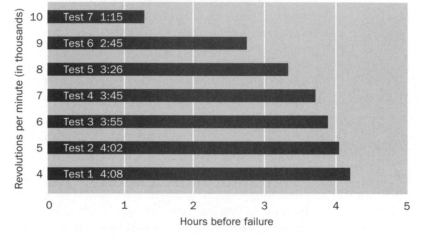

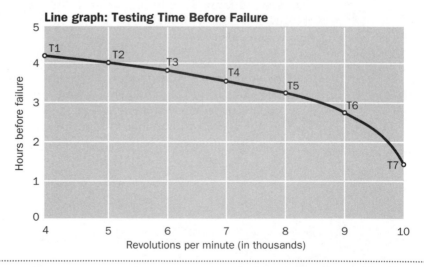

Figure 10-45   Table–Graph Relationship. The two graphs show clearly the relationship between rpm and time before failure. The line graph shows the relationship as a continuous variable and is well suited to technical and expert audiences.

Graphics Checklist

Choosing Graphics

- Make sure the graphic communicates what you want it to convey quickly and accurately.
- Be sensitive for ways to use graphics to enhance the effectiveness of your reports. Choose the graphic that will do the following best:
  - Clarify information
  - Summarize information
  - Emphasize a specific idea
- If information requires your reader's immediate attention, look for ways to present this information graphically to help your reader see the urgency of your purpose.

- If your reader will not be motivated to read your report, graphics and visual design can encourage him or her. Seeing is easier than reading.
- Use tables rather than bar graphs or line graphs if you have to present extensive data.
- Use flowcharts if the progression of ideas is complex.
- Use bar graphs and circle graphs if you want to show large comparisons.
- Use creative visuals to emphasize or portray important ideas, but use these sparingly.

Drawing Graphics

- Make the graphic aesthetically pleasing.
- Keep decoration from interfering with the message.
- Avoid overuse of colour or shading.
- Select colours and shades carefully to show connections and similarities as well as differences.

- Eliminate from the graphic any information not relevant to your point.
- Watch for graphics that are text-heavy.
- Avoid using too many typefaces and fonts. Avoid use of italics, open type, Olde English, and other typefaces that are difficult to read.

Evaluating Graphics for Accuracy

- Check for distortion. You, not the computer, must make the final decision.
- If you choose three-dimensional graphics, check the accuracy of each segment to ensure that the size suggested is what the data suggest.

- Choose scales that are regular and logical.
- Keep the graphic as simple as possible. Avoid the tendency to overuse the technology available in computer programs. Excessive detail obscures or distorts the point of the graphic.

Planning and Revision Checklists

The following questions are a summary of the key points in this chapter, and they provide a checklist when you are planning and revising any document for your readers.

Planning a Report That Will Include Graphics

- How important are graphics to your presentation?
- How complex are your graphics likely to be?
- How expert is your audience in reading graphics?
- Based on your answers to the previous questions, how much prose explanation of your graphics are you likely to need?
- Do you have objects to portray?
- What do you have to illustrate about the objects?
- Do you want to draw attention to certain aspects of the objects and not to others?
- Will exploded or cutaway drawings of the objects serve your purpose?
- Would photographs of the objects add realism or drama to your report?
- Based on your answers to the previous questions about objects, what kinds of photos and drawings are you likely to need?
- Will any of your photos or drawings need a scale reference?
- Will any of your photos or drawings need annotation?
- Are you working with any concepts that can be best presented visually or in a combination of words and graphics?
- Do you have any definitions that should be presented visually in whole or in part?
- Do you have any processes or algorithms that should be depicted visually?
- Would a flowchart of any of your processes or algorithms aid your readers?
- Will you be presenting information on trends or relationships? Should some of the information be presented in tables and graphs?
- Do you have masses of statistics that should be summarized in tables?
- Would some informal tables help you present your data?
- Which are your readers most likely to comprehend: bar and circle graphs or line graphs?
- For each graph you plan, ask this question: Is this graph intended to give the reader a general shape of a trend, or should the reader be able to extract precise information from the graph?

Revising Report Graphics

- Are your graphics suited to your purpose and audience?
- Are your graphics well located and easy to find?
- Have you shown scale on your photos when necessary?
- Are your annotations horizontal? Are they easy to read and find?

continued >>

- Will your readers grasp the concepts you have shown visually? Do your verbal and graphic elements complement each other?
- Will your readers easily follow any processes you have shown graphically?
- Do you have any blocks of data that should be converted to informal or formal tables?
- Are your tables and graphs properly titled and properly numbered?
- Are your tables and graphs simple, clear, and logical?
- Have you referred to your tables and graphs in your text?
- Have you, when necessary, included units of measure in your tables and graphs?
- Are the numbers in your tables aligned correctly? Whole numbers on right-hand digits? Fractional numbers on the decimal points?
- Have you acknowledged the sources for your tables and graphs?
- Are your graphs legible?
- Are your graphs attractive?
- When necessary, have you helped your readers to interpret your graphs with commentary or annotations?
- Do your graphs need a grid for more accurate interpretation?
- Have you avoided the use of keys? If not, have you kept them simple?
- Have you plotted your graphs according to the conventions—independent variable horizontally, dependent variable vertically? If not, do you have a good reason for your arrangement?
- If you have used a suppressed zero, will it be obvious to your reader?
- Do your tables and graphs complement each other?

Weblinks

Technical Illustration
www.arcm.com/illustra.html

Graphical Excellence
www.darkstar.engr.wisc.edu.zwickel/397/graphexc.html

Graphics Guidelines
www.darkstar.engr.wisc.edu.zwickel/397/graphguide.html

Icon Bazaar
www.iconbazaar.com/

Exercises

1. Analyse the effectiveness of the two graphics on the next page, both of which were designed to appear in reports to investors. In what ways could each be redrawn to eliminate distortion?

2. Mega Corp., which designs and test markets word processing programs, had the following sales figures for the years 1991, 1992, 1993, 1994, and 1995 in the six provinces in which it does business

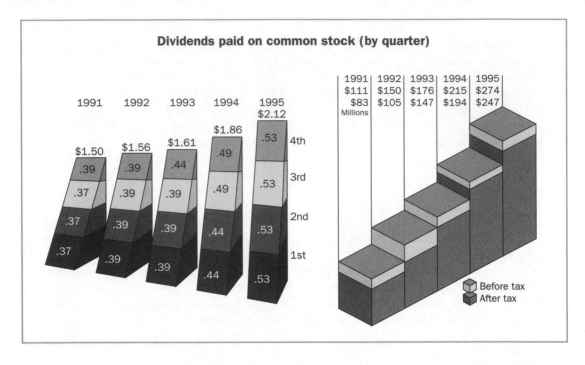

Dividends paid on common stock (by quarter)

(see pages 271-272). The company has two divisions: Alberta, Saskatchewan, and Manitoba make up Division I; Ontario, Quebec, and New Brunswick make up Division II.

Use line graphs, bar graphs, or circle graphs to show the following:
a) Total sales of CW1, CW2, and CW3 for each year.
b) Comparison of total sales for Division I and Division II for each year.
c) Comparison of performance for Division I and Division II for each CorrectWrite version.
d) Which division has the largest percentage of gains in sales.

3. Redraw Figures 10-15 and 10-16 to improve the comparisons suggested by the divided bars.

4. Reexamine Figure 10-19. Could you redesign this graphic so that it better presents the information?

5. Reexamine Figure 10-25. In what other way could you present the same information shown here?

6. Reexamine Figure 10-38. Can you suggest other ways to show the complexities of the food web?

7. Examine several technical publications in your field of study. Choose examples of good or bad graphics. Write a report that analyses the effectiveness (or ineffectiveness) of these graphics. Be sure to integrate a copy of the graphic with your analysis of each.

MEGA SALES 1991—INDIVIDUAL UNITS

Province	CorrectWrite 1	CorrectWrite 2	CorrectWrite 3
Alberta	904	741	318
Saskatchewan	713	751	722
Manitoba	823	755	720
Ontario	679	596	483
Quebec	552	396	246
New Brunswick	327	219	435

MEGA SALES 1992—INDIVIDUAL UNITS

Province	CorrectWrite 1	CorrectWrite 2	CorrectWrite 3
Alberta	804	700	299
Saskatchewan	703	720	799
Manitoba	923	875	825
Ontario	655	543	450
Quebec	502	380	236
New Brunswick	315	380	495

MEGA SALES 1993—INDIVIDUAL UNITS

Province	CorrectWrite 1	CorrectWrite 2	CorrectWrite 3
Alberta	740	738	466
Saskatchewan	803	800	789
Manitoba	843	769	790
Ontario	773	555	490
Quebec	525	453	426
New Brunswick	337	287	488

MEGA SALES 1994—INDIVIDUAL UNITS

Province	CorrectWrite 1	CorrectWrite 2	CorrectWrite 3
Alberta	888	902	500
Saskatchewan	800	845	876
Manitoba	819	803	865
Ontario	723	505	390
Quebec	500	353	326
New Brunswick	330	300	495

MEGA SALES 1995—INDIVIDUAL UNITS			
Province	CorrectWrite 1	CorrectWrite 2	CorrectWrite 3
Alberta	940	838	766
Saskatchewan	930	900	889
Manitoba	634	567	590
Ontario	673	455	290
Quebec	425	353	226
New Brunswick	237	187	288

Oral Exercises

See Chapter 17, "Oral Reports," before doing these exercises.

8. Assume that you are Director of Marketing for Mega Corporation. You receive a call from Megan Pierce, Vice President of Operations of Mega, who wants you to give an oral sales report to the board of directors. Your presentation should be approximately 10 minutes. Prepare graphics as visual aids to explain the sales performance of Mega for 1991 to 1995.

9. Evaluate the effectiveness of the graphics in a journal in your major field of study. Prepare an oral presentation assessing the effectiveness of the graphics. Reproduce sample graphs, tables, drawings, and other graphic elements, and perhaps sample pages for use as overhead transparencies to explain your evaluation.

Report Exercise

See Chapter 13, "Development of Reports," and Chapter 14, "Development of Analytical Reports," before doing this exercise.

10. Assume that, after your sales presentation, Megan Pierce asks you to write a report to her. She wants to share your information with the Executive Committee. She also wants you to make projections for 1996 based on the 1991 to 1995 figures.
    • Should the report be formal or informal?
    • Based on your sales analysis, what kind of report will you write? How will you structure it? What elements will you include?

PART IV

APPLICATIONS

PART IV puts the basic writing, design, and graphic techniques of the first three parts to work and covers most forms of technical communication. The first six chapters discuss correspondence, the job hunt, and various types of reports, including instructions, progress reports, and proposals. Chapter 17 discusses techniques for preparing oral reports.

CHAPTER 11
Correspondence

CHAPTER 12
The Strategies and Communications of the Job Hunt

CHAPTER 13
Development of Reports

CHAPTER 14
Development of Analytical Reports

CHAPTER 15
Instructions

CHAPTER 16
Proposals and Progress Reports

CHAPTER 17
Oral Reports

CORRESPONDENCE

> **Letter and Memorandum Reports**
> Introduction
> Summary
> Discussion
> Action

Even in these days of instant communication through telephones, fax machines, and e-mail, letters and memos still play a major role in getting an organization's work done. For example, executives may reach a decision in a telephone conversation or a teleconference, but that decision has to be documented. People may forget or incorrectly remember what the decision was. A letter or memo records the decision for everyone.

In fact, as we pointed out in Chapter 8, "Document Design," it's a myth that electronic technology is creating the paperless office. Canadian business and government turn out more paper in the electronic age than ever before. Much of that paper consists of correspondence. On the job, you will often be responsible for a share of your organization's letters and memorandums.

In this chapter, we discuss the composition of business letters and memorandums, their style and tone, and their format. We pay special attention to e-mail, the newest form of correspondence. Then we show you how to write letters of inquiry, replies to letters of inquiry, letters of complaint and adjustment, and letter and memorandum reports.

Composing Letters and Memorandums

Composing letters and memorandums—memos, for short—is little different from composing any piece of writing as we describe the process in Chapter 2, "Composing." But a few points about topic, purpose, and audience might be worth reemphasizing because of their importance to good correspondence.

Topic and Purpose

People on the job use letters and memos to inform, to instruct, to analyse and evaluate, to argue—the whole range of communication activities that occupy people at work. Letters go to people outside the company or organization; memos go to people within. Any of the following would be a typical topic and purpose:

- Instructing office managers how to complete the new travel payment requests
- Convincing the boss that the office needs two new microcomputers
- Answering a complaint

Unless you expect hostility or resistance from your readers, be sure to announce your topic and purpose immediately. Nothing irritates a reader more than to read through several paragraphs of details with no idea of where the letter or memo is heading. Be direct. Tell your reader what your topic and purpose are with an opening like this one:

> Additional report writing responsibility in our office has increased our need for greater word processing capability. This memo describes the problems caused by the increased work load and shows the benefits of purchasing two new microcomputers and a second laser printer for the use of our staff.

The only exception to such a clear statement of topic and purpose may be when the recipient is likely to be hostile to your conclusions. We discuss this possibility and how to handle it when we discuss bad-news letters on pages 294–298.

Audience

In composing your letter or memo, consider your readers: Who are they and what do they know already? What is their purpose in reading your letter or memo?

WHO ARE THE READERS? Letters and memos may be addressed to one person or to many. Even when you address a letter or memo to one person, you may send copies of it to many others. In such cases, you have to think about the knowledge and experience of those receiving copies as well as those receiving the original. If those receiving copies lack background in the topic under discussion, you may have to take time to fill them in.

In another common situation, you may be explaining a technical problem and its solution to a colleague with technical knowledge equal to your own. However, you may also be sending a copy to your boss, who lacks that technical knowledge. When such is the case, you would be wise to lead your discussion with what amounts to an executive summary. (See pages 214–215.) Fill your boss in quickly on the key points, and tell him or her the implications of what you are saying.

WHAT IS THE READER'S PURPOSE?   You have a purpose in writing your letter or memo, but your reader has a purpose as well. Be sure to match your purpose to your reader's. For instance, your reader may be reading to evaluate your recommendation and accept or reject it. Your purpose must be to provide enough information to make that evaluation and decision possible.

In another situation, your purpose may be to explain why a project is running late. Your reader, somewhat skeptically no doubt, will be reading to determine whether your reasons are valid and acceptable. Provide enough information to justify your position. If you don't match your purpose to your reader's, you may not achieve the result you intended.

Style and Tone

In your correspondence, work for a clear style and a human tone.

Clear Style

Everything we say about clear and readable style in Chapter 5 goes doubly when you are writing letters and memos. Letters must be clear, so clear that the reader cannot possibly misunderstand them. Use short paragraphs, lists, clear sentence structure, and specific words. Above all, avoid pomposity and the cold formality of the passive voice.

Do not make your letters and memos a repository for all the clichés that writers before you have used. Avoid expressions like these:

- We beg to advise you that ...
- We are in receipt of your letter that ...
- It is requested that you send a copy of the requested document to our office.

There are hundreds of such expressions that weigh down business correspondence. To protect yourself from such prose pachyderms, remember the closing advice from Chapter 5: ask yourself whether you would or could say in conversation what you have written. If you know you would strangle on the expression, don't write it. Restate it in simpler language, like this:

- We'd like you to know that ...
- We received your letter that...
- Please send us a copy of your latest tax return.

Human Tone

To get a human tone into your correspondence, focus on the human being reading your letter or memo. Develop what has been labelled the *you-attitude*.

To some extent, the you-attitude means that your letters and memos contain a higher percentage of *you's* than *I's*. But it goes beyond the mechanical use of certain pronouns. With the you-attitude, you see things from your reader's point of view. You think about what the letter or memo will mean to the reader, not just what it means to you. We can illustrate simply. Suppose you have an interview scheduled with a prospective employer and, unavoidably, you must change dates. You could write as follows:

> Dear Ms. Moody:
>
> A change in my final examination schedule makes it impossible for me to keep our appointment on May 2.
>
> I am really disappointed. I was looking forward to coming to Calgary. It's a great inconvenience, but I hope we can work out an appointment. Please let me know when we can arrange a new meeting.

Now this letter is clear enough, and it may even get a new appointment for its writer. But it has the I-attitude, not the you-attitude. The persona projected is of a person who thinks only of himself or herself. The reader may be vaguely or even greatly annoyed. This next version will please a reader far more:

> Dear Ms. Moody:
>
> A change in my final examination schedule makes it impossible for me to keep our appointment on May 2. When I should have been talking with you, I'll be taking an exam in chemistry.
>
> I hope this change will not seriously inconvenience you. Please accept my regrets.

Will you be able to work me in at a new time? Final exam week ends on May 5. Please choose any later date that is convenient for you.

Mechanically, the second letter contains more *you's*, but more to the point, it considers the inconvenience caused the reader, not the sender. It also makes it easy for the reader to set up a new date.

Notice also that the second letter is a bit more detailed than the first. Many people have stressed the need for brevity in letters and memos, and certainly it is a good thing to be concise. But do not get carried away with the notion. Letters and memos are not telegrams. When they are too brief, they give an impression of brusqueness, even rudeness. Often, a longer letter or memo gives a better impression. Particularly avoid brevity when you must refuse people something or disappoint their expectations. People appreciate your taking time to explain in such a situation.

Our advice about style and tone can be summed up with what we call the four **C's** of correspondence: Correspondence should be **clear, concise, complete,** and **courteous**. Sometimes, *concise* and *complete* may be in conflict. If in doubt, opt for completeness. And always remember the importance of being courteous. Taking time for the you-attitude is the good and human way to act. Luckily, it's also very good business.

Format

Almost any organization you join will have rules about its letter and memo formats. You will either have an assistant to do your correspondence, or you will have to learn the rules for yourself. In this section, we give you only enough rules and illustrations so that you can turn out a good-looking, correct, and acceptable business letter or memo. You will find this an especially valuable skill when you go job hunting.

Figures 11-1 and 11-2 illustrate the block and semiblock styles on non-letterhead stationery. Figures 11-3 and 11-4 illustrate the block style and the simplified style on letterhead stationery.

The chief difference between memos and letters is format. Figure 11-5 illustrates a typical memo format. Figure 11-7 illustrates the heading used for the continuation pages of a letter or a memo. We have indicated in these samples the spacing, margins, and punctuation you should use. In the text that follows, we discuss briefly the different styles and then give you some of the basic rules you should know about the parts of a letter or memo. Before continuing with the text, look at Figures 11-1 to 11-5 and Figure 11-7. Particularly observe the spacing, placement, and punctuation of the various parts of a letter or memo.

For most business letters you write, any of the styles shown would be acceptable. In letters of inquiry or complaint, where you probably do not have anyone specific in a company to address, we suggest the simplified style. For letters of application, we suggest the block or semiblock style without a subject line. Some people still find the simplified letter without

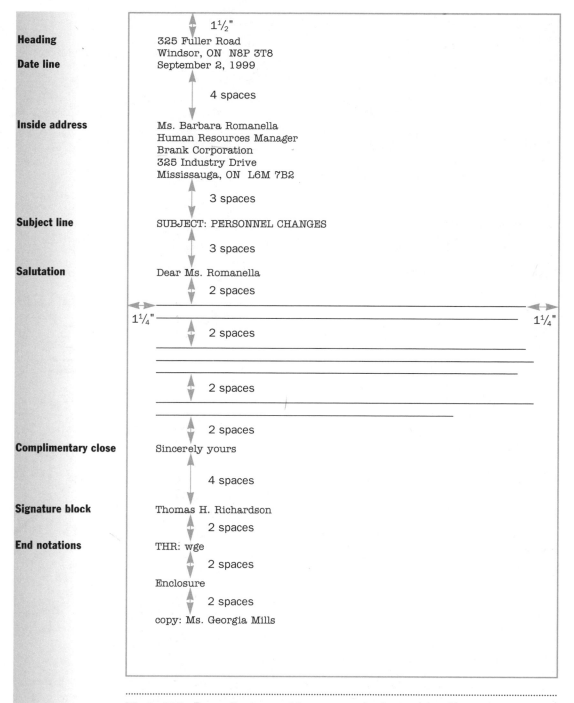

Heading

1½"

325 Fuller Road
Windsor, ON N8P 3T8

Date line

September 2, 1999

4 spaces

Inside address

Ms. Barbara Romanella
Human Resources Manager
Brank Corporation
325 Industry Drive
Mississauga, ON L6M 7B2

3 spaces

Subject line

SUBJECT: PERSONNEL CHANGES

3 spaces

Salutation

Dear Ms. Romanella

2 spaces

1¼"   1¼"

2 spaces

2 spaces

2 spaces

Complimentary close

Sincerely yours

4 spaces

Signature block

Thomas H. Richardson

2 spaces

End notations

THR: wge

2 spaces

Enclosure

2 spaces

copy: Ms. Georgia Mills

Figure 11-1 BLOCK LETTER ON NONLETTERHEAD STATIONERY. VERY SHORT LETTERS SOMETIMES REQUIRE A MORE FLEXIBLE APPROACH TO SPACING IN ORDER TO ACHIEVE A BALANCED PAGE.

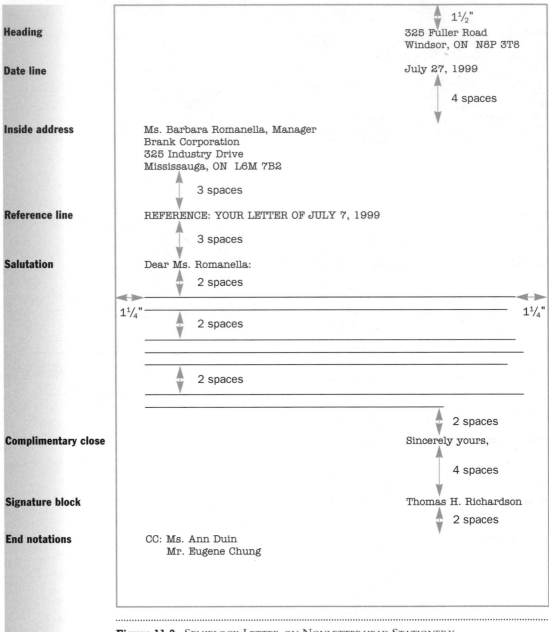

Heading

1½"

325 Fuller Road
Windsor, ON N8P 3T8

Date line

July 27, 1999

4 spaces

Inside address

Ms. Barbara Romanella, Manager
Brank Corporation
325 Industry Drive
Mississauga, ON L6M 7B2

3 spaces

Reference line

REFERENCE: YOUR LETTER OF JULY 7, 1999

3 spaces

Salutation

Dear Ms. Romanella:

2 spaces

1¼"   1¼"

2 spaces

2 spaces

2 spaces

Complimentary close

Sincerely yours,

4 spaces

Signature block

Thomas H. Richardson

2 spaces

End notations

CC: Ms. Ann Duin
    Mr. Eugene Chung

Figure 11-2 SEMIBLOCK LETTER ON NONLETTERHEAD STATIONERY

the conventional salutation and complimentary close a bit too brusque. Unless you know for certain that the company you are applying to prefers the simplified form, do not take a chance with it.

If you are doing your own word processing, we suggest the block style as the best style. All the conventional parts of a letter are included, but everything is lined up along the left margin. You do not have to bother with tab settings

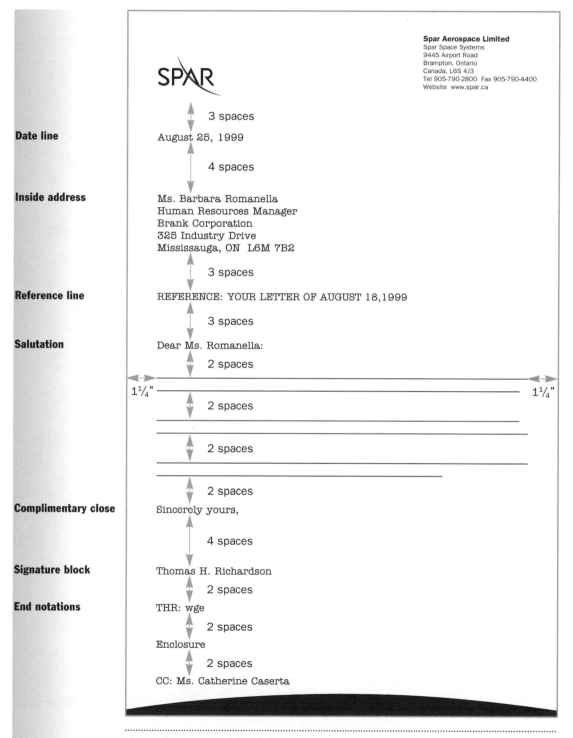

Date line

Inside address

Reference line

Salutation

Complimentary close

Signature block

End notations

3 spaces

August 25, 1999

4 spaces

Ms. Barbara Romanella
Human Resources Manager
Brank Corporation
325 Industry Drive
Mississauga, ON L6M 7B2

3 spaces

REFERENCE: YOUR LETTER OF AUGUST 18,1999

3 spaces

Dear Ms. Romanella:

2 spaces

1¼"   1¼"

2 spaces

2 spaces

2 spaces

Sincerely yours,

4 spaces

Thomas H. Richardson

2 spaces

THR: wge

2 spaces

Enclosure

2 spaces

CC: Ms. Catherine Caserta

Spar Aerospace Limited
Spar Space Systems
9445 Airport Road
Brampton, Ontario
Canada, L6S 4J3
Tel 905-790-2800 Fax 905-790-4400
Website www.spar.ca

SPAR

Figure 11-3 BLOCK STYLE ON LETTERHEAD STATIONERY
Source: Courtesy Spar Aerospace Limited.

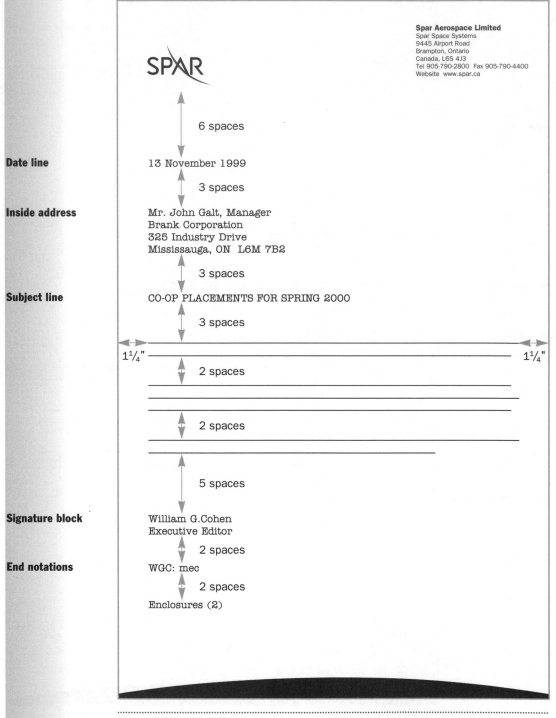

Figure 11-4 SIMPLIFIED STYLE ON LETTERHEAD STATIONERY
Source: Courtesy Spar Aerospace Limited.

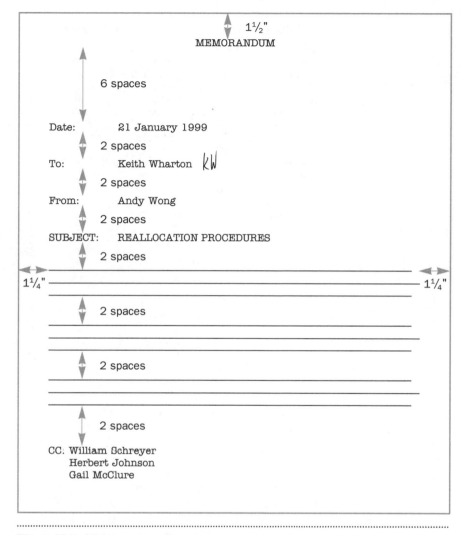

Figure 11-5 MEMORANDUM FORMAT

and other complications. Some people feel that a block letter looks a bit lopsided, but it is a common style that no one will object to. No matter which style you choose, leave generous margins, from from one to two inches (2.5 cm to 5 cm) all around, and balance the first page of the letter vertically on the page. Because letters look more inviting with lots of white space, you should seldom allow paragraphs to run more than seven or eight lines.

Heading

When you do not have letterhead stationery, you will have to type your heading. In the semiblock style, the heading is approximately flush right. In the other formats shown, the heading is flush left. Do not abbreviate words such as *street* or *road*. Write them out. You may abbreviate the names of

Canada		United States			
Alberta	AB*	Alabama	AL	Montana	MT
British Columbia	BC	Alaska	AK	Nebraska	NE
Labrador	LB	American Samoa	AS	Nevada	NV
Manitoba	MB	Arizona	AZ	New Hampshire	NH
New Brunswick	NB	Arkansas	AR	New Jersey	NJ
Newfoundland	NF	California	CA	New Mexico	NM
Nova Scotia	NS	Colorado	CO	New York	NY
Northwest Territories	NT	Connecticut	CT	North Carolina	NC
Ontario	ON	Delaware	DE	North Dakota	ND
Prince Edward Island	PE	District of Columbia	DC	Ohio	OH
Quebec (Province		Florida	FL	Oklahoma	OK
de Quebec)	PQ	Georgia	GA	Oregon	OR
Saskatchewan	SK	Guam	GU	Pennsylvania	PA
Yukon Territory	YT	Hawaii	HI	Puerto Rico	PR
		Idaho	ID	Rhode Island	RI
		Illinois	IL	South Carolina	SC
		Indiana	IN	South Dakota	SD
		Iowa	IA	Tennessee	TN
		Kansas	KS	Texas	TX
		Kentucky	KY	Utah	UT
		Louisiana	LA	Vermont	VT
		Maine	ME	Virginia	VA
		Maryland	MD	Virgin Islands	VI
		Massachusetts	MA	Washington	WA
		Michigan	MI	West Virginia	WV
		Minnesota	MN	Wisconsin	WI
		Mississippi	MS	Wyoming	WY
		Missouri	MO		

*Notice that both letters of the abbreviation are capitalized and that no period is used.

Figure 11-6 GEOGRAPHIC ABBREVIATIONS FOR CANADA AND THE UNITED STATES

provinces and states, however. Figure 11-6 lists the province abbreviations for Canada and state abbreviations for the United States.

The postal code is the last item in the address. It should be placed two spaces after the name of the province. There is a space (not a hyphen) between the two parts of the postal code.

If you have business letterheads made up, have them printed on good quality bond in a neutral colour and simple style. With word processing and most new printers, you can print your own letterheads. If you choose to do so, be careful not to design anything too elaborate; use a simple, standard design.

Date Line

In a letter without a printed letterhead, the date line is part of your heading in the block, semiblock, and simplified styles. When you do have a printed letterhead, the date line is flush left in the block and simplified styles and approximately flush right in semiblock. Place it three to six spaces below a printed letterhead in a manner to help balance the letter vertically on the page. Write the date out fully, as in either June 3, 1999, or 3 June 1999.

Do not abbreviate the month or add st or nd (e.g., 1st, 2nd) to the number of the day.

Inside Address

The inside address is placed flush left in all the formats shown. Make sure the inside address is complete. Follow exactly the form used by the person or company you are writing to. If your correspondent abbreviates *Company* as *Co.*, you should also. Use *S. Edward Smith* rather than *Samuel E. Smith* if that is the way Smith wants it. Do use courtesy titles such as *Mr., Ms.*, and *Dr.* before the name. The abbreviations usually used are *Mr., Ms.*, and *Dr.* (*Miss* and *Mrs.* are still in use, but *Ms.* is standard usage in the workplace.) Place one-word titles such as *Manager* or *Superintendent* immediately after the name. When a title is longer than one word, place it on the next line by itself. Do not put a title after the name that means the same thing as a courtesy title. For example, don't write *Dr. S. Edward Smith, Ph.D.*

Attention Line

You may wish to write to an organizational address but also draw your letter to the attention of some individual. It's a way of saying, in effect, "Anyone there can answer this letter, but if Mr. Smith is there he is the best person to handle the matter." When you use an attention line, type it flush left two spaces below the inside address. Capitalize only the A. You can use a colon or not between *Attention* and the name:

Attention Ms. Barbara Romanella

or

Attention: Ms. Barbara Romanella

Reference Line

Use the reference line to refer to the letter or memo you are answering; for example,

REFERENCE: YOUR LETTER OF MAY 12, 1999

Place the reference line heading (sometimes abbreviated *RE.* or *REF.*) flush left in all styles. Type the heading and the reference line itself in capital letters. Generally, you will follow the heading with a colon, although sometimes the colon is omitted. A letter may have both a reference line and a subject line, or the two may be combined:

REFERENCE: YOUR LETTER OF 12 JULY 1999

APPLICATION FOR A MORTGAGE AT 452 LITTLE COMFORT ROAD

Subject Line

Place the subject line flush left in all the styles. In the block and semi-block styles, it is usually preceded by the heading *SUBJECT*, although sometimes you will see it with no heading. Generally, the heading is followed by a colon, but sometimes the colon will be omitted. Type the heading and the subject line in capital letters. In the simplified style, omit the heading, and type the line in all-capital letters.

If you are answering a letter that has a subject line, repeat the subject line from the original letter. If you are making up your own subject line, be sure it is complete enough to be useful. If, for example, you are reporting progress on an architectural design for a building at 452 Little Comfort Road, don't write merely "452 LITTLE COMFORT ROAD." Rather, write "PROGRESS REPORT ON THE ARCHITECTURAL DESIGN FOR THE BUILDING AT 452 LITTLE COMFORT ROAD."

Both subject lines and reference lines get your letter or memo off to a good start. They allow you to avoid clichéd openers like "With regard to your letter of April 5, 1999."

Salutation

Place the salutation flush left. Convention still calls for the use of *Dear*. Always use a name in the salutation when one is available to use. When you use a name, be sure it is in the inside address as well. Also, use the same courtesy title as in the inside address, such as *Dear Dr. Sibley* or *Dear Ms. McCarthy*. You may use a first-name salutation, such as *Dear Samantha*, when you are on friendly terms with the recipient. Follow the salutation with a colon.

What do you do when you are writing a company blindly and have no specific name to address? Some people use *Dear* followed by the name of the department being written to, such as *Dear Customer Relations Department*. Some use *Dear Sir or Madam*. One solution, perhaps the best, is to choose the simplified style, where no salutation is used. In any case, do **not** begin letters with *Dear Sir* alone, which is sexist, or *To Whom It May Concern*, which is old-fashioned.

Body

In word processing the body of an average-length letter or memo, single-space between the lines and double-space between the paragraphs. In a particularly short letter, double-space throughout the body and use five-space indentations to mark the first lines of paragraphs. Avoid splitting words between lines. Never split a date or a person's name between two lines.

Complimentary Close

In the block style, place the complimentary close flush left. In the semiblock style, align the close with the heading (or with the date line in a letterhead letter). Settle for a simple close, such as *Sincerely*, or *Sincerely yours*, or *Very truly yours*. Capitalize only the first letter of the close and place a comma after the close.

Signature Block

Place your name four spaces below the complimentary close in the block and semiblock styles, five spaces below the last line in the simplified style. Use your first name, middle initial, and last name or, if you prefer, your first initial and middle name, as in *M. Lillian Smith*. We don't recommend the use of initials only, as in *M. L. Smith*, because this form puts your correspondents at a disadvantage. People who don't know you will not know whether to address you as *Dear Mr.* or *Dear Ms.*

If you have a title, place it below your name. Sign your name immediately above your printed name. Your signature and your printed name should agree. In memos it's customary to initial next to your printed name in the "From" line.

End Notations

Various end notations may be placed at the bottom of a letter or memo, always flush left. The most common ones indicate identification, enclosure, and copy.

IDENTIFICATION   The notation for identification is composed of the writer's initials in capital letters and the typist's initials in lowercase:

DHC: lnh

ENCLOSURE   The enclosure line indicates that additional material has been enclosed with the basic letter or memo. You may use several forms:

Enclosure

Enclosures (2)

Encl: Employment application blank

COPY   The copy line informs the recipient of a letter or memo when you have sent a copy of the letter to someone else. The copy notation looks like this:

cc: Ms. Georgia Mills

See Figures 11-1 to 11-5 for proper spacing and sequence of these three notations.

Continuation Page

Use a continuation page or pages when you can't fit your letter or memo onto one page. Do not use letterhead stationery for a continuation page. Use plain bond of the same quality and colour as the first page.

As shown in Figure 11-7, the continuation page is headed by three items: page number, name of addressee, and date. When you have a continuation page, the last paragraph on the preceding page should contain at least two lines. The last continuation page must have at least three lines of text to accompany the complimentary close and the signature block.

E-Mail

E-mail is somewhere between paper mail and a telephone call. As we note in Chapter 7, "Electronic Communication," an e-mail message is transmitted

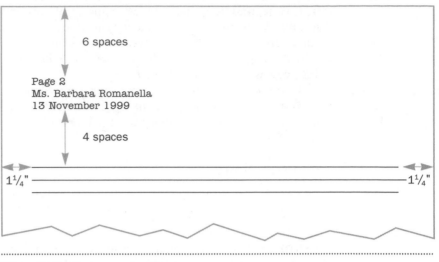

Page number
Addressee
Date

Continuation page must have at least three lines of text.

6 spaces

Page 2
Ms. Barbara Romanella
13 November 1999

4 spaces

1¼"   1¼"

Figure 11-7 Continuation Page

instantaneously, or nearly so, but it differs from a phone call because the recipient does not have to deal with e-mail right away. Recipients can read their e-mail messages at a convenient time, formulate a reply, and then dispatch the reply electronically.

The various Internet services all follow a similar memo format, with a space for address, subject, and message. The service automatically puts the time and date of transmission on the message. Correspondents can send copies to others if they wish.

E-mail is a highly effective way to send a concise memo. Through e-mail, correspondents can communicate quickly and conversationally about routine matters. Like memos, e-mail messages can be used to discuss a matter briefly and come to some agreement. However, they are probably not suited to expressing long, complex arguments. Although e-mail style encourages informality, be careful your style doesn't slip into faulty grammar and bad spelling. Sloppiness may lead to a loss of clarity. Furthermore, the recipient may forward your message to someone who doesn't appreciate sloppiness. Because confidentiality is low in e-mail, you probably should not deal with sensitive matters via this medium.

Because of the speed and ease with which you can send e-mail messages all over the globe, keep in mind our advice about communicating internationally. Remember that North American style in letters and memos does not always work outside of the United States and Canada.

You would be wise to make print copies of important e-mail messages, both those you send and those you receive. As with conversation, whether by phone or face-to-face, people may forget what they said or agreed to in an e-mail message. Printed copies remind all concerned of what the facts, opinions, disagreements, and agreements really were. (See also pages 143–146.)

International Correspondence

In Chapter 4, "Writing for Your Readers," we discuss the importance of understanding the culture of your readers. We advise you to adjust your communication style for the differences between North American and other cultures, particularly those of Asia, Mexico, and Latin America (see pages 71–74). The adjustments we advise are these:

- Be more indirect. Deemphasize the main point or place it at the end of the message.
- Use a more formal, even elegant style.
- Deemphasize structure and the use of headings.
- Recognize that messages may be shared with others.
- Avoid placing direct blame on any one person or group. Allow your reader to save face.
- Discuss business in terms of larger human and organizational concerns.
- Don't rush people to decisions. Allow time for group consensus to build.

Obviously, correspondence with people from cultures different from your own calls for adjustments in approach and style.

In the two letters below, a Canadian executive is answering a request for an increase in the contract price the Canadian company pays a Pakistani sugar supplier. The first letter reflects the courteous but analytical way the executive might answer the request if it had come from a North American company. The second letter is the letter that should be written if the executive takes the styles of different cultures in account.

1. Dear Mr. Singh:

   We have your letter requesting an increase in the contract price we pay Peshawar Sugar Mills, Ltd. for sugar. We have considered your request, and our findings are as follows:

   Findings
   - Our contract, which expires on 31 December 1999, calls for us to pay you 12,950 rupees per metric ton.
   - This price is comparable with the price we pay our other suppliers. In fact, in several cases, it is a higher price.
   - In general, the world price of sugar is declining, not rising.

   To remain competitive in the Canadian market we have to buy our sugar at a cost that reflects the world market. Therefore, we must decline increasing the contract price.

   Our current contract expires at the end of this year, and we will begin negotiations in a few months on a new contract. However, if world sugar prices remain stable or lower still further, a price increase in the new contract seems unlikely.

   Sincerely,

2. Dear Mr. Singh:

   Thank you for your letter of 22 July 1998. We have long appreciated our association with your company. Your sugar shipments have consistently been of high quality, reflecting the expertise of both Pakistani agriculture and your refinery.

> We regret that the current contract price we pay for your sugar no longer seems satisfactory. However, the contract price does reflect the world sugar market. In fact, it might actually be slightly higher than the rest of the world market.
>
> In order to continue buying sugar from your company, we have to remain competitive in our primary market here in Canada. We know you understand our dilemma.
>
> Our current contract expires at the end of this year. We will begin negotiations on a new contract in a few months. At that time we will know more accurately than we do now where world sugar prices are heading. In the meantime, we hope that our long relationship will continue to the mutual benefit of both our companies.
>
> Yours sincerely,

The second letter is much more indirect than the first. It emphasizes the good relationship between the two companies rather than the problem of the price increase. The second letter is less structured than the first and uses more formal language. The conclusion reached is the same as in the first letter, but the refusal is implied rather than directly stated.

Letters of Inquiry

As a student, businessperson, or simply a private individual, you will often have occasion to write letters of inquiry. Students often overlook the rich sources of information for reports that they can tap with a few well-placed, courteous letters. Such letters can bring brochures, photographs, samples, and even very quotable answers from experts in the field the report deals with.

Sometimes companies solicit inquiries about their products through their advertisements and catalogues. In such cases your letter of inquiry can be short and to the point:

> Your advertisement on page 89 of the January 1999 <u>Saturday Night</u> invited inquiries about your new Film-X developing process.
>
> I am a college student and president of a 20-member campus photography club. The members of the club and I would appreciate any information about this new process that you can send us.
>
> We are specifically interested in modernizing the film-developing facilities of the club.

As in the letter just quoted, you should include three important steps:

- Identify the advertisement that solicited your inquiry.
- Identify yourself and establish your need for the information.
- Request the information. Specify the precise area in which you are interested.

Obviously, in this step you also identify the area in which the company may expect to make a sale to you. You thus, in a subtle way, point out to the company why it is in its best interest to answer your inquiry promptly and fully: a good example of the you–attitude in action.

An unsolicited letter of inquiry cannot be quite so short. After all, in an unsolicited letter you are asking a favour, and you must avoid the risk of appearing brusque or discourteous. In an unsolicited letter you include five steps:

- Identify yourself.
- State clearly and specifically the information or materials you want.
- Establish your need for the requested information or materials.
- Tell the recipient why you have chosen her or him as a source for this information or material.
- Close courteously, but do not say "thank you in advance." Many feel that this phrase is presumptuous.

The first four steps may be presented in various combinations rather than as distinct steps, or in different order, but none of the steps should be overlooked.

Identification

In an unsolicited letter, identify yourself. We mean more here than merely using a title in your signature block. Rather, you should identify yourself in terms of the information sought. That is, let your reader know that you are not merely a student; you are a student in a dietetics class seeking information for a paper about iron enrichment of flour. Or you are a member of a committee investigating child abuse in your town. Or you are an engineer for a provincial ministry of transportation seeking information for a study of noise walls on expressways. Certainly, the more prestigious your identification of yourself, the more likely you are to get the information you want, but do not misrepresent yourself in any way. Misrepresentation will usually lead to embarrassment.

Some years ago, one of the authors of this text wrote for information on bookshelves using his college letterhead instead of his private stationery. He was deluged with brochures that were followed up by a long-distance telephone call from a sales manager asking how many shelves the college was going to need: "Is the college expanding its library facilities?"

"No," the feeble answer came, "I just wanted to put up a few shelves in my living room."

Do not misrepresent yourself, but do honestly represent yourself in the best light you can. Most companies are quite good about answering student inquiries. They recognize in students the buyers and the employees of the future and are eager to court their goodwill.

Inquiry

State clearly what you want. Be very specific, and do not ask for too much. Avoid the shotgun approach of asking for "all available information" in some wide area.

Particularly, do not expect other people to do your work for you. Do not, for example, write to someone asking for references to articles on some subject. A little time spent by you in the library will produce the same information. On the other hand, it would be quite appropriate to write to a sociologist asking for a clarification or amplification of some point in a recent article that he or she had written. Science thrives on the latter kind of correspondence.

If you do need detailed information, put your questions in an easy-to-answer questionnaire form. If you have only a few questions, include them in your letter. Indent the questions and number them. Be sure to keep a copy of your letter. The reply you receive may answer your questions by number without restating them.

For a larger group of questions, or when you are sending the questionnaire to many people, make the questionnaire a separate attachment. Be sure in your letter to refer the reader to the attachment. Questionnaires are tricky. Unless they are presented properly and carefully made up, they will probably be ignored. Do not ask too many questions. If possible, phrase the questions for yes or no answers or provide multiple-choice options. Sometimes, meaningful questions just cannot be asked in this objective way. In such cases, do ask questions that require the respondent to write an answer, but try to phrase your questions so that answers to them can be short. Provide sufficient space for the answer expected. If you are asking for confidential information, stress that you will keep it confidential. The questionnaire should be typed, printed, or photocopied.

Need

Tell the recipient why you need the information. Perhaps you are writing a report, conducting a survey, buying a camera, or simply satisfying a healthy, scientific curiosity. Whatever your reason, do not be complicated or devious here. Simply state your need clearly and honestly. Often this step can best be combined with the identification step. If there is some deadline by which you must have an answer, say what it is.

Choice of Recipient

Tell the recipient of the letter why you have chosen that person or company as a source for the information. Perhaps you are writing a paper about stereo equipment and you consider this company to be one of the foremost manufacturers of FM tuners. Perhaps you have read the recipient's recent article on space medicine. Obviously, this section is a good place to pay the recipient a sincere compliment, but avoid flattery or phoniness.

Point out any benefit the recipient may gain by answering your request. For example, if you are conducting a survey among many companies, promise the recipient a tabulation and analysis of results when the survey is completed.

Courteous Close

Close by expressing your appreciation for any help the receiver may give you. But do not use the tired, old formula, "Thanking you in advance, I remain ...." Later, do write a thank-you note even if all you get is a refusal. Who knows? The second letter may cause a change of heart.

Sample Letter

Dear Mr. Hanson:

Identification
Need

I am a second-year student at Ryerson Polytechnic University. I am seeking information for a paper I am writing on the use and conventions of e-mail.

Choice of recipient

You were cited in a recent <u>Maclean's</u> article as an authority in this area. Would you be kind enough to give me your ideas on reasons why some people in business and industry are having trouble communicating through e-mail and are becoming hostile toward it? For instance, two professionals I interviewed complained about how "rude" and "disruptive" much of the e-mail they receive is while a third said that the tone and intention of several of her messages to others had often been misunderstood. What, to your knowledge, are the principal causes of frustration and annoyance in e-mail?

Specific information
requested

Courteous close
including due date

Any help you can give me would be greatly appreciated, and I will of course cite you in my paper, which is due on March 3.

Replies to Letters of Inquiry

In replying to a letter of inquiry, be as complete as you can. Probably you will be trying to avoid a second exchange of questions and answers. If you can, answer the questions in the order in which they appear in the inquiry. If the inquirer represents an organization and has written on letterhead stationery, you may safely assume that a file copy of the original letter has been retained. In that case, you don't have to repeat the original questions—just answer them. If the inquirer writes as a private person, you cannot assume that a copy of the letter has been kept. Therefore, you will need to repeat enough of the original question or questions to remind the inquirer of what has been asked.

You might answer the earlier letter about e-mail etiquette in the following fashion:

Dear Ms. Mallette:

Repetition of
question

Your questions about the frustration and hostility surrounding e-mail are of increasing concern to many people in the workplace.

Answer to question

My own interviews with working people—and my personal experience as a keen e-mail correspondent—have led me to conclude that users, once they get over the initial excitement at the immediacy of communication, gradually feel pressured ("being bombarded with messages" is the way one respondent expressed it). I can make two very broad comments:

1. For the recipient, it is important to hold on to a sense of control, to let one's own schedule and priorities dictate one's timing in checking and responding to e-mail.

2. For the sender, there seem to be roughly four problem areas: timing (false urgency, impossible deadlines), subject identification (ambiguous or general headings that beg to be ignored), message forwarding (repetitious and tedious for readers), and concern over privacy and security.

Source of additional
information

I hope this helps you in your own thinking. I am enclosing for you a copy of a paper I delivered last month to a group of Ford Canada managers in Oakville. If you missed last Saturday's <u>Globe and Mail</u>, you might also want to check the "Facts & Arguments" page for a tongue-in-cheek look at the subject. Its author makes the very valid point that those who complain most bitterly about the irritations of e-mail seem to be the same people who are most deeply dependent on it!

Good luck with your paper.

Because the writer of the letter of inquiry wrote as a private person, she is, in this answer, reminded of the original question. The tone of the letter is friendly. The question is answered succinctly but completely. An additional source of information is mentioned, an excellent idea that should be followed when possible.

When you can, include as enclosures to your letter previously prepared materials that provide answers to the questions asked. If you do so, provide whatever explanation of these materials is needed.

Letters of Complaint and Adjustment

Mistakes and failures happen in business as they do everywhere else. Deliveries don't arrive on time or at all. Expensive equipment fails at a critical moment. If you're on the receiving end of such problems, you'll probably want to register a complaint with someone. Chances are good that you'll want an adjustment—some compensation—for your loss or inconvenience. To seek such an adjustment, you'll write a letter of complaint or, as it is also called, a claim letter.

Letter of Complaint

Your attitude in a letter of complaint should be firm but fair. There is no reason to be discourteous. You'll do better in most instances if you write the letter with the attitude that the offending company will want to make a proper adjustment once they know the problem. Don't threaten to withdraw your business on a first offence. Of course, after repeated offences you will seek another firm to deal with, and that should be made clear at the appropriate time.

Be very specific about what is wrong and about any inconvenience you suffered. Be sure to give any necessary product identification such as serial numbers. At the end of your letter, motivate the receiver to make a fair adjustment. If you know exactly what adjustment you want, spell it out. If not, allow the company you are dealing with to suggest an adjustment. Figure 11–8 shows you what a complete letter of complaint looks like. Note that it is in simplified format and addressed to the Customer Relations Department. You can safely assume that most companies have an office or an employee specifically responsible for complaints. In any case, if the letter is addressed in this manner, it will reach the appropriate person much more rapidly.

Letter of Adjustment

What happens at the other end of the line? You have received a letter of complaint and must write the adjustment letter. What should be your attitude?

26 Shady Woods Road
White Bear Lake MB R3M 1L9
28 October 1999

Customer Relations Department
Chapman Products, Inc.
1925 Jerome Street
Toronto, ON M5M 2X3

BROKEN SANDING BELTS

Product information

This past September, I purchased two Chapman sanding belts, medium grade, #85610, at the Fitler Lumber Company in Flin Flon, Manitoba. I paid a premium price for the Chapman belts because of your reputation. However, the belts have proved to be unsatisfactory, and I am returning them to you in a separate package (at a cost to me of $7.46).

Problem

The belt I have labelled #1 was used only 10 minutes before it broke. The belt labelled #2 was used only 5 minutes when the glue failed and it broke.

Inconvenience caused

I attempted to return the belts to Fitler's for a refund. The manager refused me a refund and said I'd have to write to you.

I am disturbed on two counts. First, I paid a premium price for your belts. I did not expect an inferior product. Second, does the retailer have no responsibility for the Chapman products he sells? Do I have to write to you every time I have a problem with one of your products?

Motivation for fair adjustment

I'm sure that Chapman is proud of its reputation and will want to adjust this matter fairly.

John Griffin

John Griffin

Figure 11-8 LETTER OF COMPLAINT

Oddly enough, most organizations welcome letters of complaint. They prefer customers who complain rather than customers who think "never again" when a mistake occurs and take their business elsewhere. Most organizations will go out of their way to satisfy complaints that seem at all fair. A skillful writer will use the adjustment letter as a means of promoting future business.

Letters of adjustment fall into two categories: those that grant the adjustment requested and those that refuse it. The first type contains good news and is easy to write. The second type is more difficult, as indicated by its common name: the bad-news letter.

THE GOOD-NEWS LETTER   When you are granting an adjustment, be cheerful about it. Remember, your main goal is to build goodwill and future business. Follow these three steps:

- Begin by expressing regret about the problem or stating that you are pleased to hear from the customer—or both. Keep in mind our earlier comments about the you-attitude while writing an adjustment letter.
- Explain the circumstances that caused the problem. State specifically what the adjustment will be.
- Handle any special problems that may have accompanied the complaint and close the letter.

Figure 11-9 shows you such a letter.

THE BAD-NEWS LETTER   A letter refusing an adjustment is obviously more difficult to write. You want, if possible, to keep the customer's goodwill. You want at the very least to forestall future complaints. In stating your refusal, you must exercise great tact.

Bad-news letters usually consist of five steps:

- Begin with a friendly opener. Try to find some common ground with the complainant. Express regret about the situation. Even though you may think the complaint is totally unfair, don't be discourteous. Incidentally, not everyone writes a letter as courteous as the one in Figure 11-8. Sometimes, people are downright abusive. If so, attempt to shrug it off. Just as you would not pour gasoline on a fire, don't answer abuse with abuse. Pour on some cooling words instead.
- Second, explain the reason for the refusal. Be very specific here and answer at some length. The very length of your reply will help convince the reader that you have considered the problem seriously.
- Third, at the end of your explanation, state your refusal in as inoffensive a way as possible.
- Fourth, if you can, offer a partial or substitute adjustment.
- Finally, close your letter in a friendly way.

Companies selling products are not the only organizations that receive letters of complaint. Public service organizations do, also. The letter that follows illustrates a refusal from such an organization—a provincial ministry of transportation. In this case, a citizen had written stating that a curved section of highway near her home was dangerous. She requested that the curve be rebuilt and straightened. The reply uses the strategy that we have outlined.

The goal of this letter is not to keep a paying customer, but to keep a taxpayer friendly. In either case, the strategy is to offer an honest, detailed, factual explanation in a cheerful way.

CHAPMAN PRODUCTS, INC.
1925 Jerome Street
Toronto, ON M5M 2X3

November 11, 1999

Mr. John Griffin
26 Shady Woods Road
White Bear Lake, MB R3M 1L9

Dear Mr. Griffin:

Expression of regret

Thank you for your letter of October 28. We're sorry that you had a problem with a Chapman product. But we are happy that you wrote to us about your dissatisfaction. We need to hear from our customers if we are to provide them satisfactory products.

Explanation of circumstances

The numbers on the belts you returned indicate that they were manufactured in 1990. Sanding belts, like many other products, have a "shelf life," and the belts you purchased had exceeded theirs. Age, heat, and humidity had weakened them.

Statement of adjustment

Mr. Griffin, we stand behind our products. Although we are sure that the belts you purchased were not defective when we shipped them, we wish to replace them for you. You are being shipped a box of 10 belts, medium grade. We're sure that these belts will live up to the Chapman name.

Handling of special problems

We also suggest that you look in the yellow pages of your telephone directory under "Hardware-Retail" for authorized Chapman dealers. We can only suggest to independent dealers how they should shelve and sell our products. We can exert more quality control with our own dealers. We know that you can find a Chapman dealer who will give you excellent service.

Sincerely,

Ahmad Attallah

Ahmad Attallah
Customer Service

AA/ay

copy: Fitler Lumber Company

Figure 11-9 Good-News Letter of Adjustment

Dear Mrs. Ferguson:

Friendly opener

Thank you for your letter concerning the section of Highway 50 near your home. The Ministry shares your concern about the safety of the highway, particularly the section between Prestonburg and St. Dennis, near which your home is located.

Reasons for refusal

Highway 50, as you mentioned, has many hills and curves and, because of the terrain, some steep embankments. However, its accident rate—3.58 accidents per million vehicle km—is far from the worst in the province. In fact, there are 64 other provincial highways with worse safety records.

We do have studies under way that will result ultimately in the relocation of Highway 50 to terrain that will allow safer construction. These things take time, as I'm sure you know. We have to coordinate our plans with municipal authorities and the federal government. Money is assigned to these projects by priority, and based on its accident rate, Highway 50 does not have top priority.

Accidents along Highway 50 are not concentrated at any one curve. They are spread out over the entire highway. Reconstruction at any one location would cause little change in the overall accident record.

Statement of refusal

Offer of substitution

For all the above reasons we do not anticipate rebuilding any curves on Highway 50. However, we are currently evaluating the need for guardrails along the entire length of the highway. Within a year we will probably construct guardrails at a number of locations. Most certainly, we will place a guardrail at the curve that concerns you. This should correct the situation to some extent.

Friendly close

We appreciate your concern. Please write to us again if we can be of further help.

The five-step strategy of the bad-news letter can be useful on many occasions. Any time you have to disappoint someone's expectations or you expect a hostile audience, consider using the bad-news approach.

Letter and Memorandum Reports

Many business reports run from two to five pages. They are too short to need the elements of more formal reports, such as title pages and tables of content. Instead, these short reports are often written as a letter or memo. Figure 11-10 shows a short report in memo form, and Figure 11-11 illustrates a report presented as a letter. All of the reports we discuss in Chapters 3 through 6 can be and often are written as memos or letters. All of the strategies discussed in Chapter 6, used singly or in combination, are found in letter and memorandum reports.

A common plan for either a letter report or a memo report calls for an introduction, a summary, a discussion, and an action step.

Introduction

Begin by telling the reader the subject and purpose of the report. Perhaps you are reporting on an inspection tour or summarizing the agreements reached in a consultation between you and the recipient. You may be reporting the results of a research project, or the beginning of one. Or you may be writing a progress report on a project that is under way but not

To:	Council Committee
FROM:	Operations Department
DATE:	April 27, 1995
SUBJECT:	BLUE BOX RECYCLING INFORMATION

Introduction

The new solid waste collection contract with Mid Ontario Disposal has resulted in some Blue Box recycling program improvements. It is hoped that these improvements will make the program easier to use, thereby increasing the number of people participating and the amount each household recycles.

Effective use of capitals and boldface

Newspaper, magazines and mixed paper can now be set out for collection mixed. As well, paperback books can now be included. The current description for these items is:

PAPER, MAGAZINES & NEWSPAPER

(Beside the Blue Box)

ALL PAPER INCLUDING NEWSPAPER, MAGAZINES, CATA-LOGUES and MIXED PAPER (including telephone books, paperback books, paper received in mail, writing paper, egg cartons and clean paper packaging) should be bundled and tied, or placed in an open grocery bag (if stacked) or placed in a clear plastic bag. Newspaper, magazines and mixed paper may be placed out for collection separately if desired. Brown paper (bags and packing paper) should be included with corrugated cardboard and boxboard.

Do **NOT** include windowed envelopes, hardcover books or soiled papers. No waxed paper or plastic or foil wrappings. No Christmas or party wrapping paper.

Cardboard and boxboard can now be set out for collection mixed. This will eliminate confusion, increase participation and capture rates. Cardboard and boxboard can still be set out for collection separately, if desired. The current description for these items is:

CORRUGATED CARDBOARD & BOXBOARD

(Beside the Blue Box)

CORRUGATED CARDBOARD & BOXBOARD must be flattened and tied in bundles no larger than 75 cm x 120 cm (30" x 48") and up to 25 cm (10") thick, or flattened and stuffed in a boxboard container (cereal box or

Figure 11-10 MEMORANDUM REPORT

Source: Reprinted with permission of the City of Orillia.

detergent box), or flattened and placed in an open grocery bag. Include
brown paper and boxboard tubes. Remove wood, plastic, metal, all food,
and liners from cereal boxes.

Do **NOT** include drinking boxes, milk cartons, waxed or coated boxes.

Program Costs And Revenue

Due to improving markets for recyclable material, revenue received by the City
for recycled materials now exceeds the cost of collection and processing. Even
without considering the cost of disposal of garbage, replacement landfill space, or
post-closure costs, it is now more economical for the City to collect recyclable
material than to collect garbage.

Collection Tonnage

In 1994, the City collected 6056 tonnes of garbage and 2387 tonnes of recyclable
material. It is hoped that with these program improvements that an additional 250
tonnes of material will be recycled in 1995.

Program Participation

The success of our diversion programs is a direct result of the enthusiastic response of the public to these relatively new programs. Our survey conducted
by Environment Youth Corps students last summer indicated that nearly all
households participated in the Blue Box program to some extent. As the public
become aware of the program improvements outlined above, higher participation
rates are expected for these materials.

PREPARED BY: RECOMMENDED BY:

P.G. Dance   *R.C. Erickson*
_____   _____
P.G. Dance, P.Eng.   R.C. Erickson.
Manager of Environmental Services   Director of Operations

PGD/pbj
bbinfo.rec

Figure 11-10   (CONTINUED)

April 17, 1995

City of Orillia
Public Works Operations Division
35 West Street North
P.O. Box 340
Orillia, Ontario
L3V 6J1

Attention: Mr. Peter Dance, P.Eng
               Manager of Environmental Services

Dear Mr. Dance:

Re: City of Orillia Landfill, 1994 Monitoring Report

Introduction

We are pleased to present our 1994 Monitoring Report for the City of Orillia Landfill. The report discusses the interpretation of the results of the 1994 monitoring program with consideration to historical results as well.

Conclusions

Based upon the interpretation, the following conclusions have been made:

a) The peat soils surrounding the site continue to attenuate the bulk of the contaminant load from the landfill;

b) The effect of the landfill on the on-site ground water in the peat and in the sand aquifer continues to slowly increase as predicted. The increasing concentrations of contaminants in the shallow ground water remain confined to the immediate vicinity of the landfill site. Landfill impact within the sand aquifer is detected within the limit of refuse and also at downgradient monitors;

c) Based on the observations of City of Orillia staff who visited the business operations of Granco Fuels and Huronia Tool and Machine, the elevated chloride and sodium levels in monitor 25 did not originate from these premises. Additional visit to Huronia Regional Center revealed a composting facility and snow dump area, but City of Orillia staff determined that surface water discharge would be towards Lake Simcoe, in the opposite direction of monitor 25. Notwithstanding, this monitor is not impacted by the landfill because it is upgradient from the waste;

d) The effect of the landfill on the inland waters (Mill Creek and Ben's Ditch) is negligible in comparison to the background water entering the site or to the water discharging from the Waste Water Treatment Centre. No measurable effect of the landfill on the inland surface water courses has been detected;

Figure 11-11 LETTER REPORT
Source: Reprinted with permission of the City of Orillia.

Page 2
City of Orillia
April 17, 1995

e) Lake Simcoe is not affected to a measurable degree by discharge of ground water from the landfill property; and

f) The surface water sampling program carried out to supplement Condition 15 has confirmed previous findings. The poor surface water quality at S7 and S8 is typical of urban settings and no specific discharges were detected.

Recommendations

Based upon the findings of the monitoring report, it is recommended that:

a) The existing swamp be maintained as a buffer in its present state and extent;

b) The 1995 monitoring program should remain the same as the 1994 program;

c) Monitors 2I-I, 24 and 27-II need to be replaced. The monitor pipe at 2I-I is able to spin within its casing. This indicates that the pipe could be broken and pose a potential pathway for monitor installation material to enter the monitor. Monitor 24 had been damaged by vandalism. Due to the low swampy area of this location, the most effective time to replace this monitor would be in the winter when frozen ground would permit easier access. An additional piezometer into the sand unit is proposed at this location. At monitor 27-II, the PVC pipe has probably shifted due to the settling of refuse, resulting in a bailor being stuck in the monitor and preventing ground water sampling. This monitor should be replaced in order for proper ground water sampling and determination of its chemistry. Also, future ground water collections at monitor 27-II should be performed with a stainless steel bailer to prevent cross contamination from successive sample events;

d) There is now a sufficient data base of water quality information to confirm previous findings. Condition 15 has therefore been met. It is recommended that further up-stream station sampling and testing be terminated. Stations S16 and S17 should continue to be part of the routine testing program but further refinement of upstream flow points is not justified;

e) No other remedial measures are required at this time; and

f) This report should be submitted to the MOEE for their approval.

Please contact us should you have any questions.

Yours very truly,
GARTNER LEE LIMITED

Steven Usner, M.Sc.,P.Eng.
Senior Hydrogeologist, Associate

TWWL:jw
Encl.

Figure 11-11 (CONTINUED)

completed. Whatever the subject and purpose are, state them clearly. If someone has requested the report, name that person. Typically, the introduction in a letter or memo report will not have a heading.

Summary

In most cases, the summary will be an executive summary and will have a heading labelling it as a summary. (See pages 214–215.) It will emphasize the things in the report important to an executive's decision-making process and state clearly any conclusions, recommendations, and decisions that have been reached. Often, the functions of the introduction and the executive summary are combined. When this is the case, the combination usually will not have a heading.

Discussion

Give your discussion a heading. You might label it simply as "Discussion," or perhaps call it "Findings," "Results and Discussion," or the like. Develop your discussion using the same techniques and rhetorical principles that you would use in a longer report. Remember to consider your audience as you do in longer reports. For example, if you are writing to an executive, do not fill your letter or memo with jargon and technical terms.

If you must report a mass of statistics, try to round them off. If absolute accuracy is necessary, perhaps you can give the figures in an informal table. Take advantage of word processing programs that make it possible to incorporate graphs into memos and letters following the principles developed in Chapter 10, "Graphical Elements." You may also find listing a useful technique in letters and memos. (See pages 81–82 and page 168.) Use subheadings just as you would in a longer report. (See pages 189–192.)

Action

If your letter or memo report recommends action on someone's part, include an action section with an "Action" or "Recommendation" heading. In this section, state—or sometimes, more diplomatically, suggest—what that action should be.

Planning and Revision Checklists

You will find the planning and revision checklists that follow Chapters 2 and 4, valuable in planning and revising any presentation of technical information. The following questions specifically apply to correspondence. They summarize the key points in this chapter.

General

Planning
- What is your topic and purpose?
- Who are your primary readers? Secondary readers? Do they have different needs? How can you satisfy all your readers?

continued >>

- Why will your readers read your letter or memo?
- What format will best suit the situation?
- Do you have all the information you need to address your letter or memo? Names, title, addresses, and so forth?

Revision
- Have you stated your topic and purpose clearly in the first sentence or two of your letter or memo?

- Have you met your readers' purpose?
- Have you avoided jargon and clichés?
- Does your correspondence demonstrate a you-attitude?
- Is your letter or memo clear, concise, complete, and courteous?
- Have you used your chosen format correctly? Checked for correct punctuation and spacing?

E-Mail

Planning
- Is your content suitable for e-mail transmission? Can you answer yes to these questions?
  Can your content be handled concisely?
  Is it of a fairly routine nature?
  Is confidentiality of no importance?
  If your e-mail message is going to an international reader, do you understand the style and content adjustments you may have to make?

Revision
- Does your e-mail message suit the medium? Is it concise, routine, and non-confidential?

International Correspondence

Planning
- Do you understand the major differences between North American business culture and the business culture of your correspondent?
- What adjustments will the cultural differences require? Will you need to deemphasize time constraints and emphasize human and organizational relationships?
- Will your style need to be more indirect, more formal, and less structured than similar correspondence with North American readers?

Revision
- Have you adopted a style suitable to your correspondent's culture? If need be, is your style more indirect, more formal, and less structured than it would be to a North American correspondent? Have you avoided placing blame for any problems? Have you emphasized human and organizational concerns and deemphasized time constraints?

Letters of Inquiry

Planning
- In what capacity are you making your request?
- What specifically do you want?

- Why do you need what you are requesting?
- Why are you making your request to this particular source?

continued >>

Revision
- Does your letter of inquiry identify you, state specifically what you want, establish your need for the information or material you request, tell the recipient why you have chosen him or her as a source, and close graciously?

Reply to a Letter of Inquiry

Planning
- Has the inquirer written to you as a private citizen or as a member of an organization?
- Can you answer the inquirer's questions point by point?
- Do you have or know of additional information or material that the inquirer would find useful?

Revision
- If you are replying to a letter of inquiry, have you answered it completely? Is there additional information you could refer the reader to or additional material you could send?

Letter of Complaint

Planning
- What specifically is the problem?
- What inconvenience or loss has the problem caused you?
- Do you have all the product information you need?
- What is the adjustment you want?
- How can you motivate the recipient to make a fair adjustment?

Revision
- Do you use a firm but courteous tone in your letter of complaint? Are you specific about the problem and about the adjustment you seek? Have you motivated the recipient to grant your request?

Letter of Adjustment

Planning
- Is the letter of adjustment good news or bad news?
- If good news, what circumstances caused the problem? Are there special problems that must be handled? What adjustment has been asked for? What adjustment can you offer?
- If bad news, what are the reasons for refusing the request for adjustment? Can you offer a substitute in place of the requested adjustment?

Revision
- Is your letter of adjustment courteous? Is the you-attitude evident?
- If your letter of adjustment is a bad-news letter, have you explained your refusal in an honest, detailed way? Have you expressed the refusal clearly but courteously? Have you offered a substitute adjustment? Have you opened and closed the letter in a friendly way?

continued >>

Letter and Memorandum Reports

Planning

- What are the occasion, subject, purpose, and audience for the report?
- Would lists, tables, and graphs help your discussion?
- What conclusions, recommendations, and decisions do you have to report?
- What action should be the outcome of the report?

Revision

- Is your letter or memorandum report well introduced and summarized? Do your headings reflect the content of the report? Have you used lists, tables, and graphs if they would help? Are your conclusions and recommendations clearly stated? Is any action needed or desired clearly stated?

Weblinks

How to Write Business Letters That Get Results
www.smartbiz.com/sbs/arts/bly48.html

Writing the Adjustment Letter
www.wuacc.edu:80/services/zzcwwctr/adjustltr-intro.txt

Writing Focused and Organized Memos
www.wuacc.edu:80/services/zzcwwctr/wrtmemos.txt

Exercises

1. Compose the letter called for in the following situation.

   You are a member of the permissions department at Educational Books, Inc. One of your responsibilities is to be sure that books published by your company are not unfairly copied for classroom use. You have learned from an American exchange professor at a Chinese university that one of the Chinese professors there is copying several chapters of one of your company's textbooks for distribution to his students. The book, *Communicating in Technology and Business*, by Jane Fisher, is available for worldwide sale. Such extensive copying clearly violates international copyright law, as covered by the Berne Convention and the Universal Copyright Convention. However, you also know that China routinely ignores such conventions.

   You learn from your informant that the Chinese professor, Li Kua-fan, teaches English. He is in his sixties and is a senior and respected member of the faculty. You wish to persuade the professor that buying the book for his students would be fairer to your company and the book's author and also in the best interest of his students. Write the body of a letter to the professor to accomplish that goal.

Before you compose your letter, see examples on pages 289–290 of how a letter written for a Canadian reader might be modified for a foreign reader. Review the information on pages 68–71. Check your library for books and articles on doing business with China. See what you can find on the World Wide Web. Accompany your letter with a note to your instructor detailing the sources you used and how they affected your audience analysis and the style and content of your letter.

2. Write an unsolicited letter of inquiry to some company asking for sample materials or information. If you really need the information or material, you may wish to mail the letter.

3. Imagine that you are working for a firm that provides a service or manufactures a product you know something about. Someone has written the firm a letter of inquiry asking about the service or product. Your task is to answer the letter.

4. Think about some service or product that has recently caused you dissatisfaction. Find out the appropriate person or organization to write to and write that person or organization a letter of complaint.

5. Swap your letter of complaint written for Exercise 4 for the letter of complaint written by another member of the class. Your assignment is to answer the other class member's letter. You may have to do a little research to get the data you need for your answer.

6. Write a memo to some university or college official or to an executive at your place of work. Many of the papers you have written earlier in your writing course are probably suitable for a memorandum format. Or you could choose some procedure, such as fall registration, and suggest a new and better procedure. Perhaps your memo could be to a professor suggesting course changes. A look at Figure 4-1 on page 53 could also suggest a wide range of topics and approaches that you could use in a memo.

THE STRATEGIES AND COMMUNICATIONS
OF THE JOB HUNT

If you are a student or a recent graduate, unfortunately, you can't take it for granted that you will get a good job immediately. In some cases, you may be competing with experienced workers for the same job. To help you in this difficult environment, in this chapter we cover the major steps of the job hunt: preparation, letters of application, résumés, and interviews.[1]

Preparation

What you can take for granted is that job hunting is nearly a full-time occupation. If you are still a student, it has to be at least a part-time occupation. Most professional jobs require that you follow a regular schedule and work 40 to 50 hours a week. Job hunting also requires that you schedule your time around various activities and, if you are still a student, that you spend at least 15 to 20 hours a week in the hunt. Your first task is to prepare for the hunt. That involves **self-assessment, gathering information about possible jobs**, and **networking**.

Self-Assessment

The goal of **self-assessment** is twofold. First and most important, you want to avoid pounding a square peg (you) into a round hole (the wrong job). You want to determine what jobs among the many possible would suit you the best: What kind of work can you do well and what kind of work pleases you? Secondly, in the job hunt, you'll be creating résumés, completing applications, and answering interview questions. Self-assessment will help you to list necessary details, such as dates, names, and job responsibilities, about past work and educational experiences.

In your self-assessment, you may ask yourself the following questions:

What are my strengths?
What are my weaknesses?
How well have I performed in past jobs?
Have I shown initiative?
Have I improved procedures?
Have I accepted responsibility?
Have I been promoted or given a merit raise?
Have I supervised or trained other staff?
How can I present myself most attractively?
What skills do I possess that relate directly to what the employer seems to need?
How and where have I obtained those skills?

To perform your self-assessment in a serious and systematic way, use the questionnaire provided in Figure 12-1.

When you have completed the questionnaire, you will have a good record of your work and educational experiences. You should have a good idea of what skills you have and what you like to do.

Using that information, match jobs and careers that you might have to your skills and interests. Two Human Resources Development Canada publications can help you make this match:

- *Job Futures: An Occupational Outlook.* Describes the educational requirements, duties, and job prospects for most occupations.
- *National Occupational Classification.* Describes in detail more than 12 000 occupations.

You can find these books in most university libraries and placement offices and in any Canada Employment Centre.

What if at the end of your self-assessment you either can't decide what you want to do or, worse, have decided that your major is in a field that no longer interests you? In either case you might seek professional job counselling. Many campus placement offices offer such help. You can also find counselling services through Canada Employment Centres throughout the country.

Software programs and Internet sites provide additional approaches to self-analysis. Programs such as Systems of Interactive Guidance and Information (Sigiplus), DISCOVER, and CHOICES provide modes of discovery and self-assessment for job preparedness. Additionally, when you use an Internet search engine and enter "career" and then "self-assessment," you gain access to an array of potentially useful sites. Locate those that meet your needs in helping you build the foundation for your application strategy.[2]

If you are reasonably sure of your career direction, your next step is to find where the jobs are that will lead in that direction.

Education and Training

College/University   Date   Specialization/Program   Degree/Diploma

_____   _____   _____   _____

Career-Related Courses: _____   _____
                          _____   _____
                          _____   _____

Supplementary Courses: _____   _____
                          _____   _____
                          _____   _____

Thesis   Projects   Presentations   Labs

_____   _____   _____   _____
_____   _____   _____   _____

Honours, Awards, Accomplishments: _____
                                    _____

Other Training: _____   _____
                  _____   _____

Skills, Knowledge Gained: _____   _____
                            _____   _____

Accomplishments: _____   _____

Work Experience

Career-related Positions:

Company   Dates   Position   Duties & Responsibilities

_____   _____   _____   _____
_____   _____   _____   _____
_____   _____   _____   _____

Other Positions:_____
Skills, Knowledge Gained: _____
                            _____
Accomplishments: _____

Activities

Professional (membership in associations,
positions held, committees served on): _____   _____
                                        _____   _____

Volunteer: Positions/Duties   Experience Gained

                    _____   _____
                    _____   _____

Extra-curricular (student groups and community involvement):

                    _____   _____
                    _____   _____

Other (athletics, hobbies, personal activities, and accomplishments):

                    _____   _____
                    _____   _____

Figure 12-1   SELF-ASSESSMENT QUESTIONNAIRE

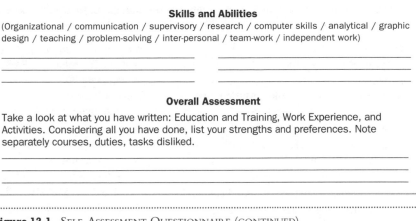

Skills and Abilities

(Organizational / communication / supervisory / research / computer skills / analytical / graphic design / teaching / problem-solving / inter-personal / team-work / independent work)

Overall Assessment

Take a look at what you have written: Education and Training, Work Experience, and Activities. Considering all you have done, list your strengths and preferences. Note separately courses, duties, tasks disliked.

Figure 12-1 SELF-ASSESSMENT QUESTIONNAIRE (CONTINUED)

Source: Material adapted from Bev Kahn, Manager of Community Services, U of T Career Centre, in *Career Options: The Graduate Recruitment Annual 1995/96 CACEE, ACSEE; Job Search Guide: Strategies for Professionals* (U.S. Dept. of Labor, Washington, D.C.: GPO 1993); *Looking at Yourself* (Take Charge-Self-Help Series #2 of 6); Government of Canada Human Resources; *Self-Assessment* (Looking for Work Series, #1) ACCIS—The graduate workforce professionals, 1991.

Information Gathering

Two good ways exist to discover and gather information about companies and organizations that offer the jobs you are seeking: You can research print publications, and you can research on the Internet. Both sources contain the information you need about where the jobs are, how much they pay, and how big a future such jobs have.

PRINT PUBLICATIONS In addition to the sources listed in Figure 12-2, consult magazines and newspapers that regularly carry business news such as the *Financial Post, The Globe and Mail,* and *Canadian Business.* To see what has recently appeared in the business press about a company, see the *Canadian Index* or *Canadian Business* and *Current Affairs* (CD-ROM version). Analyse the company to see what achievements it is most proud of and to determine its goals.

On-campus recruitment files and company literature binders, found in all campus placement offices, are a major source of information. They contain profiles of most major companies and many governmental organizations and include information about their products, services, locations, job opportunities, and even their management philosophy. For example, Dupont Canada's literature binder includes the statement you see in Figure 12-3.

THE INTERNET Online access to job sources is now available in all Canada Employment Centres and most campus career centres. The principal online source of employment information in Canada is the Electronic Labour Exchange, made available by Human Resources Development Canada. The Labour Exchange is a clearing house of information on job opportunities,

---

Company Websites, Annual Reports, Company Directories, Current Full-Text Business Databases, Electronic Job Searches

Annual Report Gallery
  www.reportgallery.com

Business City
  www.businesscity.com/doc/Mktinfo.htm

Canadian Company Capabilities
  www.strategis.ic.gc.ca/cdncc

Canadian Job Source Directory. Scarborough, ON:
Tri International, 1995 – (Annual).

Canadian Key Business Directory [CD-ROM].
  Toronto: Dun & Bradstreet of Canada (Annual).

Canadian Trade Index [CD-ROM]. Toronto:
  Canadian Manufacturer's Association (Annual).
  or **www.palantir.ca/the-alliance/public/cti.html**

CBCA Business and Current Affairs [CD-ROM].
  Toronto: Micromedia, 1996 – (Monthly).

Compact/D Canada [CD-ROM]. Bethesda, MD:
  Disclosure (Monthly).

Companies Online
  www.lycos.com

Corporate Affiliations Plus [CD-ROM]. New
  Providence, NJ: Reed Reference Electronic
  Publishing (Annual).

Forbes 500 Top Private Companies
  www.forbes.com:80/Privates/50index.htm

*Get Wired, You're Hired: The Canadian Guide to
Job Hunting Online.* Mark Swartz. Scarborough,
ON: Prentice-Hall Canada, 1997.

Hoovers Guide to Computer Companies [CD-ROM].
  Austin, TX: Reference Press in Association with
  Upside (Annual).

Hoovers Online
  www.hoovers.com

Lexis-Nexis [Online Database].
  Canada/CANCO/BUSFIN/ABI (Daily).

Moody's International Annual Reports [CD-ROM].
  New York: Moody's Investor's Service (Annual),
  or **www.moodys.com**

Moody's International Company Data [CD-ROM],
  or **www.moodys.com**

Scott's All Selectory [CD-ROM]. Don Mills, ON:
  Scott's Directories (Annual).

Sources
  www.sources.com

Strategis
  www.strategis.ic.gc.ca/engdoc/maintxt.html

Thomas Register [CD-ROM]. Palo Alto, CA: DIALOG
  Information Services (Annual), or
  www1.thomasregister.com/index.html

Wall Street Research Net
  www.wsrn.com/home/company/Research.html

Web 100
  www.w100.com

Yahoo Business and Economy
  yahoo.com/Business_and_Economy

Figure 12-2 CANADIAN JOB INFORMATION SOURCES AND STRATEGIES

serving both employers, who provide descriptions of the type of staff they need, and job-seekers, who are able to learn about local employment opportunities. The Electronic Labour Exchange can be used as a self-serve recruiting tool that matches employer job profiles with job-seeker profiles. It also provides access to the Job Bank, an electronic listing of job and business opportunities phoned in to Human Resource Centres of Canada by employers around the country.

Another useful site, available to students anywhere in Canada, is the University of Waterloo's Online Career Development Manual (**www.adm.uwaterloo.ca:80/infocecs/CRC/manual-home.html**). If you are in a high-tech field, you may also want to check the sites of the CEO Group (**www.hitechcareer.com**) and The Lendman Group (**www.lendman.com**). Many companies advertise their technical positions on these sites.[3]

We believe that employees are the Company's most important assets. Some of the key commitments we make are to:

- Attract, challenge and retain highly talented people
- Build strong positive relationships with employees
- Live the principles of pay and employment equity
- Make safety excellence a priority
- Create stimulating and exciting jobs
- Give employees opportunities for maximum personal growth and development
- Encourage our people to be initiators, to self-manage, and to set challenging objectives in line with corporate goals.
- Recognize and reward employee contributions to Company results
- Provide compensation and benefits which compete favourably in our communities and business areas
- Establish an open and participative atmosphere

Figure 12-3 DuPont Canada's Management Philosophy

Source: Human Resources & Communications Department, DuPont Canada, *People and Business Together* (DuPont, n.d.).

We cannot emphasize enough how important this preparation is. Most job seekers do not even know such rich information sources exist. Many who do know do not take advantage of them. You now know what some of the sources are; the rest is up to you.

Networking

Networking is a way of finding both job information and job opportunities. Networking starts with broadcasting the news that you are looking for a job. Whom do you tell? Start with family and friends, including grandparents, aunts, uncles, cousins, and in-laws. Talk to professors, clergy, and favourite teachers. Don't overlook family doctors, dentists, lawyers, bankers, barbers, and hairdressers. If there are professional associations that cover fields you are interested in, join them. Figure 12-4 lists some associations by province and territory. For information about these organizations and those in other fields, see *Directory of Associations in Canada*.

Visit or phone local businesses or organizations, particularly those that have jobs you might be interested in, and ask for the names of people who have or manage jobs like the ones you want. Call such people and ask if you can come by for a talk. Make it clear that you are not looking for a job interview but rather an informational interview to seek advice about looking for work or how to prepare for a certain kind of job.

If you have a name you can use, such as a relative or teacher, it will help in making the initial contact. But don't let not having a name deter you. Try to make the contact anyway. Expect a lot of people to put you off, but you

British Columbia

Applied Science Technologists
and Technicians of British
Columbia
10767-148 Street
Surrey, British Columbia V3R 0S4
(604) 585-2788
www.asttbc.org

Association of Professional
Engineers and Geoscientists of
British Columbia
Sperling Plaza #7, #210,
200-4010 Regent Street
Burnaby, British Columbia
V5C 6N2
(604) 430-8035
www.apeg.bc.ca

Alberta

Alberta Society of
Engineering Technologists
2100 Canada Trust Tower,
10104-103 Avenue North West
Edmonton, Alberta T5J 0H8
(403) 425-0626
www.aset.ab.ca

The Association of Professional
Engineers, Geologists and
Geophysicists of Alberta
15th Floor, Tower One,
Scotia Place
10060 Jasper Avenue
Edmonton, Alberta T5J 4A2
(403) 426-3990
www.apegga.com

Saskatchewan

Saskatchewan Applied Science
Technologists and Technicians
363 Park Street
Regina, Saskatchewan S4N 5B2
(306) 721-6633

Association of Professional
Engineers & Geoscientists
of Saskatchewan
#104, 2255-13 Avenue
Regina, Saskatchewan S4P 0V6
(306) 525-9547

Manitoba

Certified Technicians and
Technologists Association of
Manitoba Inc.
602-1661 Portage Avenue
Winnipeg, Manitoba R3J 3T7
(204) 783-0088
www.cttam.com

Association of Professional
Engineers of Manitoba
850A Pembina Highway
Winnipeg, Manitoba R3M 2M7
(204) 474-2736

Ontario

Ontario Association of Certified
Engineering Technicians and
Technologists
#404, 10 Four Season Place
Etobicoke, Ontario M9B 6H7
(416) 621-9621
www.oacett.org

Professional Engineers of Ontario
25 Sheppard Ave. W. Ste. 1000
North York, Ontario M9B 6H7
(416) 224-1100
www.peo.on.ca

Québec

Ordre des inginieurs du Québec
2020, rue University, 18e étage
Montréal, Quebec H3A 2A5
(514) 845-6141

Nova Scotia

Society of Certified Engineering
Technicians and Technologists
of Nova Scotia
PO Box 159 DMPS
Dartmouth, Nova Scotia B2Y 3Y3
(902) 463-3236

Association of Professional
Engineers of Nova Scotia
1355 Barrington Street
PO Box 129
Halifax, Nova Scotia B3J 2M4
(902) 429-2250
www.apens.ns.ca

New Brunswick

New Brunswick Society of
Certified Engineering Technicians
& Technologists
535 Beaverbrook Court, Ste. 105
Fredericton, New Brunswick
E3B 1X6
(506) 454-6124

Association of Professional
Engineers of New Brunswick
535 Beaverbrook Court, Ste. 105
Fredericton, New Brunswick
E3B 1X6
(506) 458-8083
www.apenb.ca

Prince Edward Island

Association of Professional
Engineers of Prince Edward
Island
549 North River Road
Charlottetown, Prince Edward
Island C1E 1J6
(902) 566-1268

Figure 12-4 PROFESSIONAL ASSOCIATIONS

Source: "Career Options in Hi-Tech and Engineering," 1998–99 edition published by
The Canadian Association of Career Educators and Employers (CACEE).

Newfoundland	Yukon	Northwest Territories
Association of Professional Engineers and Geo-Scientists of Newfoundland 120 Torbay Rd. PO Box 21207 St. John's, Newfoundland A1A 5B2 (709) 753-7714	Association of Professional Engineers of the Yukon Territory PO Box 4125 Whitehorse, Yukon Y1A 3S9 (867) 667-6727	Association of Professional Engineers, Geologists and Geophysicists of the Northwest Territories #5, 4807-49 Street Yellowknife, Northwest Territories X1A 3T5 (867) 920-4055

Figure 12-4 (CONTINUED)

will likely be pleasantly surprised at how many people will talk to you. People like to give advice, and, in particular, they like to talk about their occupation. Furthermore, organizations are on the lookout for enterprising self-starters. In calling on the organization, you are showing yourself to be such a person. In these interviews, you are the interviewer. To help people remember you, make up business cards that look like the one in Figure 12-5. If you have a profession, such as computer programmer, add it to the card beneath your name. To help yourself remember whom you have seen and what you have learned, keep good records as you proceed. Write down names (accurately spelled), addresses, and phone numbers. Record what seems to be important to the people you talk to about work in general and the specific work that interests you.

All this may strike you as an informal way of looking for work, and it is. But research shows that 80 to 85% of people find work in precisely this way. Partly, this is true because many jobs never reach a formal search. They are filled through contacts of the kind we are telling you to develop. Also, two-thirds of all jobs are in companies with fewer than 25 employees.[4] Small companies

James (Jimmy) Chow

B. Eng., Mechanical Engineering

2382 Dundas Street West
Toronto, Ontario M6S 1A8

(416) 555-8444

e-mail **jchow@hotmail.com**

Figure 12-5 BUSINESS CARD

often don't participate in formal searches such as sending recruiters to university and college campuses. You have to search them out, and networking is probably the best way to do it.

More formally, you can network with organizations specifically set up to help people find work. Foremost among these, if you are a student, is your placement office. Many large firms regularly call on placement offices to seek new employees. The placement office schedules campus interviews for graduating students, and many offices have job fairs once or twice a year. Job fairs, to which many companies send representatives, are good places to gather information and to network. In addition, the placement office maintains a library of books about how to seek employment and usually has a file of brochures and articles about companies and organizations that might interest you.

Hunting for a job is a hard job in itself. There is a great deal of help out there, but you can't be passive. You have to actively search out job information and opportunities. Another way to do that is with letters of application and résumés, which we discuss next.

The Correspondence of the Job Hunt

In some cases, the first knowledge prospective employers will have of you is the **letter of application** and **résumé** that you send to them. A good letter of application, sometimes called a *cover letter*, and résumé will not guarantee that you get a job, but bad ones will probably guarantee that you do not. In this section we'll describe how to prepare letters of application and résumés, and then discuss several follow-up letters needed during the job hunt.

Letter of Application

Plan the mechanics of your **letter of application** carefully. Buy the best quality neutral (white, ecru, grey) bond paper. This is not the time to skimp. Plan to type or word process your letter, of course, or have it done. Use a standard typeface; do not use italics. Make sure your letter is mechanically perfect, free from erasures and grammatical errors. Be brief but not telegraphic. Keep the letter to one page. Don't send a letter duplicated in any way. Accompany each letter with a résumé. We have more to say about résumés later.

Pay attention to the style of the letter and the résumé that accompanies it. The tone you want in your letter is one of self-confidence. You must avoid both arrogance and humility. You must sound interested and somewhat eager, but not fawning. Do not give the impression that you must have the job, but do not come across as though you don't care, either.

When describing your accomplishments in the letter and résumé, use action verbs. They help to give your writing brevity, specificity, and force. For example, don't just say that you worked as a sales clerk. Rather, tell how you maintained inventories, sold merchandise, prepared displays, implemented new procedures, and supervised and trained new clerks. Here's a sampling of such words:

administered	edited	oversaw
analysed	evaluated	planned
assessed	exhibited	produced
conducted	expanded	reduced costs
created	improved	reorganized
designed	managed	supported
developed	operated	was promoted
directed	organized	wrote

You cannot avoid the use of "I" in a letter of application, but take the you–attitude as much as you can. Think about what you can do for the prospective employer. The letter of application is not the place to be worried about salary and pension plans. Above all, be mature and dignified. Forget about tricks and flashy approaches. Write a well-organized, informative letter that highlights the skills the company most desires, according to your analysis. We will discuss the application letter in terms of a beginning, a body, and an ending.

THE BEGINNING   Beginnings are tough. Do not begin aggressively or cutely. Beginnings such as "WANTED: An alert, aggressive employer who will recognize an alert, aggressive young forester" will usually send your letter into the wastebasket. If it is available to you, a bit of legitimate name dropping is a good beginning. Use this beginning only if you have permission and if the name dropped will mean something to the prospective employer. If you qualify on both counts, begin with an opener like this:

Dear Ms. Marchand:

Professor P.K. Rathor of Cambrian University's Food Sciences faculty has suggested that I apply for the position of Assistant Dietician. In June I will receive my Bachelor of Science degree in Food Sciences from Cambrian University. Also, I have spent the last two summers working in food preparation for Memorial Hospital here.

Remember that you are trying to arouse immediate interest about yourself in the potential employer. Another way to do this is to refer to something about the company that interests you. Such a reference demonstrates that you have done your homework. Then try to show how some preparation on your part ties you into this special interest. See Figure 12-6 on page 320 for an example of such an opener.

Sometimes the best approach is a simple statement about the job you seek accompanied by something in your experience that fits you for the job, as in this example:

Your opening for an assistant dietician has come to my attention. In June of this year, I will graduate from Cambrian University with a Bachelor of Science in Food Sciences. I have spent the last two summers working in food preparation for Memorial

Hospital here. I believe that my education and work experience qualify me to be assistant dietician on your staff.

Be specific about the job you want. As the vice-president of one firm told us, "We have all the people we need who can do anything. We want people who can do something." Quite often, if the job you want is not open, the employer may offer you an alternative one. However, employers are not impressed with vague statements such as, "I'm willing and able to work at any job you may have open in research, production, or sales."

THE BODY   In the body of your letter, select items from your education and experience that show your qualifications for the job you seek. Remember always, you are trying to show the employer how well you will fit into the job and the organization. In selecting your items, it pays to know what employers value the most. One thorough piece of research[5] shows that for recent graduates, employers give priority as follows:

First priority
Major field of study
Academic performance
Work experience
Plant or home-office interview
Campus interview

Second priority
Extracurricular activities
Recommendations of former employer
Academic activities and awards

Third priority
Type of university or college attended
Recommendations from faculty or school official

Fourth priority
Standardized test scores
In-house test scores

Try to include information from the areas that employers seem to value the most, but emphasize the areas in which you come off best. If your grades are good, mention them prominently. If you stand low in your class—in the lowest quarter, perhaps—maintain a discreet silence. Speak to the employer's interests, and at the same time highlight your own accomplishments. Show how it would be to the employer's advantage to hire you. The following paragraph, an excellent example of the you-attitude in action, does all these things:

I understand that the research team of which I might be a part works as a single unit in the measurement and collection of data. Therefore, team members need a general knowledge and ability in fishery techniques as well as a specific job skill. I would like to point out that last summer I worked for Fisheries and Oceans on a fish population study. On that job, I gained electro-fishing and seining experience and learned how to collect and identify aquatic invertebrates.

By being specific about your accomplishments, you avoid the appearance of bragging. It is much better to say, "I was president of my senior class," than to say, "I am a natural leader."

One tip about job experience: The best experience is that which relates to the job you seek, but mention job experience even if it seems unrelated. Employers feel that a student who has worked is more apt to be mature than one who has not.

Do not forget hobbies that relate to the job. You are trying to establish that you are interested in, as well as qualified for, the position.

Do not mention salary unless you are answering an advertisement that specifically requests you to. Keep the you–attitude. Do not worry about pension plans, vacations, and coffee breaks at this stage of the game. Keep the prospective employer's interests in the foreground. Your self-interest is taken for granted.

If you are already working and not a student, construct the body of your letter in much the same fashion. The significant difference is that you will emphasize work experience more than education. Do not complain about your present employer. Such complaints will lead the prospective employer to mistrust you.

In the last paragraph of the body, refer the employer to your enclosed résumé. Mention your willingness to supply additional information such as references, letters concerning your work, research reports, and transcripts.

THE ENDING   The goal of the letter of application is an interview with the prospective employer. In your ending, request this interview. Your request should be neither humble nor overaggressive. Simply indicate that you are available for an interview at the employer's convenience and give any special instructions needed for reaching you. If the prospective employer is in a distant city, indicate (if you can) some convenient time and place where you might meet a representative of the company, such as at the convention of a professional society. If the employer is really interested, you may be invited to visit the company at its expense.

THE COMPLETE LETTER   Figure 12-6 shows the complete letter of application. Take a minute to read it now. The beginning of the letter shows that the writer has been interested enough in the company to investigate it. The desired job is specifically mentioned. The middle portion highlights the course work and work experience that relate directly to the job sought. The close makes it convenient for the employer to arrange an interview.

The word processor is a great convenience when you are composing application letters. It allows you to store basic paragraphs of your letter that you can easily modify to meet the needs and interests of the organization you are writing to. Such modification for each organization is truly necessary. Human resources officers read your letter and its accompanying résumé in about 30 seconds or so. If you have not grabbed their interest in that time, you are probably finished with that organization.

March 23, 1999

635 North River Road
Watertown, P.E.I. C6A 7N1

Mr. Morrell R. Solem
Director of Research
Price Industries, Inc.
2163 Airport Drive
Mississauga, ON M4K 2L8

Dear Mr. Solem:

Opener showing knowledge of company

Specific job mentioned

I read in the January issue of <u>Metal Age</u> that Dr. Charles E. Gore of your company is conducting extensive research into the application of X-ray diffraction to problems in physical metallurgy. I have conducted experiments at Watertown Polytechnic Institute in the same area under the guidance of Professor John J. O'Brien. I would like to become a research assistant with your firm and, if possible, work for Dr. Gore.

Highlights of education

In June, I will graduate from WPI with a Bachelor of Science degree in Metallurgical Engineering. At present, I am in the upper 25 percent of my class. In addition to my work with Professor O'Brien, I have taken as many courses relating to metal inspection problems as I could.

Highlights of work experience

For the past two summers, I have worked for Watertown Concrete Test Services, where I have qualified as a laboratory technician for hardened concrete testing. I know how to find and apply the specifications of the A.S.T.M. This experience has taught me a good deal about modern inspection techniques. Because this practical experience supplements the theory I learned at school, I could fit into a research laboratory with a minimum of training.

Reference to résumé

You will find more detailed information about my education and work experience in the résumé enclosed with this letter. I can supply job descriptions concerning past employment and the report of my X-ray diffraction research.

Request for interview

In April, I will be in Toronto to attend this year's conference on Developments in Physical Metallurgy. Would it be possible for me to talk with some member of Price Industries at that time?

Sincerely yours,

Jane E. Lucas

Jane E. Lucas

Enclosure

....

Figure 12-6 LETTER OF APPLICATION

The Résumé

A résumé provides your prospective employer with a convenient summary of your education and experience. As in the letter of application, good grammar, correct spelling, neatness, and brevity—ideally, only one page—are of major importance in your résumé. Although the traditional paper résumé is still commonplace, more and more organizations are using electronic media for screening their job candidates. Therefore, it's important to have versions of your résumé available in the following formats:

- Traditional paper
- E-mail format
- Scannable format
- World Wide Web format

Because the content and organization of different kinds of résumés are similar, regardless of format, we discuss those aspects first and then discuss the different formats.

CONTENT AND ORGANIZATION   The résumés shown are in the three formats most commonly used in Canada: **chronological, functional,** and **combination.** All have advantages and disadvantages.

CHRONOLOGICAL FORMAT   The advantages of a chronological résumé such as the one shown in Figure 12-7, are that it's traditional and acceptable. If your education and experience show a steady progression toward the career you seek, the chronological résumé portrays that progression well. Its major disadvantage is that your special capabilities or accomplishments may sometimes get lost in the chronological detail. Also, if you have holes in your employment or educational history, they show up clearly.

Contact Information   In a chronological résumé, put your name and address at the top. Give your phone number, including the area code. If you have a fax number or e-mail address, include that as well.

A heading like "Résumé" is still sometimes used, but we advise against it because it competes with the applicant's name for prominence. Don't waste space stating the obvious.

CAREER OBJECTIVE   Some applicants use the career objective entry to specify the kind of work they want to do and sometimes the industry or service area where they want to do it, like this:

A challenging food service management position in a metropolitan hospital.

The career objective is often omitted since it is stated in the letter of application. If you choose to use it, place the career objective entry immediately after the address and align it with the rest of the entries.

EDUCATION   For most students, educational information should be placed before business experience. People with extensive work experience, however, may choose to put that first. List the colleges or universities you have attended in reverse chronological order: in other words, list the institution you attended most recently first, the previous one next, and so on. Include

Highlights of education in reverse chronological order

Fragmentary sentences used

Summary of work experience in reverse chronological order

James (Jimmy) Chow

2382 Dundas St. West, Toronto, Ontario, M6S 1A8

(416) 555-8444

e-mail jchow@hotmail.com

EDUCATION

| 1995 to 1998 | Bachelor of Engineering (Mechanical Engineering) |
| | Ryerson Polytechnic University, Toronto, Ontario |

Major Areas of Study

| Design | Mechanical Components, Experimental Stress Analysis, Mechanics of Materials, Engineering Graphics |
| Computer Systems | FORTRAN, BASIC, CAD/CAM, APT, Manual N/C Programming |

Engineering Projects

- Wrote N/C program to produce cross-section of centrifugal pump
- Co-ordinated team of four to design chainsaw/auger conversion kit and consulted with design staff for several major firms; received offer from manufacturer to test prototype

| 1994 to 1995 | First year Applied Science |
| | University of Windsor, Windsor, Ontario |

CAREER-RELATED WORK EXPERIENCE

Summer 1997   **Assistant Technologist**

American Motors Diesel Division, Oshawa, Ontario

- Thoroughly researched and correlated Canadian and American safety standards (CMVSS and MVSS) to determine acceptability
- Completed technical and economic feasibility studies pertaining to employee suggestions

OTHER WORK EXPERIENCE

PART-TIME   **Sales Clerk**
1993 to 1997   North West Clothing, Rexdale, Ontario

- Increased sales by 10% through congenial manner and effective response to customer needs

PROFESSIONAL   OACETT – Associate Member
MEMBERSHIPS   SAE – Affiliate Member

INTERESTS   Technical and scientific magazines, particularly <u>Road and Track</u> and <u>Popular Mechanics</u>

Active member of High Park Tennis Club

REFERENCES   Available on request

Figure 12-7 CHRONOLOGICAL RÉSUMÉ

Source: Adapted with permission from *Career Options: The Graduate Recruitment Annual* (Science & Engineering).

your high school if you plan to include high school accomplishments else-where in the résumé or if its identity or location has significance.

Give your degree or diploma, your major, your minor if you have one, and the date or expected date of your graduation. List core or elective courses only if that information is a useful supplement to the name of the degree. Add anything distinctive such as honours, and special projects, in addition to the program information. If included, the G.P.A. goes in this section.

EMPLOYMENT HISTORY   As you did with your educational experience, put your work experience in reverse chronological order. To save space and to avoid the repetition of I throughout the résumé, use phrases rather than complete sentences. The style of the sample résumés makes this technique clear. As we advise you to do in the letter of application, emphasize the ex-periences that show you in the best light for the kinds of jobs you seek. Use active verbs in your descriptions.

Do not neglect less important jobs of the sort you may have had in high school, but use a summary approach for them. You would probably put col-lege placements and work-study programs here, although you might choose to put them under education. Indicate achievements, for example, positions of progressive responsibility, supervisory roles, significant accomplishments that added value to the position.

PERSONAL BACKGROUND   You may wish to provide personal information about yourself. Such information can be presented under a number of differ-ent headings: "Skills," "Community Involvement," "Hobbies & Activities," and the like. Personal information can complement work experience, indicating de-sirable qualities and skills you possess. Volunteer experience—as a Big Brother or Big Sister, for example—can demonstrate your maturity, compassion, and sense of responsibility, along with more practical assets like time management. Volunteer experience may also allow you to highlight specific skills that you have not yet had the opportunity to put to use at work: chairing a committee, plan-ning a major fundraiser, editing a newsletter.

Knowledge of a second or third language can be a selling point in this age of globalization. Recent travels indicate an interest in broadening knowledge and experience. Even hobbies and sports, carefully selected, can show you are a well-rounded person. But be cautious: A "generic" list of hobbies ("reading, sports, movies, spending time with my friends") is not going to impress an in-terviewer with your ability to make a unique contribution to his or her firm.

Certain kinds of personal information—age, marital status, ethnic back-ground among them—are not appropriate for inclusion in résumés. Interviewers are prohibited by Canadian human rights legislation from ask-ing such questions, and many do not welcome résumés that cloud hiring decisions by answering questions that cannot be asked. When in doubt, check with your university or college career centre or the human rights commis-sion in your province.

REFERENCES   You have a choice with references. You can list several ref-erences with addresses and phone numbers or simply put in a line that says

"References available on request." Both methods have an advantage and a dis-advantage. If you provide information on references, a potential employer can contact them immediately, but you use up precious space that might be better used for more information about yourself. Conversely, if you don't pro-vide the reference information, you save the space but put an additional step between potential employers and information they may want. It's a judgment call, but, on balance, we favour saving space by omitting the ref-erence information. Your first goal is to interest the potential employer in yourself. If that happens, then it will not be difficult to provide the reference information at a later time. It's smart to have a list of references ready to hand over at the interview.

In any case, have at least three references available. Choose from among your professors and past employers people who know you well and are likely to say positive things about you. Get their permission, of course. Also, it's a smart idea to send them a copy of your résumé. If you can't call on them personally, send them a letter that requests permission to use them as a ref-erence, reminds them of their association with you, and sets a time for their reply, like this:

> Dear Ms. Shar:
>
> In June of this year, I'll graduate from Watertown Polytechnic Institute with a B.Sc. in metallurgical engineering. I'm getting ready to look for work. May I have permission to use you as a reference?
>
> During the summers of 1993 and 1994, I worked as a laboratory technician in your testing lab at Watertown. They were good summers for me, and I qualified, with your help, to carry out several ASTM tests.
>
> I will send my résumé out to some companies by March 15 and will need your reply by that time. I enclose a copy of my résumé for you, so that you can see what I've been doing.
>
> Thanks for all your help in the past.

FUNCTIONAL FORMAT   A main advantage of the functional résumé (Figure 12-8) is that it allows you to highlight the experiences that show you to your best advantage. Extracurricular experiences show up particularly well in a functional résumé. Its major disadvantage is that you don't show as clearly a steady progression of work and education. Also, the functional résumé is a newer format than the chronological and some employers may not find it as acceptable.

The address portion of the functional résumé is the same as in the chrono-logical. After the address, you may provide a career objective line if you like.

For education, simply give the university from which you received your degree, your major, and your date of graduation.

The body of the résumé is essentially a classification. You sort your expe-riences—educational, employment, extracurricular, volunteer—into categories that reveal capabilities related to the jobs you seek. Remember that in addition to professional skills, employers want good communication skills and good interpersonal skills. Possible categories are *technical, professional, team building, communication, research, sales, production, administration,* and *consulting.*

Francine LeBlanc
512 Cliffside Boulevard
Halifax, NS B3H 4L5
(902) 555-5996
leblanc@sympatico.ca

JOB OBJECTIVE

To work as part of an environmental research team with a focus on Aquatic Ecology and Fish Biology.

SKILLS AND ABILITIES

ANALYTICAL

– transferred, set up and maintained a microsatellite DNA fingerprinting laboratory at the Halifax Museum
– used qualitative and quantitative methods to analyse parasites as part of field and laboratory research for Memorial University

RESEARCH

– snorkelled and SCUBA dived as part of extensive field work research project on fish reproductive behaviour for Memorial University
– collected behavioural data, samples of fish, and tagged fish as part of field and laboratory research for Memorial University
– conducted extensive field work in Terrestrial and Freshwater Biology, Tropical Ecosystems, Marine Biology, and Tropical Marine Biology

INTERPERSONAL

– interacted with academic professionals in the biological field and worked as part of an academic team (Memorial University)
– developed excellent public relations skills dealing with parents while acting as Lifeguard and Swimming Instructor at the Glenview Swim Club, Toronto, ON

LEADERSHIP/TRAINING

– organized creative and safe learning environments for swimming lessons (Glenview Swim Club)
– provided exercise and health expertise to new members at the St. Clair Fitness Club,Wolfville, N S
– designed personalized exercise programs (St. Clair Fitness Club)
– instructed in the use of weight lifting equipment (St. Clair Fitness Club)

EDUCATION

B.Sc., Honours Environmental Science, 1998

Dalhousie University

ADDITIONAL INFORMATION

– SCUBA Licence
– Swim Team–Gold Medal 1994
– Rock Climbing Club
– Enjoy travel, cooking, skiing

REFERENCES

Available on request

Figure 12-8 Functional Résumé

Source: Adapted with permission from *Career Options: The Graduate Recruitment Annual.* (Science & Engineering).

Summary of work experience in reverse chronological order

Achievements that suggest skills and abilities listed

Carmen Santos

102 Patterson Street   Home: (403) 555-3504
Calgary, Alberta T2P 4X9   Fax: (403) 555-4988
                                                          csantos@hotmail.com

EDUCATION
June 1998   Mechanical Engineering Diploma
                   Southern Alberta Institute of Technology

EXPERIENCE

Summer 1997   ASSISTANT PROJECT MANAGER
                   Ibiscus Steel Ltd., Calgary, Alberta

1995-Present   PARTS DEPARTMENT SALESPERSON
                   Canadian Tire, Calgary, Alberta

Summer 1994   SALESPERSON
                   Canoe Express, Calgary, Alberta

SKILLS AND ABILITIES

TECHNICAL
- Produced detail drawings of mechanical equipment for course project
- Specified materials to meet static/dynamic load and stress for Ibiscus Steel Ltd.
- Led team on project to specify machining operations, production methods and tooling for the manufacture of innovative car wash equipment
- Applied time and method study techniques to production of centrifugal pump for final year project

SALES
- Researched product availability for clients at Canadian Tire
- Named employee of the month at Canadian Tire
- Increased sales by 20% at Canoe Express
- Responded effectively to customer inquiries at Canoe Express

TIME MANAGEMENT
- Effectively managed a part-time job, full-time studies, volunteer work and maintained a GPA of 3.85
- Handed in all assignments on time
- Increased sales while training new staff at Canoe Express

INTERPERSONAL
- Displayed tact and diplomacy dealing with Canadian Tire customers
- Commended for professionalism, sensitivity and poise in dealing with a very difficult parts department supplier at Canadian Tire

ADDITIONAL INFORMATION

Elected President of the Mechanical Engineering Club
Student member of the Mechanical Engineering Association
Nominated Team Leader on all final year projects
Voted most popular student in high school graduating class
Team captain of high school hockey team
Enjoy tennis, squash, hiking, painting and auto repair

REFERENCES

AVAILABLE ON REQUEST

Figure 12-9 COMBINATION RÉSUMÉ

Source: Adapted with permission from *Career Options: The Graduate Recruitment Annual.* (Science and Engineering).

The best way to prepare a functional résumé is to brainstorm. Begin by listing some categories that you think might display your experiences well. Brainstorm further by listing your experiences in those categories. When you have good listings, select the categories and experiences that show you in the best light. Remember, you don't have to display everything you've ever done, just the things that might strike a potential employer as valuable.

COMBINATION FORMAT   The combination résumé (Figure 12-9) is just what its name implies: a combination of the chronological and functional formats. The combination résumé highlights skills and achievements (like the functional résumé), while placing them in a chronological context. Its main advantage is its flexibility: It allows you to emphasize the strongest side of your application. Like the chronological résumé, though, the combination résumé exposes gaps in your work experience, and should therefore be used cautiously.

PAPER RÉSUMÉS   Use good paper in a standard colour and make sure that the print is sharp and clear. It's best if your letters and résumés are on matching paper. Make the résumé visually pleasing. Leave generous margins and allow for ample spacing. Use distinctive headings and subheadings. The samples in Figures 12-7, 12-8, and 12-9 provide you with good models of what a résumé should look like. Take a look at them now before you read the following comments.

To whom should you send letters and résumés? When answering an advertisement, follow whatever instructions are given there. When operating on your own, send them, if at all possible, to the person within the organization for whom you would be working; that is, the person who directly supervises the position. This person normally has the power to hire for the position. Your research into the company may turn up the name you need. If not, don't hesitate to call the company switchboard and ask directly for the name and title you need. Write to human resources directors only as a last resort. Whatever you do, write to *someone* by name. Don't send "To Whom It May Concern" letters on your job hunt. It's wasted effort. Sometimes, of course, you may gain an interview without having sent a letter of application—for example, when recruiters come to your campus. When you do, bring a résumé with you and give it to the interviewer at the start of the interview. He or she will appreciate this help tremendously. Furthermore, the résumé gives the interviewer a point of departure for questions, which often helps to structure the interview to your best advantage.

ELECTRONIC RÉSUMÉS   Not surprisingly, with the increasing use of computers and the Internet in business, traditional paper formats frequently have to be modified to become electronically useful. We describe three such modifications: the scannable résumé, the e-mail résumé, and the World Wide Web résumé.

Scannable Résumé   A scannable résumé is a paper résumé that has been modified so that it can be electronically scanned. Many organizations now scan the paper résumés they receive and enter their information into a special database for quick retrieval by key words. (See Figure 12-10.) For example, if the company needs an environmental specialist, the hiring manager scours the database for words such as *environment, ecology*, and the like. Only job candidates with the key words on their résumés will be considered. In a scannable résumé, therefore, you must make sure that the key words of your occupation, often nouns, are present in abundance. You must get through the computer to be considered by a human reader.

For your résumé to be scannable, you must also modify its format. Ordinarily, a scanner reads résumés from left to right and often makes mistakes if it encounters such features as italics, underlining, changes of typeface, and small sizes of type. In designing your scannable résumé, therefore, adopt the following guidelines:

- Display all information in a single column.
- Align all information on the left margin.
- Use spaces instead of tabs to separate headings from text, or place headings on a separate line.
- Use a single typeface.
- Use all capital letters for your name and major headings.
- Use 12-point type.
- Do not use italics and underlining.
- Do not use rules and borders.
- Submit a clean and crisp laser-printed copy.
- Do not fold or staple the résumé.

E-Mail Résumé   Often organizations bypass paper résumés entirely, preferring to solicit and receive candidate information electronically. Such organizations, for example, might announce their job openings on the World Wide Web and invite applications with a link to the e-mail address of the hiring manager.

Like the scannable résumé, the e-mail résumé is subject to key-word searches. Compose it accordingly, being sure to include the appropriate key words. (See Figure 12-11.)

E-mail uses none of the formatting elements and special characters available in typical word processing programs—no boldface, italics, variations in type size or typeface, and so forth. Essentially, creating an e-mail résumé is like typing with a typewriter, including the uniform spacing of letters. In addition, the line length is restricted to sixty-five characters (including spaces), or approximately five inches (12.7 cm). If you are creating your résumé with a word processing program, keep these restrictions in mind: Set the width of your page for five inches, and eliminate all special characters and formatting. Follow these guidelines:

- Display all information in a single column.
- Align all information on the left margin.
- Use spaces instead of tabs to separate headings from text or place headings on a separate line.
- Use all capital letters for your name and major headings.

FRANCINE LEBLANC
512 Cliffside Boulevard
Halifax, N.S.
B3H 4L5
(902) 555-5996
leblanc@sympatico.ca

JOB OBJECTIVE
To work as part of an environmental research team with a focus on Aquatic
Ecology and Fish Biology.

SKILLS AND ABILITIES
Analytical:
Transferred, set up and maintained a microsatellite DNA fingerprinting laboratory
at the Halifax Museum.
Used qualitative and quantitative methods to analyse parasites as part of field
and laboratory research for Memorial University.

Research:
Snorkelled and SCUBA dived as part of extensive field work research project on
fish reproductive behaviour for Memorial University.
Collected behavioural data, samples of fish, and tagged fish, as part of field
and laboratory research for Memorial University.
Conducted extensive field work in Terrestrial and Freshwater Biology, Tropical
Ecosystems, Marine Biology, and Tropical Marine Biology.

Interpersonal:
Interacted with academic professionals in the biological field and worked as
part of an academic team (Memorial University).
Developed excellent public relations skills dealing with parents while acting as
Lifeguard and Swimming Instructor at the Glenview Swim Club, Toronto, ON.

Leadership/Training:
Organized creative and safe learning environments for swimming lessons
(Glenview Swim Club).
Provided exercise and health expertise to new members at the St. Clair Fitness
Club, Wolfville, NS
Designed personalized exercise programs (St. Clair Fitness Club).
Instructed in the use of weight lifting equipment (St. Clair Fitness Club).

EDUCATION
B.Sc., Honours Environmental Science, 1995
Dalhousie University

ADDITIONAL INFORMATION
SCUBA Licence
Swim Team—Gold Medal 1994
Rock Climbing Club
Enjoy travel, cooking, skiing.

REFERENCES
Available on request.

Figure 12-10 FUNCTIONAL RÉSUMÉ IN SCANNABLE FORMAT

CARMEN SANTOS
102 Patterson Street
Calgary, Alberta
T2P 4X9
Home: (403) 555-3504
Fax: (403) 555-4988
csantos@hotmail.com

EDUCATION
June 1998: Mechanical Engineering Diploma, Southern Alberta
Institute of Technology.

EXPERIENCE
1997, Summer: Assistant Project Manager, Ibiscus Steel Ltd.,
Calgary, Alberta.
1995-Present: Parts Department Salesperson, Canadian Tire,
Calgary, Alberta.
1994, Summer: Salesperson, Canoe Express, Calgary, Alberta.

SKILLS AND ABILITIES
Technical:
Produced detail drawings in mechanical equipment for course
project.
Specified materials to meet static/dynamic load and stress for
Ibiscus Steel Ltd.
Led team on project to specify machining operations, production
methods, and tooling for the manufacture of innovative car
wash equipment.
Applied time and method study techniques to production of
centrifugal pump for final year project.

Sales:
Researched product availability for clients at Canadian Tire.
Named employee of the month at Canadian Tire.
Increased sales by 20% at Canoe Express.
Responded effectively to customer inquiries at Canoe Express.

Time Management:
Effectively managed a part-time job, full-time studies, and volun-
teer work and maintained a GPA of 3.85.
Handed in all assignments on time.
Increased sales while training new staff at Canoe Express.

Interpersonal:
Displayed tact and diplomacy dealing with Canadian Tire customers.
Commended for professionalism, sensitivity and poise in dealing
with a very difficult parts department supplier at Canadian Tire.

ADDITIONAL INFORMATION
Elected President of the Mechanical Engineering Club.
Student member of the Mechanical Engineering Association.
Nominated Team Leader on all final year projects.
Voted most popular student in high school graduating class.
Team captain of high school hockey team.
Enjoy tennis, squash, hiking, painting, and auto repair.

REFERENCES
Available upon request.

Figure 12-11 COMBINATION RÉSUMÉ IN E-MAIL FORMAT

World Wide Web Résumé   Technologically sophisticated companies all over the world use the search engines of the World Wide Web (WWW) to scour for résumés of promising job candidates. Creating a World Wide Web résumé, therefore, offers you a worldwide opportunity to locate a job. (See Figure 12-12.)

In designing your résumé, adopt all the guidelines for creating a WWW site (see pages 155–159). Incorporate a variety of internal links so that visitors to your résumé site will interact with the pages. For example, the address of a former employer could be a link that opens a window to his or her e-mail address. The listing of your major and minor could link to a page that identifies pertinent courses. The mention of a special project could link to a detailed description of the online version of that project.

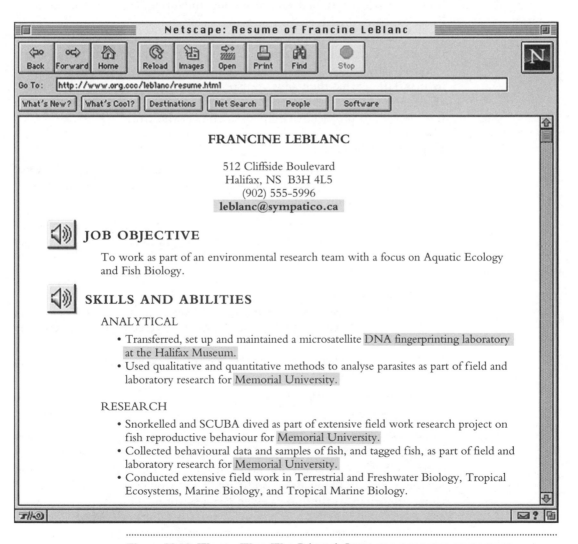

Figure 12-12 WORLD WIDE WEB RÉSUMÉ. LINKS ARE INDICATED BY SHADING.

A WWW résumé has multimedia possibilities. In addition to the usual listing of information, you could add pertinent graphics, sound, and animation. Use audio to speak directly to prospective employers about your most important job skills.

Especially remember to register your site with all appropriate search engines—this is how prospective employers will locate you. Also, remember to fill your résumé with the key words that prospective employers will use to conduct their search. Finally, be sure to include a link to your e-mail address. That is how interested employers will most likely contact you.

Those who are reluctant to make such personal information available on the Net might prefer to post their résumé on a job-seeker's register. One such site is the National Graduate Register (http://ngr.schoolnet.ca/ngr/house), which is designed exclusively for students and recent graduates and matches résumés with employers across the country.

The WWW offers a rich variety of job finding services. When you e-mail your résumé to such a service or submit specific biographical information electronically, it is then automatically compiled in a standardized résumé format. The service then adds your résumé to its international database of available employees, thus making your résumé readily accessible through the Internet to prospective employers all over the world.

Follow-Up Letters

Write follow-up letters (1) when you have had no answer to your letter of application in two weeks; (2) after an interview; (3) when a company refuses you a job; and (4) to accept or refuse a job.

NO ANSWER   When a company has not answered your original letter of application, write again. Be gracious, not complaining. Say something like this:

April 26, 1999

Dear Mr. Souther:

On April 12, I applied for a position with your company. As I have not heard from you, I have enclosed copies of my letter and résumé, in case the originals have been misplaced.

If you have already reached some decision concerning my application, could you please let me know.

I look forward to hearing from you.

Sincerely yours,

AFTER AN INTERVIEW   Within a day, follow up your interview with a letter. Such a letter draws favourable attention to yourself as someone who understands business courtesy and good communication. Express appreciation for the interview. Draw attention to any of your qualifications that seemed to be important to the interviewer. Express your willingness to live with any special conditions of employment such as relocation. Make clear you want the job and feel qualified to do it. If you include a specific question in your letter, it may hasten a reply. Your letter might look like this one:

Dear Ms. Marchand:

Thank you for speaking with me last Tuesday about the position you have open for an assistant dietician.

Working in a hospital food service relates well to my experience and interests. The job you have available is one I am qualified to do. A feasibility study I am currently writing as a senior project deals with a hospital food service's ability to provide more varied diets to people with restricted dietary requirements. May I send you a copy next week when it is completed?

I understand that my work with you would include alternating weekly night shifts with weekly day shifts. This requirement presents no difficulty for me.

Tuesdays and Thursdays are best for me for any future interviews you may wish, but I can arrange a time at your convenience.

Sincerely yours,

AFTER A JOB REFUSAL   When a company refuses you a job, good tactics dictate that you acknowledge the refusal. Express thanks for the time spent with you, and state your regret that no opening exists at the present time. If you like, express the hope that they may consider you in the future. You never know; they might.

ACCEPTING OR REFUSING A JOB   Writing an acceptance letter presents few problems. Be brief. Thank the employer for the job offer and accept the job. Settle when you will report for work and express pleasure at the prospect of working for the organization. A good letter of acceptance might read as follows:

Dear Mr. Solem:

Thank you for offering me a job as research assistant with your firm. I happily accept. I can begin work by 1 July as you have requested.

I look forward to working with Price Industries and particularly to the opportunity of doing research with Dr. Gore.

Sincerely yours,

Writing a letter of refusal can be more difficult. Be as gracious as possible. Be brief but not so brief as to suggest rudeness or indifference. Make it clear that you appreciate the offer. If you can, give a reason for your refusal. The employer who has spent time and money in interviewing you and corresponding with you deserves these courtesies. And, of course, your own self-interest is involved. Some day you may wish to reapply to an organization that for the moment you must turn down. A good letter of refusal might look like this one:

Dear Ms. Lofranco:

I enjoyed my visit to the research department of your company. I would very much have liked to work with the people I met there. I thank you for offering me the opportunity to do so.

After much serious thought, however, I have decided that the research opportunities offered me in another job are closer to the interests I developed at the University. Therefore, I have accepted the other job and regret that I cannot accept yours.

I appreciate the courtesy and thoughtfulness that you and your associates have extended me.

Sincerely yours,

Interviewing

The immediate goal of all your preparation and letter and résumé writing is an interview with a potential employer. Interviews come about in various ways. If you network successfully, you will obtain interviews that allow you to ask questions of people already on the job. Although these are information-seeking interviews, if you impress the person you are talking to, they may turn into interviews that assess your potential as an employee. Your letters and résumés may get you interviews. Recruiters may come to your campus and schedule screening interviews with graduating students. As their name suggests, screening interviews are preliminary interviews from which the recruiters choose people to continue the process.

Continuing the interview process often means multiple interviews at the organization's headquarters. In one day you might interview with human resources people, the person who would be your boss if you were employed, and perhaps his or her boss. If you make it to the point where you are offered a job, you will probably have an interview in which you negotiate the details of your job, salary, and benefits. All this can be quite stressful. The better prepared you are, the more easily it will go. The screening and follow-up interviews follow a somewhat similar pattern. We discuss them first and then give you some advice about negotiation.

The Interview

If you have prepared properly, you should show up at the interview knowing a good deal about the organization. As one interviewer stated: "If they don't know anything about our company—are they really interested in us?"[6]

For interviews you should be well groomed and dressed professionally. Arrive at the place of the interview early enough to be relaxed. Shake hands firmly but not aggressively, and make eye contact. Give the interviewer a copy of your résumé, and, when the interviewer sits down, sit down comfortably. Body language is important. Be neither tense nor too casual.

Most interviews follow a three-part pattern. To begin with, the interviewer may generate small talk designed to set you at ease. Particularly at a screening interview, the interviewer may give some information about the company. This is a good chance for you to ask some questions that demonstrate that you have done your homework about the company. But don't force your questions on the interviewer.

Most of the interview will be taken up with questions aimed at assessing your skills and interests and how you might be of value to the organization. A well-done self-assessment obviously is a necessity in answering such questions. Figure 12-13 lists some commonly asked questions. If you prepare answers for them, you should be able to handle most of the questions you are likely to receive. In your answers, relate always to the organization. To the question, "What do you want to be doing five years from now?" the answer "Running my own consulting firm" might bring the interview to an early close.

To the question, "What can you tell me about yourself?" the interviewer really doesn't expect an extended life history. This question provides you with the opportunity to talk about your work and educational experiences and your skills. Try to relate your skills and experience to the needs of the organization. Don't overlook those interpersonal and communication skills essential to nearly every professional job. In your answer to this and other questions, be specific in your examples. If you say something like "I have good managerial skills," immediately back it up with an occasion or experience that supports your statement.

The question "Why do you want to work for us?" allows you to display what you have learned about the organization. In answering this question, you should again show that what you have to offer meshes with what the company needs.

The question about how you would spend your life if you won ten million dollars is an interesting one. "Lolling around the beach" is obviously the wrong answer, but so might be "I'd continue to work for your corporation." What the question is intended to get at are those worthwhile things in your life that you really enjoy doing and would do even without pay. Building houses for Habitat for Humanity or setting up sports programs for inner-city youths might qualify as good answers.

In answering questions about your strengths and weaknesses, be honest, but don't betray weaknesses that could eliminate you from consideration. "I can't stand criticism," would likely finish you off. "Sometimes, I don't know when to quit when I'm trying to solve a problem," given as a weakness could be perceived as a strength.

- What can you tell me about yourself?
- What are your strengths and weaknesses?
- What do you want to be doing five years from now?
- Do you know much about us? Why do you want to work for us?
- We're interviewing ten people for this job. Why should you be the one we hire?
- What in your life are you most proud of?
- Here is a problem we had (interviewer describes problem). How would you have solved it?
- If you won ten million dollars in a lottery, how would you spend the rest of your life?
- Why do you want a career in your chosen field?
- Which school subjects interested you the most/least? Why?

Figure 12-13 FREQUENTLY ASKED INTERVIEW QUESTIONS

In the last part of the interview you will likely be given a chance to ask some questions of your own. It's a good time to get more details about the job or jobs that may be open. Ask about the organization's goals. "What is the company most proud of?" is a good question. Don't ask these questions just to ask questions. The interview is a good time for you to find out if you really want to work for an organization. Not every organization is going to be a good fit for what you have to offer and what you want to do. Unless the interviewer has raised the question of salary and benefits, don't ask questions about these matters.

If you really want to go to work for the organization, make that clear before the interview ends. But don't allow your willingness to appear as desperation. At some point in the interview, be sure to get the interviewer's name (spelled correctly!), title, address, phone number, and fax number (usually, you can simply ask the interviewer for his or her card). You'll need them for later correspondence. When the interviewer thanks you for coming, thank him or her for seeing you and leave. Don't drag the interview out when it's clearly over.

Negotiation

Interviewers seldom bring up salary and benefits until either they see you as a good prospect or they are sure they want to hire you. If they offer you the job, the negotiation is sometimes done in a separate interview. For example, your future boss may offer you the job and then send you to negotiate with the human resources staff.

Sometimes, the negotiator may offer you a salary. At other times, you may be asked to name a salary. How do you know what to accept or what to ask for? You may have received useful salary information through your networking activities. Also, you can find such information through research. Figure 12-14 shows the Statistics Canada information categories for salary ranges. Research will give you not a specific salary but a salary range. If asked to name a salary, do not ask for the bottom of the range. Ask for as near the top as you reasonably can. The negotiator will respect you for knowing what you are worth. However, balance the compensation package—vacations,

---

Salaries & Ranges, 72-002

Average Hourly Wages of Full-time Jobs, by Firm Size, 75-001E

Employment Income, by Detailed Occupation, by Sex, by Activity, 93-332

High Technology Industries, Average Annual Earnings, 75-100E

Labour Market, Distribution of Jobs by Wage Level, 71-538E

Workers, Rates, by Industry, by Unionization, 75-001E

Figure 12-14 SOURCES FOR SALARY RANGES
Source: Statistics Canada, Library Services Division, *Statistics Canada Catalogue,* 1994.

pension plans, health care, educational opportunities, and so forth—against the salary. Some compensation packages are worth a good deal of money and may allow you to take a lower salary.

Before and After the Interview

If you have not participated in job interviews before, you should practise them. Get together with several friends. Using the information you have gathered, roleplay several interviews. As two of you play interviewer and interviewee, the others act as observers. Appraise each other honestly. In particular, look for strengths and weaknesses in the interviewees' answers, diction, grammar, and body language. Practise until you feel comfortable with the process.

When interviews are over, write down your impressions as soon as you can. Were there unexpected questions? How good were your answers? What did you learn about the organization? What did you learn about a specific job or jobs? Did anything make you uncomfortable about the organization? Do you think you would fit in there? By the next day, get a thank-you note (letter or fax) off to the interviewer (See page 332).

Planning and Revision Checklists

You will find the planning and revision checklists that follow Chapter 2, "Composing" (pages 11-34), and Chapter 4, "Writing for Your Readers" (pages 50-77), and at the back of the book valuable in planning and revising any presentation of technical information. The following questions specifically apply to the job hunt. They summarize the key points in this chapter and provide a checklist for planning and revising.

Preparation

- Have you completed the self-assessment questionnaire in Figure 12-1?
- Do you have a complete record of your past job and educational experiences?
- Do you know your strengths and weaknesses, your skills, and your qualifications for the jobs you seek? Do you have clear career objectives?
- Do you need professional career counselling?
- Have you researched the Internet and the sources in Figure 12-2 to find job information?
- Have you found organizations that fit your needs?
- Have you started your networking?
- Have you had business cards made?
- Have you called on businesses and set up informational interviews?

continued >>

- Have you joined a professional organization relevant to your career field?
- Have you located agencies and individuals who can help you in your job hunt?

- Have you kept good records of your networking?

Correspondence

Planning

For your letter of application:
- Do you have the needed names and addresses?
- What position do you seek?
- How did you learn of this position?
- Why are you qualified for this position?
- What interests you about the company?
- What can you do for the organization?
- Can you do anything to make an interview more convenient for the employer?
- How can the employer reach you?

For your résumé:
- Do you have all the details needed of your past educational and work experiences? Dates, job descriptions, schools, majors, degrees, extracurricular activities, etc.?
- Which résumé form will suit your experience and capabilities best? Chronological? Functional? Combination?
- Do you need to prepare your résumé in electronic formats? What key words will you use?
- In a functional or combination résumé, which categories would best suit your experience and capabilities?
- Do you have three references and permission to use their names?
- What follow-up letters do you need to write?

Revision

- Do your letter of application and résumé reflect adequate preparation and self-assessment?

- Are your letter of application and résumé completely free of grammatical and spelling errors? Are they well designed and visually appealing?

For the letter of application:
- Have you the right tone: self-confident without arrogance?
- Does your letter show how you could be valuable to the employer? Will it raise the employer's interest?
- Does your letter reflect a sure purpose about the job you seek?
- Have you highlighted the courses and work experience that best qualify you for the job you seek?
- Have you made it clear you are seeking an interview and made it convenient for the employer to arrange one?

For the résumé:
- Have you chosen the résumé type that best suits your experiences and qualifications?
- Have you limited your résumé to one page or at most two pages?
- Have you put your educational and work experience in reverse chronological order?
- Have you given your information in phrases rather than complete sentences?
- Have you used active verbs to describe your experience?
- Does the personal information presented enhance your job potential?
- Do you have permission from three people to use their names as references?

continued >>

- If you are using a functional résumé, do the categories reflect appropriately your capabilities and experience?
- Has your combination résumé zeroed in on a recognizable career objective? Do the achievements listed under each heading demonstrate that skill or capability?
- Are the follow-up letters you have written gracious in tone?

- Have you followed up every interview with a letter? Does that letter invite further communication in some way?
- Does your letter of acceptance of a job show an understanding of the necessary details, such as when you report to work?
- Does your letter of refusal make clear that you appreciate the offer and thank the employer for time spent with you?

Interviews

Planning

- Have you found out as much about the organization as you can? Its products, goals, locations, and so forth?
- Have you practised interviewing, using the questions in Figure 12-13?
- Do you have clothes appropriate for interviewing?
- Do you have good questions to ask the interviewer?
- Do you know the salary range for the jobs you seek?

Revision

- Did you answer questions well? Which answers need improving?
- Did the interviewer ask any unexpected questions?
- How did the interviewer respond to your questions? Did he or she seem to think they were relevant?
- How well do you think you did? Why?
- Do you think your career goals and this organization are a good fit?

Weblinks

Archeus Online: Resume Writing Resources
www.golden.net/~reswri.htm

Canadian Jobs Catalogue
www.kenevacorp.mb.ca

Translating Resumes for the Internet
www.nytimes.com/library/jobmarket/0107sabra.html

Exercises

1. Work out a schedule for your job hunt. Allocate time and set dates for the following stages:
   - Self-assessment
   - Job information

- Networking
- Letter of application
- Résumé
- Interview practice

2. Complete for yourself a summary of your self-assessment. Complete and turn in to your instructor a summary of your job information search, a networking plan, a sample letter of application and résumé, and a summary of the salary ranges for entry-level jobs in your field.

3. In groups of four, plan and carry out practice interviews as described on page 337. Everyone in the group should get the chance to play interviewer and interviewee once.

4. Write a letter to some organization applying for full- or part-time work. Brainstorm and work out in rough form the three kinds of résumés: chronological, functional, and combination. Choose the one that suits your purposes best, and work it into final form to accompany your letter. It may well be that you are seeking work and can write your letter with a specific organization in mind.

5. Write one of the following job-search letters, then exchange letters with a classmate and provide constructive advice on each other's letter:
   a) A *Networking* letter (used to initiate informational interviews in order to research a particular career area or type of job).
   b) A *Thank-you* letter (used to follow up a job interview or informational interview).
   c) An *Acceptance* letter (used to accept a job offer and confirm terms of employment).
   d) A *Withdrawal* letter (used to withdraw your application from consideration by other organizations).
   e) A *Refusal* letter (used to decline an offer of employment).
   f) A *Rejection follow-up* (used in cases where you are not selected for a position and to investigate the potential for an opportunity in the future).[7]

DEVELOPMENT OF REPORTS

Although reports may generally be classified as informative or analytical, many reports that you write as part of your job will not fall neatly into one of these two categories. In fact, your greatest challenge as a writer will be to determine how to design a report that is best suited for whatever assignment you receive. A report assignment may not call precisely for an information report, a recommendation report, a feasibility study, or an empirical research report. For example, you may be told to "write a report summarizing what we have done in our meetings this week"; "write a report discussing our major problems in choosing the best toxic clean-up plan for this neighbourhood of 200 single-family houses"; "write a report explaining to our client the cheapest way we have found for providing utilities"; "explain the best design for a pump that will remove 1100–1900 litres of flood water per hour from golf course fairways located along creeks." Each of these situations incorporates characteristics of the different report types listed above. The question, then, is how do you go about designing any report, for any purpose?

To help you answer that question, we provide two sample reports in this chapter, each developed to meet a different situation. Study and analysis of each report will show you how the writers developed their reports to meet their situations. Applying what you learn will help you write your reports to meet your situations.

The Variable Nature of Reports

Any type of report can be presented as a formal report or a letter or memo report.

Formal reports include all or most of the elements discussed in Chapter 9—transmittal letter, title page, list of illustrations, abstract, summary, glossary, and appendices. Chapter 14 discusses the formal report format.

Letter and memo reports are short reports, seldom more than five pages long. Because they are shorter, they do not need the complex format of formal reports. Memo reports remain within the organization; letter reports go outside the organization. You can find examples of letter and memo reports in Chapter 11, "Correspondence," and Chapter 14, "Development of Analytical Reports." Figures 13-1 and 13-2 are memo reports.

Liability and Report Writing

Before discussing report design, we want to stress that all reports carry legal responsibility. Reports, like letters and instructions, can be used as legal documents. They document your activities as an employee and suggest your competence in pursuing your work. For those reasons, your reports should always be carefully written. They should be accurate, mechanically correct, effectively designed, and visually pleasing. In short, they should testify to your competence and your ability to think logically and precisely. When you write a report to a client, he or she will expect your information to be accurate. The client will expect to be able to make financial and technical decisions based on the accuracy and clarity of your reports. If your work is not clear, if it is inaccurate, the client can hold you legally responsible for any costs incurred as a result of your reports.

Because reports become permanent records of your work, you want to be sure that if they are read by litigants, by readers you do not know, or by anyone at any time, they present a positive picture of you and the professional manner in which you approach your work.

Producing the kind of document that achieves its purpose, a communication that you can send with confidence, begins and ends with the composing process, which we emphasize throughout this book. As you analyse audiences, your relationship with these audiences, the context that prompted your report, and the contexts in which it is being written and received, always look for ways in which your report could be misconstrued. As you plan, organize, write, revise, and edit, be sure to look for other ways your message could be interpreted. When necessary, revise to avoid any misinterpretation. Care in developing every document you write is the best defence against your writing being used to discredit you or your organization.

General Structure of Reports

Writing effective reports involves four considerations, which we highlight from the general composing process:

- Understanding what you want your readers to know
- Understanding their perspective on the information you will present
- Applying your knowledge of how people read and process information to the development and presentation of the message

- Choosing content, style, and tone suitable for your audience, the message, and your relationship to both in the organizational context

In short, good report writing begins with good planning. Because employees are often overwhelmed with paperwork, your reports, like everything you write, need to be designed to encourage audiences to read them. Therefore, you will want to carefully apply the principles covered in Chapter 8 on document design and Chapter 9 on the main design elements of reports.

Sample Report #1

The following situation explains the background, rationale, and purpose of Figure 13-1, a good example of a document intended to report information.

Graham and Rosenberg is an architectural consulting firm that specializes in analysing construction problems. The membership of a historic Nova Scotian church has hired Graham and Rosenberg to determine why the chimneys of the church are leaking and to recommend what should be done about the problem. First Church is, of course, interested in the cost of correcting the problems. Tim Fong, the managing engineer on the First Church project, writes an internal report to Eben Graham, one of the principals of Graham and Rosenberg, who is dealing directly with the church committee on repairs. Tim's main purpose is to let Eben Graham know what the team has done on the First Church project so that Graham can phone the chairperson of the church committee about the progress of the study. Eben Graham requires project reports—periodic and final—from all managing engineers on all projects so that he knows what's going on and can inform clients regularly. In a sense, this is an internal status report that shows you the characteristics of a good informal memo report. Refer to Figure 13-1 as you review these characteristics.

1. *State the subject of your informal report clearly.* All reports need clear titles. Informal reports are no exception. A busy reader with a dozen items to read will often make a decision to read an internal company report based on the subject line. For example,

   SUBJECT: Description of First Church Masonry, Oldtown, NS

   is not as effective as

   SUBJECT: Status of Investigation of Masonry Deterioration and Leakage, First Church, Oldtown, NS

   The subject line below tells the reader the purpose of the report and the meeting where the report will be discussed. Adding the date of the meeting is also useful in aiding the reader's memory.

   If a report requires action by readers, you may want to add that immediately below the subject line:

   SUBJECT: Recruiting Meeting—October 1, 1999—Change in Hiring Policies for Part-Time Research Technicians.

| TO: | Eben Graham | **DATE:** | August 20, 1999 |

TO: Eben Graham   **DATE:**   August 20, 1999

FROM: Tim Fong

SUBJECT: Status of Investigation of Masonry Deterioration and Leakage, The First Church, Oldtown, NS

Jane Hazel, James Portales, and I have examined two of the chimneys of The First Church. The following points should aid you in preliminary conversations with First Church to inform them of the extent of damage. We will have a final letter report for the Church by 99 10 01 that will include repair estimates for all three chimneys and the roof.

Conclusions

The two chimneys we have examined are badly deteriorated and require extensive repairs to stop the leakage and to eliminate an increasing danger of falling debris.

(1) Leakage through faulty flashing can be stopped easily and effectively by repairing the flashings.

(2) Leakage through the stone masonry cannot be stopped effectively because the chimney masonry is badly deteriorated. The stones in the chimneys have shifted, thereby enlarging the stone joints and creating horizontal surfaces that catch water. Water entering the masonry can bypass the lead counterflashing internally and enter the building. Freeze-thaw action on the wet stone masonry has slowly pushed the stones apart. The stones in the chimneys are not mechanically tied together to prevent movement.

(3) Unless major repairs are made to the two chimneys and the bell tower, significant deterioration will occur in wood decking and masonry. The damage will cause dangerous conditions from falling debris. Eventually, the structural safety of the church will be threatened.

Recommendations

(1) We recommend removal of any chimney not needed. The work should include removal of the chimneys to below the roof level, repair of all deteriorated wood about the chimney, installation of a new roof deck, and installation of new roofing slate to match the existing roof.

(2) Any chimney scheduled to remain should be demolished and reconstructed with the exterior stones. Reconstruction should include new clay flue liners, steel reinforcing in the horizontal joints of the stone masonry, and new stainless steel or copper through-wall flashings. The roofing around the chimney should be repaired with new metal base flashing of the same metal used for the through-wall flashing.

Figure 13-1 Sample Report #1

Eben Graham   -2-   August 20, 1999

(3) The wood components of the deck should be thoroughly examined and replaced or repaired, as required by the rotted conditions. Repairs should include exploratory operations into hidden conditions to ensure all deteriorated wood is repaired.

(4) Reconstruction of the interior finishes on the church should be delayed until all repair work is complete and tested.

Field Observations

Examination of both the interior and the exterior of both chimneys shows that:

Chimney No. 1

Chimney 1 has extensive problems with wood and masonry.

Interior Observations

* The chimney is constructed of brick below the roof deck.

* The undersides of the roof deck and joists are water stained on four sides of the chimney. The heaviest staining occurs on the north side of the chimney, which is the low point of the surrounding roof.

* An eavestrough has been installed at the low side of the chimney to catch leakage water and direct it to trash barrels.

* The low header in the roof deck framing on the north side of the chimney opening is wet and extensively rotted, allowing easy insertion of a two-inch pocket knife. Large pieces of the rotted wood are easily removed by hand.

* The remaining structural components surrounding the chimney are sound, based on our visual examination from the attic space.

Exterior Observations

* The chimney is capped with roofing cement and fabric membrane (See Photo 1).

* The mortar joints have been coated with a caulking material (See Photo 1 and Photo 2).

* A cricket made of copper sheet metal is located on the roof above the chimney (See Photo 3). There is one small crack in a soldered seam on the ridge of the cricket.

* After lifting the counterflashing on the cricket, we found a large hole in the membrane (See Photo 3). Water draining over the roof and onto the cricket enters through this hole into the building.

Detailed observations *(margin note)*

Figure 13-1 (CONTINUED)

Eben Graham   -3-   August 20, 1999

* Some of the granite blocks in the chimney have shifted, and the mortar joints are open slightly.

Chimney No. 2

Our examination shows that Chimney 2 is also in a highly deteriorated state.

Interior Observations

* The roof deck and structural components surrounding the chimney are stained from water leakage, but all components are sound, as far as we can tell without removing any decking.

Exterior Observations

* The chimney is capped with roofing cement and fabric membrane.

* The mortar joints have been coated with a caulking material.

* The flue lining is brick, which has deteriorated. The mortar joints of the lining are heavily eroded (See Photo 4).

* The granite blocks that form the exterior width of the chimney have shifted outward, leaving many of the horizontal and vertical stone joints open (See Photo 5).

* Some horizontal stone joints are completely open. We examined these joints at the corners of the chimney for the presence of metal ties between stones. We found no ties.

* We saw no defects in the metal flashings at the base of the chimney.

General Observations of the Roof Structure

We are currently examining the roof surfaces of The First Church to determine the presence of deterioration resulting from the leakage about the chimneys. We will send results of these findings to you by 99 09 25 along with photos that support our observations.

We still need to examine Chimney No. 3 carefully, but our visual observations suggest that the problems with No. 3 are similar to those of No. 1 and No. 2.

Future work

We plan to provide photos for Chimney No. 3 as well as sections of the roof, if visual inspection of the roofing near No. 3 suggests that water damage has occurred.

Figure 13-1 (CONTINUED)

Contact information

> Eben Graham   -4-   August 20, 1999
>
> Please contact
>
> Jane Hazel about interior observations (ext. 2165)
>
> James Portales about exterior observations (ext. 2171).
>
> I will be in Fredericton for the structural design conference until August 25.

Figure 13-1 (CONTINUED)

ACTION REQUIRED: Attached forms must be completed by all departments by June 15, 2000.

2. *In a memo report, attempt to begin with the main information.* That way, a reader who sees nothing but the subject line and the first page will get the point of your message.

   In Figure 13-1, the subject line is followed immediately by a short introduction. The conclusions and the recommendations based on those conclusions explain precisely what needs to be done to repair the chimneys at the church.

3. *Keep additional paragraphs short to make the content easier to read,* but be sure to provide all explanation needed to support the information in the opening paragraph.

4. *Use design principles to highlight information.* In Figure 13-1, the supporting part of the report is divided into two main headings—Chimney 1 and Chimney 2. Main problems with each chimney can be seen at a glance because of the listing arrangement.

5. *Be sure to tell readers where to get additional information.* Figure 13-1 includes the names and phone numbers of the two engineers working on the First Church project so that Graham can contact the appropriate individual if he has questions about the findings in the report.

Sample Report #2

Figure 13-2 illustrates another information report. A short report in memo form, it is intended to update faculty on changes to academic computing services. The campus Computing and Communications Services issue regular bulletins to faculty and staff, informing them about changes and developments in service, announcing courses and workshops, and offering "tips and tricks" for the use of new services. Their audience covers the full range of computer (il)literacy. The manager of academic computing, who also teaches technical communication, knows that "user friendliness" is as essential in this kind of document as in a software program. Therefore he chooses a clearly straightforward prose style, using subheadings and blank space effectively to make a necessarily technical and dense document readily accessible to all his readers.

<table>
<tr><td></td><td>

Memorandum from

COMPUTING AND COMMUNICATIONS SERVICES

To: Cody, Susan
           Department of Business and Technical Communication

From: Randy Patch, Academic Computing Services

Date: May 17, 1993
</td></tr>
</table>

Subject line indicates time frame

Re: REMINDER: NEW ACADEMIC COMPUTING ENVIRONMENT
           THIS FALL

Background and purpose

In February of this year, Computing and Communications Services (CCS) distributed a memorandum to all faculty and staff, announcing the transition from the academic mainframe to a new academic computing environment for fall '93. In the intervening months, CCS has completed a large part of this project: the new machines have been installed, software purchased and configured, and faculty users given introductory training courses. The purpose of this memorandum is to remind all academic mainframe account holders that the IBM VM/CMS ROSE system will not be available for general use after September, 1993, and to inform them of the software and data migration entailed by the new system.

Headings: spacing and bolding give emphasis

Software Migration

Most instructional or administrative software currently supported on the academic mainframe has been moved to Matrix (the new academic computing system). Some mainframe software packages are not available for the new environment; these are being replaced with functionally similar products. The table below summarizes the disposition of academic mainframe software products:

Table used to summarize information

Move to AIX	C, Pascal, Fortran, Lisp, Scheme, Prolog, Adabas/Natural, CICS, SAS, SPSS, TSP, Cansim, APT, Listserv, Kermit, FTP, Gopher, Tools, Rosebud, ZETA plotter Fortran routines, Mail (replace with PineMail)
Move to DOS	APL, Basic, Cobol II, Maple, 370 Assembler, CHASE, CRASE, NUTS (replace with PDA/MDS)
Move to SunOS	GPSS
Outsource to Centennial	MVS guest, VSAM
Discontinue	RAMMIS II, Snobol, Watbol, Watfiv, PROFS (replace with AIX ClockWise), SLAMM II, Siman, Plastico, McMaster, BMDP, APL2, IMSL, Script/DCF

Figure 13-2 SAMPLE REPORT #2

Source: Reprinted with permission of Randy Patch, Manager, Academic Computing Services, Ryerson Polytechnic University.

In some cases, AIX replacements for VM software products will not be available in time for instructors to migrate by September. These products will be available on the mainframe only during the Fall '99 term, and will not be removed until December '99. The following products fall into this category: SQL/DS, CICS, Assembler 370, PL/1.

Data Migration

On April 27, members of the Advisory Committee on Academic Computing (ACAC) unanimously approved a motion to make mainframe account holders responsible for transferring their disk and archive files to the new computing system, with CCS providing instruction and assistance where required. You should begin this process as soon as possible, to ensure that your data has been safely transferred before September. For advice and/or assistance with transferring your data from the mainframe, please contact the Computing Support Centre (6806) or Academic Computing Services (Geoff Collins, 6831).

If you have any questions or concerns about the transition to the new computing environment, please call Randy Patch, Manager, Academic Computing, at extension 6835.

Contact names

Figure 13-2 (CONTINUED)

Determining Report Structure

Many times, reports do not need all the design elements discussed in Chapter 9. If they are designed for internal communication, they can be set up in memo report format (Figures 13-1 and 13-2, for example), even though they may be several pages long. Whatever the length of the report, you will want to organize it so that it will achieve its intended goals and use a logical system of headings to reveal the content to the reader, as discussed in Chapter 8.

Determining Internal Development of Reports

Reports will usually begin with an introduction that briefly states the following:

- The purpose of the report
- The reason the report was written
- The scope of the report—what will be covered
- Perhaps a short summary of the main ideas covered in the discussion

As discussed in Chapter 9, the extent of the introduction depends on your readers' needs: do they expect the report? Do they understand the circumstances surrounding the report (why it was written)? Remember: Readers have to be prepared for the information they will read before they are ready to process it.

The introduction to a report prepares the reader for the content to be presented. A reader approaching a report for the first time will ask several questions: What is this report about? What does it cover? Do I need to read it? How does it affect me? The introduction should answer those questions. Thus, any report introduction should stand alone. It should make sense to a reader who is seeing the report for the first time. The length of the introduction is determined by what your reader needs to know before moving to the conclusions or the discussion.

A report may also require a summary that gives the main highlights of the entire report. Or, the report may use a combined introduction/summary, a short paragraph that states the purpose of the report and the main ideas presented. Figure 13-2 uses this configuration. Figure 13-1 uses a brief introduction and separate sections containing detailed conclusions and recommendations to let the senior engineer know the results of the analysis of the masonry.

The discussion section presents each main category of information specified in the introduction, as shown in Figures 13-1 and 13-2.

In short, use an introduction, introduction/summary, summary, conclusions, recommendations, and discussions as purpose, audience, and situation call for them.

The two reports in this chapter, though they lack the complexity of more analytical reports, provide a good base for the study of report development. They illustrate well that the style, content, organization, and design of your report depend on your situation.

Planning and Revision Checklists

Because of the variable nature of reports, the general planning and	revision checklist at the end of the book will serve best for this chapter.

 Weblinks

A Technical Report
www.csm.uwe.ac.uk/~tdrewry/reps_bsd.htm#techrep

Webtrends (tm) Summary Report
www.jps.net

Report Sample
www.ctsports.com

Exercises

1. The following report is a poorly organized and formatted information report. Redesign the report to reflect good document design, effective style, and organization.

PLEASE READ AND INITIAL
TO: Structural Engineering Group
FROM: Program Planning Committee
DATE: September 7, 1999
RE: Construction Engineering Conference

The Construction Engineering Conference, which will be held October 28-30 at the Lancaster Hotel, will be attended by approximately 260 engineers. To give all of you some idea about how the conference will proceed, we want you to be aware of the following items.

The SE group should be on hand throughout the conference to represent our company, since we are the host company this year, and to answer any questions from participants. For our company, our group contacts will be Jim Mahann and Joanna Sturges. Their conference office will be in Suite 104. They will begin working from this office October 26.

Breakout rooms will be available for the second part of all sessions. Phones and fax machines will be available in all breakout rooms from 9:00-5:00 each day. House phones will be located only at the end of the first and second floor ballroom areas.

Structural software will be displayed by nine vendors all day October 29 and until noon October 30. Four book companies will also have displays of recent publications on structural topics. Computer consultants from IBM, Compaq, and Apple will also be on hand to discuss compatibility issues and to discuss their own products. Material for the conference packets has already begun arriving. Each folder will have brochures for at least a dozen new products.

Participants will arrive by mid-afternoon October 28. Everyone from our group is to be available to greet incoming guests. Room assignments have already been made for all guests, but if anyone has questions, be sure they are sent to Jim and Joanna. Our company will host happy hour beginning at 4:30 in the Cavanaugh Room. A buffet supper, hosted by MERK Structural Group in Montreal, will be held in the same room. Food will be available at 6:00. The film of the Paratex Building structural failure will be shown at 8:00 in the Cinema Space for those who have not had the opportunity to see this film.

Other information: Cheque cashing services are available with proper identification at the Manager's Office, Room 6. A list of suggested entertainment places is being prepared. You will receive copies for distribution.

Both days of the conference will feature both plenary and concurrent sessions. Two plenary sessions will be on the 28th and one on the 29th. Dr. Milo Nguyen and Dr. Hee Wong from McGill will conduct the 28th plenary sessions. Dr. Phillipa Rollins of the University of Toronto will be the principal speaker for the 29th. The exact schedule will be published soon. Everyone will receive a complete packet of information. Coffee and refreshments will be available during the morning and afternoon session breaks.

That's about it for now. Any questions or suggestions are welcome. Call Megan and Tracy at 2133 and 5623.

2. **Write a memo report to your instructor presenting and discussing three topics you are considering for your major report.**

DEVELOPMENT OF ANALYTICAL REPORTS

In Chapter 13 we looked at two simple information reports. In this chapter, we move on to the more complex analytical report. Although the elements of both information and analytical reports are the same, analytical reports go beyond simply reporting information, they analyse it. From the analysis, the writer may evaluate information, draw conclusions, and perhaps recommend action. The type of report you write and the extent of the analysis required depend on the topic and purpose of your report.

Analytical reports often defy rigid classification, but for the purpose of this chapter, we can classify them into the following types. If the analysis leads to a recommendation, the report may be called a **recommendation report**. If the analysis emphasizes evaluation of personnel, data, or perhaps options, the report may be called an **evaluation report**. **Feasibility reports** analyse a situation to determine the best solution to questions surrounding the situation or problem. **Empirical research reports** explain research that has been conducted, report the results, analyse the results, and sometimes recommend further work or research that is needed.

Many reports both inform and analyse. **Progress reports**, which will be discussed in Chapter 16, describe and evaluate the work that has been done on a project, the cost, and problems encountered. **Trip reports** document the information gathered on a trip, evaluate this information, and may suggest action based on the report findings. **Performance review reports** describe an employee's performance, analyse his or her effectiveness, and estimate the employee's potential for promotion. **Economic justification reports** explain the cost of a project or action and then argue for the cost-effectiveness of the project.

In this chapter, we will discuss the design of four of these types: the analytical report in general, the recommendation report, the feasibility study, and the empirical research report. Each report type will be accompanied by illustrations so that you can see how design works in specific situations. However, you should always remember that report guidelines are just that—guidelines. Your report should respond to the needs of your content and your audience.

Analytical Reports

Isolating analytical reports for study is useful for several reasons. Analytical reports usually have a more complex design than information reports. Analytical reports usually require a more extensive introduction than is needed for the information report. Analytical reports begin with an introduction that may include:

- The purpose of the report
- The reason the report was written
- The scope of the report—what issues will and will not be covered
- The procedure for investigating (analysing) the topic of the report

After the introduction, the report can be developed in several ways:

Introduction

Conclusion—results of the analysis

Recommendation—if required by the investigation

Presentation of information

Criteria for evaluation

Discussion/evaluation of information

Or,

Introduction

Presentation of information

Criteria for evaluation

Discussion/evaluation of information

Conclusion—results of the analysis

Recommendation—if required by the investigation

The organization you choose should depend on your reader or the format used by your company. Use the first plan—placing the conclusions of the analysis first—if your reader is most interested in the conclusions. Use the

TO: ENR Group   **DATE:**   March 11, 1999

FROM: Melanie Pierce

SUBJECT: Alternatives for Restructuring the FACG Team

Introduction

Recent decisions to reposition REVAC's main product line have resulted in the decision by the VP-Operations to refocus the direction of the Financial Analysis Consulting Group (FACG). Diversification of REVAC products into European markets requires that new types of financial analysis be available for sales, marketing, and product development.

My office was asked to analyse two options considered by the GOC during its fall decision to establish European markets with the goal of achieving a wider range of financial information:

1. Create a separate International Financial Analysis Office, which would report directly to the VP-Operations.

2. Create an international financial group within the existing FACG.

Current FACG Situation

The FACG has not hired new financial personnel for three years. During this time, two have left the group. Their responsibilities were absorbed by existing analysts, whose primary responsibility was to monitor North American markets. The recent shift of Marvin Perry to operations manager for general organizational planning makes a replacement for him mandatory. The upshot of the situation is that FACG cannot be responsible for more analytical data, particularly European data, without adding additional staff.

Option 1: Establishment of new FACG International Group

Creating a separate office for international financial analysis would avoid overloading the current FACG. European financial data must be considered no later than 99 10 01 to be of value to design and pre-market planning. Human Resources reports that three Eurospecialists, whose contracts expire at 00 08 15, will hear re-situation offers to REVAC. Should they begin work September 1, they could make the first cost estimates available by the October 1 deadline. All three are experienced overseas financial specialists who would need minimal instruction in what kind of financial information the VP-O needs to launch the Euromarket. The VP-O's administrative staff would be responsible for the new group's set up.

Figure 14-1 ANALYTICAL REPORT

ENR Group   -2-   **March 11, 1999**

Option 2: Expansion of FACG

Analysis of Option 2

Space is currently available in the FACG office suite on the 41st floor, if Eurospecialists with North American background could be found who would work with the current FACG team. Human Resources has been interviewing new International Business graduates at UWO and York and is ready to recommend those who meet qualifications. New graduates must have educational backgrounds that equip them to work with either domestic or Euro-markets. Two recent MBAs are under consideration to fill FACG vacancies to enable the office to assume a full range of responsibility.

Comparison of Current Alternatives

Comparison of Option 1 with Option 2

Replacing FACG management personnel because of the stringent qualifications required of these select analysts usually takes at least six months after a position vacancy has been announced. Assuming that estimate is on track, a replacement for Marvin Perry and one other experienced analyst will not likely happen until 00 01 01 at the earliest. None of the graduating students interviewed so far will be available before January 1. After start date, new analysts will still have to have time to take the required SEC exams, which means that their effectiveness date to REVAC begins about 00 01 01.

While expanding the current FACG with new hires is the most cost effective move, the effective time makes the value of recruiting new graduates less than desirable. In contrast, the cost of resituating the M-L team to REVAC would increase start-up costs for the unit by 60% and require space availability near the VP-O office. However, the fact that these analysts are fully SEC certified and ready to begin work with only minimal instruction suggests that this expenditure is worth considering.

Status as of 99 04 05

What actions need to be taken now

Cost requirements for start-up of the new unit need to be specified. The VP-O's Executive Committee authorized the creation of the international unit apparently on the assumption that salaries would be commensurate with those of existing FACS members. Since that is not the case, cost guidelines vs. the importance of the Oct 1 start time need to be clarified.

If expansion of the FACG unit is selected because of cost, Planning needs to be made aware that Euro-market data analysis will be delayed at least eight months. If this option is chosen, Human Resources needs to be informed immediately to step up recruiting efforts with an emphasis on candidates with international background. In any case, salary structure needs to be clearly specified in the event that a range of individuals becomes available.

pc: File 9104.22A
       S. Smith
       N. Ahmed
       P. Silanski

Figure 14-1   (CONTINUED)

second plan—presenting the data or information, evaluating it, then presenting the conclusions and any recommendations you have—if the analysis, rather than the conclusions, is the focus of your report.

Figure 14-1 is a report that emphasizes analysis rather than any firm conclusion. It was written by Melanie Pierce, an international market analyst for REVAC, a pipeline company that is considering expanding its sales into European markets. This expansion will require major revisions in REVAC's financial operations to handle marketing finances. Her report to the ENR (Engineering Network Reorganization) Group has no conclusion at this point, but Pierce does want to inform the group about the two options being considered for dealing with the proposed international expansion.

For that reason, Melanie does not include a summary or a conclusion at the beginning, but places the less-than-definitive conclusion at the end. Note that in this report, the writer gives several sentences of background, as several readers besides the main reader will receive the report. These readers may not be as familiar with the context of the report as the main reader.

Do not place the conclusion first if you think your reader may misunderstand or object to it; present the criteria for analysis, the analysis, and then the evaluation from which the conclusion and any recommendations evolve.

Recommendation Reports

A common type of analytical report is the recommendation report. The focus of this type of analytical report is the recommendations. You must analyse a problem or situation, present possible solutions, analyse each solution as it relates to the problem, and then recommend the one you think is best.

Figure 14-2 is a recommendation report written by a research engineer with a provincial ministry of transportation. The report summarizes his ministry's experience with an anti-icing compound tested over a 10-year period on selected highways in the province. His task is to determine the effectiveness of the compound and to recommend whether wider use of the compound is justified, given its cost. The report follows ministry guidelines (documentation page including abstract and distribution list; title page with copyright information).

He begins with background and the agreed-upon criteria for compound use. The body of the report comprises test site observations, cost, and accidents. Conclusions and recommendations come at the end of the report. (Tables summarizing data have been omitted here.)

Figure 14-3 illustrates another design for a recommendation report that provides final recommendations for solving a problem.

This report presents its conclusion and recommendations up front, after a brief introduction. Robert Collins is a mechanical engineer whose group is designing a salt water disposal system for Chemco, which manufactures agricultural chemicals such as pesticides and fertilizers. Amelia Stouffer, Robert's supervisor, has asked Robert to explain the group's work thus far and

Figure 14-2 RECOMMENDATION REPORT #1

Source: Ontario Ministry of Transportation, Research and Development Branch, *Verglimit Pavements in Ontario — An Interim Report* (Toronto, 1986).

Technical Report Documentation Page

Verglimit Pavements in Ontario
— An Interim Report

Author:	J.E. Gruspier, Research Engineer, Materials Research Office
MTC No.:	ME-86-02
Date:	August 1986
Published by:	The Research and Development Branch Ontario Ministry of Transportation and Communications
Participating Agencies/-Client:	

Abstract:

This report summarizes a decade of MTC experience with Verglimit — a European anti-icing compound incorporated in bituminous concrete. Road condition reports and accident experience are compiled for the various Verglimit test sections in southern Ontario.

Findings indicate that Verglimit has been effective in reducing icing in about 50% of the trial pavement sections and bridge decks. It was also found that Verglimit should not generally be used in combination with steel slag aggregate due to the thermal properties of the latter.

The incorporation of Verglimit in bituminous concrete pavement surface courses may triple their cost. Nevertheless, consideration of using Verglimit in asphalt surfaces on bridges, particularly prone to hazard because of icing, appears to be justified.

Key words:	Verglimit, de-icing chemicals, snow and ice control, pavements, safety
Distribution:	Environmental and municipal works engineers, MTC Districts and Regions, pavement design and maintenance engineers.
Copyright Status:	Crown copyright

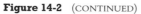

Figure 14-2 (CONTINUED)

ME-86-02

Verglimit Pavements in Ontario
— An Interim Report

J.E. Gruspier
Research Engineer
Research and Development Branch

Published by
The Research and Development Branch
Ontario Ministry of Transportation and Communications
Hon. Ed Fulton, Minister
D.G. Hobbs, Deputy Minister

For additional copies, write:
The Editor, Technical Publications
Room 320, Central Building
1201 Wilson Avenue
Downsview, Ontario
Canada M3M 1J8

Telephone: (416) 248-7226
Infotex Electronic Mail: 21:MIN006

August 1986

Figure 14-2 (CONTINUED)

1

1/ Introduction

Differential icing between a bridge deck and the approaches is a phenomenon which can occur with some frequency in late fall or early spring, or at any time there is a sudden temperature drop below the freezing point during the winter months. The bridge deck is exposed from the top and bottom and thus tends to cool off quickly with falling temperatures such that ice may form on the deck surface if the air is high in humidity or a light rain falls as the temperature drops below 0°C. The approaches, on the other hand, have sufficient heat stored in the ground to prevent ice from forming on the pavement. The difference in the condition of the bridge deck surface and the adjacent pavement may result in an unexpected hazard to safe driving before spot treatment by sanding and salting can be applied.

Verglimit is a patented compound which is designed to reduce this hazard. It is a chemical multi-component de-icer which consists primarily of calcium chloride flakes to which 5% sodium hydroxide and an unknown chemical component is added. The compounded flakes are coated with linseed oil which is polymerized to protect the flakes from water. The compound is incorporated into the asphalt mix at the plant and the surface course mix is laid on the road in the normal manner. As the pavement wears under traffic, new particles of Verglimit become exposed, providing built-in de-icing for the life of the pavement surface.

According to the manufacturer, Verglimit is not intended to melt appreciable accumulations of ice. Instead, it provides a thin film of brine which prevents ice from adhering to the pavement. As the temperature decreases, so does this effect. The Verglimit pavement on a bridge deck should freeze at about the same time as the pavement on the approaches, if it is working as designed, creating a uniform driving condition. A higher effectiveness is to be expected in the first year; however, the results should be consistent in the second, third, and subsequent years according to the manufacturer.

The criteria considered by the Ministry for potential use of Verglimit are:

1) There must be a known slippery condition due to ice formation or else where icing has been observed to occur on bridge decks.

2) Verglimit should not be used where vehicles are stopping, as at an intersection, due to the increased flow value of the mix.

Verglimit is generally added at a rate of 5% by weight to the hot mix which is laid to a compacted thickness of 36 mm. The void content of the surface course pavement is designed to be 3% to 4%.

The purpose of this report is to document Ministry experience with Verglimit trial installations over the last decade with respect to physical performance, accidents and cost.

Figure 14-2 (CONTINUED)

2

2/ Test Sites

3/ Presence of Verglimit

Verglimit was first used in Ontario in 1977 at two locations. It was placed on a trial basis as a HM patch on Hwy 48 at Ringwood and on the deck of the Black Horse Bridge on Hwy 9. It was subsequently placed at a further 11 sites during the period 1979-84. All the sites are listed in Table 1.

Most of the Verglimit pavements are still exposed and in service; however, the following are not:

Highway 11 - Vernon Narrows Bridge, Huntsville Bypass -- An uneven pavement was placed and severe ravelling occurred, possibly due to lack of compaction. The Verglimit was replaced with regular HL-1 in the spring of 1981 after only one winter in service.

Highway 22 - Medway River Bridge, west of London -- The pavement placed on the deck of this bridge was uneven and was removed and replaced.

In the summer of 1983, the Verglimit surface courses were sampled to determine if the de-icing compound was still present. The physical performance of the Verglimit at the test sites was monitored over one winter season (1983-1984). Accident reports for the sites were reviewed for the period from early 1978 to 1985.

In the summer of 1983, cores were taken from three of the test sites to determine if the de-icing compound was still present in the pavement after being exposed for a number of years. The following sites were chosen due to their proximity to Toronto and convenience in sampling:

• Highway 9 - Black Horse Bridge (1977)

• Highway 48 - HM Patch, north of Ringwood (1977)

• Highway 11 - CNR Bridge, Huntsville Bypass (1980)

The pavements were tested in the field for reaction with silver nitrate ($AgNO_3$) as were the cores after they were removed to determine the presence of the de-icing compound. The surface of the Verglimit pavements showed a moderate to good reaction in all cases. The cores were broken and $AgNO_3$ applied to the freshly broken faces. A good reaction occurred with all the cores, indicating that the calcium chloride ($CaCl_2$) was still active within the pavement at all three locations. These tests showed that the $CaCl_2$ flakes were still in solid form in the pavement after 3-6 years, indicating that the $CaCl_2$ was not migrating out of the pavement either to the surface or to the bridge deck below.

....

Figure 14-2 (CONTINUED)

3

4/ Observations of
Physical Performance

The performance of the Verglimit sections over the 83/84 winter season were monitored by MTC District Maintenance staff in accordance with procedures laid down by the Research and Development Branch. Observations were made of the following performance features:

- icing of bridge decks relative to the adjacent HM pavement on the approaches or to other structures close by;

- moisture "tracking" from the Verglimit pavement on humid days when the adjacent pavement was dry;

- in light snowfall conditions, any differences in clearing between Verglimit and the adjacent pavement;

- any visible differences in plowing between Verglimit and the adjacent pavement;

- any differences in traffic working snow and slush off the Verglimit and the adjacent pavement.

It should be noted that not all of the above features would be obvious at any one time. The assessment of these features and their effect were reported at intervals over the winter months. Table 2 summarizes the comments received for each Verglimit site.

Since the assessment of the performance of the Verglimit pavement was subjective and many different observers were involved, some variance in the reported performance might be expected for these reasons alone. Also, while the pavement performance was to have been monitored in the temperature range 0°C to -5°C, it is quite possible that some of the monitoring may have taken place at colder temperatures when the benefits of the Verglimit pavment would not have been evident. With these qualifications, it appears that the performance of the Verglimit trial sections was not uniform.

Some trial areas appeared to be performing very well. There were obvious benefits apparent at those sites, either during or after snow storms or when the temperature dropped below the freezing mark. The benefits for the Verglimit sections were noted relative to the performance of the adjacent pavements or other structures decks in the immediate vicinity.

Of the 10 Verglimit pavements monitored, four of these showed markedly better performance than adjacent pavements or nearby structures. The following types of comments were recorded:

- less icy or less prone to icing;

- no frosting compared to other decks in the area;

- deck clears faster;

- no "special" attention required;

- no complaints by public or the police as in the past.

For example, the Madawaska Bridge on Hwy 17 showed the benefits for a Verglimit bridge deck when compared to an adjacent structure deck at the Bonnechere River. However, it appears that the performance of the Verglimit was less effective during the winter of 83/84 than in previous years. The Verglimit surface was in its third winter of service when this observation was made.

Of the five remaining sites, four indicated little or no difference in the performance of the Verglimit when compared with the adjacent HM pavement. Comments such as, "some clearing off early in storms" or "dries quicker, better traction when wet," were recorded, indicating only very minor benefits at best.

There were indications that the performance of one Verglimit pavement not on a bridge deck was poorer than the adjacent pavement. The site on Hwy 8 incorporated a steel slag aggregate in the surface course. When ice developed on the pavement, it was slower to melt on the Verglimit section. Also, light snow adhered to form a 0.3 m wide ice strip at the centreline which was not apparent on other pavements with conventional aggregates.

While the reason for the above performance is not clear, it is likely that the steel slag pavement exhibits colder pavement surface temperatures than a conventional aggregate pavement due to its inherent thermal properties. Thus, ice and snow would tend to form more easily on the pavement surface and remain for longer periods. Also, steel slag aggregate makes a pavement surface more wear-resistant; hence, less Verglimit would be exposed at any one time, or during a winter season, when compared with conventional pavements. Thus, the use of steel slag or similar slower-wearing aggregate appears to be counterproductive when used in a Verglimit surface pavement.

Figure 14-2   (CONTINUED)

4

5/ Discussion of Physical Performance

In general, based on the results of the monitoring summarized in Table 3, it would appear that Verglimit is effective as a built-in de-icer in a least 50% of the trials. However, it appears that Verglimit becomes less effective with the passage of time, based on comments noted by the observers.

When Verglimit is first placed, its winter performance appears to be markedly better than the performance of the pavement which was replaced. As time passes, the Verglimit appears to lose some of its ability to reduce the icing phenomenon. This might be associated with the wearing qualities of the pavement, i.e., when a pavement is designed to be more stable and durable, less $CaCl_2$ will be exposed at the pavement surface to give the Verglimit pavement its desirable performance. This could be overcome by designing the pavement mix so that its useful life would be reduced somewhat, but so that the desirable properties of Verglimit could be utilized. However, the additional long-term cost of this compromise must be kept in mind. It should be noted that MTC Verglimit mixes have used 5.0% by weight while current design practices by the manufacturer call for a minimum of 5.5 to 6.5% Verglimit to produce the desired results.

Almost half of the trial Verglimit sites exhibited performance which was no different from the adjacent HM pavement. The monitoring of the Verglimit performance was to have been carried out in the temperature range of about 0°C to -5°C. This is the temperature range in which Verglimit is considered to be effective, according to the manufacturer. While some of the comments received from the Districts refer to the effectiveness of Verglimit at this temperature range, all comments referring to lack of any difference in performance between the Verglimit and adjacent pavements or bridge decks in the vicinity failed to mention this temperature range or near freezing conditions.

As a result, one might wonder whether some of the observers were making their observations at temperatures outside of the effective range claimed for the product. For example, at -15°C, no difference would be evident in the performance of the Verglimit compared to the adjacent pavement, but none would be expected. Since the narrow temperature range or near freezing conditions occur for a very limited period of the winter, it is important that observations should be limited to this temperature range, otherwise misleading results could be obtained as to the effectiveness of a Verglimit pavement.

The one example of Verglimit performance being poorer than that of the adjacent pavement illustrates the difficulty of trying to do two different things with one pavement design, i.e.:

1) utilizing a slow wearing aggregate for better durability; and

2) using a Verglimit design which prevents icing at near freezing temperatures but is dependent on the continual wearing of the pavement surface to expose the $CaCl_2$ particles contained within the pavement.

The two purposes are not compatible and the experience indicates that Verglimit should only be used in combination with slag aggregate where traffic volumes are very high.

While the results of the study are not conclusive, it does seem that the Verglimit placed in a surface wearing course can be effective, as claimed by the manufacturer. The reasons for its ineffectiveness at some sites are not fully understood. A further season of closer monitoring, particularly within the narrower below-freezing temperature range, would appear desirable and necessary.

Figure 14-2 (CONTINUED)

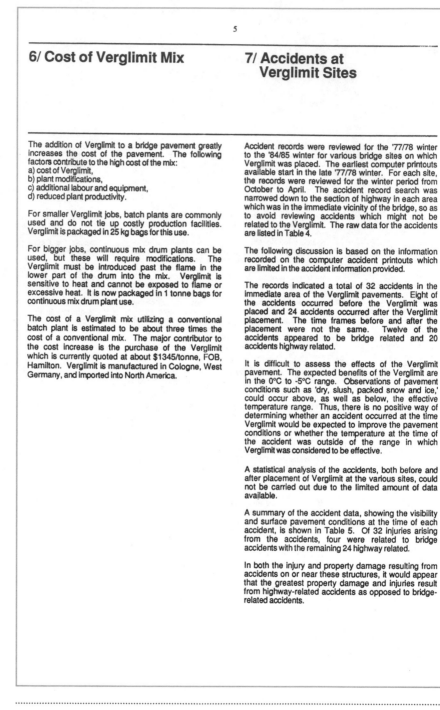

5

6/ Cost of Verglimit Mix

The addition of Verglimit to a bridge pavement greatly increases the cost of the pavement. The following factors contribute to the high cost of the mix:
a) cost of Verglimit,
b) plant modifications,
c) additional labour and equipment,
d) reduced plant productivity.

For smaller Verglimit jobs, batch plants are commonly used and do not tie up costly production facilities. Verglimit is packaged in 25 kg bags for this use.

For bigger jobs, continuous mix drum plants can be used, but these will require modifications. The Verglimit must be introduced past the flame in the lower part of the drum into the mix. Verglimit is sensitive to heat and cannot be exposed to flame or excessive heat. It is now packaged in 1 tonne bags for continuous mix drum plant use.

The cost of a Verglimit mix utilizing a conventional batch plant is estimated to be about three times the cost of a conventional mix. The major contributor to the cost increase is the purchase of the Verglimit which is currently quoted at about $1345/tonne, FOB, Hamilton. Verglimit is manufactured in Cologne, West Germany, and imported into North America.

7/ Accidents at Verglimit Sites

Accident records were reviewed for the '77/78 winter to the '84/85 winter for various bridge sites on which Verglimit was placed. The earliest computer printouts available start in the late '77/78 winter. For each site, the records were reviewed for the winter period from October to April. The accident record search was narrowed down to the section of highway in each area which was in the immediate vicinity of the bridge, so as to avoid reviewing accidents which might not be related to the Verglimit. The raw data for the accidents are listed in Table 4.

The following discussion is based on the information recorded on the computer accident printouts which are limited in the accident information provided.

The records indicated a total of 32 accidents in the immediate area of the Verglimit pavements. Eight of the accidents occurred before the Verglimit was placed and 24 accidents occurred after the Verglimit placement. The time frames before and after the placement were not the same. Twelve of the accidents appeared to be bridge related and 20 accidents highway related.

It is difficult to assess the effects of the Verglimit pavement. The expected benefits of the Verglimit are in the 0°C to -5°C range. Observations of pavement conditions such as 'dry, slush, packed snow and ice,' could occur above, as well as below, the effective temperature range. Thus, there is no positive way of determining whether an accident occurred at the time Verglimit would be expected to improve the pavement conditions or whether the temperature at the time of the accident was outside of the range in which Verglimit was considered to be effective.

A statistical analysis of the accidents, both before and after placement of Verglimit at the various sites, could not be carried out due to the limited amount of data available.

A summary of the accident data, showing the visibility and surface pavement conditions at the time of each accident, is shown in Table 5. Of 32 injuries arising from the accidents, four were related to bridge accidents with the remaining 24 highway related.

In both the injury and property damage resulting from accidents on or near these structures, it would appear that the greatest property damage and injuries result from highway-related accidents as opposed to bridge-related accidents.

Figure 14-2 (CONTINUED)

6

8/ Conclusions and Recommendations

1. The use of Verglimit pavement should be considered for those bridge decks which, based on current or previous experience, exhibit the icing phenomenon. The positive performance of the Verglimit pavement, noted in at least 50% of the trial sites, suggests that it can be effective in those bridge decks exhibiting hazardous performance in temperatures just below freezing.

2. The cost of a Verglimit mix is about three times the cost of the same mix without Verglimit. However, the quantity of surface course mix required for a bridge deck is relatively small. High cost appears to preclude the more general use of Verglimit in pavement surfaces.

3. Verglimit should be used primarily in southern Ontario. Since the effectiveness of Verglimit is limited to just below the freezing point, the maximum exposure would be obtained in the southern part of the province where the fluctuations around the freezing point would be most numerous and midwinter thaws are experienced. Verglimit's effectiveness in the northern part of Ontario would be more limited due to the colder temperatures there. However, its use might be justified on bridges which are known to "ice over" on a number of occasions early in the winter season and for which the number of accidents is high.

4. Verglimit pavement could be designed so that it will wear faster in order to provide more exposure of the Verglimit during the winter season. This may shorten pavement surface life but will give the Verglimit an opportunity to reduce the hazards of the icing phenomonon, which is its intended purpose. The additional cost of this design must be considered.

5. The Verglimit mix design used by the Ministry has differed in the minimum percentage of Verglimit used, i.e., MTC used 5.0% minimum but the manufacturer recommends a 5.5% minimum Verglimit. The optimum proportion of Verglimit in relation to effectiveness and mix design variables needs further exploration (see 4).

6. Verglimit should not be used in a pavement design utilizing steel slag aggregate except where traffic volumes are very high. The thermal properties of the slag aggregate appear to be quite different from conventional HM aggregate and result in icing or ice retention in a temperature range different to that of conventional pavement aggregates.

7. Further monitoring of the Verglimit pavement trial sections should be carried out to see if the present findings still hold with time. Emphasis should be placed on monitoring the performance of Verglimit in the just below freezing range (0°C to -5°C), which is the effective range claimed by the manufacturer.

Figure 14-2 (CONTINUED)

The introduction is brief—contains only a statement of purpose—because the reader is familiar with the report problem.

TO: Amelia Stouffer   DATE: July 13, 1999
FROM: Robert Collins
SUBJECT: Mimmstown Produced Salt Water Disposal System (SWD)

This report documents a study of past, present, and anticipated produced water from the WC 66 Field for disposal at the Mimmstown Separation Station. It also evaluates the adequacy of the present system and forecasts future needs.

CONCLUSIONS

1. The produced water disposal system at the Mimmstown Separation Station periodically receives surges from liquid dumps on FWKO and treaters above the rates 1700 BWPD capacity of the SWD system.

2. The skimmer tank and Wemco arrangement, as designed, limits the surge capacity to only what the Wemco can accommodate.

3. With workover operations still underway on the WC 66A platform, only a fraction of the expected yield of produced salt water is arriving at Mimmstown; therefore at present there are no surge problems. Workover rig is expected to move off WC 66A by October 1, 1999. Thereafter, peak rates are again expected.

4. With installation of water polishing equipment on WC 66 Field platforms, produced water will be diverted to Mimmstown P/L for treatment and disposal at Mimmstown.

5. Upon upset of polishing equipment on the WC 66 Field platforms, produced water will be diverted into Mimmstown P/L for treatment and disposal at Mimmstown.

6. Present indication from USGS and EPS is that now and in the future, produced water offshore can be treated to specific ppm and disposed of overboard.[1] See Table A.

7. Modifications are required for the existing SWD system to accommodate the surges (which create operating problems) that will continue during the interim period until water polishers are placed offshore.

[1]Information provided by LAS.

The writer gives the results of his analysis before he presents his recommended course of action on page 2.

Figure 14-3 RECOMMENDATION REPORT #2 (NOTE: FIGURES AND TABLES MENTIONED IN THIS REPORT ARE NOT INCLUDED IN THIS FIGURE.)

A. Stouffer
Page 2
July 13, 1999

RECOMMENDATION

Engineering recommends that modification to the existing SWD system include installation of a small centrifugal pump downstream of skim tank to pump into the Model 36 Wemco to provide a constant flow to the Wemco. By pumping from the skimmer tank, a lower operating level can be maintained in the tank to allow for as much as a 250 bbl instantaneous surge situation before creating operating problems.

RATIONALE FOR RECOMMENDATION

Analysis of the problem

At the Mimmstown Separation Station, produced water is separated from the product steam in the free water knock-out (FWKO) and the fired production heater treaters. The produced water then flows through a gas boot and into a 1000 bbl tank. The water gravity flows from the skimmer tank, through a water leg, into the Wemco model 36 water clarifier.

A control valve on the discharge of the Wemco regulates the flow of treated water into the 220 bbl injection pump suction tank for disposal into one of two wells. Each SWD injection pump is capable of delivering 4500 BWPD at 100 psig MAWP.

Since a relatively constant level is maintained in the Wemco it should not be expected to handle surges entering at a rate greater than 1700 B/D. The present water leg (15 cm diameter) and skimmer arrangement cannot retain the surge in the tank nor restrict the flow of water in the Wemco, as the skimmer contains no flow outlet regulating valve or pneumatic LLC device.

During adverse surge conditions, spill-over from the oil skim chamber of the Wemco flows into the oil holding tank and is pumped to the bad oil tank for recirculation to the fired production treaters.

To prevent overflow, the operator may manually by-pass the Wemco by throttling the block valve on the 15 cm by-pass line and, thus, divert a portion of the flow directly into injection pump suction tank.

Since it is undesirable to allow BS&W to enter the bad oil tank from the SWD system as well as to inject improperly treated water (in excess of 100 ppm oil content) into the disposal wells, modification to the existing system is warranted.[2]

[2]Information provided by SID office.

Figure 14-3 (CONTINUED)

A. Stouffer
Page 3
July 13, 1999

With the expected production forecast (See Table B) derived from well test data and information supplied by KWJ, the following calculations forecast the anticipated maximum daily average produced water yield for the existing and intended platforms in WC 66 Field (including WC 66A, B, C, & D platforms).

To use maximum case for expected water field

by December 5	$\dfrac{37000\ \text{BOPD}}{2.3}$	=	1610 BWPD
Produced water off H.P. gas			1500 BWPD
	Total		3110 BWPD

by June 2000	$\dfrac{4200\ \text{BOPD}}{2.3}$	=	1825 NEPF
Produced water off H.P. gas			1500 BWPD
	Total		3325 BWPD

With these estimated yields of water production, sizing Mimmstown facility for ultimate maximum BWPD @ 3400 BWPD (max.) is adequate without placing water polishing equipment offshore. As indicated in Table B, maximum daily injections rate was 2700 bbl (March 99); the maximum average per day rate was 1875 BWPD (March 99). Several methods were investigated to remedy the periodic surges that occur. For this investigation, three possible options may be available:

OPTION 1

Modify the salt water disposal as shown in Figure 3 enabling the water clarification equipment to allow for surges, in addition to the maximum skim capacity of 1700 BWPD. Installation of water polishing equipment offshore in WC 66 Field should eliminate the need for any greater skim capacity than currently exists at Mimmstown.

This modification includes:

1. Modified skimmer tank:
   a. Add external cage
   b. Add sight glasses
   c. Add level trip for pumps

Description of each option considered in solving the problem and the cost of employing each option

Figure 14-3 (CONTINUED)

A. Stouffer
Page 4
July 13, 1999

    2.   Dual pump package w/controls

    3.   Added piping, valves and fittings

Estimated cost of this installation is $23 500.

    This option will allow the 1000 bbl tank to accept periodic surges by maintaining lower level in the tank (pumping down the level to retain surges totally in the tank and not causing spillover in the Wemco).

OPTION 2

    Modify existing SWD as indicated in Figure 3 to allow for maximum average anticipated yield of 3400 BWPD to ensure adequate capacity of Mimmstown SWD facility in the event of complete upset of offshore clarification equipment or changes in OCS requirements for overboard water disposal.

    A synopsis of required items for this option includes:

    1.   Additional Wemco (1700 BWPD skim capacity)

    2.   Modified skimmer tank
        a. Add external cage
        b. Add sight glasses
        c. Add level-trip for pumps

    3.   Dual pump package w/control panel

    4.   Additional piping, valves, and fittings

The estimated cost of this equipment and installation is $64 650.

OPTION 3

    Continue to operate with the existing system and continue to utilize bad oil system for surge situations, as the intended offshore installation of water clarification equipment will eliminate the need for additional SWD equipment.

    Option 3 requires no additional equipment.

Figure 14-3 (CONTINUED)

A. Stouffer
Page 5
July 13, 1999

FINAL OBSERVATION

　　Although installation of the recommended changes in the SWD system would require temporary shutdown and emptying of the SWD skimmer tank, the length of time required for welding on the tank itself would be minimal (estimate 2 days). The remainder of the pump, piping, and valves can be installed with SWD in service (estimate 2 weeks). In addition, installation of these SWD modifications should not interfere with the intended offset workover of SWD wells 1 and 2.

　　As noted in the rationale, the planned water polishing equipment in WC 66 Field will decrease the amounts of produced water arriving at Mimmstown. However, this modification would allow for capability of handling surges whenever such situations arose as previously explained and would suffice for present needs and long-term operating problems.

Prepared by: _R. Collins_
　　　　　　　　R. Collins
Approved: _A. Stouffer_
　　　　　　　A. Stouffer

Figure 14-3 (CONTINUED)

to outline the options the group is considering for designing the salt water disposal plant. Because Amelia has requested this report, Robert does not need a detailed introduction. He includes only subject and scope and launches into the conclusions and then the recommendation of the best salt water disposal option studied thus far. In the discussion section, each option is presented and analysed. The visual design of the report allows readers to find the sections they want: They can read only the conclusions and recommendations, or they can read the analysis (or parts of it) that leads to the detailed statement of the recommendations.

Feasibility Studies

Another major type of analytical report is the feasibility study, which is launched to determine whether an organization should take an action it is considering taking. The central question involves doing something or not doing it or determining which option among several options is the best choice. The feasibility study is similar to the recommendation report, but the feasibility study is usually much more involved. A number of issues need to be presented and addressed, factors that usually produce a rather long, complex report.

The following situations call for a feasibility study.

- A university research group wants to know whether fire ants can be effectively controlled in open fields of 400 hectares or less by using chemicals such as x, y, and z.
- The provincial government wants to know whether partially treated sewage can be deposited on land in a semi-arid part of the province to improve the soil without leaking harmful bacteria into the water table.
- A company wants to know whether land it currently owns near a major highway should be developed into a shopping mall, a business park, or some combination of both.
- A major city wants to know whether building an additional airport on property it owns near a major waterway will cause flooding in residential areas downstream from the proposed airport.

Usually, the feasibility study helps organizations to make decisions based on the value of a solution as well as its cost. The feasibility report presents the written analysis and the resulting decision. Like other analytical reports, the feasibility study and the resulting report will do the following:

- Set the purpose and scope of the study
- Gather and check information
- Analyse information and data
- Reach conclusions
- Arrive at a decision

As in all composition, a good deal of back and forth movement occurs in the investigative process.

For any report, informational or analytical, you need to know how to gather, check, and study your information; how to develop a discussion, conclusions, and recommendations; and how to use principles of document design to present your study and its results. Because formulating purpose and scope is so critical to successful analytical reports, particularly feasibility studies, we discuss each of these factors at some length here.

Purpose

Feasibility and analytical reports should begin with a clear purpose, which will become part of the statement of purpose for the report. The following purpose statement shows the direction the study will take:

> This study decides whether the establishment of a local area network in the Mechanical Engineering Department is feasible given the facilities and funding available.

Although the need to articulate a clear purpose statement seems obvious, its importance to the success of the feasibility study cannot be underestimated. If investigators, as well as writers, do not have a clear direction for their study, the resulting information they gather will be incoherent.

Here are some additional examples of purpose statements:

- The purpose of this study is to determine the feasibility of using particle board to sheathe the interior of houseboats.

- The purpose of this investigation is to determine whether instructional materials are available for teaching school children about the effects of toxic pollution on water quality.

- Our primary objective is to decide what computing options will provide the best design programs for landscape architecture students, given the limited financial resources of the department.

Scope

Once the purpose of the feasibility study has been clearly decided and stated, the methods of accomplishing the purposes must be determined. These methods determine the scope of the study, the actions to be taken, the range of data to be gathered, the bounds to be set for studying the problem, and the criteria against which possible solutions will be measured. For example, a company that is deciding whether to establish a new branch in Red Deer will need to answer the following questions:

Purpose

Should X Company establish a branch plant in Red Deer?

Scope

Does X Company now have, or can it anticipate, enough profit in Red Deer to justify a plant there?

Does Red Deer offer adequate physical facilities, utilities, transportation, and communication?

What is the price of land? Is existing office space available that would be suitable?

What is the tax structure in Red Deer? Are the tax code and building regulations favourable for a plant like X?

Can the required staff be obtained, whether by local hiring or moving personnel into the area?

What is the general quality of life in Red Deer?

What effect would opening a branch plant in Red Deer have upon overall company organization, operations, policy, and financial conditions?

From this initial list of questions, the investigation can proceed, although each question will probably be broadened and rephrased as research warrants. Devising a scope statement that guides the investigation is crucial, but as an investigator you should not remain blindly committed to your initial scope statement. Reexamine it from time to time in light of the information you gather. Look for holes, overlaps, irrelevant questions. Often, a person unacquainted with the study is in a far better position than you to spot shortcomings and illogical assumptions in the scope statement. Therefore, someone outside the study should be asked to review and react to the list of scope items you compile.

Once you have carefully researched and answered the questions in your scope statement, you will need to plan the design of your report. Your written feasibility report may include all or some of the following elements, discussed in Chapter 9:

- Letter of transmittal or preface
- Title page
- Table of contents
- List of illustrations
- Glossary of terms
- Executive summary
- Introduction
- Discussion
- Factual summary
- Conclusions
- Recommendations
- Appendices
- References

How many of these elements you include will depend upon audience factors and the length and complexity of the report. For example, a long report aimed at a narrow audience of several people should have a letter of transmittal. A long report for a more general audience would have a preface instead. A short feasibility report of only several pages may be written as a memorandum or letter and essentially consist of only an executive summary, discussion, conclusions, and recommendations.

For our discussion of feasibility reports within the context of report development in general, we want to focus on the development of the key internal elements: the introduction, discussion, factual summary, conclusions, and recommendations—common elements in any feasibility report.

Introduction

Although we have already discussed the standard components of an introduction, in a feasibility study you may want to include several types of information in addition to these standard elements. For example:

- Subject, purpose, and scope
- Reasons for conducting the study
- Identification and characteristics of the person or company performing the study (if not given in a preface or letter of transmittal)
- Definition and historical background of the problem studied
- Any limitations imposed upon the study
- Procedures and methods employed in the study
- Acknowledgments to those who were instrumental in preparing the study (if not given in the transmittal letter or the preface)
- Topics that will be covered in the discussion

Discussion

When you are preparing to write the discussion section of a feasibility study, consider your purpose statement and your scope, both of which are included in the introduction. These two elements should give you clues to the arrangement of your information. To illustrate how the segments of the scope statement can lead to the plan of the discussion, let's return to the feasibility example you studied earlier.

The answer to the purpose statement—"Should X Company establish a branch plant in Red Deer?"—was deemed to depend on the answers to seven questions that made up the scope statement. Taking each of these questions and the answers to each as the bulk of the discussion, we would have the following plan for the report:

Executive Summary: Should X Company establish a branch plant in Red Deer? Why or why not?

Introduction
   Subject, purpose, and scope of the study
   Reasons for conducting the study
   Procedures used in conducting the study

Analysis of Factors Determining the Establishment of a Branch Plant in Red Deer

Estimated Profitability of a New Branch in Red Deer

Evaluation of Facilities
   Existing office space
   Utilities
   Transportation
   Communication
   Land prices and availability
   Local construction prices

Business Climate
   Tax structure
   Building codes
   Business regulation
   Economic health

Human Resources
   Local labour market
   Staff available for transfer

Quality of Life in Red Deer
   Schools
   Cost of living

Effect on X Company of Establishing a Branch Plant in Red Deer
   Existing organization
   Existing operations
   Company policy
   Financial resources

Factual Summary of Research

Conclusions

Recommendations

Appendices

References

Note that each of the main issues covered in the scope statement becomes a main segment of the discussion, which works to answer the controlling question.

Once the analysis is complete, you can begin to write the conclusion: Should X Company establish a branch plant in Red Deer? Why or why not? Based on the results of the research, we can make appropriate recommendations. For example, the analysis might suggest that a branch plant would be profitable but that X Company should wait until a new industrial park is completed because leased space can be obtained at attractive preconstruction prices. Or, the analysis might suggest that establishing a new branch is feasible only if the company can negotiate tax abatements. Without these, initial profitability could be undercut so much that the company's financial structure could be weakened. Or, lack of adequate transportation facilities might make the establishment of a branch plant totally impracticable.

Factual Summary of Research

The term *factual summary* distinguishes this type of summary from those that contain conclusions and recommendations as well as essential facts. Creating a good factual summary is one of the hardest challenges you face as a writer. In meeting that challenge, keep these principles in mind:

- You can summarize only the information appearing in the discussion of the report. A factual summary must not introduce new information.
- Every statement in a factual summary should be an assertion of facts presented. Opinions should be omitted.
- Facts, as they appear in various sections of the report, should be collected for the reader.
- The facts should become a springboard for the conclusions and recommendations that will follow.

Conclusions

The conclusions section acts as the intermediate step between the facts in the factual summary and the recommendations. Conclusions are inferences and implications you draw from your data.

Conclusions can be presented in normal essay style or in a series of short, separate statements. However you present your conclusions, you should arrange them in a clear order that reveals your thinking process to the reader. If your readers can read your introduction, factual summary, conclusions, and recommendations and believe that you have justified your recommendations, then you have probably presented your study well. Your readers should not read your conclusions and wonder how they relate to your factual summary and recommendations: They should see the connections immediately.

Recommendations

In contrast to a conclusion, a recommendation is an action statement. That is, it recommends that the report users take some proposed action or refrain from taking it. Always be sure that the first (or only) recommendation discharges the purpose set forth early in the report. If the purpose is to determine whether X Company should establish a branch plant in Red Deer, then the recommendations should address this purpose:

> X Company should establish a branch office in Red Deer.
>
> or
>
> X Company should delay establishing a branch plant in Red Deer until adequate tax abatements are offered by the City Council.
>
> or
>
> X Company should not establish a branch plant in Red Deer because an adequate work force will not be available to staff a new office.

Further recommendations expand on the initial one. If the first recommendation favours establishment of a branch plant, subsequent recommendations may detail the necessary steps to carry out the plan. If the first recommendation opposed the establishment of a branch, the reasons for the negative recommendation should be succinctly restated. Subsequent recommendations may propose alternative plans.

The **appendix** may include items such as drawings of proposed buildings, examples of building codes that would affect construction decisions, Chamber of Commerce reports on potential growth of the community, statement of tax structures secured from the city's solicitor and the local tax office—data used to support analysis and the resulting conclusions.

The **references** section lists sources of the study. These sources may include documentation of interviews, government reports, census statistics, journal articles, even unpublished studies—whatever sources of information you used to gather information under each scope statement.

Empirical Research Reports

As a student and later a technical specialist, you may be assigned the task of designing some device, determining its reliability, or testing the validity of some idea. This kind of analytical report is called the empirical research report because it analyses a problem based on extant knowledge, proposes a solution, tests that solution, and then concludes whether the solution is workable.

Examples of empirical research reports might include the following:

- A report on research conducted by a student who was attempting to design a monitor for use with infants who may be prone to Sudden Infant Death Syndrome. Like many research reports, this one reports the progress of the research up to the point at which the report had to be submitted. Thus, its conclusions are not definitive, but suggestive of what also needs to be done to pursue this research further.

This empirical study opens with the statement of the problem (introduction), the known causes of the problem, description of the problem, best known intervention method (monitoring), the design the student has chosen for the monitor, the theory by which it operates, and the conclusion about the possibility of developing this device at the time the report was submitted.

- A report summarizing research to integrate a digital computer into the control loop of an M-B shake test machine to develop a random vibration testing apparatus, using the computer to generate and control the vibration spectrum.

Following the introduction, this study begins with a discussion of the theory behind computer integration, then moves to presentation of the model studied for integration, then to results of the model studied, discussion of the results, costs of implementation, and suggestions for further improvement of the model.

An empirical research report generally includes the following elements in some form:

- Introduction and review of current knowledge
- Materials and methods for solving the problem
- Results
- Discussion
- Conclusion

To illustrate how this type of report is developed, we will show the major segments for the report described below.

Ann Underwood, a senior biochemistry major, develops a research project to study the retinoblastoma (RB) gene in normal canine tissues and in canine osteosarcoma (OS). Her goal is to see whether a relationship exists between the canine RB gene and OS. This relationship is present in human osteosarcoma. Thus, if her research can establish a firm relationship between the canine RB gene and osteosarcoma, canines may be used as research models to study ways of monitoring or slowing OS in humans. The empirical research report she writes reports the results of her research and provides a useful example for studying how empirical research is reported.

Introduction and Literature Review

Like all introductions, the empirical research report introduction gives the subject, scope, significance, and objectives of the research. The literature review explains what is known about the problem, as this knowledge has been reported in published articles and reports. The writer may also use the literature review to explain a choice of method or to show a rationale for investigation.

The introduction and the literature review may be separate sections, or they may be integrated into one section. Examine the introduction and literature review of the retinoblastoma research report.

Background and Significance

Cancer cells exhibit many abnormal traits. The most obvious trait is loss of contact inhibition. Cancer cells continue dividing even when crowded: they stack on top of each other to form an aggregated mass, eventually forming a tumor. They have a different shape from noncancerous cells, as they rely to a greater extent on anaerobic metabolism. Their outer membrane displays special tumor antigens, which confer distinct immunological properties on the cell (Weinberg, 1983). Cancer cells, unlike normal cells, will grow in semi-solid media and will form tumors when implanted into nude mice.

Oncogenes and Anti-Oncogenes—Their Relevance

A relatively small number of genes, termed oncogenes or proto-oncogenes, may profoundly influence transformation of a cellular phenotype from normal to neoplastic (Weinberg, 1983). Oncogenes are converted from normal cellular genes, the proto-oncogenes. Proto-oncogenes may be converted to active oncogenes by a number of somatic and/or hereditary events (Deion, 1984). Oncogene mutations as discrete as a single base pair change, resulting in a single amino acid substitution, have been shown, in some cases, to promote a transformed phenotype. Various oncoproteins may promote cellular growth, regular cellular signaling and/or regular transcriptional rates (Hunter, 1984). The mechanisms by which oncoproteins work are diverse and clearly involve fundamental cellular processes and changes in regulation of these processes (Goades, 1989).

More recently, a new mechanism for the development of cancer has been studied. In this mechanism, certain proteins are in normal cells not to promote proliferation but to suppress it (Weinberg, 1988). Thus, the loss of growth-suppressor proteins causes unregulated cell growth by removing a normally present control. Genes encoding such growth-suppressor proteins have been termed anti-oncogenes, or recessive oncogenes. The essential difference between a dominant and a recessive oncogene is that for the former it is the presence of the product, whereas for the latter it is the absence of the product that leads to transformation (Green, 1988).

Retinoblastoma and Osteosarcoma—Their Relationship

Retinoblastoma (RB) serves as a prototype for this recessive class of cancer genes. The normal function of the RB gene is to suppress growth. Loss of function is thus associated with the appearance of malignancy. Specific changes resulting in homozygosity or hemizygosity for the mutant or inactive allele appear to be a key mechanism leading to tumor formation (Murphree, 1984).

Retinoblastoma is a rare cancer found in the retinoblasts of children. Retinoblasts are the precursors of retinal cells. After differentiation into a specialized retinal cell, a retinoblast stops dividing and no longer serves as a target for tumorigenesis. Retinoblastoma occurs with a frequency of 1 in 10,000 (Benedict, 1988) to 1 in 20,000 live births (McFall, 1987), where the age of onset is anywhere from 0 to 7 years. No discernible geographic, racial or sex-specific clustering was apparent in the cases studied (Cavenee, 1986). Affected individuals fall into two categories: a) those having multifocal tumors that develop at an early age and b) those with unilateral tumors that appear at a later age. Individuals affected with multifocal tumors tend to be affected with the hereditary form of retinoblastoma, while those with unilateral tumors are usually affected with the sporadic form.

In 1971, Knudson hypothesized that retinoblastoma results from a mutation in both alleles of chromosome 13. Two events are necessary in the development of both the hereditary and the sporadic forms of retinoblastoma. The first event is a germinal mutation in the hereditary form and a somatic mutation in the sporadic form. The second event is somatic in both forms (Knudson, 1978). In hereditary cases, the mutant allele is usually inherited from the father (Bookstein, 1990) and is present in all cells of the body. As a result only one additional mutation must occur in the retinoblast in order for cancer to develop. With the sporadic form, both mutations must occur somatically.

The heritable form of RB is transmitted as a dominant cancer susceptibility trait (Lee, 1988). Each of the offspring of the carrier parent has a 50% chance of inheriting the trait, and, of these, 90% will develop RB. While the predisposing mutation is inherited in a dominant fashion, it is recessive at the cellular level. The gene represents the prototype for a recessive class of human tumor cancer genes. The inherited mutation is not sufficient to cause cancer. It merely predisposes the cell to the development of retinoblastoma. For cancer to develop, the second allele must also undergo mutation.

The method by which the second mutation occurs is not known. Possibilities include nondisjunction, nondisjunction with reduplication of the mutated allele and mitotic recombination. Any of these events results in homozygosity or hemizygosity for the abnormal chromosome 13 (Figure 1). The mutation apparently can be caused by either a microscopic or submicroscopic change (Knudson, 1978). Whether or not these tumors have identifiable structural changes within the RB gene, they either have an absence or abnormal expression of the RB transcript (Benedict, 1988). Through reverse transcription, it has been shown that 470 nucleotides are lost near the 5' end of the gene. As the size of the deletion is only about 50kb, it is often too small to be cytogenetically visible (Lee, 1988).

In contrast, the normal protein produced by the RB gene is 110 kD in size (Lee, 1988). RB tumors lack this protein.

Experiments have shown that in normal cells, the protein is located within the nucleus, where it is associated with DNA binding activity. This association supports the proposed role of the protein in regulating other genes. It is these genes which, when unregulated, cause the uncontrolled proliferation seen in cancer cells.

Studies have shown that individuals affected with the hereditary form of retinoblastoma show a greatly increased risk of developing independent secondary neoplasms (Herd, 1987). The most common of these secondary neoplasms is osteosarcoma (OS). Studies show that cells in some osteosarcoma tumors exhibit a deletion at the Rb1 locus. It is therefore thought that some OS arises by the same mechanism as retinoblastoma (Cavenee, 1986). Other etiologic possibilities have been suggested for OS, such as radiation effects (Baack, 1990), but other studies have also revealed cases in which OS developed outside the field of radiation in the absence of such treatment (Hansen, 1985).

Comparative Features of Canine OS and Human OS

Osteosarcoma in dogs is the most commonly occurring skeletal neoplasm. It affects 7 in 100,000 dogs annually. Dogs diagnosed with OS have a very poor prognosis, with only 10-20% surviving one year following amputation. As in humans, OS readily metastasizes, with the most common site being the lungs.

Many other similarities exist between OS in man and OS in dogs. (See Table 1). OS primarily affects the appendicular skeleton of both species. The bones most often affected are the proximal humerus, the distal femur, the proximal tibia, and the distal radius. A genetic correlation is seen according to size: breeds of large dogs (over 80 lbs.) and tall humans. Familiar trends are also evident. A high occurrence of OS is found among families of St. Bernards and rottweilers as well as in several pairs of human siblings (Haines, 1989).

Treatment of Osteosarcoma

Current treatment for human osteosarcoma involves removal of the tumor followed by radiation therapy and chemotherapy. In vitro research is currently underway to test the possibility of gene therapy as a mode of treatment. Huang et al. (1988) demonstrated that by inserting a functional RB protein into cells containing inactivated endogenous RB genes, the neoplastic phenotype was suppressed. Cells were infected with a retrovirus carrying the functional RB gene. Infected cells in culture subsequently expressed a RB protein indistinguishable from the native RB in terms of molecular weight, cellular location and phosphorylation. Infected cells also became enlarged and exhibited severely inhibited growth. When injected into nude mice, the infected cells lacked the ability to form tumors.

Furthermore, Bookstein et al. (1990) successfully restored normal RB expression in human prostate cancer cell line DU145, which was shown to possess a RB mRNA transcription that lacked 105 nucleotides by exon 21. Normal RB expression was restored in DU145 cells using retrovirus mediated gene transfer. The transformed cells, expressing exogenous RB protein, subsequently lost their ability to form tumors in nude mice.

The results obtained by Huang and Bookstein illustrate the possibility of gene therapy as a new form of treatment of malignant cancers. Gene therapy would be beneficial in that it is based on the permanent correction of an underlying defect in tumor cells. Unlike conventional cytotoxic cancer therapies, gene therapy should not be harmful to normal cells and therefore need not be specifically targeted.

Research Goals

My research focuses on OS in canines with the hope that such a study will lead to discovery of a correlation between canines and humans. If OS in dogs is shown to share molecular features with human RB and OS, dogs with hereditary diseases may then be considered as research models for the benefit of both species.

My research will thus have three specific aims:

1. Using Northern analysis, to characterize RB gene transcription in normal canine tissues.
2. Using Northern analysis, to characterize RB gene transcription in canine osteosarcoma.
3. To determine if the RB transcript from canine osteosarcoma differs from the transcript of normal tissues, and then to determine the frequency of RB mRNA changes in canine osteosarcoma.

Note that the student uses parenthetical references to show what is known about retinoblastoma and osteosarcoma, as these findings relate to the proposed research. Extant research shows the rationale for the proposed research on canines.

The objectives of the research are sometimes stated as a hypothesis. They can often be stated as questions. The important point to note is that the study has a rationale, based on the existing literature.

In much research reporting, passive voice and past tense are used to report what is known from previous research. Present tense is used to indicate current knowledge or status of the problem. You may wish to examine the use of tense and voice in the student report.

Materials and Methods

The researcher's goal in this section is to allow other experienced researchers to duplicate the research. This section usually contains the following parts:

- Design of the investigation—what you planned to do in your research (perhaps one sentence)
- Materials—objects and equipment you used for the research
- Procedures—how you conducted the research
- Methods for observation and interpretation of what you found

However, not every part may be distinctly titled. In the retinoblastoma research report, the investigation involved seven steps, as indicated by the seven subheadings under Materials and Methods. Within each step, the writer states what materials were used for that step, the procedure used (with explanation added when she deems that to be necessary), with the final step devoted to analysis of the data collected.

Materials and Methods

The research required seven major phases. Crucial analysis occurred during RNA Extractions, Nucleic Acid Electrophoresis, and Northern Hybridization.

Description of each research phase

Tissue Sample and Cell Lines Utilization

Normal tissues (n = 6) were collected from terminal teaching dogs immediately after euthanasia. No history was available on these animals.

Canine osteosarcoma tissue was collected from animals presented for tumor biopsy or removal at Colorado State University Veterinary Teaching Hospital (n = 24) and the Texas A&M Veterinary Teaching Hospital (n = 6). All tissue and tumor samples were stored at -80° C until use.

Two human cells were also utilized. Human retinoblastoma cell line, Y-79, is known to express a truncated RB message of 4.0kb. A human fibroblast cell line, CDD-45, is expected to express a normal RB transcript of 4.7kb. Both cell lines served as homologous controls for hybridization with the human RB cDNA probe. Y-79 cells were grown in RPMI with 15% fetal calf serum; CDD-45 cells were grown in MEM with 10% FCS. Both cell lines were grown at 37° C in 5% CO_2 and 95% O_2.

RNA Extractions

Approximately 0.5g of frozen tissue and tumor samples was ground under liquid N2 using a mortar and pestle. Following grinding, the samples were denatured and solubilized in guanidinium thiocyanate solution (4M guanidinium thiocyanate, 2-mercaptoethanol). The tissue was passed through a 16G needle followed by a 20G needle to reduce viscosity. Sodium acetate was added to lower pH. The samples were extracted with phenol followed by chloroform: isoamyl alcohol (24:1). The aqueous phase was precipitated with equal volume isopropanol at -20° C for 1.5 hrs. The pellet was resuspended in guanidinium solution and reextracted with phenol and chloroform: isoamyl alcohol. The aqueous phase was precipitated again under the same conditions. The pellet was resuspended and precipitated with 2.5 vol. ethanol. The new pellet was washed in 70% ethanol, dried, and resuspended in 100mcl 0.5% SDS.

Quantification of RNA

Extracted RNA was diluted 1:20 in 0.5% SDS and quantitated using a Beckman DU-70 spectrophotometer. The spectrophotometer was used on the dual wavelength program and set to compare O.D.260 and O.D.280. The 260/280 ratio should be close to 2.0 and not less than 1.6 for acceptable RNA purification. Calculations used were as follows:

mcg RNA = (O.D.260) (constant) (dilution factor) (ml. sample)

constant = 40mcg/ml

dil. factor = 20 (5mcl/100mcl = 1/20)

ml. sample = 100mcl-5mcl = 0.095

Nucleic Acid Electrophoresis

10mcg of sample were dried and resuspended in 10mcl sample buffer [37% formalde-hyde (17.5% vol), 2x di-formaldehyde (50%), 5x MOPS running buffer (10%), TE pH8.0 (22.5%)]. 5mcl of 6x tracking dye was added and the samples were loaded into the wells of an 0.5% agarose horizontal gel; 4mcl ethidium bromide were added to the gel to stain the nucleic acids during electrophoresis. The gel was run in 1x MOPS running buffer at 50V for 3-4 hrs. A UV-illuminated photograph was taken of each gel for comparison of rRNA band size. The nucleic acids were then transferred overnight from the gel to a Nytran membrane using 1x sodium transfer buffer (pH 6.5).

Probe Labelling

3.8R and 0.9R human cDNA probes were prepared; 3.8R hybridizes to the 3' end and 0.9R to the 5' end of the Rb transcript. The probes were labelled using the BRL Random Primers DNA Labeling System. Fifty ng of DNA was added to 23mcl 1xTE and denatured. Six mcl dNTPs, 15mcl random primer buffer solution, and 5mcl ^{32}P dCTP were added on ice and mixed; 1 mcl Klenow fragment was added and the mixture briefly centrifuged. The probe was allowed to incubate at 37° C for 30 min. Equal vol-ume stop buffer was added and the resulting mixture was separated through a column of Sephadex G50 with TE. The labelled probe was collected. 1 mcl was spotted on a glass filter (Whatman GF/C) and counted using a LKB 1211 Rack-Beta Liquid Scintillation Counter.

Northern Hybridization

Membranes were hybridized using a rapid hybridization protocol. Northern blots were prehybridized with shaking at 65° C for 15 min in rapid hybridization buffer (pre-warmed to 65° C). The probe was denatured at 95-100° C for 2-5 min. The probe was added to the hybridization buffer at a concentration of 1¥10^6 cpm/mcl. The membranes were allowed to hybridize with shaking at 65° C overnight (minimum of 2 hrs. recom-mended in protocol). The membranes were washed once at room temperature for 15 min. in 1% SDS and 1xSSC, then twice at 65° C for 30 min. in 0.5% SDS and 0.5xSSC. The washed membranes were placed in a seal-a-meal bag and autoradiographed with 2 intensifying screens at -80° C for 48-120 hrs.

Analysis

The developed autoradiographs were analysed by comparison to known molecular weight markers to determine the size of the RB transcript in normal tissues and in canine osteosarcoma.

Results

You may begin your results section with an overview of what you have learned. In a results section, the supporting details, if at all possible, are presented in tables and graphs. (We have omitted those included in the student report.) You do not need to restate these details, but you may want to refer to key data, both to emphasize their significance and to help your readers compre-hend your tables and graphs.

Note that in the Results section of the retinoblastoma report, the student specifically states her results from the three crucial analysis phases she mentions at the beginning of Materials and Methods:

The main results occurring in the three crucial phases.

Results

The results of the three crucial analytical phases are as follows:

RNA Extraction

Total RNA was extracted from normal canine tissues, control cell lines, and canine osteosarcomas. RNA was quantitated and evaluated for intactness (Tables 2 and 3).

Since nucleic acids absorb at a wavelength of 260 nm and proteins absorb wavelengths of 280 nm, the desired range for the 260/280 ratio is 1.6 to 2.0. Most samples yielded a ratio in the desired range, while some (103573, 105989, 106463, 106685, 106899-B, OS2.7) had lower ratios, indicating the presence of excess protein. Only 3 samples did not yield at least 10mcg of RNA (091091, 099580, 107393). The entire quantity of RNA available for these three samples was loaded per lane during electrophoresis.

Nucleic Acid Electrophoresis

CCD-45 is a normal human fibroblast cell line and as such is expected to express a typical RB mRNA of 4.7kb. Y-79, a cell line derived from human retinoblastoma, expresses a shortened mRNA transcript (4.0kb). RNA from both of these cell lines were included as controls.

The integrity of RNA from all samples was evaluated. Following electrophoresis for 3-4 hours, the gels were examined under UV light for bands in the regions of the 18S and 28S subunits of rRNA, indicating the presence of intact RNA. These bands were seen for all normal tissues (Figs. 4 and 5), 3 lanes of CCD (Figs. 4-9), one lane of Y-79 (Fig. 7), and 14 lanes of tumors (Figs. 6-9). Other lanes indicated the presence of degraded RNA. (See Figs. 4-9 and Tables 2 and 3.)

Northern Hybridization

Nucleic acids were transferred from gels to Nytran membranes. Following transfer, the membrane was probed using 3.8R and 0.9R. At no time were acceptable hybridization signals apparent with the 3.8R probe. Using 0.9R, signals were obtained for CCD45 and 5 normal tissues (lymph node, liver, testes, kidney, uterus) (Fig. 10). However, no signal was seen with any of the later membranes. Possible signals were obtained on some tumors, but were so faint as to be inconclusive.

Discussion

The discussion interprets the results. It answers questions such as these:

- Do the results really answer the questions raised?
- Are there any problems with the results? If so, why?
- Were the research objectives met?
- How do the results compare with results from previous research? Are there disagreements? Can these disagreements be explained?

Although the discussion section may cover a lot of ground, keep it tightly organized around the answers to the questions that need to be asked. In the retinoblastoma report, the writer directs the discussion to the three main research steps and explains the problems she encountered and the possible explanation:

The writer is clear
and specific about
the results.

For each of the
crucial phases in the
research, the writer
explains the negative
results, the possible
reasons for the
results, and ways
that better results
could be obtained.

Discussion

Problems occurred within all three analytical phases. These problems affected the results of the research.

RNA Extraction

Total cellular RNA was extracted from six normal canine tissues, 30 osteosarcoma tumors, and two human cell lines. The quantity and quality of RNA obtained were calculated and are shown in Tables 2 and 3. The majority of samples yielded high amounts of RNA, with the exception of 091091, 099580, and 107393. Ratios obtained for 260/280 were primarily between 1.6 and 2.0. Ratios less than that indicate the presence of unextracted protein contaminating the DNA.

Nucleic Acid Electrophoresis

All electrophoresis was accomplished using an RNA ladder for determination of transcript size and RNA from CCD-45 cells for comparison to typical human RB transcript. RNA from Y-79 cells was included on three of the gels, until the available quantity ran out. Y-79 RB transcripts are known to be truncated and thus represent an important positive control for RB gene mutation. Following electrophoresis for 3-4 hours, the gels were examined for the presence of intact rRNA. Bands localized at the 18S and 28S subunits of rRNA suggest the presence of undegraded RNA. In some cases where the bands were not seen, clumps of degraded RNA were observed at the end of the lane. Other lanes showed no evidence of nucleic acids (Figs. 4-9).

The rRNA bands were seen for all normal tissues, CCD-45, Y-79, and for 14 out of 30 tumors. There are many possible explanations for the lack of intact RNA. Twenty-four of the tumors were sent to Texas A&M from Colorado State University. It is not known how the tumors were handled before their arrival. Perhaps they were allowed to sit at room temperature for a period of time before freezing. The manner in which the samples were shipped could also have been less than ideal. If at any time the samples were allowed to thaw, it would allow time for endogenous RNA to degrade the RNA.

The error may also lie within the extraction procedure. I extracted the tumors in 3 batches of 10. From the first extraction, 5 tumors indicated intact RNA; from the second, only 2 had intact RNA; and from the third, 7. One might assume that mishandling occurred, especially during the second batch. However, mistakes made during the extraction cannot account for the degradation seen in all the samples as some from each batch, as well as all normal tissues and cells, had intact RNA.

Northern Hybridization

The success with which the probe bound to the canine RNA was minimal. All membranes were hybridized first with 3.8R then with 0.9R. It was hoped that the size of the mRNA could be determined by analyzing the location of the bands. However, as none of the mRNA was successfully labelled with the radioactive probe, no bands were found.

When using the 0.9R probe, which binds to the 5' end of the transcript, hybridization was seen with one membrane. Signals were detected with CCD-45 and 5 normal tissues (lymph node, liver, testes, kidney, and uterus) (Fig. 10). The approximate transcript size of mRNA from normal tissues and CCD-45 cells was 2.4kb. Another band around 6.5kb was found for the CCD-45 cells and for LN-4, U-5, and L-2. One tumor (107393) did hybridize to the 0.9R probe. The approximate transcript size was 2.5kb, with another band at 7.5kb (Fig. 11).

I am unsure as to exactly why the hybridizations were unsuccessful. Lack of homology between canine RNA and a human DNA probe was one possibility. However, the human probe should have labelled the RNA from the CCD and Y-79 cells, both of which were derived from human samples. Also, the 0.9R probe hybridized with normal canine tissues at an earlier date. It would therefore be reasonable to expect a signal from the other normals probed with 0.9R at a later date. In addition, if homology exists between human probe and normal canine tissue RNA, the same homology should exist with canine tumor RNA.

Since lack of homology can essentially be ruled out, other reasons must be explored. A problem may have existed with the probe itself. Perhaps the ^{32}P dCTP was not fresh or did not incorporate adequately into the DNA. However, on the basis of the specific activity, it is thought that the probe should have been adequate.

The probe DNA may not have been allowed to denature long enough before being added to the membrane. Repetition of this technical error on all blots would have been unlikely.

Another possible cause lies in the transfer of the nucleic acids from the gel to the Nytran membrane. All transfers were allowed to proceed overnight, and all were set up in the manner detailed in the protocol. When dismantling the transfer, in each case it was noted that the tracking dye had transferred from the gel to the membrane, indicating that the nucleic acid should also have transferred.

Steps that can be taken in the future to help increase hybridization include a) cloning the canine RB gene to create a homologous cDNA probe, b) preparing oligonucleotide probes to conserved areas of human RB gene that might be expected to hybridize more efficiently with canine transcripts and/or c) using a reverse polymerase chain reaction (rPCR) to amplify the canine RB message. These methods increase the possibility of documenting a hybridization for the canine RB transcript.

Cloning of the canine RB gene would require the production of a canine cDNA library from canine mRNA. Screening using nucleic acid probes would require production of a canine cDNA library from canine mRNA. Screening using nucleic acid probes to RB sequences or antibodies to expressed RB fusion proteins should allow selection of positive clones with subsequent sub-cloning and RB cDNA purification. This procedure would eventually allow for a homologous Northern screening system of canine osteosarcomas using a canine RB cDNA probe. The investment of time and energy for this approach would be substantial.

A more practical method would be to prepare oligonucleotide probes for conserved segments of the human RB gene. Since the sequence of the human RB gene is known and functional regions of the gene delineated, a specific sequence from a conserved region of the gene can be synthesized. Conserved gene sequences in the human gene would presumably be represented in canines, allowing more efficient hybridization.

Another possibility would be to use reverse polymerase chain reaction to amplify canine RB mRNA. Canine mRNA would be reverse transcribed to DNA, which would then be used in the PCR reactions. Two oligonucleotide primers flanking the desired segment of RB DNA and oriented with their 3' ends facing each other would be designed so that DNA synthesis extended across the DNA segment between them. The template DNA would be denatured in the presence of the oligo primers and the 4 dNTPs. The mixture would be cooled, allowing the oligos to anneal to the target segment. Annealed primers would then be extended by DNA polymerase. After repeating the cycle several times (~30x), an amplification level of 106 of the desired segment should have occurred. This procedure would yield a much greater amount of canine RB mRNA available for Northern hybridizations (23).

Conclusion

A conclusion, if necessary, allows you to add any final evaluating remarks about the project in general. In the retinoblastoma report, the writer explains the partial success (as well as the partial failure) of the research and what might be done in subsequent research. The conclusion can state the value of the research in this project.

Conclusion

With the data collected, the RB gene can be characterized in the canine species and research into osteosarcoma and possible treatments, including gene therapy, can continue. Using the data already collected, it has been possible to characterize RB transcripts as found in normal canine tissue as compared to normal human fibroblast cell line CCD-45.

While many explanations exist for lack of adequate hybridization with the RB probe, none provides an adequate explanation in itself. The cause may be a factor of all those reasons detailed or may be something I have not considered. However, while no signal was obtained for the tumors, signal was obtained for some normal tissues. Also, the RNA from the tumors remaining after electrophoresis has been quantitated and stored at -80° C. Thus, it is feasible that given more time, the errors and drawbacks encountered could be worked out and sufficient data collected from the tumors to allow analysis of RB transcripts.

A Final Word

In this section we have given you general advice about reporting empirical research. If you are to become a professional in any field that requires such reporting, doing it well will be of vital importance to you. Therefore, we strongly urge you to examine representative journals and student theses in your discipline. Observe closely their format and style. Most journals have a section labelled something like "Information for Contributors." This section will inform you about manuscript preparation and style.

Many disciplines in engineering and science require senior students to pursue an empirical research project. If you are assigned such a project, you may well find that your empirical research can be the topic of a formal report assignment in your technical writing class. Professors in your disciplinary courses will guide you in the development of your research, and the above guidelines should guide you in planning how to report your research.

Planning and Revision Checklists

The following questions are a summary of the key points in this chapter, and they provide a checklist when you are planning and revising any document for your readers.

Planning

• What is the purpose of your report? Have you stated it in one sentence?

continued >>

- What is the scope of your report?
- Who is your reader? What is your reader's technical level?
- What will your readers do with the information?
- What information will you need to write the report?
- How long should the report be?

- What format should you use for the report?
- What report elements will you need?
- What elements do you need to include in your introduction?
- What arrangement will you use to present your report?
- What graphics will you need to present information or data?

Revision

- Have you stated your purpose clearly and specifically?
- Has the information in your discussion fulfilled your purpose?
- Is your information correct?
- Is your information clearly stated?
- Does your introduction adequately prepare your reader for what will come in the report itself?

- Do your conclusions follow logically from your discussion?
- Do your recommendations follow logically from your conclusions?
- Is the presentation of your report logical?
- Do your graphics immediately show what they are designed to show?
- Have you adequately documented all information sources?

 ## Weblinks

Academic Writing: Scientific Reports
www.wisc.edu/writing/Handbook/ScienceReport.html#top

Thesis Development in Analytical Writing
www.rpi.edu/dpt/llc/writecenter/web/text/thesis.html

Writing an Analytic Research Paper
www.urich.edu/~writing/rsrchppr.htm

Exercises

1. Locate a journal in your field that reports empirical studies of major issues in your field. Survey issues during the last two years. Write an informal information report to your instructor describing the kinds of topics covered and the approach required by the journal for reporting the research.

2. Choose one empirical research article. Write an information report describing how the writer develops each part: introduction

and literature review, materials and methods, results, and discussion. Add a final section summarizing the instructions to authors for papers submitted to this journal.

3. Reports for the situations below may be written either individually or collaboratively. Your instructor may divide the class into work groups to develop a report responding to each issue. If you have such a collaborative assignment, be sure that your group works separately from the other groups. After completing individual or group reports, you may want to compare reports written by other individuals or other groups, raising these questions:

- What design differences do you see?
- Are the differences significant as they affect the overall effectiveness of each report?
- Based on how writers perceive the report situation, how do these differences reflect content and structure?

As you begin the planning process for each report, answer the following questions:

- Who will be the readers of this report? What are the differences among these readers in terms of their knowledge about what you will say?
- What is your purpose in writing this report?
- What main ideas do you want to include?
- Should this be an informal report or a formal report?
- What main sections do you want to include?
- How should these sections be arranged?
- Where will you place the ideas you listed in question 3?
- Will any visual presentations, such as tables or graphs, be important in presenting your information?
- What kind of format considerations do you want to use?

Report Situations

A. Your professional society has just received a letter from the dean of your faculty explaining that a wide-ranging study is underway to evaluate the required courses in each department. As part of this evaluation, he asks your organization to submit a report explaining what you found to be the worst required courses you have taken. He also asks you to evaluate the best courses you have taken. The dean states that a committee composed of faculty and students from each department, from outside each department, and from the dean's office will be examining all required courses in each department. He definitely wants input from students with majors in each department, as these evaluations are deemed important in the institution's examination of its programs.

B. By April 15 of every academic year, your professional society is required to submit a budget and an action plan for the coming year to the university. In this budget report, you must describe what activities the society will pursue the next academic year, the expenditures planned for these activities, and any extra funding the society will need for special projects or for other activities. The dean of students must approve the action plan and the budget by the first meeting in September.

C. The student professional societies on campus have been asked to write reports listing and describing the major problems students confront on the campus and suggesting any recommendations. These reports will be sent to the Officer of Student Affairs, who will compile the reports from student groups and submit one report to the board of governors.

D. You are a student assistant in the main office of your department. Your department chair has decided that the department needs to develop a brochure telling new students how to survive their first year. You have been asked to work with other majors in the department to develop such a document, which will be given to new students by the department's advisors. The department chair asks you to keep the document to under 10 pages, fewer if at all possible, as the department plans to make several hundred copies.

E. Write a report that defines and then describes your major field or discipline. This report, which should be four pages or fewer, will be available at the university's Open House. Students like you will be there to answer questions about your department and the majors available in the department. This report will be available for high school students who are thinking about what discipline they would like to study in college or university. As you plan such a document, you might want to discuss the importance of this discipline and its subfields, job opportunities available for new graduates in this discipline, coursework required for a major in this discipline, etc. In short, what would a high school student be interested in knowing about your major field of specialization?

F. The chair of your department has asked you to write a report recommending the best calculator for students in your major. Write a report to your department's advisor explaining the kind(s) of calculators you believe students should purchase. Explain the rationale for your views.

Oral Exercises

Before you attempt either oral exercise, please consult the guidelines in Chapter 17, "Oral Reports." These reports are based on B and C above.

- *Report Situation B.* Assume that as an officer in your professional society, you are asked to give an oral version of your budget report to the dean of students and her staff. Your presentation should be 10 minutes maximum. Be sure to include visual aids to explain your proposed expenditures.
- *Report Situation C.* The Officer of Student Affairs has invited your professional organization to give an oral briefing describing your concerns about campus issues to the university's academic council. You will be allowed 10 minutes to give an oral summary of your written report. Use visual aids if they will enhance your points.

INSTRUCTIONS

Instructing others to follow some procedure is a common task on the job. Sometimes the instructions are given orally. When the procedure is done by many people or is done repeatedly, however, written instructions are a better choice. Instructions may be very simple, as in Figure 15-1, or exceedingly complex, requiring a bookshelf full of manuals. They may be highly technical, dealing with operating machinery or programming computers, for example. Or they may be executive- or business-oriented, such as explaining how to complete a form or how to route memorandums through a company. The task is not to be taken lightly. A Shakespearean scholar who had also served in the British Army wrote the following:

> The most effective elementary training [in writing] I ever received was not from masters at school but in composing daily orders and instructions as staff captain in charge of the administration of seventy-two miscellaneous military units. It is far easier to discuss Hamlet's complexes than to write orders which ensure that five working parties from five different units arrive at the right place at the right time equipped with the proper tools for the job. One soon learns that the most seemingly simple statement can bear two meanings and that when instructions are misunderstood the fault usually lies with the original order.[1]

To use Call Waiting:

To answer a second call while you are talking on the phone:

When you hear a beep:

1. Press (**Link**) . Your existing call is placed on hold.

To return to the original call:

1. Press (**Link**) .

Note: Call waiting does not work if a Three-Way Calling conversation is in progress.

Figure 15-1   SIMPLE INSTRUCTIONS

Source: Bell Canada, "Vista" brochure (PQ 733 734 Issue 02). © 1995 Bell Canada.

This chapter discusses situational analysis for instructions, possible components of instructions, creating an accessible format, and the importance of checking with your readers.

Situational Analysis for Instructions

In preparing to write instructions, follow the situational analysis we describe on pages 13–17 in Chapter 2, "Composing." In addition, pay particular attention to the answers to the following questions.[2]

- What is the purpose of my instructions?
- What is my reader's point of view?
- How and where will my readers use these instructions?
- What content does my reader really need and want?
- How should I arrange my content?

What Is the Purpose of My Instructions?

Be quite specific about the purpose of your instructions. Keep your purpose in mind because it will guide you in choosing your content and in arranging and formatting that content. State your purpose in writing, like this:

> To instruct the plant managers, the corporate treasurer, and the plant accountant in the steps they need to follow to establish a petty cash fund.

What Is My Reader's Point of View?

Don't be satisfied with a general description of a reader, such as "the average consumer" or "a typical car owner." You'll gain more accurate insights if you put yourself in the place of someone you know who fits that general description. For example, if I were my grandfather, what would be my point of view if I had to work with these instructions on how to complete this form? What questions and problems might I have? In what order might these questions and problems arise? Are there terms and concepts involved that I might not understand? What information do I really need? What information would be irrelevant? And so forth.

How and Where Will My Readers Use These Instructions?

Will your readers read your instructions carefully from beginning to end? Evidence indicates that they will not.[3] Readers most often scan instructions and then read them closely at those points where they need clarification. In other words, they usually read them as a reference work rather than as an essay or a novel. Where will your readers use these instructions? In a comfortable, well-lighted workshop, well stocked with tools? In a cold, drafty, poorly lighted garage with only those tools they thought to bring from the workshop? In the cockpit of a boat under emergency conditions, reading by a flashlight? Standing in line in a government office? The answers to such questions will help you organize and format your instructions.

What Content Does My Reader Really Need and Want?

Understanding your purpose and your reader's point of view is essential for answering this question. You can include many things in a set of instructions: theory, descriptions of mechanisms, troubleshooting advice, and so forth. We discuss such things in the next section, "Possible Components of Instructions." You should include everything that is really relevant and nothing that is not relevant. If your reader has a need or a desire for theory, then furnish it. If theory is not needed or desired, furnishing it would be wasted effort for all concerned. Unneeded material is worse than irrelevant. It may obscure the relevant information to the point where the reader has difficulty finding it.

How Should I Arrange My Content?

Answers to all the previous questions help you to make decisions about arranging the content. If a good deal of theory is important and needed, your arrangement should probably include a separate section for it. If only brief explanations of theory are needed for the reader to understand a few steps in the instructions, place the explanations with the steps. For example, you might put the whys and wherefores of using a carpenter's level at the point in the instructions where the reader needs to use a level.

For arranging the actual instructions on how to perform the process, you must understand the process fully. If you can perform the process, taking notes as you go, do so. If that is not possible or convenient, analyse the process in your mind. Break it into its major steps and substeps. Be alert for potential trouble spots for your reader.

Possible Components of Instructions

Sets of instructions may contain as many as eight components:

- Introduction
- Theory or principles of operation
- List of equipment and materials needed
- Description of the mechanism

- Warnings
- How–to instructions
- Tips and troubleshooting procedures
- Glossary

We do not present this list as a rigid format. For example, you may find that you do not need a theory section, or you may include it as part of your introduction. You may want to vary the order of the sections. You may want to describe or list equipment as it is needed while performing the process rather than in a separate section. Often, nothing more is needed than the how-to instructions. We present the components primarily as a guide to your discovery of the material you will need.

Introduction

Normally, introductions to instructions state the purpose of the instructions and preview the contents. Frequently, they provide motivation for reading and following the instructions. They may also directly or indirectly indicate who the intended readers are. The following, from a publication on legislation regarding lead in the workplace, does all these things:

Intended audience

Purpose

The guide has been prepared to help employers, workers, members of joint health and safety committees, supervisors and occupational health personnel meet the requirements of the designated substance regulation respecting lead in the workplace and to understand the responsibilities this regulation places on all participants in the workplace health and safety system.

General reference to contents

The advice in this guide is the interpretation, by officials of the Occupational Health and Safety Division, of the <u>Occupational Health and Safety Act</u> (the Act) and regulations.

The advice does not have binding effect but is intended to provide general answers to possible questions asked in the context of a specific situation. It is being used by staff of the ministry to assist in the administration of the lead regulation.

Questions of construction and application will find their ultimate answer given by the courts where a contest ensues as to construction or application of a legislative provision.[4]

Introductions to instructions are often not much different from the introductions we describe for you in Chapter 9, "Design Elements of Reports." However, short sets of instructions may have very abbreviated introductions or, in some cases, no introduction at all. On the other hand, when introductions are longer than the one we have shown you, it is usually because the writers have chosen to include theory or principles of operation in the introduction. This is an accepted practice, and we tell you how to give such information in our next section.

Theory or Principles of Operation

Many sets of instructions contain a section that deals with the theory or principles of operation that underlie the procedures explained. Sometimes historical background is also included. These sections may be called "Theory" or "Principles of Operation," or they may have substantive titles such as "Colour Dos and Don'ts," "Purpose and Use of Conditioners," and "Basic Forage Blower Operation." Information about theory may be presented for several reasons. Some people have a natural curiosity about the principles behind a procedure. Others may need to know the purpose and use of the procedure. The good TV repair technician wants to know why turning the vertical control knob steadies the picture. Understanding the purposes behind simple adjustments enables the technician to investigate complex problems. What if nothing happens when the vertical control knob is turned? With a background in theory, the technician will know more readily where to look in the TV set to find a malfunction.

Such sections can be quite simple. In the following section, headed "Application," from a pamphlet on caulking and weatherstripping, some basic theory is presented in easy-to-understand language as part of the instructions:

Application

Cut the tube nozzle at a 45° angle. The closer to the tube you cut the nozzle, the larger the bead. So start small; you can always cut it bigger.

Hold the gun at a 45° angle to the work and exert a constant pressure. Pushing the gun forward works well in small cracks because it helps to force caulking in. Pulling the gun allows you to apply a heavier bead.

The bead should be at least as deep as it is wide. It should have a convex surface and should adhere well to both sides of the crack. Many caulks (such as silicone and latex) can be smoothed with a wet finger or tooled before they cure (a skin forms on the bead). Most caulks will require a solvent for cleaning.

Remember to release the pressure on the plunger after each run. Otherwise, you will get messy drips.[5]

As simple as this excerpt is, it presents useful principles. Readers are told not only what to do, but why.

Theory sections can be more complex. Figure 15-2 presents a portion of the theory section from the lead brochure. It describes the damage that overexposure can do to the human body. Understanding the theory helps readers to understand the need for lead regulation and motivates them to follow the regulations. The entire section is written in a very straightforward way: What does this theory mean for the reader? Through the careful use of format and simple language, the writers of the brochure make the theory quite accessible for the intended audience.

As our two excerpts illustrate, many diverse items of information can be placed in a theory or principles section. Remember, however, that the main purpose of the section is to emphasize the principles that underlie the actions later described in the how-to instructions. In this section, you're telling your readers *why*. Later, you'll tell them *how*. Theory is important, but don't get carried away with it. Experts in a process sometimes develop this section at too great length, burying their readers under information they don't need and obscuring more important information that they do need. Make

Why Is Lead a Health Hazard?

Lead can cause serious damage to a number of systems in the body. These harmful effects are preventable by diligent adherence to a comprehensive lead control program.

Overexposure to lead can affect:

The Blood: Lead can interfere with the body's ability to manufacture hemoglobin, the molecule in red blood cells responsible for carrying oxygen to the tissues.

The Kidneys: Lead can reduce the ability of the kidneys to filter wastes from the bloodstream.

The Gastro-intestinal System: Lead poisoning may result in complaints of abdominal pain, loss of appetite, vomiting, nausea, constipation or diarrhea.

The Nervous System: Lead can cause peripheral nerve damage that results in muscle weakness. It may also lead to behavioural changes and to impairment of vision and hearing. At very high levels, lead can affect the brain, causing convulsions, coma, and even death.

The Reproductive System: Lead may harm the developing fetus and may cause impaired sperm production.

Like many other poisons, lead may be harmful following a high dose received in a short period of time (acute poisoning), or after long-term exposure to lower doses (chronic poisoning).

Symptoms of **acute lead poisoning** include a metallic taste in the mouth and gastro-intestinal symptoms such as vomiting, abdominal cramps, constipation or diarrhea. The major effect of acute organic poisoning by either TEL or TML is on the central nervous system, with symptoms such as disturbed sleep, headache and psychosis.

The earliest signs of **chronic lead poisoning** may not be noticed because they are similar to many common complaints. These include headache, fatigue, irritability, pains in joints and muscles, abdominal pain and constipation. More severe chronic poisoning leads to several characteristic symptoms, including a blue line on the gums, wrist drop (the inability to hold the hand extended), severe abdominal pain and pallor.

Although all forms of lead are potentially harmful if absorbed, some are more toxic than others. However, it is the amount of lead that enters the body that really matters. This is largely dependent on the solubility and physical form of the lead. For example, fine lead dust or powder is a major hazard whether it is pure lead or a lead compound such as lead oxide.

Figure 15-2 THEORY SECTION

Source: Ontario Ministry of Labour, Health & Safety Division, *Designated Substances in the Workplace: A Guide to the Lead Regulation* (1985, rev. 1988): 4–5.

this section, if you have it at all, only as full and as complex as your analysis of purpose and audience demands.

List of Equipment and Materials Needed

In a list of equipment and materials, you tell your readers what they will need to accomplish the process. A simple example would be the list of cooking utensils and ingredients that precedes a recipe. Sometimes, in straightforward processes or with knowledgeable audiences, the list of equipment is not used. Instead, the instructions tell the readers what equipment they need as they need it: "Take a rubber mallet and tap the hubcap to be sure it's secure."

When a list is used, often each item is simply listed by name. Occasionally, however, your audience analysis may indicate that more information is needed. You may want, for instance, to define and describe the tools and equipment needed, as is done in Figure 15-3. If you think your readers are really unfamiliar with the tools or equipment being used, you may even give instruction in their use, as in Figure 15-4. If the equipment cannot be easily obtained, you'll do your readers a service by telling them where they can find the hard-to-get items. As always, your audience analysis determines the amount and kind of information you present.

To install an air-vapour retarder, you might need:

Caulking material that will adhere to the poly and remain flexible. By far the best material is acoustical sealant, which can be bought in tubes. A sub-floor adhesive or butyl caulk can also be used to seal the poly.

A caulking gun, usually the large size, if you are using the acoustical sealant. Some manufacturers now make acoustical sealant in smaller containers. You should buy a good caulking gun that will not break easily and will hold the caulking tube securely in place.

A staple gun and staples.

Extruded polystyrene, an impermeable insulation that you can use where the poly is difficult to place, such as between joints and between floors.

Vapour retarder paint or vinyl wallpaper, in combination with caulking, for places where you can't install a new poly sheet.

Foamed-in-place polyurethane for places that are hard to reach. This comes in small aerosol cans and is both an air barrier and vapour retarder.

Other equipment for specific applications, such as **poly-vapour boxes**, to provide a continuous air-vapour retarder around electrical boxes.

Figure 15-3 LIST OF EQUIPMENT AND MATERIALS

Source: Ontario Ministry of Environment and Energy, *Where and How to Install Air-Vapour Retarders* (Toronto:MEE, n.d.): 5.

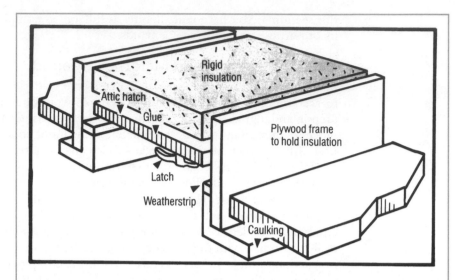

Weatherstripping

While caulking stops air leakage at fixed joints that swell and shrink with the seasons, weatherstripping controls air leakage at joints that open, such as windows, doors and attic hatches. There are many kinds of weatherstripping.

Foam strips are generally the cheapest and least durable. They can be used in areas such as attic hatches and old wooden storm windows, where there is compression fit and not much movement. They are not recommended for sliding units or on doors (except as noted below).

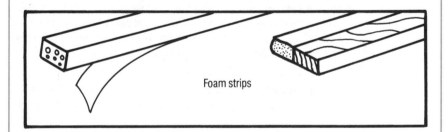

Spring vinyl or spring metal strips provide an excellent seal and are very durable. They work well on sliding or double-hung windows and doors. The traditional bronze strip is the longest-lasting, but is expensive and tricky to install. Vinyl strips that fold in half to form a V-shaped pattern with an adhesive on one side can be quickly and easily installed. Stapling the vinyl or using contact cement will ensure it remains in place.

Figure 15-4   INSTRUCTION IN EQUIPMENT USE

Source: Ontario Ministry of Environment and Energy, *Where and How to Caulk & Weatherstrip* (Toronto: MEE, n.d.): 14–15.

Tubular gaskets come in several types. The hollow or core-filled, flexible type provides a good seal. They must be fitted carefully to ensure a strong closing pressure on doors and swinging windows.

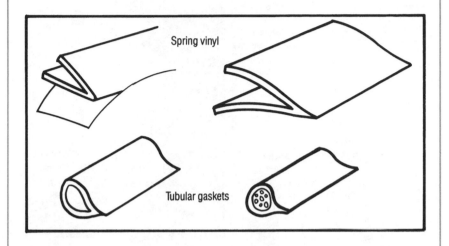

Attachment strips that allow a compression seal come in several varieties. Some of the common types are hollow tubes on attachment strips, polyester piles and spring vinyl tubes. These can provide an excellent seal and are very durable, though they can be expensive.

If you can't find the weatherstripping you want, try a glass or window repair shop. Or call the manufacturer to obtain the names of the distributors in your area.

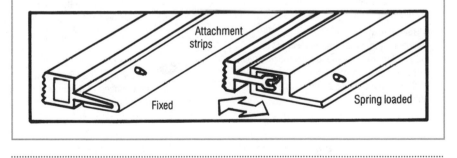

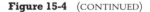

Figure 15-4   (CONTINUED)

Description of the Mechanism

Instructions devoted to the operation and maintenance of a specific mechanism usually include a section describing the mechanism. Also, the mechanism is frequently described when it is central to some process. In such sections, follow the principles for technical description given in Chapter 6. Break the mechanism into its component parts and describe how they function.

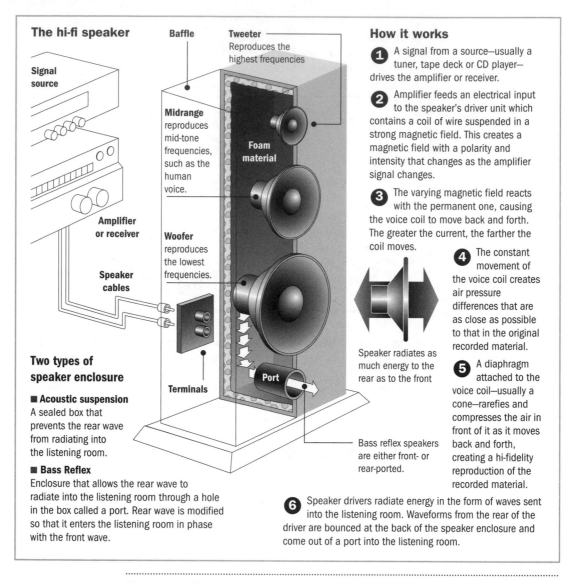

The hi-fi speaker

Signal source

Amplifier or receiver

Speaker cables

Baffle

Tweeter
Reproduces the highest frequencies

Midrange reproduces mid-tone frequencies, such as the human voice.

Foam material

Woofer reproduces the lowest frequencies.

Terminals

Port

Two types of speaker enclosure

■ **Acoustic suspension**
A sealed box that prevents the rear wave from radiating into the listening room.

■ **Bass Reflex**
Enclosure that allows the rear wave to radiate into the listening room through a hole in the box called a port. Rear wave is modified so that it enters the listening room in phase with the front wave.

How it works

❶ A signal from a source—usually a tuner, tape deck or CD player—drives the amplifier or receiver.

❷ Amplifier feeds an electrical input to the speaker's driver unit which contains a coil of wire suspended in a strong magnetic field. This creates a magnetic field with a polarity and intensity that changes as the amplifier signal changes.

❸ The varying magnetic field reacts with the permanent one, causing the voice coil to move back and forth. The greater the current, the farther the coil moves.

❹ The constant movement of the voice coil creates air pressure differences that are as close as possible to that in the original recorded material.

Speaker radiates as much energy to the rear as to the front

❺ A diaphragm attached to the voice coil—usually a cone—rarefies and compresses the air in front of it as it moves back and forth, creating a hi-fidelity reproduction of the recorded material.

Bass reflex speakers are either front- or rear-ported.

❻ Speaker drivers radiate energy in the form of waves sent into the listening room. Waveforms from the rear of the driver are bounced at the back of the speaker enclosure and come out of a port into the listening room.

Figure 15-5 DESCRIPTION AND ILLUSTRATION OF A HI-FI SPEAKER

Source: Ian G. Masters, "What Makes a Speaker Tick?", *The Toronto Star* (8 May, 1997): G3.

Figure 15-5 shows a mechanism description that explains how a hi-fi speaker functions. With the help of a graphic, the description divides the speaker into its component parts and describes how these parts function individually and in relation to one another.

Mechanism descriptions are generally accompanied by numerous illustrations like those in Figures 15-5, 15-6, and 15-7. Such illustrations show only necessary detail, and to be effective they normally have to be well annotated.

Hazards

Spilled mercury may be absorbed by porous surfaces or fabrics and will penetrate small cracks. Mercury can be brought home on clothing and shoe soles. Mercury forms explosive compounds in the presence of ammonia, acetylene and ethanol/nitric acid. Liquid mercury when mixed with chlorine dioxide will explode violently. Mercury is also incompatible with other substances as listed on the mercury data sheet for inspectors.

Mercury liquid evaporates readily in air. Mercury vapour is odourless, colourless and very toxic.

Vaporization increases significantly with increased temperature. High levels of mercury in air may occur in poorly ventilated areas.

Untrained workers may be seriously injured.

High levels of mercury in air may occur in the clean-up area.

Spilled mercury releases vapour. Dry sweeping spreads mercury.

Mercury is difficult to remove from wooden floors, cracks, and carpeted areas.

High levels of mercury in air may occur if mercury has been missed during clean-up.

Waste mercury releases vapour.

Controls

Use care in handling mercury. Use unbreakable, sealed containers. Handle and store mercury in well ventilated areas with non-porous surfaces. Avoid contact with mercury. Cover mercury with water or preferably oil to slow vaporization. Keep mercury away from chemicals which react violently with it.

Evacuate area of all unnecessary persons.

Open windows and doors to outdoors and turn on exhaust fans. Keep doors to other rooms closed.

Instruct and train every worker required to clean up mercury in the hazards of mercury exposure and in the use of respiratory equipment and protective clothing.

Every worker required to be in an area where high levels of mercury may occur shall use a respirator that meets or exceeds requirements set out in the Code for Respiratory Equipment for mercury. Protective clothing shall be provided.

Collect all visible spilled mercury with suction apparatus equipped with charcoal filters to prevent escape of mercury vapour. A water trap may be used to collect mercury for reuse.

Mop spill area with 20% calcium sulphide or 20% sodium thiosulphate solution to neutralize mercury that may have been missed. Allow 24 hours before removing the neutralizing agent.

Monitor the air to determine if decontamination is complete. Treat spill area again if necessary or discard contaminated material.

Recycle waste mercury. Keep containers labelled and closed. Do not incinerate. Keep waste mercury covered with water or preferably oil to slow vaporization.

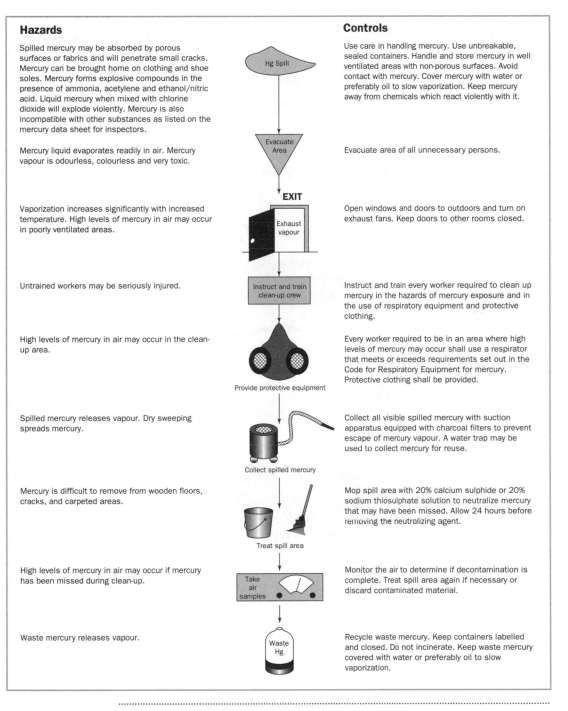

Figure 15-6 FLOW CHART FOR MERCURY SPILL CLEAN-UP

Source: Ontario Ministry of Labour, Health & Safety Division, *Designated Substances in the Workplace: A Guide to the Mercury Regulation* (1986): 38–39.

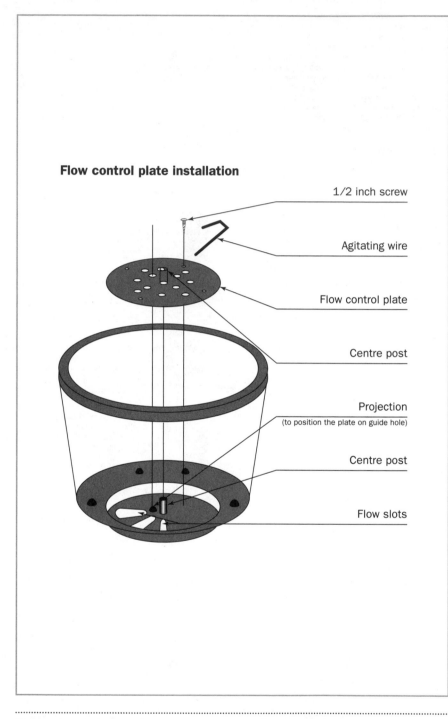

Flow control plate installation

1/2 inch screw

Agitating wire

Flow control plate

Centre post

Projection
(to position the plate on guide hole)

Centre post

Flow slots

Figure 15-7 EXPLODED DIAGRAM: INSTALLATION OF FLOW CONTROL PLATE

Source: Forest Research Section, Forestry Branch, Nova Scotia Department of Natural Resources, *Forest Research Report 55* (February 1995).

IMPORTANT SAFETY INSTRUCTIONS

When using electrical appliances, basic safety precautions should be followed, including the following:

Warning—To reduce the risk of burns, electric shock, fire, injury to persons or exposure to excessive microwave energy:

1. Read all instructions before using the appliance.

2. Read and follow the specific "PRECAUTIONS TO AVOID POSSIBLE EXPOSURE TO EXCESSIVE MICROWAVE ENERGY" found on Page 2.

3. As with most cooking appliances, close supervision is necessary to reduce the risk of a fire in the oven cavity.

   NOTE: If a fire should start:
   - KEEP THE OVEN DOOR CLOSED
   - TURN THE OVEN OFF
   - DISCONNECT THE POWER CORD OR SHUT OFF POWER AT THE FUSE OR CIRCUIT BREAKER PANEL.

   a. Do NOT overcook foods. Since many overcooked foods will cause fires in the oven cavity, carefully monitor the oven especially if paper, plastic, or other combustibles are placed inside the oven.

   b. Do NOT store combustible items such as bread, cookies, etc. inside the oven because if lightning strikes the power lines, it may cause the oven to turn ON.

   c. Do NOT use wire twist-ties in the oven. Be sure to inspect purchased items for wire twist-ties and remove them before the item is placed in the oven.

4. This appliance must be grounded. Connect only to properly grounded outlet. See "GROUNDING IN-STRUCTIONS" found on Page 6.

5. Install and locate this appliance only in accordance with the provided installation instructions.

6. Some products such as whole eggs and sealed containers, closed jars, for example, may explode and should not be heated in this oven.

7. Use this appliance only for its intended use as described in this manual.

8. As with any appliance, close supervision is necessary when used by children. Do not leave microwave unattended when cooking.

9. Do not operate this appliance if it has a damaged cord or plug, if it is not working properly, or if it has been damaged or dropped.

10. This appliance should be serviced only by qualified service personnel. Contact your nearest authorized service center for examination, repair or adjustment.

11. Do not cover or block any openings on the appliance.

12. Do not use outdoors.

13. Do not immerse cord or plug in water.

14. Keep cord away from heated surfaces.

15. Do not let cord hang over edge of table or counter.

16. When cleaning surfaces of door and oven use only mild, non abrasive soaps or detergents applied with a sponge or soft cloth. (See "Care and Cleaning" instructions on Page 32.)

SAVE THESE INSTRUCTIONS

Figure 15-8 WARNING SECTION

Source: Sears Canada Inc., *Kenmore Microwave Oven Use and Care* (Sears Canada, n.d.): 3.

Figure 15-6 is a flowchart summarizing the steps in a mercury spill clean-up (see Figure 15-12 for the actual instructions). Figures 15-5 and 15-7 provide an *exploded* view. In this context, of course, *exploded* means that the mechanism is drawn in such a way that its component parts are separated and thus easier to identify.

Warnings

People who hurt themselves or damage their equipment when following instructions in the use of that equipment often sue for damages. If they can prove to a court's satisfaction that they were not sufficiently warned of the dangers involved, they will collect large sums of money. For this reason, warnings have become an increasingly important part of instructions.

How seriously do corporations take this need to warn people of possible dangers? One of the authors of this book recently saw a shoe box that contained boating shoes. The box was decorated with an oceanographic chart. On the side of the box was a warning stating, "This chart is not intended to be used as a navigational aid and is not reliable for that purpose."[6] Figure 15-8 shows that something as simple to operate as a microwave oven comes with a set of warnings.

If they are extensive enough, the warnings may be put into a separate section, as they are in Figure 15-8. But often they are embedded in the how-to instructions. In either case, be sure they are prominently displayed in some manner that makes them obvious to the reader. You may surround them with boxes, print them in type different from and larger than the surrounding text, print them in a striking colour, or mark them with a symbol of some sort. Often, you will use some combination of these devices.

Not only must you make the warnings stand out typographically, you must also use language and, when appropriate, graphics that are absolutely clear about the nature, severity, and consequences of the hazards involved. You must clearly state how to avoid the hazard. Any lack of clarity can result in a preventable accident, almost certainly followed by a costly lawsuit against your employer.[7]

No terminology is completely agreed upon for warnings. However, three levels of warning have been widely accepted, designated by the words *caution, warning*, and *danger*.[8]

CAUTION   Use **caution** to alert the reader that not following the instructions exactly may lead to a wrong or inappropriate result. In a caution, no danger to people or equipment is involved. Figure 15-9 shows how a caution might be used to advise a technician to follow the steps of a procedure in proper order. Sometimes **note** is used for this level of warning.

WARNING   Use **warning** to alert the reader to faulty procedures that may cause minor or moderate personal injury or that may damage equipment, as in the warning from a compact disc player manual shown in Figure 15-10. The exclamation point inside the triangle in Figure 15-10 is a commonly accepted symbol to attract the reader's attention and to stress the importance of the message. You will see it used on all three levels of warnings.

Check Valve Test

- Place the mouthpiece shut-off valve in the **Diving** position.
- Place the mouthpiece in your mouth, squeeze the inhalation hose closed, and attempt to inhale through the mouthpiece. If it is possible to inhale with the inhalation hose closed off, the check valve is missing or defective.

CAUTION

If the mouthpiece shut-off valve is in the **Open** position, the test will incorrectly indicate a defective or missing check valve.

Figure 15-9 A CAUTION MESSAGE

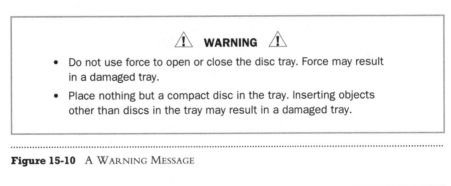

⚠ **WARNING** ⚠

- Do not use force to open or close the disc tray. Force may result in a damaged tray.
- Place nothing but a compact disc in the tray. Inserting objects other than discs in the tray may result in a damaged tray.

Figure 15-10 A WARNING MESSAGE

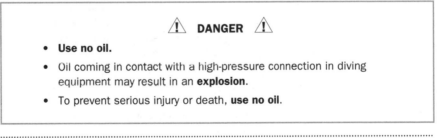

⚠ **DANGER** ⚠

- **Use no oil.**
- Oil coming in contact with a high-pressure connection in diving equipment may result in an **explosion**.
- To prevent serious injury or death, **use no oil**.

Figure 15-11 A DANGER MESSAGE

DANGER   Use **danger** for the highest level of warning: a warning to prevent major personal injury or death. Obviously, you must make danger messages stand out typographically and write them with utter clarity. Figure 15–11 presents a good example of a danger message.

How-to Instructions

The actual instructions on how to perform the process lie at the heart of any set of instructions. For sample sets of how-to instructions, see Figures 15–12 through 15–15. The same general principles apply to all how–to instructions.

1. Evacuate all people from the area of the spill.

2. Contain the mercury vapour in the smallest area possible by:
   - closing all doors between the spill area and the rest of the workplace; and
   - shutting off any ventilation equipment that circulates air from the spill area to the rest of the workplace.

3. Post signs warning of the spill and forbidding entry of the spill area by all unauthorized persons.

4. When entering the spill area, wear appropriate respiratory protection and protective clothing. Open all doors and windows in the spill area to the outdoors. Turn on all exhaust fans that vent air directly outdoors. Turn off the heat to reduce vaporization of mercury.

5. Assess the extent of the hazard. This can include:
   - determining the quantity of mercury that has spilled in relation to the volume of the spill area;
   - taking readings of mercury vapour concentrations with a direct reading instrument (see page 26);
   - assessing ventilation in the spill area; and
   - determining the temperature in the spill area and whether there are any warm surfaces that would promote vaporization of mercury.

6. Contact the appropriate inspection branch of the Ministry of Labour. Phone numbers are listed at the back of this guide.

7. On the basis of the assessment of the hazard decide on appropriate safety precautions, personal protective equipment and clean-up procedures.

8. Make sure everyone involved with the clean-up is aware of proper procedures and the hazards of mercury.

9. Equip anyone who must enter the spill area with appropriate respirators and protective clothing. The **Code for Respiratory Equipment for Mercury** specifies the type of respirator that must be used, depending on the concentration of mercury in the air. If the concentration cannot be determined, respiratory equipment required for "escape" must be worn.

10. Collect all visible spilled mercury with a vacuum device equipped with a charcoal filter or a water trap. Make sure all mercury trapped in cracks and crevices is picked up. Do not sweep, as this can cause the mercury to break into smaller beads.

11. Wash the spill area with a neutralizing solution that will convert the mercury into a form that will not vaporize. This may be done with a solution of 20 per cent calcium sulphide, 20 per cent sodium thiosulphate or another preparation designed for this purpose. Allow 24 hours before removing the neutralizing solution.

12. After the spill has been cleaned, monitor the air again for mercury concentration. If levels are high, repeat vacuuming and neutralizing procedures.

Figure 15-12 INSTRUCTIONS FOR CLEAN-UP ACTION AFTER MERCURY SPILL

Source: Ontario Ministry of Labour, Health & Safety Division, *Designated Substances in the Workplace: A Guide to the Mercury Regulation* (1986): 21-22.

DELUXE CHECK PRINTERS. INC. STANDARD OPERATING PROCEDURES

Procedure C-9
Establishing, Changing, or Eliminating the Petty Cash Fund
Accounts Payable and Purchasing Manual—C

SUMMARY: The petty cash fund is a fixed cash fund reserved for minor expenditures of $50 or less. This procedure explains how to establish, change, or eliminate the petty cash fund.

NOTE: When a petty cash fund is established, the plant manager should assign responsibility to no more than two cash drawer custodians, with one individual having primary responsibility. The accounts payable clerk must not be a custodian of the petty cash fund.

See Procedure C-17 to disburse petty cash. See Procedure C-18 to replenish the petty cash fund. See Appendix J for petty cash fund controls.

RESPONSIBILITY	ACTION
Plant manager	1. Request authorization from corporate treasurer for one of the following: • establish petty cash fund • change amount of existing petty cash fund • eliminate existing petty cash fund
Corporate treasurer	2. Review request and approve or disapprove and notify plant accountant of decision.
Plant accountant	3. Notify plant manager of decision. 4. If establishing fund or increasing existing fund, have check prepared from Account 1030 (Regular Cash Account) for authorized amount, payable to cash, debiting Account 1010 (Petty Cash Account) on check voucher. 4a. Place check in check cashing fund box and withdraw authorized amount of cash. 4b. Place cash in petty cash fund, and notify plant manager that petty cash fund is established or increased. –OTHERWISE– 5. If decreasing or eliminating existing fund, use Daily Report of Cash, form A-30-Q (Exhibit 24), to credit Account 1010.

Rewritten by: Kathy Huebsch

Figure 15-13 STANDARD OPERATING PROCEDURES

Source: Reprinted by permission of Deluxe Check Printers, Inc.

STYLE   When you are writing how-to instructions, one of your major concerns is to use a clear, understandable style. To achieve this, write your instructions in the active voice and imperative mood: "Turn the mouse upside down and rotate the plastic dial counterclockwise as far as it will go." The imperative mood is normal and acceptable in instructions. It's clear and precise and will not offend the reader. (For more on the active voice and imperative mood, see Chapters 5 and 6.)

Figure 15-13 shows how you can create a single set of instructions to co-ordinate the interrelated tasks of multiple participants in a given procedure. Here, the procedure is divided into responsible actions, identified in the left-hand column, and related actions, described in the imperative mood in the right-hand column.

Notice that the sets of how-to instructions in this chapter all use a list format. The list may use numbers, bullets, or simply white space to keep each step distinct. Each step usually contains only one instruction and at the most two or three closely related instructions. The list format keeps each step in a series clear and distinct from every other step. Listing has several other advantages as well:

- It makes it obvious how many steps there are.
- It makes it easy for readers to find their place on the page.
- It allows the reader to use the how-to instructions as a checklist.

Use familiar, direct language and avoid jargon. Tell your readers to *check* things or to *look them over*. Don't tell them to *conduct an investigation*. Tell your readers to *use* a wrench, not to *utilize* one. Fill your instructions with read-ily recognized verbs such as *adjust, attach, bend, cap, centre, close, drain, install, lock, replace, spin, turn,* and *wrap*. For more on good style, see Chapter 5, "Achieving a Readable Style."

If your how-to instructions call for calculations, include sample calcula-tions to clarify them for the reader. See Figure 15-14 for an example of such calculations.

GRAPHICS   Be generous with graphics. Word descriptions and graphics often complement each other. The words tell *what* action is to be done. The graphics show *where* it is to be done and often *how* to do it. Our samples demonstrate well the relationship between words and graphics. Note that graphics are often annotated to allow for easy reference to them.

ARRANGEMENT   When writing performance instructions, arrange the process being described into as many major routines and subroutines as needed. For example, a set of instructions for the overhaul and repair of a piece of machinery might be broken down as follows:

- Disassembly of major components
- Disassembly of sub-components
- Cleaning
- Inspection
- Lubrication

Method of Determining Media Porosity

You will need: (1) your normal pot; (2) a way to cover or plug the pot drain holes; (3) a graduated cylinder or other liquid measure; and (4) some dry mix. Use this method to test new mixes. Plant growth in your standard mix and a new one, each with its respective aeration value, will be your guide as to the best mix. Select mixes with high aeration porosity (in the range of 20-25) for items such as pine and yew. Somewhat lower values can be tolerated by junipers and white cedar.

1. With drain holes covered or plugged fill container with water to the normal potting level. This amount of water is total container volume (A).

2. Empty the water and fill the pot with slightly moist mix. Be sure the pot is level. Add water very slowly until a slick of water appears on the surface. The water added is (B), the pore volume. Record the amount of water added.

3. Without moving the pot remove the drain hole covers or plugs, allowing the water to drain into a bucket. Measure the water drained (C), the aeration pore volume.

$$\text{Total porosity} = \frac{B \times 100}{A}$$

$$\text{Aeration porosity} = \frac{C \times 100}{A}$$

— To determine the water retention porosity, which is similar to the moisture at field capacity of a soil, subtract aeration porosity from total porosity.

— Example
pot volume = 5180 mL (A)
water added to saturate mix = 3354 mL (B)
water drained when holes
uncovered = 1080 mL (C)

Total porosity = 65%
$\frac{3354}{5180} \times 100 = 65\%$

Aeration porosity = 21%
$\frac{1080}{5180} \times 1200 = 21\%$

Water retention porosity = 44%
65 − 21 = 44%

Calculation of Parts per Million (PPM) in a dilute liquid feed

$$\text{ppm nutrient} = \frac{\text{weight of fertilizer (in kg)} \times \% \text{ nutrient (in fertilizer)} \times 100}{\text{volume of stock solution (in litres)} \times \text{dilution rate}}$$

Calculation of weight of fertilizer required per litre of stock solution to obtain a given level of nutrient in the dilute feed

$$\text{kg of fertilizer per litre} = \frac{\text{ppm (of diluted feed)} \times \text{dilution rate}}{\% \text{ nutrient (in fertilizer)} \times 1000}$$

Figure 15-14 SAMPLE CALCULATIONS

Source: Ontario Ministry of Agriculture, Food and Rural Affairs, *Production Recommendations for Nursery and Landscape Plants* (Toronto, rev. 1994): 19.

THREATS TO ONTARIO'S WATERS

Harmful Exotic Species

Ontario's fish and the waters that support them are threatened by several exotic species that can be spread unknowingly by anglers and boaters.

Whenever you move your boat from one waterbody to another, exotic species may tag along for the ride. There are some important things you can do to prevent the transport of harmful exotic species from one lake or river to another:

- **Inspect** your boat, motor, trailer, and boating equipment (anchor, centreboards, rollers, axles) and remove any zebra mussels and other animals and plants that are visible before leaving any waterbody;

- **Drain** water from the motor, livewell, bilge and transom wells while on land before leaving the waterbody.

- **Wash/dry** your boat, tackle, downriggers, trailer, and other boating equipment to kill harmful species that were not visible at the boat launch. Some aquatic nuisance species can survive more than 2 weeks out of water so it is important to:
  — rinse your boat and equipment that normally gets wet with hot tap water (greater than 40° C); or
  — spray your boat and trailer with high pressure water (250 psi); or
  — dry your boat and equipment for at least 5 days before transporting to another water body.

- **Empty** your bait bucket on land before leaving any waterbody. **Never** release live bait into a waterbody, or release aquatic animals from one waterbody into another;

- **Learn** how to identify zebra mussels and other exotic species. If you suspect a new infestation report it to the **Ministry of Natural Resources or the Invading Species Hotline (1-800-563-7711)**— this hotline is a partnership between the Ontario Ministry of Natural Resources and the Ontario Federation of Anglers and Hunters.

Figure 15-15 INSTRUCTIONS TO BOATERS FOR REDUCING SPREAD OF HARMFUL AQUATIC SPECIES

Source: Recreational Fishing Regulations Summary (© Queen's Printer of Ontario, 1998): 9. Reproduced with permission.

- Repair
- Reassembly of components
- Testing of components
- Reassembly of major components

Notice that in this case the steps are in chronological order. Our samples also demonstrate chronological order.

If there are steps that are repeated, it is sometimes a legitimate practice to tell the reader to "Repeat steps 2, 3, and 4." But whether you do so depends upon your analysis of the reader's situation. Visualize your reader. Maybe he or she will be perched atop a shaky ladder, your instructions in one hand, a tool in the other. Under such circumstances, the reader will not want to be flipping pages around to find the instructions that need to be repeated. You will be wiser and kinder to print once again all the instructions of the sequence. If the reader will be working in a comfortable place with both feet on the ground, you will probably be safe enough saying, "Repeat steps...."

Such reader and situation analysis can help you make many similar decisions. Suppose that your readers are not expert technicians, and the process calls for them to use simple test equipment. In such a situation, you should include the instructions for operating the test equipment as part of the routine you are describing. On the other hand, suppose your readers are experienced technicians following your instructions at a comfortable workbench with a well-stocked library of manuals nearby. You can assume that they know how to operate any needed test equipment, or you can refer them to another manual that describes how to operate the test equipment.

For the most part, instructions have no conclusions. They simply end with the last instruction. On occasion, particularly when writing for lay people, you might wish to close with a summary of the chief steps of the process or, perhaps, a graceful close. However, such endings are not general practice.

Tips and Troubleshooting Procedures

Many sets of instructions contain sections that give the reader helpful tips on how to do a better job or that provide guidance when trouble occurs.

TIPS   You may present tips in a separate section, as illustrated in Figure 15-16. Or you may incorporate them into the how-to instructions, as in this excerpt on setting flexible tile. In the excerpt, the last sentence in instructions 1, 2, 3, and 5 gives the reader a tip that should make the task go more easily:

1. Remove loose or damaged tile. A warm iron will help soften the adhesive.
2. Scrape off the old adhesive from the floor or wall. Also from the tile if you're to use it again.
3. Fit tiles carefully. Some tile can be cut with a knife or shears, others with a saw. Tile is less apt to break if it's warm.
4. Spread adhesive on the floor or wall with a paint brush or putty knife.
5. Wait until adhesive begins to set before placing the tile. Press tile on firmly. A rolling pin works well.[9]

TROUBLESHOOTING PROCEDURES   You may incorporate troubleshooting procedures into your how-to instructions, as in this excerpt:

Tighten screws in the hinges. If screws are not holding, replace them one at a time with a longer screw. Or insert a matchstick in the hole and put the old screw back.[10]

Perhaps more often, troubleshooting procedures will have a section of their own, as in Figure 15-17. Notice that the remedies are given as instructions in the active voice, imperative mood, while a page reference is also provided to guide the reader to additional related information.

INSTALLATION TIPS

❏ Continuity and integrity are the two principles behind the proper installation of an air-vapour retarder. The retarder should be run unbroken
throughout the house and should not be pierced by wiring, vents or
accidental tears. If this happens, it should be properly repaired.

❏ Make the air-vapour retarder as continuous as possible between floors
and past partition walls, stairways and cupboards.

❏ Completely seal the air-vapour retarder to all openings in the house
envelope, such as window and door frames and venting and wiring
penetrations. Patch all holes.

❏ Use the widest sheets of poly to reduce the number of seams; 10-foot
rolls are generally available.

❏ Overlap seams and staple them through the caulking over a solid surface.

❏ Let the outside wall of the house "breathe". It should not act as a
vapour retarder. This will prevent "vapour locks," where moisture becomes trapped between two vapour retarders, causing moisture damage. For example, if you are insulating on the inside over an old plaster
wall with several coats of oil-based paint, you should first score the
plaster with a skill saw. Be careful not to damage the studs.

Figure 15-16   INSTALLATION TIPS

Source: Ontario Ministry of Environment and Energy, *Where and How to Install Air
Vapour Retarders* (Toronto): 5-6.

Electrical System

PROBLEM	POSSIBLE CAUSE	POSSIBLE REMEDY	PAGE REFERENCE
Battery will not charge	Loose or corroded connections	Clean and tighten connections	66
	Sulfated or worn-out battery	Check electrolyte level and specific gravity	67
	Loose or defective alternator belt	Adjust belt tension or replace belt	52
"CHG" indicator glows with engine running	Low engine speed	Increase speed	
	Defective battery	Check electrolyte level and specific gravity	67
	Defective alternator	Have your John Deere dealer check alternator	

Figure 15-17   TROUBLESHOOTING CHART

Source: Reprinted by permission of Deere and Company.

Glossary

If your audience analysis tells you that your reader will not comprehend all the terminology you plan to use in your instructions, you'll need to provide definitions. If you need only a few definitions, you can define terms as you use them. You can even provide graphic definitions.

If you must provide many definitions, you'll probably want to provide a glossary as a separate section. Figure 15-18 shows a portion of a longer glossary that defines terms related to the Internet. See also Chapter 6, where we discuss definitions, and Chapter 9, where we discuss glossaries.

Accessible Format

Your major goal in formattting your instructions should be to make the information accessible for your readers. Part III, Document Design, is especially helpful in this regard.

The theory section shown in Figure 15-2 on page 396 demonstrates excellent accessibility. The type is clear and plain, and the format is especially helpful for readers who scan the document. The headings in boldface type allow the reader to scan quickly, looking for points of interest.

Look now at Figure 15-19, instructions to readers who have been summoned to a hearing of a government body. There are no headings. There is no visual interest or emphasis on the page. The language is legalistic, obscure, and intimidating. In other words, the format violates most of the principles discussed in Chapter 8, "Document Design," and the style of the instructions violates most of the principles discussed in Chapter 5, "Achieving a Readable Style."

Now look at Figure 15-20, which is the same document after it has been revised and given a new format to make it accessible. Certain things are immediately obvious. The print is bigger and there is more white space. There are meaningful and informative headings. They are phrased from the reader's point of view. Such new headings guide and inform, rather than confusing the reader. The format and style of the instructions now demonstrate a knowledge and application of the principles discussed in Chapters 5 and 8. The result is a readable document.

Finally, when a set of instructions runs more than several pages, you should furnish a table of contents (TOC) to help your readers find their way and to provide an overview of the instructions. The headings in the TOC should duplicate those in the instructions. Figure 15-21 shows a useful TOC in which the headings are meaningful and informative to the readers.

Reader Checks

When you are writing instructions, check frequently with the people who are going to use them. Bring them a sample of your theory section. Discuss it with them. See if they understand it. Does it contain too much theory or

A Guide to the E-Business Lexicon

ANS

Advance Notification of Payment is used in e-business by buyers to notify sellers of impending electronic cash transfers, improving treasury management and cash flow forecasting.

ASN

Advance Shipment Notice is a detailed electronic document used to outline specifics of shipments, orders, packing and individual items purchased. ASNs are an essential component in an EDI system.

ANSI X12

These "transaction sets" are created by the American National Standards Institute and are basic building blocks used in EDI in the U.S. to format transfer of data. Several hundred types of X12 "sets" exist for specific business activities.

Authentication

An electronic method to verify the source of transmitted data; like an electronic fingerprint. It should not be confused with encryption, which disguises data but does not verify who sent it.

Blind Signature

A form of authentication that allows a customer to remain anonymous while verifying the electronic transfer of funds.

Certificate

A certificate is a digital "signature" issued by a financial institution to an organization or individual to ensure secure online trading. It is typically a unique alphanumeric code that authenticates a transaction and prevents others from fraudulently posing as customers or merchants.

Certification Authority

A third-party entitled by government or trading partners to issue encryption and authentication "keys" to buyers and sellers.

Commerce Server

Software turning a computer workstation into a World Wide Web site handling online transactions, database and inventory management, order taking, billing, security and customer service.

Cookies

A small file sent to your computer when visiting some Web sites that identifies you on subsequent visits. Useful for tracking frequent users, but controversial as an invasion of privacy.

Dial-Up Access

As it suggests, connecting to the Internet or a private network by dialing through a modem.

Figure 15-18 A GUIDE TO THE E-BUSINESS LEXICON

Source: The Definitive Guide to Emerging Electronic Business Solutions (Bell Global Solutions Inc., December 1997): 22.

Disintermediation

An e-business term referring to the cutting out of middlemen or others in the traditional buying chain.

Domain Name

The unique electronic address of your Web site, such as www.yourcompany.com. Domain names are registered for a small annual fee with InterNIC, the Internet's non-profit overseer of Web addresses.

E-Cash

Electronic currency that can be used as a substitute for money in online transactions. Also known as secured credit cards, electronic cheques and digital coins. Also the name for a digital payment system licensed by DigiCash.

EDI

Electronic Data Interchange is a private, proprietary system of computer-to-computer data transfer first used in the 1960s and 1970s to connect large corporations and their trading partners. EDI can exchange electronic versions of order forms, invoices and other structured documents between computers.

EDIFACT

Touted as the global standard for EDI, it has been developed by the United Nations and works with ANSI and most other standards.

Electronic Purse

An electronic purse stores a set amount of "cash" electronically on a microchip embedded in a plastic credit card or "smart card," creating a cashless pre-payment card to buy goods and services. The idea is now being tested in Guelph, Ont., by Mondex and will likely be one of several e-business payment methods.

E-Mail

Electronic mail allows connected computer users to exchange unstructured information, such as pure text or multimedia graphics. It is fast becoming a preferred alternative to memos, faxes, telephones, voice mail and even face-to-face meetings.

Encryption

A process of encoding or disguising data traveling over networks to ensure confidentiality. A password or electronic "key" unlocks the data.

ERS

Evaluated Receipt Settlement is an EDI method that eliminates invoices based on the receipt of an ASN saying goods have been shipped. Cost savings can be huge compared with invoice-based systems.

Extranet

A community of users—business partners, suppliers, distributors or customers—using the same tools as the Internet to privately and securely exchange information.

FAQ

Frequently Asked Questions are online lists of common queries and answers about an Internet service, feature or site.

Figure 15-18 (CONTINUED)

NOTICE TO WITNESS

You have been served with a Summons to Witness to compel your attendance at a hearing before the Workers' Compensation Board (the "Board") at the location, date, and time indicated on the summons to give evidence.

Pursuant to section 81(a) of the Workers' Compensation Act (the "Act") the Board has the power to summon and enforce the attendance of witnesses and to compel them to give oral or written evidence under oath in the same manner as a court of record in civil cases.

If you fail to attend without lawful excuse you may have contempt proceedings against you in the Supreme Court of Ontario.

The attendance money that has been served with the summons is to facilitate your attendance at the hearing. If as a result of your attending the hearing you incur a loss of wages or salary, you may be entitled to an additional payment subject to the limits and guidelines in effect from time to time.

If you have any questions regarding the summons or your attendance before the Board, please contact:

Supervisor, Administrative Services
Review Services
2 Bloor Street East
Toronto, Ontario
M5W 2V1

Tel: 416-555-4150
Toll Free: 1-800-555-0050
Fax: 416-555-4146

Figure 15-19   GOVERNMENT NOTICE BEFORE REVISION

too little? Submit your how-to instructions to the acid test. Let members of the audience for whom the instructions are intended—but who are not familiar with the process—attempt to perform the process by following your instructions. Encourage them to tell you where your instructions are confusing. A procedure called **protocol analysis** can be a help at this point. In this procedure, you ask the person following your instructions to speak into a tape recorder, giving his or her observations about the instructions while attempting to follow them. Here is an excerpt from a set of such observations made by someone trying to use a computer manual and online help to aid him in a word processing exercise:

> Somehow I've got the caps locked in here. I can't get to the lowercase. OK, I'm struggling with trying to come off those capitals. I'm not having any luck. So, what do I need to do. I could press help. See if that gets me anything. Using the keyboard.

Important

You must appear as a witness at a hearing
of the Workers' Compensation Board.
The attached summons tells you where and when.
Please read these two pages carefully right away.

Information for witnesses

1. The law says all witnesses must attend.
Under the Workers' Compensation Act (Section 81a), the Workers'
Compensation Board has the same powers as a court. It investigates
accidents that happen on the job. If you are summoned as a witness,
you must attend the hearing and give your evidence under oath.

It is against the law to miss this hearing without a lawful reason.
You can be charged with contempt of court. If you have a lawful
reason why you can't attend, you must advise the Board as soon
as possible.

2. You may have to miss work.
You must appear at the time and place listed on the attached summons
and stay as long as you are needed.

3. Your expenses will be paid.
The money attached to the summons is to cover your expenses to attend the hearing. If you lose any pay for the time you are a witness,
the Board may also pay part or all of your wages or salary.

4. If you have questions
Please contact: Supervisor, Administrative Services
Review Services
Workers' Compensation Board
2 Bloor Street East
Toronto, Ontario M5W 2V1
Tel: 416-555-4150 (Toronto calls)
Toll Free: 1-800-555-0050 (Long distance calls)
Fax: 416-555-4146

Figure 15-20 GOVERNMENT NOTICE AFTER REVISION

I'll try that. 2.0. I can't do that because it's in this mode. I'm getting uppercase on
the numbers so I can't type in the help numbers. So I'll reset to get rid of that. Big
problem. Try reset. Merging text, formatting, setting margins, fixing problems. I
can't enter a section number because I can't get this thing off lock. Escape. Nothing
helps. Well, I'm having trouble here.[11]

Such information pinpoints troublesome areas in instructions. If you
were writing instructions that were to be used by many people, protocol

Table of Contents

Figure 15-21 TABLE OF CONTENTS

Source: Ontario Ministry of Environment and Energy, *Where and How to Caulk & Weatherstrip.*

analysis would be a worthwhile investment in time and money. In any case, whether you use protocol analysis or not, if your readers can't follow your instructions, don't blame them. Rather, examine your instructions to see where you have failed. Often, you will find you have left out some vital link in the process or assumed knowledge on the part of your readers that they do not possess.

Planning and Revision Checklists

You will find the planning and revision checklists that follow Chapter 2 and Chapter 4 valuable in planning and revising any presentation of technical information. The questions here specifically apply to instructions. They summarize the key points in this chapter and provide a checklist for planning and revising.

Planning

- What is the purpose of your instructions?
- What is your reader's point of view?
- How and where will your readers use these instructions?
- What content does your reader really need and want?
- How should you arrange your content? Which of the following components should you include as a separate section? Which should you omit or include within another component, such as theory in the introduction?

    Introduction

    Theory or principles of operation: How much theory do your readers really need or want?

    List of equipment and materials needed: Are your readers familiar with all the needed equipment and materials? Do they need additional information?

    Description of the mechanism: Does some mechanism play a significant role in these instructions?

Warnings: Are there expected outcomes that will be affected by improper procedure? Are there places in the instructions where improper procedure will cause damage to equipment or injury or death to people?

How-to instructions: Can your instructions be divided and grouped?

What is the proper sequence of events for your how-to instructions?

Tips and troubleshooting procedures: Are there helpful hints you can pass on to the reader? What troubles may come up? How can they be corrected?

Glossary: Do you need to define enough terms to justify a glossary?

- What graphics will help your instructions? Do you have them available or can you produce them?

Revision

- Have you made the purpose of your paper clear to your readers?
- Can your readers scan your instructions easily, finding what they need?

- Do you have sufficient headings? Do your headings stand out? Are they meaningful to your readers? Would it help to cast some as questions?

continued >>

- Is all terminology unfamiliar to the reader defined somewhere?
- Is your print size large enough for your readers and their location?
- Is all your content relevant? Is it needed or desired by your readers? Have you made it easy for your readers to scan and to skip parts not relevant to them?
- Have you covered any needed theory adequately?
- Do your readers know what equipment and materials they will need? Do they know how to use the equipment needed? If not, have you provided necessary explanations?
- Have you provided any necessary mechanism description?
- Are your caution, warning, and danger messages easy to see and clear in their meaning? Are you sure you have alerted your readers to every situation in which they might injure themselves or damage their equipment?
- Have you broken your how-to instructions into as many routines and subroutines as necessary?
- Are your steps in chronological order, with no steps out of sequence?
- Are your how-to instructions written in the active voice and imperative mood?

- Have you used a list format with short entries for each step of the instructions?
- Have you used simple, direct language and avoided jargon?
- If needed, have you provided sample calculations?
- Have you used graphics whenever they would be helpful? Are they sufficiently annotated?
- Have you provided helpful tips that may help your readers to do the task more efficiently?
- Have you anticipated trouble and provided troubleshooting procedures?
- If troubleshooting is covered in a separate section, is the section laid out in a way to clearly distinguish among problem, cause, and remedy?
- Do you have enough definitions to warrant a glossary?
- Are your instructions long enough to warrant a table of contents?
- Have you checked with your readers? Have you allowed a typical reader to attempt the procedure using your instructions? Have you corrected any difficulties such a check revealed?
- Have you checked thoroughly for all misspellings and mechanical errors?

Weblinks

How to Write Instructions
www.niu.edu/acad/english/wac/instr.html

Notes on Instruction Writing
www.terra.cc.oh.us/sharla/notes1.html

Writing Instructions
www.witc.tec.wi.us/write/winst.htm

Exercises

1. Writing instructions offers a wide range of possible papers. Short papers might consist of nothing more than an introduction and a set of how-to instructions. Examples—good and bad—of such short instructions can be found in hobby kits and accompanying such things as toys, tents, appliances, and furniture that must be assembled. Textbook laboratory procedures frequently are examples of a short set of instructions. Using the Planning and Revision Checklists for this chapter, write a short set of instructions. Here are some ideas:
   - Developing film
   - Drawing a blood sample
   - Applying fertilizer
   - Setting a bicycle gear
   - Completing a form
   - Accomplishing some do-it-yourself task around a house
   - Replacing a part in an automobile or some other mechanism
   - Cleaning a carpet
   - Balancing a chequebook

2. Using the Planning and Revision Checklists for this chapter, write a set of instructions that includes at least six of the eight possible components listed on pages 393-394. The components do not have to be in separate sections, but they must be clearly recognizable. Here are some suggested topics:
   - Testing electronic equipment
   - Writing (or following) a computer program
   - Setting up an accounting procedure for a small business
   - Conducting an agronomy field test
   - Checking blood pressure
   - Painting an automobile

PROPOSALS AND PROGRESS REPORTS

M any times as an employee in an organization, you will generate a variety of documents relating to one particular problem or situation. You may send several e-mail memorandums to colleagues within the organization; you may write letters to individuals outside the organization concerning the problem or situation; you may write memo reports "To File" that document your activities on the problem or situation; you may also write a detailed formal report, such as a formal feasibility study, discussed in Chapter 14, at the conclusion of your work on the situation. In short, you will write various documents to different audiences about one project, problem, or topic. Proposals and progress reports are two additional documents that are often written in response to one project.

The Relationship Between
Proposals and Progress Reports

The proposal, as its name implies, describes the work that will be done, the reasons it should be done, and the methods that will be used to accomplish the work. The progress report, as its name implies, describes and evaluates the project as the work is being done. Thus, if an individual or an organization decides to begin a work or research project, particularly one that requires several months or even several years to complete, the individual or organization will usually need to *propose* the project and then *report the progress* on that project at intervals agreed upon when the proposal is accepted and the resulting agreement or contract is being negotiated. When the topic of the progress report emanates from the project that is proposed, the content and organization of the progress report are often directed by the content and organization of the written proposal.

However, in other instances, employees may need to report progress on a variety of projects or problems on which they are working. In situations like these, the employee writes a progress report (or status report, as it may be called) to inform supervisors or other individuals about what has been accomplished in completing a job or solving a problem. By keeping these individuals up-to-date on work activities, the employee uses the status report to document what has been accomplished and by whom. The progress or status report thus becomes an official and even a legal record of work.

This chapter explains how to design and write proposals and progress reports. First, we discuss the development of proposals in the context of a specific project. We will show you the letter that initiated the project—a writing-instruction workshop in an agricultural chemical company—as well as the instructor's informal status report to the president of Write, Inc., who had submitted the proposal.

Next, we discuss progress reports. We will present two situations in which someone must report the status of a project. The first example shows a report designed to describe and evaluate the work completed on a student research project. The second example shows a report designed to describe, evaluate, and document the status of work on a routine project to which an employee has been assigned.

After you study this chapter, you should be able to develop the typical sections included in proposals as well as in progress reports. As the following examples will show you, proposals and progress reports—in fact any kind of document we discuss in this book—can be submitted in memo or letter format, as discussed in Chapters 11 and 13, or as a longer, more formal document, as discussed in Chapter 14. The length of each document, as well as the audience and the context in which the document is generated and received, will determine which format you use.

Proposals

All projects have to begin somewhere and with someone. In universities, in business, and in research organizations, the starting point is often a proposal. In simplest terms, a proposal is an offer to provide a service or a product to someone in exchange for money. When an organization—frequently a federal, provincial, or municipal government or a business enterprise—decides to have some sort of work done, it naturally wants the best job for the best price. To announce its interest, the soliciting organization may advertise the work it wants done and invite interested individuals or organizations to contact the organization.

In a university setting, the research and grants office may notify departments that money is available for research projects in a specific area. Faculty members are invited to submit project proposals that explain how much time they will need to complete the project; any financial resources required for equipment, salaries, and release time from regular teaching duties; and the goals and benefits of the research to the individual researcher and the university.

Thus, the proposal process usually begins with an organization that is interested in work or research being done in response to a specific need or problem. The proposal is the written document that launches a proposed solution to this need or problem by individuals or groups qualified to deal with the matter.

When an organization disseminates a description of the work it wants done, this document is usually called a request for a proposal (RFP) or a request to bid (RTB). The soliciting organization may send selected companies an RFP that includes complete specifications of the work desired, or it may describe the needed work in general terms and invite interested firms to submit their qualifications. This type of request is usually called a request for qualifications (RFQ). The responding organization explains its past accomplishments, giving the names of companies for which the work was performed, describing the work it did, and giving references who can substantiate the organization's claims. Based on the qualifications of the responding firms, the soliciting organization will send full descriptions of the work to the groups it believes to be best qualified.

Alternatively, the soliciting organization may describe the kind of work it wants done and invite interested companies to describe briefly what they offer, how they would do the work, and approximately how much it will cost. This kind of request is called a request for quote (also referred to as an RFQ). Responding firms that give a price that best approximates what the soliciting organization wants to pay will be sent a full description of the work needed and will be invited to submit full proposals.

To understand some of the many ways that proposals initiate projects, consider the following examples.

1. Professor Ng of the university's sociology department learns that the provincial Ministry of Community and Social Services is soliciting studies of educational problems experienced by school-age children of single-parent families. Because Professor Ng has established a research record in this field and is looking for new projects, she decides to request a copy of the RFP. After studying it carefully, she decides to submit a proposal. In her proposal she describes her planned research and explains its benefits. She states her qualifications to conduct the research and details the costs of the project.

2. A municipality in Saskatchewan decides that it wants to repave a heavily used rural road and extend the paving another five km beyond the existing pavement. The public works office runs an advertisement in several local and province-wide newspapers briefly describing the work. Public works officials also send copies of the advertisement to road construction firms that have reputations for doing quality work at a fair price. The construction companies interested in submitting bids will notify the municipal officials and will be invited to attend a bidder's conference in which requirements of the job are discussed further. Public works officials may take potential contractors on a tour of the area. Those who decide to bid on the paving project will have four weeks to submit bids that meet the minimum specifications given in the published RFP as well as in the bidder's conference.

3. Alvin Cranston, a manager for a local telephone company, is charged with redesigning the operator service facilities for the company. Alvin knows that he will need to consider a number of issues (lighting, furniture, computers, as well as building layout), so he decides to publish a request for qualifications in telephone trade publications. He also asks the company's marketing department to help him locate a list of companies that specialize in ergonomic design. With a list of these companies, he writes each one and explains, in general terms, what his company wants to do. He then invites the ergonomic design firms to submit their qualifications for performing such work.

4. Biotech Corporation is considering the development of a new organic dispersant for combatting major oil spills in fresh water industrial lakes. They want to know how much containers for transporting this new dispersant would cost, what kinds of containers are currently available to transport the dispersant by rail or air freight, and whether chemical transport container companies would be interested in providing the containers and shipping the dispersant to purchasers.

In short, each aspect of the solicitation process, the RFP, the RFQ, or the RTB, has an appropriate use, but one or more of them are necessary to initiate action on a project.

The Context of Proposal Development

Because proposals are time consuming to write—most require substantial research, analysis, and expense on the part of the proposing organization—individuals and organizations wishing to respond to an RFP study it carefully. They do not want to submit a proposal that is not likely to be accepted. Thus, the proposer—whether a university professor seeking research funds or a highway construction firm seeking to win a contract from a municipality to repave its rural roads—will approach the decision to prepare a proposal carefully.

The responding company must decide whether to respond to the proposal. This decision is based on careful study of the RFP or the RFQ with a number of questions in mind: Can we do the work requested? Can we show that we can do this work, based on what we have already done? Can we do it within the time limit given in the RFP? Businesses responding to RFPs are also interested in economic issues: How much will our proposed approach cost? How much money can we make? Who else will be submitting proposals? What price will they be quoting for the same work? Will we be competitive? What other projects are we currently involved in? Could problems arise that would make us unable to complete the job on time and at the price we quote? Do we have the staff qualified for this project?

Many business entities requesting proposals will hold a bidder's conference where companies interested in submitting a proposal can ask questions about the project or seek clarification of the needs described in the RFP. Most RFPs require that proposals be submitted by a deadline and contain specific information. Proposals that do not contain the information requested may be omitted from consideration. Therefore, once an organization decides to submit a proposal, the RFP is carefully studied and the information requirements are separated. Each information requirement is given to an individual or a group who will be responsible for furnishing necessary material and data.

Some proposals, such as university research proposals, may be written by one person. In complex proposals, however, different sections may be written by individuals in different areas of the organization. An editor or proposal writer will then compile the final document. This writer/editor may be assisted by readers, who help check the accuracy of the developing proposal to be sure that all requested information is included and that the information is correct. Once the proposal is written and submitted, it becomes a legally binding document. The proposing company or individual is legally committed to do what it says it will do at the cost stated and within the time limit stated. For that reason, the proposing organization carefully checks all information for accuracy. Figure 16-1 will help you visualize the proposal process.

In requests for proposals in which a large number of bidders submit proposals, the soliciting organization may select several finalists and allow each finalist to give an oral version of the proposal. During this oral presentation, the soliciting group asks questions; the proposing group has one more opportunity to argue for the value of what they are proposing, the merits of their organization to do the work, and the justification for the cost attached to the proposed work.

Effective Argument in Proposal Development

All writing is persuasive in that it must convince the reader that the writer has credibility and that the writer's ideas have merit. However, the success of the proposal rests totally on the effectiveness of the argument—how convincingly the writer argues for a plan, an idea, a product, or a service to be rendered and how well the writer convinces the reader that the proposing organization is the best one to do the work or research needed. In

Soliciting Company: **Submitting Company:**

RFQ

RTB

RTB—**Bidder's Conference** ──────▶ **Decision to Submit Proposal**
- project clarification   - analysis of RFP/RTB requirements
- Q&A between soliciting organiza-   - analysis of cost
  tions and potential bidders   - analysis of capability vs. RFP
                                             requirements

                                           Planning Process
                                           - RFP requirements separated
                                           - RFP requirements assigned
                                             to work groups
                                           - outline of technical, management,
                                             and cost sections
                                           - assignment to proposal writing team

                                           First Draft—all segments combined
                                           - Review by evaluation team
                                           - Revisions

                                           Final Draft
                                           - Review by evaluation team
                                           - Revisions and editing

                                           Corrections, Printing, Binding

Proposals from other companies ◀────── Copies to soliciting company

Evaluation by soliciting company

Selection of finalists

Oral presentation by finalists

Decision by soliciting company;
    finalist selected and announced

Figure 16-1 PROPOSAL CYCLE IN AN ORGANIZATION

planning the content of the proposal, the proposer must harmonize the soliciting company's needs with the proposer's capabilities. The writer must be acutely sensitive to what readers will be looking for but not propose

action that cannot be done because it is outside the capability of the proposing individual or organization. The proposing individual or organization has
an ethical responsibility to explain accurately and specifically what work can
be done and not done so that there is no intent to deceive readers with
promises that cannot be fulfilled.

The following questions are useful in analysing the effectiveness of the argument, whether in a written or oral proposal:

> What does the soliciting organization really want?
> What is the problem that needs to be solved?
> What approaches to the solution will be viewed most favourably?
> What approaches will be viewed unfavourably?
> What objections will our plan elicit?
> Can we accomplish the goals we propose?

To answer these questions, the proposer may be required to do research on
the organization, its problems, its corporate culture and the perspective and attitudes stemming from its corporate culture, its current financial status, goals,
and problems. As each part of the proposal is developed, you should examine
it from the intended readers' perspective:

> What are the weaknesses of the plan, as we—the writer(s)—perceive them?
> How can we counter any weaknesses and readers' potential objections?
> How can we make our plan appealing?
> How can we show that we understand their needs?
> How can we best present our capability to do this project?
> What are our strengths?
> From our own knowledge of our organization, what are our weaknesses—
>   in personnel, in overall capability to complete this project as proposed?
> Do we need to modify our proposed plan to avoid misleading readers
>   about our ability to perform certain tasks on time, as proposed, and at cost?
> Can we sell our idea without compromising the accuracy of what we
>   can actually do?

As you consider each question, you should determine what evidence
you will need to support the merits of your idea and the arguments needed
to refute any objections. Every sentence should argue for the merits of your
plan and your—or your organization's—ability to complete it. Although
the proposal is designed to be a sales document, the writer is still ethically
obligated to present a plan that meets the soliciting organization's needs
and requirements. In considering the ethical issues that confront proposal
writers, you will want to review Chapter 2 on ethical considerations in
technical writing.

Standard Sections of Proposals

Proposals generally include three main divisions: a summary, main body, and
attachments. Major proposals are submitted in complete report format, which
requires a letter of transmittal, a title page, a submission page (perhaps), a table

of contents, and a summary. The main body focuses on the three main parts of the proposal: what the proposal's objectives are (technical proposal), how the objectives will be achieved (management proposal), and how much the project will cost (cost proposal). You may find it helpful to visualize the structure in this way:

Project summary

Project description (technical proposal)
    Introduction
    Rationale and significance
    Plan of the work
    Facilities and equipment

Personnel (management proposal)

Budget (cost proposal)

Appendices

Shorter proposals may be written in a memo or letter format. Whatever the format, the main elements will be required, although how they appear will vary with each proposal. In most RFPs, the soliciting organization will explain what should be included in the proposal, either specific information to be included or major elements (as shown in the RFP in Figure 16-6 at the end of this chapter). Often, RFPs indicate the maximum number of pages allowed in a proposal. Writers are well advised to follow these instructions carefully to ensure that the proposal is not rejected during the initial screening process.

SUMMARY The summary is by far the most important section of the proposal. Many proposal consultants believe that project approval can be won or lost according to the effectiveness of the summary, which is your readers' first introduction to what you are proposing. The summary should concisely describe the project, particularly how your work meets the requirements of the soliciting organization, your plan for doing the work, and your or your company's main qualifications. The summary should be a concise version of the detailed plan, but it should be written to convince readers that you understand what the soliciting firm needs and wants; that what you are proposing can be done as you describe; and that your approach is solid because you have the required knowledge and expertise. From reading the summary, readers should want to read more of your proposal.

PROJECT DESCRIPTION (TECHNICAL PROPOSAL) The project description, or technical proposal, usually includes any or all of the following: an introduction; a description of the rationale and significance of the project; a detailed plan of how the work will proceed; a description of the work and the methods you will use; a breakdown of the tasks involved; analysis of any foreseeable problems; and perhaps a description of what facilities or resources will be used to complete the project.

Introduction The proposal introduction should explain what you are proposing, why you are proposing this idea, and what you plan to accomplish.

The introduction contains the same elements as any introduction. In short proposals, the summary and introduction can be combined.

Rationale and Significance   Much of your success in convincing readers that you should be granted permission to do the work you propose rests on your success in convincing them that you understand the project. In this section, you need to make it clear that you understand their needs—as stated in the summary or introduction—and that you have designed your goals by analysing and defining their needs. Although you will clearly be selling your idea, you should recognize and answer any questions your readers may have as you argue the merits of your project. Convincing your readers that you fully understand what they are looking for is critical in establishing your credibility. In short,

- You may want to define the problem, to show that you understand it.
- You may want to explain the background of the problem, how it evolved, by providing a historical review of the problem.
- If you are proposing a research project, you may want to explain why your research needs to be done and what results can be expected from your research.
- You may want to describe your solution and the benefits of your proposed solution.

Of greatest importance, however, is the *feasibility* of the work you propose. Is your proposed work doable? Is it suitable, appropriate, economical, and practicable? Have you given your readers an accurate view of what you can and will do?

Plan of the Work   This section is also critical, particularly to expert readers who will attempt to determine whether you understand the breadth of the work you are proposing. In this section, you will describe how you will go about achieving the goals you have stated. You will specify what you will do in what order, explaining and perhaps justifying your approach as you believe necessary. A realistic approach is crucial; a knowledgeable reader will sense immediately if your plan omits major steps. A flawed work plan can destroy your credibility as well as the merits of the goals or the solution you are proposing.

Scope   The work plan section may need to describe the scope of the proposed work. What will you do and not do? What topics will your study or your work cover and not cover? What are the limits of what you are proposing? What topics will be outside the scope of your project? Readers need to know, from an ethical and a legal perspective, the limits of your responsibility.

Methods   A work plan may also require a statement of the methods you will use. If you are going to do on-site research, how will you do this research? If you plan to collect data, how will you analyse it? How will you guarantee the validity of the analysis? If you are going to conduct surveys, how will you develop them? If you plan to do historical research or a literature review of a topic, how will you approach such a review to ensure that your findings are representative of what is currently known about a subject area? A precise, carefully detailed description of your work methods can add to your credibility as one who is competent to perform the proposed work.

Task Breakdown   Almost all proposals require you to divide your work into specific tasks and to state the amount of time allotted to each task. The task breakdown further subdivides the work to show how much time you plan to devote to each task. A realistic time schedule also becomes an effective argument. It suggests to readers that you understand how much time your project will take and that you are not promising miracles just to win approval of your proposal or business plan.

If a project must be completed by a deadline, the task breakdown and work schedule need to indicate exactly how you plan to fit every job into the allotted time. However, do not make time commitments that will be impossible to meet. Readers who sense that your work plan is artificial will immediately question your credibility. Remember, too, that a proposal is a binding commitment. If you cannot do what you propose within the required time, you can destroy your professional credibility and leave yourself open to litigation.

Problem Analysis   Few projects can be completed without problems. If you have carefully analysed the problem or work you intend to do, you should be able to anticipate where difficulties could arise. Problems that may be encountered can often be discussed in the rationale sections. However, if you discover major obstacles that you believe will occur during the course of the project, you may wish to isolate and discuss these in a separate section. Many organizations that request work or solicit research proposals are aware of problems that may arise. Reviewers in these organizations look carefully at the problem analysis section, wherever it occurs, to see whether the proposer has anticipated these problems and explained the course of action he or she will use to deal with them. Anticipating and designing solutions to problems can further build your credibility with readers, who will not be impressed if you fail to diagnose points in your work plan that could be troublesome and even hinder your completion of the project.

Facilities   The facilities section of the proposal is important if you need to convince the reader that the proposing company has the equipment, plant, and physical capability to do the proposed work. Facilities descriptions are particularly crucial if hardware is to be built at a plant site owned by the proposing organization. Even in study proposals, your readers may want to know what research resources you will use. Sometimes existing facilities are not adequate to do a particular job and the company must purchase specific equipment. The facilities section enables the proposer to explain this purchase and how it will be included in the cost proposal.

In study proposals, researchers may need to visit special libraries or research sites that require travel. The amount of money needed for this travel will be part of the cost proposal. Thus, the nature of any extra research support, its importance, and its cost to the project will need to be explained here.

HUMAN RESOURCES (MANAGEMENT PROPOSAL)   Any technical proposal or project is only as good as the management strategy that directs it. The management proposal should explain how you plan to manage the project: who will be in charge and what qualifications they have for this kind of work. Management procedures should harmonize with the methods of pursuing the work described in the technical proposal.

Descriptions of the proposer's management philosophy and hierarchy may need to be related to the company's management philosophy and culture. Readers should see the same kind of management applied to the proposed work as to the company and other projects it manages. Any testimony to or evidence of the effectiveness of the management approach will lend credibility to the technical proposal. Proposal reviewers must be convinced that you and the organization have a sound approach supported by good management.

In research proposals, the researcher who is soliciting funds will want to explain his or her expertise in the subject area proposed. This support may include educational background, previous projects successfully undertaken, published research on the topic, and general experience.

COST (COST PROPOSAL)   The cost proposal is usually the final item in the body of the proposal, even though cost may ultimately be the most crucial factor in industrial proposals. Cost is usually given last and appears as a budget for the length of the proposal period. The technical and management proposals, with their descriptions of methods, tasks, facilities, required travel, and personnel, should help justify the cost. They should have already explained the rationale for items that will produce the greatest cost. However, any items not previously discussed in the technical and management proposals, such as administrative expenses, additional insurance benefit costs, and unexpected legal costs, should be explained.

An itemized budget is often submitted as a separate document. It includes items such as the proposing organization's liability for not meeting project deadlines, for cost overruns, and for unforeseen strikes and work stoppages. Many budget sections include standard statements, such as descriptions of union contracts with labour costs, insurance benefits costs, non-strike costs, and statements of existing corporate liability for other projects—any existing arrangements that affect the cost of the proposed contract. Clearly, the goal is to explain exactly how much the project will cost and where the cost is determined. How extensive the budget will be depends on the magnitude of the project.

CONCLUSION   Like any report, the proposal includes a final section that reiterates what the proposal offers the potential client or the soliciting agency, why the proposer should be selected to perform the work, and the benefits that the project, when completed, will yield for the client. The conclusion presents the final restatement of the central argument.

APPENDICES   Again, as in any report, the appendix section will include supporting materials for information given in the main body of the proposal—in the technical, management, or cost proposal. For example, the appendix might include résumés of principal investigators, managers, or re-searchers. These résumés should highlight their qualifications as they pertain to a specific project.

Progress Reports

When a soliciting organization requests a proposal, it often states that a specific number of progress reports will be required, particularly if the project covers a long time period. As their name suggests, progress reports, sometimes known as status reports, tell readers how work is progressing on a project. They are usually submitted at specific intervals agreed upon at the beginning of a project that requires several months or even years to complete. Their immediate purpose is to inform the authorizing person of the activities completed on a project, but their long-range purpose should be to show the proposing organization's or the individual's competence in pursuing a task and completing it.

As we mentioned at the beginning of this chapter, an employee may write progress reports routinely to report the status of projects on which he or she is working. These progress reports explain what the employee has done so that others interested in the progress are kept informed. They also help the employee or work group provide evidence of their activities. Whether a progress report is written to describe work done on a proposed project or to report activity on any job, it has three main purposes that provide *documentation* of work accomplished:

- They explain to the reader what has been accomplished and by whom, the status of the work performed, and problems that need attention.
- They explain to the client how time and money have been spent, what work remains to be done, and how any problems encountered are being handled.
- They enable the organization or individual conducting the proposed work to assess the work and plan future work.

Several different strategies are used in designing progress reports. Three of the most popular are to organize the report by work performed, by chronological order, or by main project goals. All begin with an introduction and a project description followed by a summary of work completed. The middle section varies according to the strategy chosen. The final section assesses the work done thus far. Any problems that are encountered are also presented, along with methods of addressing those problems in the form of conclusions and recommendations. Cost can be dealt with in either the middle or final section.

STRUCTURE BY WORK PERFORMED   Most often, progress reports follow one of the two basic plans portrayed below. In the left-hand column, the middle is organized around work completed and work remaining. In the right-hand column, the middle is organized around tasks.

In both structures, the writer emphasizes what has been done and what remains to be done and supplies enough introduction to be sure that the reader knows what project is being discussed.

Beginning

- Introduction/project description
- Summary

Middle

- Work completed
  Task 1
  Task 2, etc.

- Work remaining
  Task 3
  Task 4
- Cost

- Task 1
  Work completed
  Work remaining

- Task 2
  Work completed
  Work remaining
- Cost

End

- Overall appraisal of progress to date
- Conclusions and recommendations

Let's take the example of a senior engineering technology student who is developing his semester research project. He is surveying current industrial methods of controlling sulfate-producing bacteria in oil wells to explain current control methods. In the progress report shown in Figure 16-2, he divides his research into three main areas and reports his progress in each area. Because he is one of 35 students, he includes a detailed introduction to refresh the instructor's memory about his purpose and justification for pursuing this topic.

The structure of Figure 16-2 is as follows:

Beginning

- Introduction
- Summary

Middle

Progress on work by phases

- Phase 1
  (Work completed)

- Phase 2
  Work completed
  Work remaining

- Phase 3
  Work completed
  Work remaining

- Cost Analysis
- Final outline

End

- Evaluation of Research

DATE: APRIL 10, 1999

TO: ELIZABETH TEBEAUX

FROM: KARIM TEDESCO

SUBJECT: PROGRESS ON FORMAL REPORT

INTRODUCTION

Subject and Purpose

I am completing work on the study and development of a growing problem in the production and recovery of oil and natural gas: bacterial control. As the major outcome of
the proposed investigation, I will recommend from among the options the method most
feasible for identifying and controlling oilfield bacteria.

Background

Petroleum microbiology is a relatively new field of interest. Because research is in its infant
stages, conclusive data are somewhat scarce. Currently, however, petroleum production
and recovery companies are financing research on a large-scale basis. Oilfield engineers, in
conjunction with microbiologists, are directing research toward the accurate identification
of petroleum bacteria, oil and natural gas recovery problems, and methods of eliminating
and/or controlling bacterial infestation.

What is the significance of bacteria in petroleum production? Oilfield bacteria corrode
pumping machinery, storage tanks, and other installations. They contaminate natural gas
associated with oil deposits; they grow in injection waters and may clog the system; and
they may have roles in the formation, release, and transformation of oil hydrocarbons.

SUMMARY

My investigation concerning feasible methods of identifying and controlling oilfield bacteria
has progressed slowly, attributable primarily to limited sources, highly technical information,
and conflicting data. I have, however, obtained invaluable information from Tretolite
Chemicals, a corrosion inhibiting company. Additionally, I have acquired needed supplementary data from the University of Texas Library in Austin.

PROGRESS ON WORK BY PHASES

I have constructed what I consider to be an effective procedure for conducting the research,
which has fallen into three separate phases:

> Phase 1: Description of Various Bacterial Groups
>
> Phase 2: Recognition of Bacterial Problems
>
> Phase 3: Alleviation of Bacterial Problems

Figure 16-2 ROUTINE PROGRESS REPORT

Elizabeth Tebeaux   -2-   April 10, 1999

Various Bacterial Groups

I have completed the general description of the three bacterial groups proven most detrimental to the oilfield industry. My report will focus primarily on the sulfate-reducing bacteria. These organisms represent the bulk of oilfield related problems. Additionally, two less prevalent bacterial species, the iron-oxidizing bacteria and the slime-forming bacteria, will be presented in this report. My two primary sources used in compiling this information are Zobell's Ecology of Sulfate Reducing Bacteria and Anderson's Petroleum Microbiology.

Recognition of Bacterial Problems

Work Completed

My analysis of the various methods of identifying bacterial problems is partially complete. I have successfully compiled a list of techniques for identifying bacterial problems. Tretolite Chemicals' "Training Manual for Sales Engineers" has proven extremely beneficial.

Work Remaining

I have not started my analysis concerning the feasibility of the various problem identification techniques. I plan to use Tretolite's training manual in conjunction with relevant data found in Producers Monthly.

Alleviation of Problems

Work Completed

I have compiled sufficient information pertaining to methods of eliminating and/or controlling oilfield bacteria. Producers Monthly and Tretolite Chemicals' "Recognition and Chemical Treatment of Bacterial Problems in the Oilfield" represent the bulk of my source.

Work Remaining

The work remaining in regard to this aspect of my investigation consists of a discussion of the feasibility of each method according to three criteria: effectiveness (desired results), financial considerations, and ease of application.

COST ANALYSIS

My estimated costs proposed on March 12 and my costs to date are outlined below.

Item	Estimated Cost	Cost to Date
Travel	$ 43.20	$ 35.00
Phone calls	6.00	5.00
Typing	60.00	20.00
Salaries	1000.00	700.00
	$ 1109.20	$ 760.00

Figure 16-2 (CONTINUED)

Elizabeth Tebeaux   -3-   April 10, 1999

FINAL OUTLINE

I. Introduction

II. Summary of Findings

III. Type of Organisms

   A. Sulfate-Reducing Bacteria

      1. What are SRB?
      2. Where are they found?
      3. When is their presence a problem?
      4. Why do SRB cause problems?

   B. Slime-Forming Bacteria

   C. Iron-Oxidizing Bacteria

IV. Recognition of Bacterial Problems

   A. Primary Indicators

      1. Microscopic observations
      2. Bacterial enumeration methods
      3. Advantages and disadvantages of each
         a. Economic feasibility
         b. Ease of application
         c. Desired results

   B. Secondary Indicators

      1. Corrosion
      2. Plugging
      3. Sulfide build

V. Alleviation of Problems

   A. Physical and Mechanical Changes

   B. Chemical Treatment

      1. Initiate with microbiocide
      2. Criteria for microbiocide treatment
      3. Compounds known to possess microbiocidal properties
      4. Mode of action

   C. Maintaining Control and Monitoring

VI. Conclusions

EVALUATION OF RESEARCH

The number of sources I will use may be less than I anticipated. Industry journals are difficult to retrieve. However, the research I have gathered is extensive and detailed. My research shows that industry research has made rapid strides in identifying bacteria and finding cost-efficient ways of dealing with these bacteria. Costs of implementing these control methods are also reasonable.

Figure 16-2 (CONTINUED)

Figure 16–3 uses a simpler version of this standard progress report. Its author is Dean Smith, a training manager for a software development company, who is responsible for developing training sessions for new sales staff. His main responsibilities are to provide training to employees, to decide what training should be conducted, and then to develop the training courses. Dean routinely writes progress reports to the Director of Human Resources, Beth Allison, to keep her informed of his activities—training he thinks will need to be offered, training programs he is currently developing or planning to develop, and training programs he and other training staff are currently teaching or directing.

Dean writes these reports to Beth about once a month (or whenever he has something he wants her to know about). Because she is familiar with what Dean does, he does not need to include an elaborate introduction. He begins with a concise summary and then proceeds to describe pertinent activities. In this particular report, he is asking for increased funding for a training program. Thus he includes an "action required" statement in the heading.

For this routine progress report, Dean modified the general plan as follows:

Beginning
- Introduction

  Purpose of the report—to report the status of a project
  Purpose of the work being performed
  Summary of current status

Middle
- Tasks completed on the project

  Task A
  Task B
  Task C

End
- Conclusions and perhaps recommendations

For progress reports that cover more than one period, the basic design can be expanded as follows:

Beginning
- Introduction
- Project description
- Summary of work to date
- Summary of work in this period

Middle
- Work accomplished by tasks (this period)
- Work remaining on specific tasks
- Work planned for the next reporting period
- Work planned for periods thereafter
- Cost to date
- Cost in this period

End
- Overall appraisal of work to date
- Conclusions and recommendations concerning problems

DATE: November 19, 1999

TO: Beth Allison

FROM: Dean Smith

SUBJECT: TQI Workshop Plans for Spring 2000
               ACTION REQUIRED BY December 10, 1999

Summary of Plans

Planning for our TQI workshops, scheduled for April and May, is nearly complete. Our TQI facilitators have produced detailed training schedules for technical service and customer relations. I have approved these, and materials are being ordered and prepared. A TQI program package, developed by HI-TOP Sales Materials, specifically for computer sales personnel, can be purchased for $3600. The format would be an excellent follow-up for all employees. As you and I have already discussed, quality off-the-shelf TQI packages should be considered.

TQI Workshop Activities as of November 19, 1999

TQI Preparations for Technical Service Personnel

Johnette Darden and her group have been preparing materials for the technical service employees. The workshop will help the staff to look at software purchases from the customer's perspective and to begin to look for ways of decreasing the time required to resolve customer complaints. The second part of the workshop will encourage TSP to examine faulty products and find ways of eliminating the problems by working with design. We will probably recommend a quality control unit be formed that uses people from both technical service and design.

TQI Preparations for Customer Relations

Responding to customer needs and filling orders rapidly will be the main focus of the TQI workshop for CR employees. Robert Choi will be working with the group (1) to reassess what we are doing in our current customer relations efforts, and then (2) to improve and even eliminate processes that do not help us serve customers quicker and better.

HI-TOP Sales Program Available for Purchase by December 15

HI-TOP developed a superb TQI program for sales staff about two years ago. The program was so effective that HI-TOP is now selling the program, which has received rave reviews from a half-dozen companies that sell hardware and software. I reviewed the program two days ago and think it would be an excellent follow-up for any TQI work we do. I would like to purchase the program and use it with both Technical Services and Customer Relations. We can continue to use the package with other TQI training.

An outline of the program is attached. As you can see, it addresses the major issues we believe our own TQI programs need to emphasize.

Figure 16-3 SIMPLIFIED ROUTINE PROGRESS REPORT

Beth Allison
Page 2
99 11 19

Please Note

   HI-TOP will sell us the program package priced at $4500 for $3600 if we act before December 10. They are currently redesigning the program to include extensive teaching aids, which are nice but unnecessary for our purposes. The new package will be available January 1 for $6000. **The original package will not be available after December 15.**

   Please give me a call so that we can discuss.

Figure 16-3 (CONTINUED)

STRUCTURE BY CHRONOLOGICAL ORDER   If your project or research is set up by time periods, your progress report can be structured to emphasize the periods:

Beginning

- Introduction/project description
- Summary of work completed

Middle

- Work completed

  Period 1 (beginning and ending dates)
       Description
       Cost

  Period 2 (beginning and ending dates)
       Description
       Cost

- Work remaining

  Period 3 (or remaining periods)
       Description of work to be done
       Expected cost

End

- Evaluation of work in this period
- Conclusions and recommendations

   Figure 16-5, pages 447–449, illustrates a progress report structured by periods.

STRUCTURE BY MAIN PROJECT GOALS   Many research projects are pursued by grouping specific tasks. Then, when progress is reported, the writer describes progress according to work done in each major group and perhaps the amount of time spent on that group of tasks. Alternatively, a researcher may decide to present a project by research goals—what will be accomplished during the project. Thus, progress reports will explain activities performed relevant to the achievement of those goals. In the plans below, the left-hand column is organized by work completed and remaining and the right-hand column by goals.

Beginning
- Introduction/project description
- Summary of progress to date

Middle

- Work completed
  Goal 1
  Goal 2
  Goal 3, etc.
- Work remaining
  Goal 1
  Goal 2
  Goal 3, etc.
- Cost

- Goal 1
  Work completed
  Work remaining
  Cost
- Goal 2
  Work completed
  Work remaining
  Cost

End
- Evaluation of work to date
- Conclusions and recommendations

Physical Appearance of Proposals and Progress Reports

The importance of the appearance of any proposal or progress report cannot be overestimated. The competence of the proposing organization or individual is suggested by a report that is neat and effectively formatted. Proposals and progress reports that exceed letter or memorandum length should have a protective cover. The title page should be attractively presented. The type or print quality should be high quality. Coloured paper and covers should convey the professional attitude of the individuals or the organization. A professional outward appearance is the first method of arguing for the merits of the proposal.

Style and Tone of Proposals and Progress Reports

The proposal and its related documents are sales documents, but writers have an ethical commitment to present information about a project clearly and accurately. Proposals, once accepted, become legally binding documents. Because contracts are based on proposals, organizations must be prepared to stand behind their proposals. Thus, the style should be positive and suggest the competence of the proposer. The writing should be vigorous, firm, and authoritative. Do not resort to vague language. Bolster any generalizations with detailed factual accomplishments. You should discuss any problems honestly, but stress positive solutions.

Other Forms of
Proposals and Progress Reports

Proposals and progress reports can be prepared in a variety of formats: as memo reports, as formal reports, and as letters. Yet, no matter what the format, proposals and progress reports will incorporate the same elements described above and illustrated in the report written by the engineering technology student (Figure 16-2). To see how proposals and progress reports might operate in another format and another context, examine the situation that follows, which illustrates a letter proposal and a memo status report on the project.

Write, Inc. specializes in helping companies improve employee writing. The company will design workshops tailored to each organization's particular writing problems. Write, Inc. will also rewrite or edit manuals, such as computer manuals, technical manuals, and policy and procedure manuals.

The company depends on referrals: satisfied client organizations who then recommend Write, Inc. to other companies. However, repeat business is also important. Write, Inc. attempts to provide continuing teaching or writing services to its clients, and the company seeks to make its services appealing through reasonable fees and instruction that achieves results—employees whose writing shows improvement because of the instruction the company provides.

Jon Sigurdson, president of Write, Inc., recently received a call from Cindy Hunter, Personnel Vice-President for Lambert Chemical Company in Manitoba. Cindy tells Jon that she has heard good things about the workshops conducted by Jon's instructors and is interested in having Write, Inc. do a workshop for all the technical sales staff on how to design effective correspondence. Cindy says that about 11 salespeople have shown a definite interest in the workshop because of several instances in which Lambert correspondence was interpreted as rude or misleading by customers. Mark Clayton, one of Write, Inc.'s instructors, makes an appointment with Cindy, examines the types of technical sales letters that Lambert has to write, and sees two letters that Cindy describes as "problematic," as well as several internal memoranda written by various individuals. Cindy tells Write, Inc.'s president, Jon, that she would like the workshops held early in the mornings, but that she is open to the number of workshop sessions that will be necessary to correct the sales correspondence problems. Cindy suggests that Jon drop her a letter that includes details—course content, time schedule, and cost—which she will then present to the president for approval.

Jon asks Mark to write the letter proposal, which he will examine and possibly revise before sending it on to Cindy. Even though Mark writes the letter, it will bear Jon's signature. See Figure 16-4 for Mark's proposal. Note that this proposal is developed by specific tasks.

Cindy Hunter accepts Write, Inc.'s proposal. Mark spends three weeks developing the cases and instructional materials before the teaching sessions begin. After the third week of the writing workshop, Mark faxes the status report shown in Figure 16-5 to Jon, who is currently on vacation but who plans to visit with Cindy Hunter during week four to offer another proposal to write the safety policy manual for Lambert. Jon is particularly interested in the participants' responses to the workshop as he plans his meeting with Cindy.

Note that the progress report specifically deals with each proposed task—those accomplished, those remaining, and the problems that have occurred in planning the workshop.

W R I T E, Inc. ────────────────▶ Instruction
1765 Portage Avenue   Writing
Winnipeg, MB   R5J 6P9   Editing
(204) 555-2921

November 2, 1998

Ms. Cindy Hunter, Vice-President for Personnel
Lambert Agricultural Chemical Co.
Brandon, MB   R8B 5R5

Dear Ms. Hunter:

We enjoyed visiting with you last Thursday and discussing how our instructional programs can improve the quality of your technical correspondence at Lambert. After assessing your description of the kind of instruction you would like to make available for all sales staff, and after again reviewing copies of several of the problem letters you sent us for further examination, I would like to submit our proposal.

Proposed Workshop for Lambert Agricultural Chemical Co.

Write, Inc. will present a correspondence workshop designed specifically for Lambert. Because of the schedule of your officers, the workshop will be presented from 8-10 a.m. for five Tuesdays. In addition to presentation of basic strategies for the design of all correspondence, the workshop will require participants to develop three letters to two case problems that simulate actual company situations requiring letter responses. We will evaluate each response, make transparencies of these responses, and share each participant's response with the group to allow group analysis of each response. A fourth and final assignment will divide participants into groups of three or four to collaboratively develop and then present a single shared response to a third case. Each group will critique these responses and suggest revisions.

In addition to in-class instruction, practice, and assignments, each participant will receive a notebook of readings and instructional materials that will be useful during the workshop and afterward as a reference.

Figure 16-4 PROPOSAL LETTER

Ms. Cindy Hunter   -2-   November 2, 1998

Workshop Schedule

The workshop will be organized as follows:

First Tuesday

Principles of Effectiveness for all Writing: Analysis of readers, definition of purpose, relationship of writer and reader, attitude and tone in writing. Assignment 1: Reading and practice in notebook.

Second Tuesday

Discussion of reading and practice assignment.

Organization of business writing. Organization of business correspondence. Analysis of cases and letter responses in notebook.

Assignment 2: Develop a letter responding to the situation in Lambert Case #1.

> We will collect all assignments during the week and evaluate them before the third class. Each participant will receive an evaluation of his/her response.

Third Tuesday

Peer review and critique of each assignment. Analysis of cases and letter responses in notebook, Section 2. Review of tone, organization, audience needs and perception.

Assignment 3: Develop two letters responding to the situations described in Lambert Case #2.

> Again, all assignments will be collected and evaluated prior to the fourth class.

Fourth Tuesday

Peer review and critique of each assignment. Practice on tone and clarity of sentences and paragraphs.

Assignment 4: Collaboration exercise. Participants will be divided into groups of three or four and will develop a shared response to Lambert Case #3. Groups will have at least one hour to develop their response and submit it. We will type all responses and have these ready for distribution at the final meeting.

Figure 16-4 (CONTINUED)

Ms. Cindy Hunter   -3-   November 2, 1998

Fifth Tuesday

Presentation of each group's response. Explanation of rationale for content, organization, tone, and style.
Peer review of each response.

Wrap-Up. Final review of principles of effective design of business correspondence. Evaluation of workshop. Write, Inc. will provide each participant an evaluation form to allow everyone to respond anonymously to the workshop. These will be collected and given immediately to you or your representative. After you have seen them, we would appreciate your sharing them with us.

Cost

As we discussed, the workshop will have 15–16 sales people. Because notebooks will be developed specifically for this workshop, much of the fee is allocated to case preparation, notebook preparation, instructional time, and assignment evaluation. Please note, however, that the fee covers all costs.

Preparation Fee	$2000.00
Case development	
Assignment development	
Notebook preparation	
Instructional time	
five 2-hr. sessions at $150/hr.	1500.00
Assignment Evaluation	
Complete analysis of two assignments for each	
participant; analysis of collaborative assignment	300.00
Total	$3800.00

Course Materials

Each participant in a Write, Inc. workshop receives a notebook of teaching materials and practice exercises. Material in the notebook will be the focus of class discussion and will have space for participants to take notes. All exercises will be done in the notebook, which also features cases and responses for each participant's analysis. After the workshop is complete, each participant has an instructional guide that can later be used for reference and review of correspondence design strategies.

Each participant will also receive a complimentary copy of <u>A Canadian Pocket Style Manual</u> by Diana Hacker, a handy guide to correctness. This guide will be placed in the front pocket of each folder.

Figure 16-4 (CONTINUED)

Ms. Cindy Hunter　　　　　　-4-　　　　　　November 2, 1998

Rationale for Write, Inc.'s Approach

Individuals learn to write by writing, not just by listening. Unlike many writing instruction services, we require participants to practice the concepts we present. We evaluate each person's work, not once, but three times, to be sure participants understand the strategies we present as well as the logic that underlies these strategies.

Qualifications of Write, Inc.

Materials for the Lambert notebook will be developed by the instructional materials group of Write, Inc. Each member of this group holds an M.A. in English and has had at least three years' experience teaching professional writing. Your workshops will be conducted in their entirety by Mr. Mark Clayton, who has been with our organization for four years. Mark holds a B.A. and an M.A. in English from the University of Manitoba, where he taught professional writing for three years. Mark has taught 19 workshops for business organizations throughout the prairie provinces.

Conclusion

Ms. Hunter, if you accept our proposal, I need to meet with you or someone in Lambert to begin developing cases for the letter exercises. We believe that writing assignments that mirror common situations within an organization provide the most meaningful contexts in which employees can improve their writing skills. Development of cases that will help your employees address common customer questions and problems will require several days, as we will need to work with Lambert managers to refine the cases. We have used this method for five years and found that workshop participants are pleased with this approach.

If you have further questions about the approach I have proposed, or if you would like to see sample materials we have developed for use by other organizations, please give me a call. As we discussed, the day and times can be arranged at your convenience.

Sincerely,

Jon Sigurdson

Jon Sigurdson
President, Write, Inc.

Figure 16-4 (CONTINUED)

TO: Jon Sigurdson   DATE: January 24, 1999

FROM: Mark Clayton

SUBJ: Status Report on Workshop at Lambert Chemical

SUMMARY

I have currently completed instruction for Week 3 of the Lambert workshop. While I am confident that the workshop will be deemed successful for the 21 participants, you need to know about two issues that might influence your discussion with Ms. Hunter about our redoing her policy manual. Employee attitude about communications is typical of what I have seen in companies that have communications problems: underestimation of what is required to write any technical report or letter effectively. With this lack of understanding come problems in explaining cost for our services.

WORK COMPLETED

First Tuesday

Principles of Effectiveness for all Writing: Analysis of readers, definition of purpose, relationship of writer and reader, attitude and tone in writing. Assignment 1: Reading and practice in notebook.

Second Tuesday

Discussion of reading and practice assignment.
Organization of business writing. Organization of business correspondence. Analysis of cases and letter responses in notebook.
Assignment 2: Develop a letter responding to the situation in Lambert Case #1.

These cases were evaluated and returned. The responses exhibited the usual problems that writers have when they do not think in terms of their customer's perspective.

Third Tuesday

Peer review and critique of each assignment. Analysis of cases and letter responses in notebook, Section 2. Review of tone, organization, audience needs and perception.

Participants had difficulty during the first hour understanding the concept of tone and audience perception. However, by the end of the session, about half the class were catching on to the problems in some of the letters I showed them.

Figure 16-5 STATUS REPORT

Jon Sigurdson—2   January 24, 1999

Assignment 3: Develop two letters responding to the situations described in Lambert Case #2.

I have collected and evaluated both letters on this case. The improvement is extraordinary.

WORK REMAINING

Fourth Tuesday

Peer review and critique of each assignment. Practice on tone and clarity of sentences and paragraphs.
Assignment 4: Collaboration exercise.

Fifth Tuesday

Presentation of each group's response. Explanation of rationale for content, organization, tone, and style.
Peer review of each response.

Wrap-Up. Evaluation of workshop.

MAJOR CONCERNS

Excessive Enrollment

Lambert representatives were not amenable to my request for two workshops of ten people each. With 21 people enrolled, I am having to redesign the collaborative response for Week 4 to divide the group into seven groups of three each. We will discuss as many of the responses as possible. I will provide detailed written critiques for each group to ensure that the response of each group is evaluated.

The size of this workshop, to my mind, reduces its effectiveness. Participants do not feel comfortable discussing examples or asking questions. We are using one of Lambert's instructional rooms, which contains 25 seats arranged in theatre style. As you well know, we usually want our workshops to be conducted in seminar room arrangement to improve communication.

Perspective on Writing

Lambert, like many other technical firms, seems to have few people who are what I would call good writers. Developing the cases was extremely time consuming and required about 11 hours more than I had expected to spend. The senior environmental engineers seem to think that good writing is simply a matter of correct mechanics and were not enthusiastic about the need for cases.

Figure 16-5 (CONTINUED)

Jon Sigurdson—3   January 24, 1999

Participants, however, seem interested in what I have to say, and I am fairly confident that they will view the workshop as a success. Their writing, and their attitudes, on what is required to communicate effectively, are definitely changing for the better.

Cost Overruns

Because of the time overruns for case development and the large class, we will lose money on this workshop. I will have to expend about 15 hours extra for case development and grading.

RECOMMENDATIONS

In your forthcoming conversations with Ms. Hunter, you may want to emphasize step-by-step what will be required to redesign their safety manual. Before we submit a proposal, we need to know if they will comply with our requests for information, if they have available the government and industry documentation we need, and if they will supply the company liaison required. In short, we need to be better prepared to estimate how much time we will need to do the policy manual so that our cost proposal is fair to us and to Lambert.

I believe that the evaluations will show that participants have had difficulties in writing sales letters because they have underestimated the writing process. If this fact comes through in the evaluations, you should be able to use this information in your discussion with Hunter.

You can reach me at 2125.

Figure 16-5 (CONTINUED)

Planning and Revision Checklists

The questions here are a summary of the key points in this chapter, and they provide a checklist when you are planning and revising any document for your readers.

Proposals

Planning
- Have you studied the RFP carefully?
- Have you made a list of all requirements given in the RFP?
- Who are your readers? Do they have technical competence in the field of the proposal? Is it a mixed audience, some technically educated, some not?
- What problem is the proposed work designed to remedy? What is the immediate background of the problem? Why does the problem need to be solved?

continued >>

- What is your proposed solution to the problem? What benefits will come from the solution? Is the solution feasible (both practical and applicable)?
- How will you carry out the work proposed? Scope? Methods to be used? Task breakdown? Time and work schedule?
- Do you want to make statements concerning the likelihood of success or failure and the products of the project?
- What facilities and equipment will you need to carry out the project?
- Who will do the work? What are their qualifications for doing the work? Can you obtain references for past work accomplished?
- How much will the work cost? Consider such things as materials, labour, test equipment, travel, administrative expenses, and fees. Who will pay for what?
- Will you need to include an appendix? Consider such things as biographical sketches, descriptions of earlier projects, and employment practices.
- Will the proposal be better presented in a report format or a letter or memo format?
- Do you have a student report to propose? Consider including the following in your proposal:

      Subject, purpose, and scope of report
      Task and time breakdown
      Resources available
      Your qualifications for doing the report

Revision

- Does your proposal have a good design and layout? Does its appearance suggest the high quality of the work you propose to do?
- Does the project summary succinctly state the objectives and plan of the proposed work? Does it show how the proposed work is relevant to the readers' interests?
- Does the introduction make the subject and the purpose of the work clear? Does it briefly point out the so-whats of the proposed work?
- Have you defined the problem thoroughly?
- Is your solution well described? Have you made its benefits and feasibility clear?
- Will your readers be able to follow your plan of work easily? Have you protected yourself by making clear what you will do and what you will not do? Have you been careful not to promise more results than you can deliver?
- Have you carefully considered all the facilities and equipment you will need?
- Have you presented the qualifications of project staff in an attractive but honest way? Have you asked permission from anyone you plan to use as a reference?
- Is your budget realistic? Will it be easy for the readers to follow and understand?
- Do all the items in the appendix lend credibility to the proposal?
- Have you included a few sentences somewhere that urge your readers to take favourable action on the proposal?
- Have you satisfied the needs of your readers? Will they be able to comprehend your proposal? Do they have all the information they need to make a decision?

Progress Reports

Planning

- Do you have a clear description of your project available, perhaps in your proposal?
- Do you have all the project tasks clearly defined? Do all the tasks run in sequence or do some run concurrently? In general, are the tasks going well or badly?

continued >>

- What items need to be highlighted in your summary and appraisal?
- Are there any problems to be discussed?
- Can you suggest solutions for the problems?
- Is your work ahead of or behind schedule?
- Are costs running as expected?
- Do you have some unexpected good news you can report?

Revisions
- Does your report present an attractive appearance?

- Does the plan you have chosen show off your progress to its best advantage?
- Is your tone authoritative with an accent on the positive?
- Have you supported your generalizations with facts?
- Do you have a good balance between work accomplished and work to be done?
- Can your summary and appraisal stand alone? Would they satisfy an executive reader?

Weblinks

Progress Reports
www.io.com/~hcexres/tcm1603/acchtml/progrep.html

Proposals
www.io.com/~hcexres/tecm1603/acchtml/props.html

Proposals
www.darkstar.engr.wisc.edu/zwickel/397/397/refs.html

Exercises

1. Examine the excerpts in Figure 16-6 (cover letter, table of contents, sections 1 and 2) from an RFP released by a university's computing services department. Then answer the questions that follow.
   - What work does the RFP want done? What problem does the RFP present to be solved?
   - Does it specify a length for the proposal?
   - Does the RFP make clear the information the proposal must contain?
   - Does the RFP furnish an outline to follow? If so, what does the outline require?
   - Does the RFP require a specific format for the proposal? What is it?
   - Does the RFP make clear the criteria by which submitted proposals will be evaluated and who will do the evaluation?

2. Write an information report based on Figure 16-6 to your professor summarizing what content items the proposal should emphasize and what criteria will be used to evaluate the proposals.

September 14, 19xx

ABC Company
   Address

You are invited to submit proposals to the Telecommunications Services department at Northern University for additional CBX9000 telephone equipment. CBX8000/9000 maintenance and house cable.

The telephone equipment, maintenance and cable will be in accordance with the specifications outlined in the enclosed Request for Proposal.

All proposals must be submitted to:

                    [name and address]

Proposals must be received at this address no later than 3:30 p.m. E.D.S.T. on October 26, 19xx.

Late proposals will not be considered regardless of the reason. Re-bids on proposals will not be allowed.

The evaluation of the proposals should be completed by November 16, 19xx. The evaluation criteria will be based upon several factors and not cost alone.

Costs should be valid for ninety days from October 26, 19xx.

A single contract may be assigned for a complete proposal or multiple contracts may be assigned by category.

Please indicate the costs for

- CBX9000 telephone equipment only
- CBX8000/9000 maintenance only
- house cable only
- a complete proposal (PBX.maintenance.cable)

Tentative installation dates are as follows:

telephone equipment	– one phase only	– January 25, 19xx
	– two phases	– January 25, 19xx
		– May 19xx
cable	– first phase	– December 19xx
	– second phase	– May 19xx

Individual meetings can be set up to discuss details of cabling as well as PBX requirements and maintenance coverage. Please contact me to schedule a meeting, which in turn will indicate your interest in submitting a proposal.

If during any meeting significant alternative solutions or needs become evident, all vendors who have indicated interest by scheduling a meeting will be notified of such addition or alteration.

I look forward to reviewing your proposal.

Sincerely,

_____

[name]

Manager, Communications Services

Enclosure

Figure 16-6 EXAMPLE REQUEST FOR PROPOSAL

Source: Adapted from RFP, Computing and Communications Services, Ryerson Polytechnic University.

Northern University   Response Due By: October 26, 19xx
RFP—CBX9000/Maintenance/Cable

1.0 INTRODUCTION AND PURPOSE

1.1 GENERAL REQUIREMENTS AND OBJECTIVES

The purpose of this document is to provide interested parties with information to enable them to prepare and submit proposals for CBX9000 telephone equipment, and/or CBX8000/9000 maintenance, and/or house cable for Northern University (hereafter referred to as Northern) campus.

2.0 PROPOSAL, PROCEDURE, STRUCTURE AND TIMETABLE

2.1 ADMINISTRATOR

This RFP is issued by Northern by their Telecommunications Services department. The RFP administrator will be:

[name and address]

2.2 SUBMISSION PROCEDURES

Proposals must be submitted consistent with the format and structure as indicated in this section.

Since it is our intent to detail the minimum requirements, all vendors are invited to elaborate on the additional features or functionalities available on their proposal solutions. However, all vendors must propose the basic configuration as specified.

Consideration will be given to all additional features, and the acquisition of the PBX, maintenance package and cable will be based upon, as part of the overall consideration, the dollar value for all features or functionalities provided.

2.3 REVISIONS TO REQUEST FOR PROPOSAL

In the event it becomes necessary to provide additional clarifying data or information, or to revise any part of this RFP, supplements or revisions will be provided to those vendors who by requesting a meeting prior to September 28, 19xx, indicate their interest in submitting a proposal.

2.4 CLARIFICATION OF THE SPECIFICATIONS

A meeting can be scheduled by any vendor interested in submitting a proposal. Scheduling a meeting indicates the vendor's interest in submitting a proposal.

If during any of these meetings, significant alternate solutions or needs become evident, all vendors who have indicated interest by scheduling a meeting will be notified of such additional or alternate solutions.

Figure 16-6 (CONTINUED)

Northern University   Response Due By: October 26, 19xx
RFP—CBX9000/Maintenance/Cable

Any vendor interested in submitting a proposal should telephone to schedule a
meeting prior to September 28, 19xx contacting:

[name and address]

Vendors submit proposals at their own risk. If prior to the date fixed for submission
of proposals, a vendor fails to notify Northern of a known error in their RFP submission and if a contract is awarded to the vendor, the vendor shall not be entitled
to additional compensation or time by reason of the error or its later correction.

2.5   RESPONSE PREPARATION AND CONTENT

2.5.1   RESPONSE ORGANIZATION

Any proposal submitted should provide a straightforward concise description
of the vendor's proposed delivery of materials, equipment, or services and the
ability to achieve the same. Emphasis should be on completeness and clarity of
the proposal. Proposals must be organized and presented in the order and by
the number assigned in the RFP. Unnecessarily elaborate brochures, art work,
expensive paper and bindings or other presentations beyond that sufficient to
present a complete and effective proposal are not desired.

2.5.2   RESPONSE PREPARATION

Each category's detailed requirements stated in Section 5.0 must be responded to in the form and order presented. Failure by a vendor to respond
to a category's specific requirement may be the basis for elimination from
consideration for that category during the comparative evaluation process.

2.5.3   RESPONSE COSTS

Northern is not liable for any cost incurred by vendors replying to the RFP.

2.6   RESPONSE SUBMISSION

In order to be considered in the proposal evaluation process, one (1) original and two
(2) copies of the proposal(s) shall be submitted to the campus contact. All proposals
must be packaged, sealed and show the following information on the outside of the
package: Vendor's Name and Address and "RFP for CBX9000".

Figure 16-6 (CONTINUED)

Northern University   Response Due By: October 26, 19xx
RFP—CBX9000/Maintenance/Cable

The original proposal package must be delivered to:

[name and address]

Original proposals and copies must be received by Northern no later than October 26, 19xx, 3:30 p.m. Eastern Daylight Saving Time. Vendors must allow sufficient time for delivery of their proposal by the time specified. Proposals that are not submitted on time will be rejected.

Proposals submitted must contain a non-collusion affidavit. (See Section 8.0 for a copy of document and signature blocks).

2.7   RESPONSE RE-SUBMISSION

Vendors may not re-submit proposals or re-bid costs, regardless of the reason. Northern, if significant alternate solutions or needs become evident, may request interested vendors (those vendors who have indicated interest by scheduling a meeting) to resubmit proposals or re-bid on cost(s).

2.8   ANTICIPATED TIMETABLE

RFP published and available	September 14, 19xx
All vendor meeting scheduled by	September 28, 19xx
Proposal delivery deadline	October 27, 19xx
Evaluation complete	November 16, 19xx
Notification of Award	November 19, 19xx

2.9   FIXED PRICE PERIOD

All prices, costs, and conditions outlined in the proposal shall remain fixed and valid for ninety (90) days, commencing on October 26, 19xx.

2.10   ORAL PRESENTATIONS

Vendors may be required to make oral presentations to supplement proposals if requested by Northern. Northern will schedule a time and location for each oral presentation it requests. Should a vendor refuse to honour the request for oral presentation, it may result in the rejection of the proposal.

2.11   DESTINATION—INSTALLED

The product/service required is to be delivered to the Telecommunications telephone switch room, AB50. Proposal prices are to include all packing, transportation, installation, instructional, and manual charges (if applicable).

Figure 16-6 (CONTINUED)

3. You will probably be required to write a complete technical report as one of the requirements for your course in technical writing.
   - Choose two or three potential topics you would consider to be suitable for a one–semester project.
   - Write a feasibility report to your instructor examining each topic in terms of availability of information, suitability of the topic for the amount of time available during the semester, and the significance of each topic to your discipline or to your career goals. Decide which topic seems most feasible.
   - Once your instructor has approved your choice of topic, write a proposal to your instructor, using memo format. In your proposal, include all elements commonly found in proposals.
   - Write a progress report to explain the status of your semester report project. Design the progress report to reflect the tasks or project goals you have used in developing your project report.

4. The following progress report is poorly organized and formatted. Reorganize it and rewrite it. Use a letter format, but furnish a subject line and the headings readers need to find their way through the report.

Forestry Research Associates
222 University Avenue
Vancouver, B.C. V8K 2G7
June 30, 1999

Mr. Lawrence Campbell, Director
Council for Peatlands Development
420 Princess Street
Sudbury, ON P6R 3X3

Dear Mr. Campbell:

Well, we have our Peatland Water-Table Depth Research Project underway. This is our first progress report. As you know, by ditching peatlands, foresters can control water-table depths for optimum growth of trees on those peatlands. Foresters, however, don't have good data on which water-table depths will encourage optimum tree growth. This study is an attempt to find out what those depths might be. We have to do several things to obtain the needed information. First, we have to measure tree growth on plots at varying distances from existing ditches on peatland. Then we have to establish what the average water-table depth is on the plots during the growing season of June, July, August, and September. To get meaningful growth and water-table depth figures, we have to gather these data for three growing seasons. Finally, we have to correlate average water-table depth with tree growth. Knowing that, foresters can recommend appropriate average water-table depths.

When the snow and ice went out in May, we were able to establish 14 tree plots on Ontario peatlands. Each plot is one-fortieth of a hectare. The distances of the plots from a drainage ditch vary from 1 to 100 metres. The plots have mixed stands of black spruce and tamarack. During June, we measured height and diameter at breast height (DBH) of a random selection of trees on each plot. We marked the measured trees so that we can return to them for future measurements. We will measure them again in September of this year and in June and September of the next two years.

While we were measuring the trees, we began placing two wells on each plot. The wells consist of perforated plastic pipes driven eight feet into the mineral soil that underlies the plot. We should have all the wells in by the end of next week. We'll measure water-table depths once a month in July, August, and September. We will also measure water-table depths any time there is a rainfall of one inch or more on the plots.

We have our research well underway, and we're right on schedule. We have made all our initial tree measurements and will soon obtain our first water-table depth readings.

By the way, the entire test area seems to be composed of raw peat to a depth of about twenty cm with a layer of well-decomposed peat about a metre thick beneath that. However, to be sure there are no soil differences that would introduce an unaccounted-for variable into our calculations, we'll do a soil analysis on each of the 14 plots next summer. We will do this additional work at no extra cost to you. During the cold-weather months, between growing seasons, we'll prepare water-table profiles that will cover each plot for each month of measurement. At the completion of our measurements in the third year, we'll correlate these profiles with the growth measurements on the plots. This correlation should enable us to recommend a water-table depth for optimum growth of black spruce and tamarack. We have promised two progress reports per growing season and one each December. Therefore, we will submit our next report on September 30.

Sincerely,

Robert Weaver

Robert Weaver
Principal Investigator

Oral Exercises

Before doing these exercises, see Chapter 17, "Oral Reports."

5. Prepare an oral version of your proposal, which you will deliver to your class. You will be allowed eight minutes maximum. Enhance your presentation with graphics (computer graphics or overhead transparencies) to show anticipated costs, your project schedule, and any visuals that will help explain the significance of your project or the methods you will use.

6. Prepare an oral progress report, which you will deliver to your class. You will be allowed five minutes maximum. Enhance your presentation with graphics to show work completed, work remaining, project costs to date, and the status of your project.

ORAL REPORTS

Oral reports are a major application of reporting technical information. You will have to report committee work, laboratory experiments, and research projects. You will give reports at business or scholarly meetings. You will instruct, if not in a teacher-student relationship, perhaps in a supervisor-subordinate relationship. You may have to persuade a group that a new process your section has devised is better than the present process. You may have to brief your boss about what your department does to justify its existence. In this chapter we discuss preparing and presenting your oral report, with a heavy emphasis on the ways in which you can provide visual support.

Preparation

In many ways, preparing an oral report is much like composing a written report. The situational analysis is virtually identical to that described in Chapter 2, "Composing." You have to consider your purpose and audience, discover your material, and arrange it.

For an oral report, you may have to pay even more attention to questions about persona, audience attitude, and your relationship to the audience than you do for a written report (see pages 14–17). These questions are particularly crucial ones, as you need to know whether your audience will consider you trustworthy and credible. To be an effective speaker, you must establish an effective relationship between you and the audience. You must not only be sincere and knowledgeable about your subject but also conform to the audience's expectations about dress, demeanour, and choice of language. You must be aware of the culture of the discourse community you are addressing (see pages 67–68).

If your audience is not North American, you must be aware of how it expects to be addressed (see pages 71–74). Often, such awareness requires expert guidance. For example, certain hand gestures common in Canada may be considered obscene in other cultures. In some cultures, too casual dress for men would be insulting, and bare arms on a woman would be sacrilegious. Don't overlook the obvious: How well do your listeners understand English? Will an idiomatic expression such as "we're going to shoot the works on this project" leave them wondering what violence is intended? The bibliography lists some sources that will give you a start. Your library will provide further help, as will the World Wide Web.

Find out as much as you can about the conditions under which you will speak. Inquire about the size of the room you will speak in, the time allotted for the speech, and the size of the audience. If you have to speak in a large area to a large group, will a public address system be available to you? Find out if you will have a lectern for your notes. If you plan to use visual aids, inquire about the equipment. Does the sponsoring group have projectors to show 35 mm slides or transparencies? Many speakers have arrived at a hall and found all of their vital visual aids worthless because projection equipment was not available. Find out if there will be someone to introduce you. If not, you may have to work your credentials as a speaker into your talk. Consider the time of day and day of the week. An audience listening to you at 3:30 on Friday afternoon will not be nearly as attentive as an audience earlier in the day or earlier in the week. Feel free to ask the sponsoring group any of these questions. The more you know beforehand, the better prepared and therefore the more comfortable you will be.

Delivery Techniques

There are four basic **delivery techniques**, but you really need to think about only two of them. The four are (1) impromptu, (2) speaking from memory, (3) extemporaneous, and (4) reading from a manuscript.

Impromptu speaking involves speaking "off the cuff." Such a method is too risky for a technical report, where accuracy is so vital. In speaking from memory, you write out a speech, commit it to memory, and then deliver it. This gives you a carefully planned speech, but we cannot recommend it as a good technique. The drawbacks are (1) your plan becomes inflexible; (2) you may have a memory lapse in one place that will unsettle you for the whole speech; (3) you think of words rather than thoughts, which makes you more artificial and less vital; and (4) your voice and body actions become stylized and lack the vital spark of spontaneity.

We consider the best methods to be extemporaneous speech and the speech read from a manuscript, and we will discuss these in more detail.

The Extemporaneous Speech

Unlike the impromptu speech, with which it is sometimes confused, the extemporaneous speech is carefully planned and practised. In preparing for an extemporaneous speech, you go through the planning and arranging steps described in Chapter 2. But you stop when you complete the outline stage. You do not write out the speech. Therefore, you do not commit yourself to any definite phraseology. In your outline, however, include any vital facts and figures that you must present accurately. You will want no lapses of memory to make you inaccurate in presenting a technical report.

Before you give the speech, practise it, working from your outline. Give it several times, before a live audience preferably, perhaps a roommate or a friend. As you practise, fit words to your outlined thoughts. Make no attempt to memorize the words you choose at any practice session, but keep practising until your delivery is smooth. When you can go through the speech without faltering, you are ready to present it. When you practise a speech, pay particular attention to timing. Depending upon your style and the occasion, plan on a delivery rate of 120–180 words per minute. Nothing, *but nothing*, will annoy program planners or an audience more than to have a speaker scheduled for 30 minutes go for 40 minutes or an hour. The long-winded speaker probably cheats some other speaker out of his or her allotted time. Speakers who go beyond their scheduled time can depend upon not being invited back.

We recommend that you type your outline. Use capitals, spacing, and underlining generously to break out the important divisions. Use boldface type for easier legibility. But don't do the entire outline in capitals. That would make it hard to read. As a final refinement, consider placing your outline in a looseleaf ring binder so you can be sure that it will not become scattered or disorganized.

There are several real advantages of the extemporaneous speech over the speech read from manuscript. With the extemporaneous speech you will find it easier to maintain eye contact with your audience. You need only glance occasionally at your outline to keep yourself on course. For the rest of the time you can concentrate on looking at your audience.

You have greater flexibility with an extemporaneous speech. You are committed to blocks of thought but not words. If by looking at your audience you see that they have not understood some portion of your talk, you are free to rephrase the thought in a new way for better understanding. If you are really well prepared, you can bring in further examples to clarify your point. Also, if you see you are running overtime, you can condense a block by leaving out some of your less vital examples or facts.

Finally, because you are not committed to words, you retain conversational spontaneity. You are not faltering or groping for words, but neither are you running by your audience like a well-oiled machine.

The Manuscript Speech

Most speech experts recommend the extemporaneous speech above reading from a manuscript. We agree in general. However, speaking in a technical situation often requires the manuscript speech. Papers delivered to scientific societies are frequently written and then read to the group. Often, the society will later publish your paper. Often, technical reports contain complex technical information or extensive statistical material. Such reports do not conform well to the extemporaneous speech form, and you should plan to read them from a manuscript.

Planning and writing a speech are little different from writing a paper. However, in writing your speech try to achieve a conversational tone. In speaking you will want to use the first person and active voice. Remember that speaking is more personal than writing. Include phrases like "it seems to me," "I'm reminded of," "Just the other evening, I," and so forth. Such phrases are common in conversation and give your talk extemporaneous overtones. Also, choose short sentences over long ones.

Type the final draft of your speech. Just as you did for the extemporaneous speech outline, be generous with capitals, spacing, underlining, and boldface type. Plan on about three typed pages per five minutes of speech. Put your pages in order and place them in a looseleaf binder.

When you carry your written speech to the lectern with you, you are in no danger of forgetting anything. Nevertheless, you must practise it, again preferably aloud to a live audience. As you practise, remember that because you are tied to the lectern, your movements are restricted. You will need to depend even more than usual on facial expression, gestures, and voice variation to maintain audience interest. Do not let yourself fall into a sing-song monotone as you read the set phrases of your written speech.

Practise until you know your speech well enough to look up from it for long periods of good eye contact. Plan an occasional departure from your manuscript to speak extemporaneously. This will help you regain the direct contact with the audience that you so often lose while reading.

Arranging Content

For the most part you will arrange your speech as you do your written work. However, the speech situation does call for some differences in arrangement and even content, and we will concentrate on these differences. We will discuss the arrangement in terms of introduction, body, and conclusion.

Introduction

A speech introduction should accomplish three tasks: (1) create a friendly atmosphere for you to speak in, (2) interest the audience in your subject, and (3) announce the subject, purpose, scope, and plan of development of your talk.

Be alert before you speak. If you can, mingle and talk with members of the group to whom you are going to speak. Listen politely to their conversation. You may pick up some tidbit that will help you to a favourable start. Look for bits of local colour or another means to establish a common ground between you and the audience. When you begin to speak, mention some member of the audience or perhaps a previous speaker. If you can do it sincerely, compliment the audience. If you have been introduced, remember to acknowledge and thank the speaker. Unless it is a very formal occasion, begin rather informally. If there is a chairperson and a somewhat formal atmosphere, we recommend no heavier a beginning than, "Mr. Chairman (or Madam Chairwoman, or an equivalent term), ladies and gentlemen."

Gain attention for your subject by mentioning some particularly interesting fact or bit of illustrative material. Anecdotes are good if they truly tie in with the subject. But take care with humour. Avoid jokes that really don't tie in with the subject or the occasion. Forget about risqué stories or potentially offensive remarks.

Be careful also about what you draw attention to. Do not draw attention to shortcomings in yourself, your speech, or the physical surroundings. Do not begin speeches with apologies.

Announce your subject, purpose, scope, and plan of development in a speech just as you do in writing. (See pages 215–218.) Giving your plan of development is even more important in a speech than in an essay. Listeners cannot go back in a speech to check on your arrangement the way that a reader can in an essay. So, the more guideposts you give an audience, the better. No one has ever disputed this old truism: (1) Tell the audience what you are going to tell them. (2) Tell them. (3) Tell them what you just told them. In instructional situations, some speakers provide their audiences with a printed outline of their talk.

Body

When you arrange the body of a speech, you must remember one thing: A listener's attention span is very limited. Analyse honestly your own attention span—be aware of your own tendency to let your mind wander. You listen to the speaker for a moment, and then perhaps you think of lunch, of some problem, or an approaching appointment. Then you return to the speaker. When you become the speaker, remember that people do not hang on your every word.

What can you do about the problem of the listener's limited attention span? In part, you solve it by your delivery techniques. We will discuss these in the next section of this chapter. It also helps to plan your speech around intelligent and interesting repetition.

Begin by cutting the ground you intend to cover in your speech to the minimum. Build a five-minute speech around one point, a 15-minute speech around two. Even an hour-long talk probably should not cover more than three or four points.

Beginning speakers are always dubious about this advice. They think, "I've got to be up there for 15 minutes. How can I keep talking if I have only two points to cover? I'll never make it." Because of this fear they load their speeches with five or six major points. As a result, they lull their audience into a state of somnolence with a string of generalizations.

In speaking, even more than in writing, **your main content should be concrete information—examples, illustrations, little narratives, analogies, and so forth—supporting just a few generalizations.** As you give your supporting information, repeat your generalization from time to time. Vary its statement, but cover the same ground. The listener who was tuned out the first time you said it may hear it the second time or the third. You use much the same technique in writing, but you intensify it even more in speaking.

We have been using the same technique here in this chapter. We began this section on the speech body by warning you that a listener's attention span is short. We reminded you that your listening span is short: same topic but a new variation. We asked you what you can do about a listener's limited span: same topic with only a slight shift. In the next paragraph we told you not to make more than two points in a 15-minute speech. We nailed this point down in the next paragraph by having a dubious speaker say, "I've got to be up there for 15 minutes. How can I keep talking if I have only two points to cover?" In the paragraph just preceding this one we told you to repeat intelligently so that the reader "who was tuned out the first time you said it may hear it the second time or the third." Here we were slightly changing an earlier statement that "You listen to the speaker for a moment, and then perhaps you think of lunch...." In other words, we are aware that the reader's attention sometimes wanders. When you are paying attention we want to catch you. Try the same technique in speaking, because the listener's attention span is even more limited than the reader's.

Creating suspense as you talk is another way to generate interest in your audience. Try organizing a speech around the inductive method. That is, give your facts first and gradually build up to the generalization that they support. If you do this skillfully, using good material, your audience hangs on, wondering what your point will be. If you do not do it skillfully or use dull material, your audience will tune you out and tune into their private worlds.

Another interest-getting technique is to **relate the subject matter to some vital interest of the audience.** If you are talking about water pollution, for example, remind the audience that the dirtier their rivers get, the more tax dollars it will eventually take to clean them up.

Visual aids often increase audience interest. Remember to keep your graphics big and simple. No one is going to see typewritten captions from more than three or four feet away. Stick to big pie and bar graphs. If you have tables, print them in letters from two to three inches high. If you are speaking to a large group, put your graphic materials on transparencies and project them on a screen. Prepare your transparencies with care. Don't just photocopy typed or printed pages or graphics from books. No one behind the first row will see them. To work, letters and numbers on transparencies should be at least twice normal size. Word processing makes large type fonts available. If you need an assistant to help you project visual aids, get one or bring one with you.

Do not display a visual aid until you want the audience to see it. While the aid is up, call your listeners' attention to everything you want them to see. Take the aid away as soon as you are through with it. If using a projector, turn it off whenever it is not in use. Be sure to key every visual aid into your speaker's script. Otherwise, you may slide right by it. (See also the section on visual aids, pages 469–481.)

Conclusion

As in your written reports, you have your choice of several closes. You can close with a summary, or a list of recommendations including a call for some sort of action, or what amounts to "Good-bye, it's been good to talk to you." As in the introduction, you can use an anecdote in closing to reinforce a major point. In speaking, never suggest that you are drawing to a close unless you really mean it. When you suggest that you are closing, your listeners perk up and perhaps give a happy sigh. If you then proceed to drag on, they will be resentful.

Second, remember that audience interest is usually highest at the beginning and close of a speech. Therefore, you will be wise to provide a summary of your key points at the end of any speech. Give your listeners something to carry home with them.

Presentation

After you have prepared your speech you must present it. For many people, giving a speech is a pretty terrifying business. Before speaking they grow tense, have hot flashes and cold chills, and experience the familiar "butterflies in the stomach." Some people tremble before and even during a speech. Try to remember that these are normal reactions, for both beginning and experienced speakers. Most people can overcome the effects of their apprehension, however, and in fact you can turn this nervous energy to your advantage.

If your stage fright is extreme, or if you are the one person in a hundred who stutters, or if you have some other speech impediment, seek clinical help. The ability to communicate ideas through speech is one of humanity's greatest gifts. Do not let yourself be cheated. Some of the finest speakers we have ever had in class were stutterers who admitted their problem and worked at it with professional guidance. Remember, whether your problems are large or small, the audience is on your side. They want you to succeed.

Physical Aspects of Speaking

What is the physical presentation or platform manner of good speakers? They stand securely but comfortably. They move and gesture naturally and emphatically but avoid fidgety, jerky movements and foot shuffling. They look directly into the eyes of people in the audience, not merely in their general direction. They project enthusiasm into their voices. They do not mumble or speak flatly. We will examine these characteristics in detail—first movement and then voice.

MOVEMENT   A century ago a speaker's movements were far more florid and exaggerated than they are today. Today we prefer a more natural mode of speaking, closer to conversation than oratory. To some extent, electronic devices such as amplifying systems, radio, and television have brought about this change. However, you do not want to appear like a stick of wood. Even when speaking to a small group or on television (or, oddly enough, on the radio) you will want to move and gesture. If you are speaking in a large auditorium, you will want to broaden your movements and gestures. From the back row of a 2500-seat auditorium, you look about three inches tall.

Movement during a speech is important for several reasons. First, it puts that nervous energy we spoke of to work. The inhibited speaker stands rigid and trembles. The relaxed speaker takes that same energy and puts it into purposeful movement.

Second, movement attracts attention. It is a good idea to emphasize an idea with a distinct gesture that reflects its importance; and a speaker who comes out from behind the lectern occasionally and walks across the stage or toward the audience awakens audience interest. The speaker who passively utters ideas deadens the audience.

Third, movement makes you feel more forceful and confident. It keeps you, as well as your audience, awake. This is why good radio speakers will gesture just as emphatically as if the audience were right there in front of them.

What sorts of movements are appropriate? To begin with, **movement should closely relate to your content.** Jerky or shuffling motions that occur haphazardly distract an audience. But a pointing finger combined with an emphatic statement reinforces a point for an audience. A sideward step at a moment of transition draws attention to the shift in thought. Take a step backward and you indicate a conclusion. Step forward and you indicate the beginning of a new point. Use also the normal descriptive gestures that all of us use in conversation: gestures to indicate length, height, speed, roundness, and so forth.

For most people, **gesturing is fairly natural.** They make appropriate movements without too much thought. Some beginning speakers, however, are body-inhibited. If you are in this category, you may have to cultivate movement. In your practice sessions and in your classroom speeches, risk artificiality by making gestures that seem too broad to you. Oddly enough, often at the very point where your gestures seem artificial and forced to you, they will seem the most natural to your audience.

Allow natural gestures to replace nervous mannerisms. Some speakers develop startling mannerisms and remain completely oblivious to them until a mentor or colleague points them out. Some that we have observed include putting eyeglasses off and on; knocking a heavy ring over and over on the lectern; fiddling with a pen, pointer, chalk, microphone cord, ear, mustache, nose, you name it; twisting or tapping a foot; and pointing with the elbows while the hands remain in the pants pockets. Mannerisms may also be vocal. Such things as little coughs or repeating comments such as "OK" or "You know" to indicate transitions may become mannerisms.

Listeners are distracted by such habits. Often they will concentrate on the mannerisms to the exclusion of everything else. They may know that a speaker put his eyeglasses on and off 22 times but not have the faintest notion of what he said. If someone points out such mannerisms in your speaking habits, do not feel hurt. Instead, work to remove the mannerisms.

Movement includes facial movement. **Do not be deadpan.** Your basic expression should be a relaxed, friendly look. But do not hesitate to smile, laugh, frown, or scowl when such expressions are called for. A scowl at a moment of disapproval makes the disapproval that much more expressive. Whatever you do, do not freeze into one expression. This lifeless fixity can give you the appearance of an automaton and make your speech seem disembodied.

VOICE   Your voice should sound relaxed, free of tension and fear. Tension tends to raise the pitch of your voice, making it less comfortable for the audience to listen to. In many of the speech books in the bibliography at the end of this book, you will find speech exercises that help with this and other voice elements. If, despite practice, you have not succeeded in making your voice an asset, don't despair. Many successful speakers have had undistinguished, even unpleasant, voices, and through force of character or intellect engaged their audiences with their ideas.

Many beginning speakers speak too fast, probably because they are anxious to be done and sit down. For the English language, a normal rate of speech falls between 120 and 180 words a minute. This is actually fairly slow. Generally, you will want a fairly slow delivery rate. When you are speaking slowly, your voice will be deeper and more impressive. Also, listeners have trouble following complex ideas delivered at breakneck speed. Slow down and give your audience time to absorb your ideas.

Of course, you should **vary your rate of talking.** If you normally speak somewhat rapidly, slowing down will emphasize ideas. If you are speaking slowly, suddenly speeding up will suggest excitement and enthusiasm. As you speak, **change the volume and pitch of your voice.** Any change in volume, whether from low to high or the reverse, will draw your listeners' attention and thus emphasize a point. The same is true of a change in pitch. If your voice remains a flat monotone and your words come at a constant rate, you deprive yourself of a major tool of emphasis.

Many people worry about their accent. Usually, our advice is **don't.** Listeners typically adjust very quickly to different accents and respect the individuality and distinctiveness of the speaker's voice.

If, however, you have been told your enunciation is careless—"Ya wanna cuppa coffee?"—or otherwise unclear, do something about it. Work with your teacher or seek other professional help. Take pains to speak slowly and enunciate clearly. Use visual aids to reinforce words your audience may have difficulty understanding. Before you speak, look up any words you know you must use and are uncertain of how to pronounce. Speakers on technical subjects have this problem perhaps more than other speakers. Many technical terms are jawbreakers. Find their correct pronunciation and practise them until you can say them easily.

Audience Interaction

One thing speakers must learn early in their careers is that they cannot count on the audience's hanging on every word. Some years ago an intelligent, educated audience was asked to record its introspections while listening to a speaker. The speaker was an excellent one. Despite his excellence and the high level of the audience, the introspections revealed that the audience was paying somewhat less than full attention. Here are some of the recorded introspections:

> God, I'd hate to be speaking to this group.... I like Ben—he has the courage to pick up after the comments.... Did the experiment backfire a bit? Ben seems unsettled by the introspective report.... I see Ben as one of us because he is under the same judgement.... He folds his hands as if he was about to pray.... What's he got in his pocket he keeps wriggling around.... I get the feeling Ben is playing a role.... It is interesting to hear the words that are emphasized.... This is a hard spot for a speaker. He really must believe in this research....
>
> Ben used the word "para-social." I don't know what that means. Maybe I should have copied the diagram on the board.... Do not get the points clearly ... cannot interrupt ... feel mad ... More words.... I'm sick of pedagogical and sociological terms.... An umbrella dropped.... I hear a funny rumbling noise.... I wish I had a drink.... Wish I could quit yawning ... Don't know whether I can put up with these hard seats for another week and a half or not.... My head itches.... My feet are cold. I could put on my shoes, but they are so heavy.... My feet itch.... I have a piece of coconut in my teeth.... My eyes are tired. If I close them the speaker will think I'm asleep....
>
> Backside hurts ... I'm lost because I'm introspecting.... The conflict between introspection and listening is killing me. If he really wants me to introspect, he must realize himself he is wasting his time lecturing.... This is better than the two hour wrestling match this afternoon.... This is the worst planned, worst directed, worst informed meeting I have ever attended.... I feel confirmation, so far, in my feelings that lectures are only 5% or less effective.... I hadn't thought much about coming to this meeting but now that I am here it is going to be O.K.... Don't know why I am here.... I wish I had gone to the circus.... Wish I could have this time for work I should be doing.... Why doesn't he shut up and let us react.... The end of the speech. Now he is making sense.... It's more than 30 seconds now. He should stop. Wish he'd stop. Way over time. Shut up.... He's over. What will happen now? ...[1]

As some of the comments reveal, perhaps being asked to record vagrant thoughts as they appeared made some members of the audience less attentive than they normally would have been. But most of us know that we have very similar thoughts and lapses of attention while we attend classes and speeches.

Reasons for audience inattention are many. Some are under the speaker's control; some are not. The speaker cannot do much about such physical problems as hard seats, crowded conditions, bad air, and physical inactivity. The speaker can do something about psychological problems such as the listeners' passivity and their sense of anonymity, their feeling of not participating in the speech.

AUDIENCE ANALYSIS   Even before they begin to speak, good speakers have taken audience problems into account. They have analysed the audience's education and experience level. They have planned to keep their points few and to repeat major points through timely variations. They plan interesting examples. While speaking, they attempt to interest the audience through movement and by varying the speech rate, pitch, and volume.

But good speakers go beyond these steps and analyse their audience and its reactions as they go along. In an extemporaneous speech, and even to some extent in a written speech, you can make adjustments based on this audience analysis.

To analyse your audience, you must have good eye contact. You must be looking at Winston, Bob, and Rosa. You must not merely be looking in the general direction of the massed audience. Look for such things as smiles, scowls, fidgets, puzzled looks, bored expressions, interested expressions, sleepy eyes, heads nodded in agreement, heads nodded in sleep, heads shaken in disagreement. You will not be 100% correct in interpreting these signs. But, generally, such physical actions are excellent clues to how well you are getting through to your audience.

REACTING TO THE AUDIENCE   If your audience seems engaged and interested, you can proceed with your speech as prepared. If, however, you see signs of boredom, discontent, or a lack of understanding, you must make some adjustments. Exactly what you do depends to some extent on whether you are in a formal or informal speaking situation. We will look at the formal situation first.

In the *formal* **situation** you are somewhat limited. If your audience seems bored, you can quickly change your manner of speaking. Any change will, at least momentarily, attract attention. You can move or gesture more. With the audience's attention gained, you can supply some interesting examples, a relevant personal experience, or other illustrative material to better support your abstractions and generalizations. If your audience seems puzzled, you know you must supply further definitions and explanations and probably more concrete examples. It may be appropriate to invite audience questions at this point. If your audience seems hostile, you must find some way to soften your argument while at the same time preserving its integrity. Perhaps you can find some mutual ground upon which you and the audience can agree and move on from there.

Obviously, such flexibility during the speech requires some experience. Also it requires that the speaker have a full knowledge of the subject. If every bit of material you know about the subject is in your speech already, you have little flexibility. But do not be afraid to adjust a speech in midstream. Even the inexperienced speaker can do so to some extent.

Many of the speaker's problems are caused by the fact that the speech situation is a one-way street. The listeners sit passively. Their normal desires to react, to talk back to the speaker, are frustrated. The problem suggests the solution, particularly when you are in a more informal speech situation, such as a classroom or a small meeting.

In the more *informal* **situation**, you can stop when a listener seems puzzled. Politely ask him where you have confused him and attempt to clarify the situation. If a listener seems uninterested, give her an opportunity to react. Perhaps you can treat her as a puzzled listener. Or, you can ask her what you can do to interest her more. Do not be unpleasant. Put the blame for the lack of interest on yourself, even if you feel it does not belong there. Sometimes you may be displeased or shocked at the immediate feedback you receive, but do not avoid it on these grounds. And do not react defensively to it. You will move more slowly when you make speaking a two-way street, but the final result will probably be better. Immediate feedback reveals areas of misunderstanding or even mistrust of what is being said.

In large meetings where such informality is difficult, you can build in some audience reaction through the use of informal subgroups. Before you talk, divide your audience into small subgroups, commonly called **buzz groups** or **discussion groups.** Use seating proximity as the basis for your division if you have no better one. Explain that after your talk the groups will have a period of time in which to discuss your speech. They will be expected to come up with questions or comments. People do not like to seem unprepared, even in informal groups. As a result, they will be more likely to pay attention to your speech in order to participate well in their buzz groups.

Whether you have buzz groups or not, often you will be expected to handle questions following a speech. If you have a chairperson, he or she will field the questions and repeat them, and then you will answer them. If you have no chairperson, you will perform this role for yourself. Be sure everyone understands the question. Be sure you understand the question. If you do not, ask the questioner to repeat it and perhaps to rephrase it.

Keep your answers brief, but answer the questions fully and honestly. When you do not have the answer, say so. Do not be afraid of conflict with the audience, but keep it on an objective basis; talk about the conflict situation, not personalities. If someone reveals through a question that she is becoming personally hostile, handle her courteously. Answer the question as quickly and objectively as you can and move on to another questioner. Sometimes the bulk of your audience will grow restless while a few questioners hang on. When this occurs, release your audience and, if you have time, invite the questioners up to the platform to continue the discussion. Above all, during a question period be courteous. Resist any temptation to have fun at a questioner's expense.

Visual Aids

Most technical talks require visual aids.

Purpose

You can use a visual aid (1) *to support* and *expand* the content of your message and (2) *to focus the audience's attention* on a critical aspect of your presentation.[2]

SUPPORT   The first purpose of any visual material is **to support your message**—to enlarge on the main ideas and give substance and credibility to what you are saying. Obviously, the material must be relevant to the idea being supported. Too often a speaker gives in to the urge to show a visually attractive or technically interesting piece of information that has little or no bearing on the subject.

Suppose, for the purposes of our analysis, that you were asked to meet with government people to present a case for your company's participation in a major federal contract. Your visual support would probably include information about the company's past performances with projects similar to the one being considered. You would show charts reflecting the ingenious methods used by the company's development people to keep costs down; performance statistics to indicate your high-quality standards; and your best conception-to-production times to show the audience your ability to target dates.

In such a presentation, before an audience of tough-minded officials, you wouldn't want to spend much of your time showing them aerial views of the company's modern facilities or photographs of smiling employees, antiseptic production lines, and the company's expensive air fleet. Such material would hardly support and expand your arguments that the company is used to working and producing on a tight budget.

FOCUS   Your second reason for using visual aids is **focus of attention.** A good visual can arrest the wandering thoughts of your audience and bring their attention right down to a specific detail of the message. It forces their mental participation in the subject.

When you are dealing with very complex material, as you often will be, you can use a simple illustration to show your audience a single, critical concept within your subject.

Criteria for Good Visual Aids

What about the visual aids themselves? What makes one better than another for a specific kind of presentation? Before we consider individual visual aids, let's look at the qualities that make a visual aid effective for the technical speaker.

VISIBILITY   The first criterion for a visual aid is *visibility*. If that seems so obvious that it hardly need be mentioned at all, it may be because you haven't experienced the frustration of being shown something the speaker feels is important—and not being able to read it, or even make out detail. To be effective, your visual support material should be clearly visible from the most distant seat in the house. If you have any doubts, sit in that seat and look. Remember this when designing visual material: **Anything worth showing the audience is worth making large enough for the audience to see.**

CLARITY   The second criterion for a good visual is clarity. The audience decides this. If they're able to determine immediately what they are seeing, the visual is clear enough. Otherwise, it probably calls for further simplification and condensation. Pictorial material that is out of focus, or close-ups of a complex device that will confuse the audience are obvious mistakes. But what about the chart that shows a relationship between two factors on x- and y-axes when the axes are not clearly designated or when pertinent information is unclear or missing?

One way to achieve clarity is to choose fonts, type styles, and colours wisely (see Chapter 8). The following are good ground rules:

- Use boldface type in a size that can be read easily.
- Limit yourself to two fonts per figure.
- Avoid all caps except in single-line headings.
- Avoid visuals that use too many colours—more than four in any one visual.

Visual material should be immediately clear to the audience, who should be able to understand it at a glance without specific help from the speaker.

SIMPLICITY The third criterion for good visual support is *simplicity*. No matter how complex the subject, the visual itself should include no more information than absolutely necessary to support the speaker's message. If it is not carrying the burden of the message, it need not carry every detail. Limit yourself to *one* idea per visual—mixing ideas will totally confuse an audience, causing them to turn you off in midsentence.

When using words and phrases on a visual, limit the material to key words that act as visual cues for you and the audience. A visual communications expert who wished to present the criteria for a good visual might *think* something like this:

A good visual must be visible.
A good visual must be clear.
A good visual must be simple.
A good visual must be easy for the speaker to control.

What would he show the audience? If he knows his field as well as he should, he'll offer the visual shown in Figure 17-1.

The same information is there. The visual is being used appropriately to provide emphasis while the speaker supplies the ideas and the extra words. The very simplicity of the visual has impact and is likely to be remembered by the audience.

CONTROL The fourth criterion for a visual aid is *control*, speaker control. You should be able to add information or delete it, to move forward or backward to review, and, finally, to *take it away* from the audience to bring their attention back to you.

Some very good visual aids can meet the other criteria and yet prove almost worthless to a speaker because they cannot be easily controlled. The speaker, who must maintain a flow of information and some kind of rapport with the audience, can't afford to let visual material interfere with this task. Remember, visual material is meant to *support* you as a speaker, not to replace you.

Figure 17-1 CRITERIA FOR VISUAL AIDS

Visual Content

So far we have discussed the why of visual support material. The remaining two questions of concern to you are: What do I use? How do I use it? Let's consider them in that order, applying the criteria already established as we go. Visual content falls into seven categories:

- Graphs
- Tables
- Representational art, such as line drawings
- Photographs
- Words and phrases
- Cartoons
- Hardware

Graphs, tables, representational art, and photographs are discussed in detail in Chapter 10, "Graphical Elements." You will want to apply the suggestions made there to the visuals you choose for oral reports. Apply also the visibility, clarity, simplicity, and control criteria. For example, the table in Figure 17-3 is too complicated for use as a visual aid for an oral report. The table in Figure 17-4 would work well. The graph in Figure 17-5 (page 475) is too busy. Listeners would be spending their time trying to figure it out instead of attending to the speaker. The graph in Figure 17-6 (page 476) would work well. The listener can grasp the main point of it immediately, with little help from the speaker. The hard fact is that many visuals taken from articles, books, or the Internet violate one or more of the criteria and are thus unsuitable for use in oral reports. You must either revise them or create your own visuals.

In the following sections, we discuss using words and phrases, pictorials and cartoons, and hardware.

WORDS AND PHRASES   There will always be circumstances in which you will want to emphasize key words or phrases by visual support, as in Figure 17-1. This type of visual can be effectively used to make the audience aware of major divisions or subdivisions of a topic, for instance.

There is danger, however, in the overuse of words—too many with too much detail. Some speakers tend to use visuals as a "shared" set of notes for their presentation, a self-limiting practice. Audiences who are involved in reading a long, detailed piece of information won't recall what the speaker is saying.

With technical presentations, there is still another problem with the use of words. Too often, because they may be parts of a specialized vocabulary, they do more to confuse the audience than increase their understanding. Such terms should be reserved for audiences whose technical comprehension is equal to the task of translating them into meaningful thoughts.

PICTORIALS AND CARTOONS   Pictorials illustrate people, processes, and concepts in an imaginative graphic way. Cartooning does the same, often using exaggeration to show common reactions or to emphasize the emotional dimension of a situation (see Figure 17-2). These techniques can heighten audience interest and can be specific to your purpose of illustrating actions, positions or problems.

Some situations in which you might choose to use pictorial or cartooned visual material are these:

- When dealing with subjects in which the audience's experience of a pattern or problem is highlighted.
- When showing people-oriented action in a stationary medium (any visual aid outside the realm of motion pictures or video).

The resourceful speaker will use a cartoon or pictorial to help give additional meaning to other forms of visual support. The use of cartoons as elements in a block diagram tends to increase viewer interest.

Figure 17-2 CARTOON USED TO HUMANIZE A STATISTIC (PERCENTAGE OF CANADIAN HOUSEHOLDS WITH TWO OR MORE COLOUR TELEVISIONS).

Source: Jason Schneider, artist; illustration for "Spectrum," *The Globe and Mail Report on Business Magazine* (March 1995) 112.

Medical and surgical procedures

Patients in acute-, convalescent- and chronic-care facilities receive medical and surgical procedures at differing rates across the country. The chart shows primary procedures per 10,000 population in 1995-1996 in numerical order nationally, and their provincial rates, with rankings according to frequency within each province in grey.

	Obstetrical	Diagnostic, therapeutic	Digestive, abdominal	Musculo-skeletal	Cardio-vascular	Gyneco-logical	Nose, mouth and throat	Urinary tract	Nervous system	Male genital	Respiratory system	Skin, subcu-taneous tissue	Breast	Eyes	Blood, lym-phatic Systems	Ears	Endocrine system	Other, or no procedure
Canada	136.8 1	106.6 2	97.5 3	72.4 4	53.7 5	41.6 6	21.8 7	21.5 8	13.9 9	13.6 10	12.5 11	12.1 12	10.8 13	10.7 14	5.6 15	3.1 16	2.9 17	471.9
NF	103.8 3	135.1 1	112.1 2	62.9 4	59.8 5	52.2 6	35.6 7	29.6 8	11.5 12	15.5 9	12 11	13.3 10	7.3 14	9.2 13	6.5 15	4.5 16	3.4 17	584.2
NS	116.7 2	106 3	118 1	80.5 5	80.7 4	45.5 6	34.8 7	25 8	13.2 [11]	12.7 13	15.9 9	13.2 [11]	8.8 14	14.8 10	7 15	3.9 16	3 17	495.8
PE	113.9 2	115.51 1	111 3	50 5	20 8	55.7 4	36.6 6	28 7	8.5 13	17.2 9	12.5 10	9 12	11.2 11	6.7 14	3.2 16	4.3 15	1.4 17	720.6
NB	125.3 2	122.6 3	128.9 1	78.3 4	60.7 5	48.9 6	43.3 7	35.5 8	12.8 14	18.1 9	13.7 13	14.2 11	16.8 10	14 12	6.6 15	6.1 16	3.1 17	756.6
QC	129.9 1	102 2	100.1 3	59.4 4	58.1 5	38.7 6	14.5 10	17.2 7	15.6 8	11.2 14	12.4 11	12.2 12	11.5 13	15.1 9	6.3 15	3.9 16	2.6 17	438.7
ON	142.3 1	100.5 2	90 3	73.5 4	49.9 5	39.6 6	20.9 8	22.6 7	13.6 10	14.7 9	12 11	11 12	10.4 13	8.5 14	5.6 15	2.7 17	3.3 16	430.2
MB	129.6 1	103.7 2	98.4 3	67.1 4	49.5 5	48 6	20.6 7	16.9 8	9.9 [12]	12.8 10	14.1 9	12.7 11	9.9 [12]	8.3 14	6.4 15	1.9 17	3 16	603.6
SK	153.9 1	113.9 2	118.3 2	91.7 4	44.5 6	56.2 5	32.3 7	28 8	16.4 10	16.6 9	12.4 [12]	14.5 11	12.4 [12]	9.6 14	5.2 15	1.9 17	3.1 16	752.1
AB	149.5 1	123.9 2	99.7 3	85.3 4	54.9 5	45.1 6	23.2 7	19.5 8	12.4 12	12.6 [10]	12.6 [10]	12.8 9	10.2 13	8 14	4.7 15	2.8 17	3.4 16	470
BC	135.5 1	113.7 2	93.2 3	81.5 4	51.8 5	40.4 6	23.1 7	22.7 8	14.3 9	13.8 10	12.7 12	13.4 11	11.2 13	10.8 14	4.4 15	2.3 16	2.2 17	442.8

Source: Canadian Institute for Health Information

[??] Ties—Statistically adjusted for age and sex factors in each province

Examples of procedures

OBSTETRICAL birth, amniocentesis, fetal monitoring

DIAGNOSTIC AND THERAPEUTIC nuclear medicine: ultrasound, CT, MRI and PET scan

DIGESTIVE AND ABDOMINAL appendectomy, gall bladder removal, hernia surgery

MUSCULOSKELETAL bone graft, fracture repair, hip, and knee replacement

CARDIOVASCULAR coronary bypass, heart transplant, pacemaker implantation

GYNECOLOGICAL hysterectomy and other surgery

NOSE, MOUTH AND THROAT tonsillectomy, adenoidectomy and nose surgery

URINARY TRACT kidney transplant, bladder surgery

NERVOUS SYSTEM brain and spinal cord surgery, skull repair

MALE GENITAL circumcision, prostate surgery, vasectomy

RESPIRATORY SYSTEM lung biopsy and surgery, tracheotomy

SKIN AND SUBCUTANEOUS TISSUE biopsy, skin graft, repair of lip or mouth

BREAST biopsy, lumpectomy, mastectomy

EYES cornea transplant, cataract surgery, retina attachment

BLOOD AND LYMPHATIC SYSTEMS bone marrow transplant, lymph node removal, spleen surgery

EARS biopsy repair of eardrum

ENDOCRINE SYSTEM operation on adrenal, pituitary, thyroid and other gland

OTHER operations not completed, not otherwise specified, or no procedure performed

Figure 17-3 A COMPLICATED TABLE

Source: "Medical and surgical procedures," *Maclean's* (June 15, 1998): 25.

Like any other technique, cartooning can be overdone. There are circumstances in which the gravity of the situation would suggest that you consider only the most formal kinds of visual support material. On other occasions, cartooning may distract the audience or call too much attention to itself. Your purpose is not to entertain but to communicate.

HARDWARE After all this analysis of visual support material, you may wonder if it wouldn't be somewhat easier to show the real thing instead. Certainly, there will be times when the best visual support you can have is

Canada's computer market

Unit Sales

In 1994 821,808 units were sold, up 17 percent from 700,856 in 1993.

	Units	Amount 000s
Servers	10,233	$82.4
Desktops	686,773	1,567.5
Laptops	894	4.6
Notebooks	94,443	421.2
Palmtops	1,537	0.8
Penbased	755	4.0
TOTAL	821,808	$2,080.7

Figure 17-4 A SIMPLE TABLE

Source: The Globe and Mail (March 14, 1998). Reproduced with the permission of the Minister of Public Works and Government Services Canada, 1998.

the actual object. Notably, the introduction of a new piece of equipment will be more effective if it is physically present to give the audience an idea of its

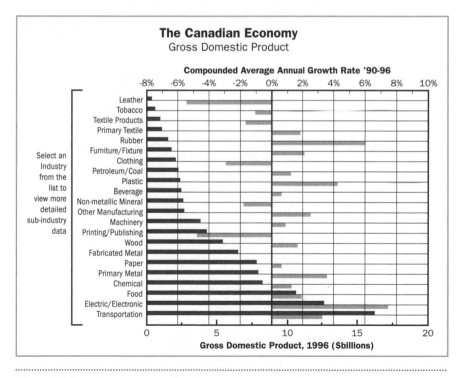

Figure 17-5 A COMPLICATED GRAPH

Source: Industry Canada, *Strategis: Trade Data Online,* http://www.strategis.ic.gc.ca/SSG/ci00015e.html, accessed on 15 May 1998. Reproduced with permission of the Minister of Public Works and Government Services Canada, 1998.

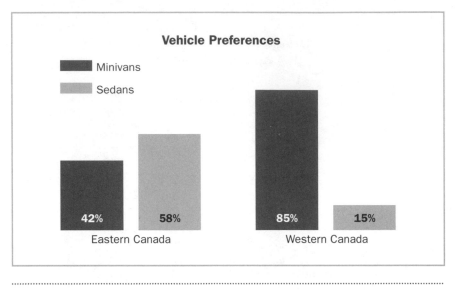

Figure 17-6 A Simple Bar Graph

size and bulk. If it is capable of some unique and important function, it should definitely be seen by the audience. (The greatest difficulty with the use of actual hardware is control. The device that is small enough for you to carry conveniently may be too small to be seen by the audience.)

Even when the physical presence of a piece of equipment is possible, it is important to back it with supplementary visual materials. Chances are the audience will not be able to determine what is happening inside the machine, even if they understand explicitly the principle involved. With this in mind, you will want to add information with appropriate diagrams, graphs, and scale drawings.

In the end, you are the one who can best decide which form of visual support is required by your message and your audience. In making your selection, use the criteria of visibility, clarity, simplicity, and control, which have been stressed over and over in this discussion of visual support.

Visual Presentation Tools

The major visual tools are these:

Computer technology   Charts
Overhead projection   Movies and videos
Slides   Chalkboards

We have listed these tools, from left to right, in descending order of importance. However, all of them are still in use and are valuable ways of presenting visual material to enhance an oral report.

COMPUTER TECHNOLOGY Computer graphics and programs—such as Harvard Graphics, Powerpoint™, or Excel™—in combination with colour printers and slide projection equipment, provide the opportunity to create visuals that meet all the criteria discussed earlier in the chapter. In addition, computer technology allows a speaker to download visuals from the World Wide Web that can be turned into slides and transparencies. In some cases, presentation rooms now have direct connections to organizational networks such as Ethernet and to the Web, allowing a speaker to download visuals while the talk is in progress and display them using an overhead projector.

The allure of such technology and the increasing ease of its use may tempt you into using unsuitable visuals. Remember, a visual that is not visible, clear, simple, and controllable is worse in most cases than no visual at all.

OVERHEAD PROJECTION   Throughout this discussion of visual support, we've stressed the importance of maintaining a good speaker–audience relationship. It's an essential in the communication process. And it's fragile. Any time you turn your back to the audience, or darken the room, or halt the flow of ideas for some other reason, this relationship is damaged.

The overhead projector effectively eliminates all of these rapport-dissolving problems. The image it projects is bright enough and clear enough to be used in a normally lighted room without noticeable loss of visibility. And just as important from your point of view, it allows you to remain in the front of the room *facing* your audience throughout your presentation. The projector itself is a simple tool that can be used without calling attention to itself.

Visual material for the overhead projector is prepared on transparent sheets the size of typing paper. The methods for preparing these transparencies have become so simple and so inexpensive that the overhead has become a universally accepted visual tool in both the classroom and industry.

Perhaps the most important advantage of the overhead projector is the total speaker control it affords. With it, you may add information or delete it in a variety of ways, move forward or backward to review at will, and *turn it off* without altering the communicative situation in any way. It is this last capability that makes the overhead projector unique among visual tools. By flipping a switch, you can literally "remove" the visual material from the audience's consideration, bringing their attention back to you and what you are saying. Because the projector is used in a lighted room, this on-and-off process seldom distracts the audience or has any effect on the speaker–audience relationship.

There are three ways to add information to a visual while the audience looks on—an important consideration when you want your listeners to receive information in an orderly fashion. In order of their discussion, they are (1) overlays, (2) revelation, and (3) writing on the visual itself.

The **overlay technique** (Figure 17-7) combines the best features of preparing your visuals in advance and creating them at the moment they are needed. You begin with a single positive transparency and add information with additional transparencies by "overlaying" them, placing each one over the first so they may be viewed by the audience as a single, composite illustration.

Figure 17-7 USING OVERLAYS WITH AN OVERHEAD PROJECTOR

Ordinarily, no more than two additional transparencies should be used this way, but it's possible to include as many as four or five.

The technical person, who must usually present more complex concepts a step at a time to ensure communication, can immediately see the applications of such a technique.

The technique of **revelation** is simpler. It is the process of masking off the parts of the visual you don't want the audience to see. A plain sheet of paper will work. By laying it over the information you want to conceal for the moment, you can block out selected pieces of the visual. Then when you're ready to discuss this hidden information, you simply remove the paper. The advantage is clear enough. If you don't want the audience to read the bottom line on the page while you're discussing the top line, this is the way to control their attention.

Writing information on a transparency is nearly as easy as writing on a sheet of paper at your desk. Felt-tipped pens available for this purpose may be used to create visual material in front of the audience. Often you can achieve your purposes by simply underlining or circling important parts of your visual—a means of focusing audience attention on the important aspects of your message.

A final way of directing audience attention with overhead-projection transparencies is simply to **use your pencil as a pointer.** The shadow of the pencil will be seen on the screen, directing the audience's attention to the proper place.

SLIDES   The 35 mm slide, with its realistic colour and photographic accuracy, has always been a popular visual tool for certain types of technical presentations. Where true reproduction is essential, no better tool is available.

Modern projectors have two notable advantages over their predecessors. First, the introduction of slide magazines has made it possible for you to organize your presentation and keep it intact. Second, remote controls allow you to operate the projector—even to reverse the order of your material—from the front of the room.

To use slide projectors effectively, however, you must turn off the lights in the room. Any time you keep your audience in the dark, you risk damaging the direct speaker-listener relationship on which communication hinges. In a sense, it takes the control of the presentation out of your hands. Long sequences of slides tend to develop a will and a pace of their own. They tire an audience and invite mental absenteeism.

There are ways to handle the built-in problems of a slide presentation, simple techniques that can greatly increase audience attention and the effectiveness of your presentation.

- When using slides in a darkened room, light yourself. A disembodied voice in the dark is little better than a tape recorder; it destroys rapport and allows the audience to exit into their own thoughts. To minimize this effect, arrange your equipment so you may stay in the front of the room and use a lectern light or some other soft, nonglaring light to make yourself visible to the audience.
- Break the presentation into short segments of no more than five or six slides.
- Always tell the audience what they're going to see, and what they should look for.

Everything considered, slides are an effective means of presenting visual material. But like any visual tool, they require control and preparation on your part. The important thing to remember is that they are there only to support your message—not to replace you.

CHARTS   Charts take a couple of forms. The first is the individual **hard-board chart**, rigid enough to stand by itself and large enough to be seen by the audience from wherever they might be seated in the room. It is always prepared before the presentation, sometimes at considerable cost.

The second chart form is the **flip chart**, a giant-sized note pad that may be prepared before or during the presentation. When you have completed your discussion of one visual, you simply flip the sheet containing it over the top of the pad as you would the pages of a tablet.

The two types of charts have a common advantage. Unlike the chalkboard, they allow for reshowing a piece of information when necessary—an important aid to speaker control.

The following techniques will help you use charts more effectively during your presentation. They're really rules of usage, to be followed each time you choose this visual form for support.

- Keep it simple. Avoid complex, detailed illustrations on charts. A three-by-five-foot chart is seldom large enough for detailed visibility.

- Ask for help. Whenever possible, have an assistant on one side of your charts to remove each one in its turn. This avoids creating a break in your rapport with the audience while you wrestle with a large cardboard chart or a flimsy flip sheet.
- Predraw your visuals with a very light-coloured crayon or chalk. During the presentation, you can simply draw over the original lines in darker crayon or marker. This allows you to create an accurate illustration a step at a time for clarity.
- Prime the audience. Tell them what they are going to see and why before you show each visual, for the same reason you would do it with the chalkboard.

MOVIES AND VIDEOS   Whenever motion and sound are important to the presentation, movies and videos are the visual forms available to the speaker that can accomplish the effect. Like slides, they also provide an exactness of detail and colour that can be critical to certain subjects. There is really no other way an engineer could illustrate the tremendous impact aircraft tires receive during landings, for instance. The audience would understand the subject only if they were able to view, through the eye of the camera, the distortion of the rubber when the plane touches down.

But movies and videos *are* the presentation. They cannot be considered visual support material in the sense developed in this book. They simply replace the speaker as the source of information, at least for their duration. If they become the major part of the presentation, the speaker is reduced to an announcer with little more to do than introduce and summarize their content.

This makes movies and videos the most difficult visual forms to control. Yet they can be controlled and, if they are to perform the support functions we've outlined, they must be. Some effective techniques are given here.

- Prepare the audience. Explain the significance of what you are about to show them.
- If a film or video is to be used, it should make up only a small part of the total presentation.
- Whenever possible, break the film or video into short three- or four-minute segments. Between segments you can reestablish rapport with the audience by summarizing what they have seen and refocusing attention on the important points in the next segment.

CHALKBOARDS   The chalkboard is perhaps the most familiar of visual tools. It has been a standard source of visual support for decades and often the only means of presenting visual information available to the classroom teacher.

As a visual aid, it leaves something to be desired. In the first place, preparing information on a chalkboard, especially technical information in which every sliding scrawl can have significance, takes time. And after the material is in place, it cannot be removed and replaced quickly.

Second, the task of writing on a surface that faces the audience requires that you turn your back toward them while you write. And people don't respond well to backs. They want you to face them while you're talking to them.

Why bother with a chalkboard then? Low cost and simplicity are its advantages. The initial cost of a chalkboard is higher than you may think; but the cost of erasers and chalk is minimal. And in spite of its drawbacks, a chalkboard is easy to use. It may take time, but there's nothing very complicated about writing a piece of information on a chalkboard. This simplicity, of course, gives it a certain flexibility, making it essentially a spontaneous visual aid on which speakers can create their visual material as they go.

There are specific techniques for using a chalkboard that can make it a more effective visual tool and help overcome its disadvantages. Let's consider them one at a time.

- **Plan ahead.** Unless there is a clear reason for creating the material as you go, prepare your visual material before the presentation. Then cover it. Later, you can expose the information for the audience at the appropriate point in your speech.
- **Be neat and keep the information simple and to the point.** If your material is complex, find another way of presenting it.
- **Prime the audience.** Before showing your information, tell them what they are going to see and why they are going to see it.

This last point is especially important when you are creating your visual support as you go. Priming your listeners will allow you to maintain the flow of information and, at the same time, prepare them mentally to understand and accept your information.

Planning and Revision Checklists

You will find the planning and revision checklists that follow Chapter 2, "Composing," and Chapter 4, "Writing for Your Readers," valuable in planning and revising any presentation of technical information. The following questions specifically apply to oral reports. They summarize the key points in this chapter and provide a checklist for planning and revising.

Planning

- What is the relationship between you and your audience?
- What is the attitude of your audience toward you and your presentation likely to be?
- Is your audience from a culture markedly different from yours? What adjustments to your persona and your presentation will any such difference require?
- What are the conditions under which you will speak?
- What equipment is available to you?
- Which delivery technique will be more appropriate? Extemporaneous? Manuscript?

continued >>

- If you are speaking extemporaneously, have you prepared a speech outline to guide you?
- If you will be reading from a manuscript, have you introduced a conversational tone into your talk? Is your typed manuscript easy to read from?
- Do you have a good opening that will interest your audience and create a friendly atmosphere?
- Have you limited your major points to fit within your allotted time?
- Does your talk contain sufficient examples, analogies, narratives, and data to support your generalizations? Have you repeated key points?
- Can you relate your subject matter to some vital interest of your audience?
- Which visual aids do you plan to use?
  Graphs?
  Tables?
  Representational art?
  Photographs?
  Words and phrases?
  Cartoons and pictorials?
  Hardware?
- Which presentation tools will you use?
  Computer programs?
  Overhead projection?
  Slides?
  Charts?
  Movies and videos?
  Chalkboards?
- Have you prepared your graphics? Do they successfully focus the listeners' attention and augment and clarify your message? Do they meet the four criteria that govern good graphics?
  Visibility   Simplicity
  Clarity   Control
- Do you have a good ending ready, perhaps a summary of key points or an anecdote that supports your purpose?
- Have you rehearsed your talk several times?

Revision

Obviously, you can't revise a talk you have already given—unless, of course, you will have an opportunity to repeat it somewhere. But you can use revision techniques in your practice sessions. Most of the questions listed above under Planning lend themselves to use during revision. Also, you can critique your speeches, looking for ways to improve your delivery techniques in future speeches. The following questions are useful for critiquing a speech. You will find it helpful to ask someone in the audience to give you friendly but honest answers to all the questions listed in the Planning and Revision sections.

- Did your gestures support your speech? Did they seem normal and relaxed? Did you avoid nervous mannerisms?

- Was your speech rate appropriate? Did you vary rate, pitch, and volume occasionally? Could everyone hear you?
- Did you pronounce all your words correctly?
- Did you have good interaction with your audience? Were they attentive or fidgety?
- Did your talk fit comfortably into the time allotted for it?
- Did the questions that followed your talk indicate a good understanding of it? Did the questions indicate friendliness or hostility to your key points?
- Were you sufficiently informed to answer the questions raised?
- Were there any indications that members of your audience could not see or readily comprehend any of your visuals?

 **Weblinks**

The Elements of a Professional Presentation
www.access.digex.net/~nuance/keystep1.html

Preparing Outstanding Presentations
www.ieee.org/pcs/creimold.html

Visual Aids in Presentations
www.darkstar.engr.wisc.edu/zwickel/397/presgraf.html

Exercises

1. Deliver the speech described in one of the following situations:
   • You are an instructor at your college or university. Prepare a short extemporaneous lecture on a technical subject. Your audience is a class of about 20 students.
   • You are the head of a team that has developed a new product or process. Your job is to persuade a group of senior managers from your own firm to accept the process or product for company use. Assume these managers have a layperson's knowledge of your subject. Speak extemporaneously.
   • You are a known expert on your subject. You have been invited to speak about your subject at the annual meeting of a well-known scientific association. You are expected to write out and read your speech. You are to inform the audience, which is made up of knowledgeable research scientists and professors from a diversity of scientific disciplines, about your subject or to persuade them to accept a decision you have reached.

2. Change one of your written reports into an oral report. Deliver the report extemporaneously. Prepare several visual aids to support major points.

PART V

HANDBOOK

Any living language is a growing, flexible instrument with rules that are constantly changing by virtue of the way the language is used by its live, independent speakers and writers. Only the rules of a dead language are unalterably fixed.

Nevertheless, at any point in a language's development, certain conventions of usage are in force. Certain constructions are considered errors that mark the person who uses them as uneducated. It is with these conventions and errors that this handbook primarily deals. We also include sections on documentation, outlining, and sexist language. To make the handbook easy to use as a reference, we have arranged it in alphabetical order. Each convention and error dealt with has an abbreviated reference tag. The tags are reproduced on the back endpapers, along with some of the more important proofreading symbols. If you are in a college writing course, your instructor may use some combination of these tags and symbols to indicate revisions needed in your reports.

Abbreviations (*Ab*)

Although most people are familiar with the kinds of abbreviations we encounter in everyday conversation and written material, from *etc.* to *Mon.* to *Dr.*, technical abbreviations are something else. Each scientific and professional field generates hundreds of specialized terms, and many of these terms are often abbreviated for the sake of conciseness and simplicity.

Canada adopted SI (Système international d'unités), the modern version of the metric system, in 1971. The symbols that represent SI units are the same in English, French, and many other languages. Anyone who shops in Canadian supermarkets, drives on Canadian highways, or listens to Canadian weather reports has learned to comprehend at least some SI units and to recognize their shortened forms. Those working in scientific and technical fields are naturally more fully conversant with SI. However, the continuing use of imperial measurement in the United States—as well as the simple truth that "old habits (of language and thought) die hard"—has meant that older terminology still crops up in business and in daily life.

Thus, before deciding to use technical abbreviations in an article or report, you must first consider your audience—laypersons, executives, experts, or technicians? Only readers with an appropriate background will be able to interpret the specialized shorthand for the field in question. When in doubt, avoid all but the most common abbreviations. If you must use a technical term, spell it out in full the first time it appears and include both the abbreviation and a definition in parentheses after it. You can then safely use the abbreviation if the term crops up again in your report. For a complete list of SI terms and abbreviations, consult one of the sources in our bibliography.

Standard technical and scientific abbreviations include the following:

absolute	abs
alternating current (as adjective)	a–c
atomic weight	at. wt
barometer	bar.
Brinell hardness number	Bhn
British thermal units	Btu or B
Canadian Standards Association	CSA
gram	g
hectare	h
kilometres per hour	km/h
metre	m
square metre	m^2
microwatt or microwatts	mu w or μW
revolutions per minute	rpm
tonne	ton

The system implied by these illustrative abbreviations can be described by a brief set of rules.

1. Use the same (singular) form of abbreviation for both singular and plural terms:

cu ft	either cubic foot or cubic feet
cm	either centimetre or centimetres

But there are some common exceptions:

no.	number
nos.	numbers
p.	page
pp.	pages
ms.	manuscript
mss.	manuscripts

2. Use lowercase letters except for letters standing for proper nouns or proper adjectives (a complete SI list will give a few other exceptions (like "M" for "nautical mile"):

cm3	*but*	K (for Kelvin)
m/s	*but*	N (for Newton)

3. For technical terms, use periods only after abbreviations that spell complete words. For example, *in* is a word, and the abbreviation for inches could be confused with it. Therefore, use a period:

ft	*but*	in.
abs	*but*	bar.
mg	*but*	at. wt

4. Remember the hyphen in the abbreviations a–c and d–c when you use them as adjectives:

This a-c motor can be converted to 28 volts dc.

5. Spell out many short and common words:

acre	rod	per	ton

6. In compound abbreviations, use internal spacing only if the first word is represented by more than its first letter:

rpm	*but*	cu ft
mph	*but*	mu w

7. With few exceptions, form the abbreviations of organization names without periods or spacing:

CSA   SSHRC

8. Abbreviate terms of measurement only if they are preceded by an arabic expression of exact quantity:

55 mph   *and*   20-lb anchor

But:

We will need an engine of greater horsepower.

Acronyms (*Acro*)

Acronyms are formed in two ways. In one way, the initial letters of each word in some phrase are combined to form a word. An example would be WYSIWYG, an acronym for the computer phrase "What you see is what you get." In a second way, some combination of initial letters or several letters of the words in the phrase are combined. An example would be *radar* for *ra*dio *d*etection *a*nd *r*anging.

Technical writing uses acronyms freely, as in this example from a description of a computer program that performs statistical analysis:

It has good procedural capabilities, including some time-series-related plots and ARIMA forecasting, but it doesn't have depth in any one area. Although it has commands to create EDA displays, these graphics are static and are printed with characters rather than with lines.[1]

Use acronyms without explanation only when you are absolutely sure your readers know them. If you have any doubts at all, at least provide the words from which the acronym stems. If you're unsure that the words are enough, provide a definition of the complete phrase. In the case of the paragraph just quoted, the computer magazine in which it was printed provided a glossary giving both the complete phrases and definitions:

ARIMA (auto-regressive integrated moving-average): a model that characterizes changes in one variable over time. It is used in time-series analysis.

EDA (exploratory data analysis): The use of graphically based tools, particularly in initial states of data analysis, to inspect data properties and to discover relationships among variables.[2]

Acronyms can be daunting to those unfamiliar with them. Even when you have an audience that knows their meaning, a heavy use of acronyms can make your writing seem dense and uninviting.

Apostrophe (*Apos*)

The apostrophe has three chief uses: (1) to form the possessive, (2) to stand for missing letters or numbers, and (3) to form the plural of certain expressions.

Possessives

Add an apostrophe and an s to form the possessive of most singular nouns, including proper nouns, even when they already end in an *s* or another sibilant such as *x*:

man's	Marx's
spectator's	Charles's
jazz's	

Exceptions to this rule occur when adding an apostrophe plus an *s* would result in an *s* or *z* sound that is difficult to pronounce. In such cases, usually just the apostrophe is added:

Xerxes'	conscience'
Moses'	appearance'

To understand this exception, pronounce *Marx's* and then a word like *Moses's* or *conscience's*.

To form plurals into the possessive case, add an apostrophe plus s to words that do not end in an s or other sibilant and an apostrophe only to those that do:

men's	agents'
data's	witnesses'
spectators'	

To show joint possession, add the apostrophe and *s* to the last member of a compound or group; to show separate possession, add an apostrophe and *s* to each member:

Gregg and Klymer's experiment astounded the class.

Gregg's and Klymer's experiments were very similar.

Of the several classes of pronouns, only the indefinite pronouns use an apostrophe to form the possessive.

Possessive of Indefinite Pronouns	Possessive of Other Pronouns
anyone's	my (mine)
everyone's	your (yours)
everybody's	his, her (hers), its
nobody's	our (ours)
no one's	their (theirs)
other's	whose
neither's	

Missing Letters or Numbers

Use an apostrophe to stand for the missing letters in contractions and to stand for the missing letter or number in any word or set of numbers where for one reason or another a letter or number is omitted:

can't, don't, o'clock, it's (it is), etc.

The class of '49 was McGill's best class in years.

Plural Forms

An apostrophe is sometimes used to form the plural of letters and numbers, but this style is gradually dying, particularly with numbers.

6s and 7s (but also 6's and 7's)

a's and b's

Brackets (*Brackets*)

Brackets are chiefly used when a clarifying word or comment is inserted into a quotation:

"The result of this [disregard by the propulsion engineer] has been the neglect of the theoretical and mathematical mastery of the engine inlet problem."

"An ideal outlet require [sic] a frictionless flow."

"Last year [1998] saw a partial solution to the problem."

Sic, by the way, is Latin for *thus*. Inserted in a quotation, it means that the mistake found there is the original writer's, not yours. Use it with discretion.

Capitalization (*Cap*)

We provide the more important rules of capitalization. For a complete rundown, see your dictionary.

Proper Nouns

Capitalize all proper nouns and their derivatives:

PLACES
Canada   Canadian   Canadianize

DAYS OF THE WEEK AND MONTHS
Monday   Tuesday   January   February

BUT NOT THE SEASONS:
winter   spring   summer   fall

ORGANIZATIONS AND THEIR ABBREVIATIONS
New Democratic Party (NDP)
Canadian Broadcasting Corporation (CBC)

Capitalize *geographic areas* when you refer to them as areas:

The Andersons toured the West.

But do not capitalize words that merely indicate direction:

We flew west over the Pacific.

Capitalize the names of *studies* in a curriculum only if the names are already proper nouns or derivatives of proper nouns or if they are part of the official title of a department or course:

Department of Geology

English Literature 25

the study of literature

the study of English literature

Note: Many nouns (and their derivatives) that were originally proper have been so broadened in application and have become so familiar that they are no longer capitalized: *boycott, macadam, spoonerism, italicize, platonic, chinaware, quixotic.*

Literary Titles

Capitalize the first word, the last word, and every important word in literary titles:

But What's a Dictionary For

The Meaning of Ethics

How to Write and Be Read

Rank, Position, Family Relationships

Capitalize the titles of rank, position, and family relationship unless they are preceded by *my, his, their,* or similar possessive pronouns:

Professor J. E. Higgins

I visited Uncle Timothy.

I visited my uncle Timothy.

Dr. Milton Weller, Head, Department of Entomology

Colon (*Colon*)

The colon is chiefly used to introduce quotations, lists, or supporting statements. It is also used between clauses when the second clause is an example or amplification of the first and in certain conventional ways with numbers, correspondence, and bibliographical entries.

Introduction

Place a colon before a quotation, a list, or supporting statements and examples that are formally introduced:

> Mr. Smith says the following of wave generation:
>
> > The wind waves that are generated in the ocean and which later become swells as they pass out of the generating area are products of storms. The low pressure regions that occur during the polar winters of the Arctic and Antarctic produce many of these wave-generating storms.

> The various forms of engine that might be used would operate within the following ranges of Mach number:

M-0 to M-1.5	Turbojet with or without precooling
M-1.5 to M-7	Reheated turbojet, possibly with precooling
M-7 to M-10+	Ramjet with supersonic combustion

> Engineers are developing three new engines: turbojet, reheated turbojets, and ramjets.

Do not place a colon between a verb and its objects or a linking verb and the predicate nouns.

> OBJECTS
>
> The engineers designed turbojets, reheated turbojets, and ramjets.

> PREDICATE NOUNS
>
> The three engines the engineers are developing are turbojets, reheated turbojets, and ramjets.

Do not place a colon between a preposition and its objects:

> The plane landed at Thunder Bay, Winnipeg, and Saskatoon.

Between Clauses

If the second clause consists of an example or an amplification of the first clause, then the colon may replace the comma, semicolon, or period:

> The docking phase involves the actual "soft" contact: the securing of lines, latches, and air locks.

> The difference between these two guidance systems is illustrated in Figure 2: The paths of the two vehicles are shown to the left and the motion of the ferry as viewed from the target station is shown to the right.

You may follow a colon with a capital or a small letter. Generally, a complete sentence beginning after a colon is given a capital.

Styling Conventions

Place a colon after a formal salutation in a letter, between hour and minute figures, between the elements of a double title, and between chapter and verse of the Bible:

Dear Ms. Jones:	<u>Working Women: A Chartbook</u>
at 7:15 p.m.	I Samuel 7:14-18

Comma (*C*)

The most used—and misused—mark of punctuation is the comma. Writers use commas to separate words, phrases, and clauses. Generally, commas correspond to the pauses we use in our speech to separate ideas and to avoid ambiguity. You will use the comma often: About two out of every three marks of punctuation you use will be commas. Sometimes your use of the comma will be essential for clarity; at other times you will be honouring grammatical conventions. (See also the entry for run-on sentences.)

Main Clauses

Place a comma before a coordinating conjunction (*and, but, or, nor, for, yet*) that joins two main (independent) clauses:

> During the first few weeks we felt a great deal of confusion, but as time passed we gradually fell into a routine.

> We could not be sure that the plumbing would escape frost damage, nor were we at all confident that the house could withstand the winds of almost hurricane force.

If the clauses are short, have little or no internal punctuation, or are closely related in meaning, then you may omit the comma before the coordinating conjunction:

> The wave becomes steeper but it does not tumble yet.

In much published writing there is a growing tendency to place two very short and closely related independent clauses (called contact clauses) side by side with only a comma between:

> The wind starts to blow, the waves begin to develop.

Sentences consisting of *three* or more equal main clauses should be punctuated uniformly:

> We explained how urgent the problem was, we outlined preliminary plans, and we arranged a time for discussion.

In general, identical marks are used to separate equal main clauses. If the equal clauses are short and uncomplicated, commas usually suffice. If the equal clauses are long or internally punctuated, or if their separateness is to be emphasized, semicolons are either preferable or necessary.

Clarification

Place a comma after an introductory word, phrase, or clause that might be over-read or that abnormally delays the main clause:

As soon as you have finished polishing, the car should be moved into the garage. **(Comma to prevent over-reading)**

Soon after, the winds began to moderate somewhat, and we were permitted to return to our rooms. **(First comma to prevent over-reading)**

If the Polar ice caps should someday mount in thickness and weight to the point that their combined weight exceeded the Equatorial bulge, the earth might suddenly flop ninety degrees. **(Introductory clause abnormally long)**

After a short introductory element (word, phrase, or clause) where there is no possibility of ambiguity, the use of the comma is optional. Generally, let the emphasis you desire guide you. A short introductory element set off by a comma will be more emphatic than one that is not.

Nonrestrictive Modifiers

Enclose or set off from the rest of the sentence every nonrestrictive modifier, whether a word, a phrase, or a clause. How can you tell a nonrestrictive modifier from a restrictive one? Look at these two examples:

Restrictive   A runway **that is not oriented with the prevailing wind** endangers the aircraft using it.

Nonrestrictive   The safety of any aircraft, **whether heavy or light**, is put in jeopardy when it is forced to take off or land in a crosswind.

The restrictive modifier is necessary to the meaning of the sentence. Not just any runway but "a runway that is not oriented with the prevailing wind" endangers aircraft. The writer has *restricted* the many kinds of runways he or she could talk about to one particular kind. In the nonrestrictive example, the modifier merely adds descriptive details. The writer does not restrict *aircraft* with the modifier but simply makes the meaning a little clearer.

Restrictive modifiers cannot be left out of the sentence if it is to have the meaning the writer intends; nonrestrictive modifiers can be left out.

Nonrestrictive Appositives

Set off or enclose every nonrestrictive appositive. As used here the term *appositive* means any element (word, phrase, or clause) that parallels and repeats the thought of a preceding element. According to this view, a verb may be coupled appositively with another verb, an adjective with another adjective, and so on. An appositive is usually more specific or more vivid than the element that it is an appositive to; an appositive makes explicit and precise something that has not been clearly implied.

Some appositives are restrictive and, therefore, are not set off or enclosed.

Nonrestrictive   A crosswind, **a wind perpendicular to the runway**, causes the pilot to make potentially dangerous corrections just before landing.

Restrictive   In some ways, Dr. Clinton **the administrator** had to behave differently from Dr. Clinton **the professor**.

In the nonrestrictive example, the appositive merely adds a clarifying definition. The sentence makes sense without it. In the restrictive example, the appositives are essential to the meaning. Without them we would have, "In some ways, Dr. Clinton had to behave differently from Dr. Clinton."

Series

Use commas to separate members of a coordinate series of words, phrases, or clauses if *all* the elements are not joined by coordinating conjunctions such as *and* or *or*:

> Instructions on the label state clearly how to prepare the surfaces, how to apply the contents, and how to clean and polish the mended article.

> To mould these lead figures you will need a hot flame, a two-pound block of lead, the moulds themselves, a file or a rasp, and an awl.

> Under the microscope the sensitive, filigree-like mould appeared luminous and transparent and faintly green.

Other Conventional Uses

> DATE
> On August 24, A.D. 79, Mount Vesuvius erupted, covering Pompeii with 50 feet of ash and pumice.

Note: When you write the month and the year without the day, it is common practice to omit the comma between them—as in June 1995.

> GEOGRAPHICAL EXPRESSION
> During World War II, Shilo, Manitoba, was the site of a military airport and supply depot.

> TITLE AFTER PROPER NAME
> A card in yesterday's mail informed us that Penny Hutchinson, M.D., would soon open new offices in Burlington.

> NOUN OF DIRECT ADDRESS
> Lewis, do you suppose that we can find our way back to the cabin before nightfall?

> INFORMAL SALUTATION
> Dear Nazreen,

Dangling Modifier (*DM*)

Many curious sentences result from the failure to provide the modifier something to modify:

> Having finished the job, the tarpaulins were removed.

In this example it seems as though the tarpaulins have finished the job. As is so often the case, a passive voice construction has caused the problem (see pages 88–89). If we recast the sentence in active voice, we remove the problem:

> Having finished the job, the workers removed the tarpaulins.

Dash (*Dash*)

In technical writing, you will use the dash almost exclusively to set off parenthetical statements. You may, of course, use commas or parentheses for the same function, but the dash is the most emphatic separator of the three. You may also use the dash to indicate a sharp transition. With typewriter print, you make the dash with two hyphens. You do not space between the words and the hyphens or between the hyphens themselves.

> The first phase in rendezvous—sighting and recognizing the target—is so vital that we will treat it at some length.

> The target must emit or reflect light the pilot can see—but how bright must this light be?

Diction (*D*)

For good diction, choose words that are accurate, effective, and appropriate to the situation. Many different kinds of linguistic sins can cause faulty diction. Poor diction can involve a choice of words that are too heavy or pretentious: *utilize* for *use*, *finalize* for *finish*, *at this point in time* for *now*, and so forth. Tired old cliches are poor diction: *with respect to, with your permission, with reference to*, and many others. We talk about such language in Chapter 5, particularly in the section on pomposity (pages 90–93).

Sometimes the words chosen are simply too vague to be accurate: *inclement weather* for *rain*, *too hot* for *600° C*. See the section on specific words in Chapter 5 (pages 89–90) for more on this subject.

Poor diction can mean an overly casual use of language when some degree of formality is expected. One of the many synonyms for *intoxicated*, such as *bombed, stoned,* or *wasted*, might be appropriate in casual conversation but totally wrong in a police or laboratory report.

Poor diction can reflect a lack of sensitivity to language—to the way one group of words relates to another group. Someone who writes that "The airlines are beginning a crash program to solve their financial difficulties" is not paying attention to relationships. The person who writes that the "Steelworkers' Union representatives are getting down to brass tacks in the strike negotiations" has a tin ear, to say the least.

Make your language work for you, and make it appropriate to the situation.

Documentation (*Doc*)

Different documentation systems are in use from program to program, campus to campus, journal to journal, company to company. Therefore, we cannot claim a universal application for the instructions that follow. Use them barring conflicting instructions from your instructor, institution, employer, or the style guide of the journal or magazine in which you hope to publish.

Before we go into the mechanics of documentation, it might be wise to discuss why and when you need to document.

First of all, documenting fulfills your moral obligation to give credit where credit is due. It lets your readers know who was the originator of an idea or expression and where his or her work is found. Second, systematic documentation makes it easy for your readers to research your subject further.

When do you document? Established practice calls for you to give credit when you borrow the following:

- Direct quotes
- Research data and theories
- Illustrations, such as tables, graphs, photographs, and so forth

You do not need to document general information or common knowledge. For example, even if you referred to a technical dictionary to find that creatinine's more formal name is methyglycocyamidine, you would not be obligated to show the source of this information. It is general information, readily found in many sources. If, on the other hand, you include in your paper an opinion that the cosmos is laced with strands of highly concentrated mass energy called *strings*, you would need to document the source of this opinion.

In general, give credit where credit is due, but do not clutter your pages with references to information readily found in many sources. If in doubt as to whether to document or not, play it safe and document.

Traditionally, documentation has taken the form of footnotes or endnotes, often combined with a bibliography which lists all sources alphabetically. In *Reporting Technical Information*, for instance, we document our sources with chapter endnotes, gathered at the end of the work.

More frequently seen these days, however, is a combination of parenthetical references—also called citations—in the text, with an alphabetized list of sources at the end. There are various names for this list: sometimes "Sources" or "References," sometimes "Work Cited" or "Works Consulted," depending on the scope of the list. Occasionally the more traditional "Bibliography" is used, but this choice is less popular because it refers only to printed sources. Footnotes or endnotes, where used, provide supplementary information, comment, or explanation, rather than documentation. Such notes offer extras, much as an appendix does.

In the discussion below, we briefly explain the conventions of documentation according to three of the most widely used guides to documentation. *The MLA Handbook for Writers of Research Papers, The Publication Manual of the American Psychological Association*, and *The Chicago Manual of Style*.

As this book is being written, the handbook and manuals we have cited do not adequately describe a way of documenting information taken from the Internet. No doubt they will in the future, but in the meantime writers are faced with the problem of how to document such sources. To help until the major documentation systems catch up with these new demands, we provide a section on how to document Internet sources. It is adapted from a Web site called *Beyond the MLA Handbook: Documenting Electronic Sources on the Internet.*[3]

Some general rules apply in the three major systems.

General Rules

The rules that follow apply whether you are using the note system or an author–date parenthetical system.

- You may use a short form of the publisher's name—for example, Wiley for John Wiley & Sons. Be consistent throughout your notes or citations, however.
- When a city of publication is not well known, include an abbreviation for the state, province, or country in your note or citation. For states and provinces, use postal abbreviations—for example, NY for New York and BC for British Columbia. (See Figure 11-6 on page 284 for a list of state and province abbreviations.) For countries, use the abbreviations that can be found in most college dictionaries—for example, Arg. for Argentina.
- When information on pagination, publisher, or date is missing in your source, at the point where you would put that information, put one of these abbreviations: n. pag. for no pagination, n.p. for no place of publication or no publisher, n.d. for no date.

MLA Style

PARENTHETICAL REFERENCES The purpose of the parenthetical reference is to provide just enough information in the body of the report to make it possible for your reader to find the source in your list of works cited at the end. The two key elements are (1) the author's last name, and (2) the page number from which the quotation or reference comes. Other material is added only as necessary. So a typical reference might look like this:

> There is a growing body of literature on the subject of travel for those confined to wheelchairs, who, since the advent of barrier-free public spaces and customized vans, have taken to the roads in increasing numbers. One such traveller has pointed out the irony of the label "accessible" applied to hotel rooms with bathroom doors precisely wide enough for a wheelchair, but not enough floor space inside to accommodate the chair (Gray 72).

Notice that there is no comma between author and page number, and no "page" or "p." before the number. Notice too that the parenthetical reference should be placed where it is least disruptive to the text, while still as close as possible to the quotation or reference. Ideally, parenthetical references appear at the end of the sentence; they should in any case be placed where there is a natural pause (usually created by a punctuation mark).

The punctuation mark comes *after* the parenthetical reference (except when the quotation is blocked off from the rest of the text).

If the author's name appears in the report, the parenthetical reference needs to include only the page number:

The special hotel requirements of the quadriplegic traveller are effectively — and humorously — summarized in Gray's recent article, "Have Chair Will Travel" (72).

If the list of sources includes more than one work by the same author, then the parenthetical reference should include a short form of the title as well as the page number:

(Gray, "Chair" 72).

WORKS CITED   In a separate section at the end of your report (see page 496 for possible titles), list all the works that you cite. Figure H-1 illustrates how it is done. We have annotated Figure H-1 to draw your attention to certain distinctive citation features, such as underlining, punctuation, and spacing.

Remember that the example below is only one way of listing your sources. Other, equally acceptable ways from other systems of documentation present the entries in the order in which the references appeared in the text, or in the order in which they were published, or in sections subdivided by subject, or medium, or type (primary or secondary). Sometimes bibliographies are annotated, meaning that the basic entry is supplemented by descriptive and/or evaluative information about the work (the "Bibliography" at the end of this textbook is an example of an annotated bibliography).

The guidelines below and the models that follow show you how to construct the citations you are likely to need in school and business.

- Use periods between the basic components of the citation.
- Transpose the author's name: last, first, middle name or initial. If you have two or three authors, print the subsequent authors' names in normal order. If you have four or more authors, list the first author's name followed by "et al." for "and others."
- Arrange the entries in alphabetical order. You need enter each source only once. Determine alphabetical order by the author's last name or, if no author is listed, by title (disregarding *the, a,* or *an*).
- Omit page numbers from whole-book entries. Give inclusive page numbers for articles in anthologies and periodicals.
- Do not number entries. Begin the first line at the left margin and indent the second and subsequent lines.

We have categorized the models under "Books," "Periodicals," and "Other."

Books   The following examples illustrate various forms of book citations.

ONE AUTHOR

Godfrey, David W.H. <u>Modern</u> *Technical Communication*. Toronto: McGraw-Hill Ryerson, 1983.

Invert order of first author's name.

Underline or italicize periodical and book titles. Capitalize first and last words and all principal words between. Do not capitalize articles, prepositions, and coordinating conjunctions unless they are a first or last word.

For anonymous books and articles, start with title.

Use normal order for all names after first.

Works Cited

Brockmann, R. John, <u>Writing Better Computer User

<u>Documentation.</u> New York: Wiley, 1986.

Burnett, Rebecca, and Ann Hill Duin. "Collaboration in

Technical Communication: A Research Continuum."

<u>Technical Communication Quarterly</u> 2 (1993): 5-21.

Byrd, David G., Paula R. Feldman, and Phyllis Fleishei. <u>The

<u>Microcomputer and Business Writing.</u> New York:

St. Martin's, 1986.

<u>Producing Quality Technical Information.</u> San Jose: IBM, 1986.

Sauer, Beverly L. "Sense and Sensibility in Technical

Communication." <u>Journal of Business and Technical

<u>Communication</u> 7 (1993): 63-83.

Schulman, Bob, Eric C. W. Dunn, and George Shackelford.

<u>Quicken.</u> Version 1.5. Computer software. Intuit, 1989.

Use quotation marks around article titles. Capitalize first and last words and all principal words between. Do not capitalize articles, prepositions, and coordinating conjunctions unless they are a first or last word.

Use periods between all major elements of citations.

Double-space all entries and between entries.

Use inclusive page numbers for articles in periodicals and anthologies.

Figure H-1 LIST OF WORKS CITED

TWO OR THREE AUTHORS

Von Koenigseck, Edward, James N. Irvin, and Sharon C. Irvin. *Technical Writing for Private Industry: The A-to-Z of O & M Manuals*. Malabar, FL: Krieger, 1991.

FOUR OR MORE AUTHORS

Burton, Lydia, et al. *Editing Canadian English*. Vancouver: Douglas & McIntyre, 1988.

Use the first author's name with et al. (and others) for four or more authors.

AN ANTHOLOGY

Rosengarten, Herbert, and Jane Flick, eds. *The Broadview Reader*. Peterborough, ON: Broadview, 1987.

Use the abbreviation *ed.* for one editor, *eds.* for two or more. Use *trans.* for one or more translators.

AN ESSAY IN AN ANTHOLOGY

Suzuki, David. "A Planet for the Taking." *The Broadview Reader.* Eds. Herbert Rosengarten and Jane Flick. Peterborough, ON: Broadview, 1987. 234-39.

SECOND OR SUBSEQUENT EDITION

Blicq, Ron S. *Technically-Write!* 3rd ed. Scarborough, ON: Prentice-Hall Canada, 1987.

ARTICLE IN REFERENCE BOOK

"Petrochemical." *The New Columbia Encyclopedia*, 1975.

When a reference work is well known, you need cite only the name of the article, the name of the reference work, and the date of publication. If the work is arranged alphabetically, do not cite page numbers.

For less well–known reference works give complete information. Cite the author of the article if known; otherwise begin with the title of the article.

"Perpetual Calendar, 1775-2076." *The New York Public Library Desk Reference.* Eds. Paul Fargis and Sheree Bykofsky. New York: Webster's New World, 1989. 10-13.

A PAMPHLET

How Does a Nuclear Reactor Work? Toronto: Ontario Hydro, 1992.

If the author of a pamphlet is known, give complete information in the usual manner.

GOVERNMENT OR CORPORATE PUBLICATION

Canada. Forestry Canada. *Annual Report, 1991-92*. Ottawa, 1993.

Treat government and corporate publications much as you would any book, except that the author is often a government agency or a division within a company.

ANONYMOUS BOOK

Producing Quality Technical Information. San Jose: IBM, 1986.

When no human, government, or corporate author is listed, begin with the title of the book.

PROCEEDINGS

Buehler, Mary Fran. "Rules that Shape the Technical Message: Fidelity, Completeness, Preciseness." *Proceedings 31st International Technical Communication Conference.* Washington, DC: Society for Technical Communication, 1984. 9-12.

UNPUBLISHED DISSERTATION

Torrey, Robert Dwayne. "Rubber-Modified Asphalt: Wet Mix Design." Diss. Ryerson Polytechnic U., 1995.

Abbreviate *University* as *U*; a university press would be *UP*, as in *McGill-Queen's UP*.

Periodicals   The following examples illustrate various forms of periodical citations.

JOURNAL WITH CONTINUOUS PAGINATION

Barker, Thomas T. "Word Processors and Invention in Technical Writing." *The Technical Writing Teacher* 16 (1989): 126-35.

JOURNAL THAT PAGES ITS ISSUES SEPARATELY

Gardner, David P. "The Future of University/Industry Research." *Perspectives in Computing* 7.1 (1987): 4-10.

In this citation, 7 is the volume number, 1 is the issue number, and 4–10 are the inclusive pages of the article.

COMMERCIAL MAGAZINES AND NEWSPAPERS

A weekly or biweekly magazine:

Johnston, Ann Dowsett. "Universities: Measuring Excellence." Maclean's 14 Nov. 1994: 17.

Monthly or bimonthly magazine:

Rose, Barbara Wade. "Danger: Software at Work." *Report on Business Magazine* March 1995: 74-82.

Newspaper:

Lewington, Jennifer. "Camp for Teachers Demystifies Sciences." *The Globe and Mail* 14 Aug. 1995: A3.

When the masthead of the paper specifies the edition, put that information in your note. Newspapers frequently change from edition to edition on the same day.

ANONYMOUS ARTICLE:

"Absolute." *New York* 18 June 1990: 28-29.

When no author is given for an article, begin with the title of the article.

Other   Here, we show you model citations for computer software, information services, letters, interviews, and two or more entries by the same author.

COMPUTER SOFTWARE

Schulman, Bob, Eric C. W. Dunn, and George Shackelford. *Quicken.* Version 1.5. Computer software. Intuit, 1989.

INFORMATION SERVICE

Berdan, R., and M. Garcia. *Discourse-Sensitive Measurement of Language Development in Bilingual Children.* Los Alamitos, CA: National Center for Bilingual Research. ERIC ED 234 636, 1982.

LETTER

Harris, John S. Letter to the author. 19 July 1993.

INTERVIEW

Adam, Julie. Personal interview. 4 Aug. 1995.

TWO OR MORE WORKS BY THE SAME AUTHOR

Barker, Thomas. "Video Field Trip: Bringing the Real World into the Technical Writing Classroom." *The Technical Writing Teacher* 11 (1985): 175-79.

———. "Word Processors and Invention in Technical Writing." *The Technical Writing Teacher* 16 (1989) : 126-35.

When you have two or more works by the same author or authors in your list of works cited, replace the author's name in the second citation with a solid line and alphabetize the entries by title.

MLA-APA Comparison

Becoming familiar with the MLA author-page system as described in this book will prepare you to use most systems used in documenting technical reports. Another system often used in the social and physical sciences is that found in the *Publication Manual of the American Psychological Association* (APA). It is sometimes referred to as the author–date system. To alert you to the kinds of variations that exist from system to system, we provide a few samples to demonstrate the differences between the MLA and APA systems.

Both systems use parenthetical references in the text, but the APA system is slightly more complex:

MLA   (Asher 93)

APA   (Asher, 1992, p. 93)

The APA system places a comma between name and date and puts a "p." for "page" before the page number.

Both systems key their parenthetical references to a list of works cited. MLA calls the list "Works Cited." APA uses the title "References." Note the differences between typical book entries and periodical entries:

MLA: Title italicized; first, last, and principal words capitalized; date concludes publication information; reverse indentation

Book Entries

——— Brockmann, R. John. Writing Better Computer User Documentation. New York: Wiley, 1986.

APA: Author's first names represented by initial; date in parentheses follows author's name; first word only capitalized in title; conventional indentation

——— Brockmann, R. J. (1986). Writing better computer user documentation. New York: Wiley.

Periodical Entries

—— Barker, T. T. "Word Processors and Invention in Technical Writing." <u>The Technical
Writing Teacher</u> 16 (1989): 126-35.

Barker, Thomas T. (1989). Word processors and invention in technical writing.

—— <u>The Technical Writing Teacher,</u> 16, 126-35.

A full comparison of the two systems would reveal similar differences
running throughout the various kinds of entries.

The Chicago Manual of Style

The system described in *The Chicago Manual of Style* is a common method of
documentation in the physical and natural sciences.

PARENTHETICAL CITATION   Refer your reader to your list of works cited
through parenthetical citations in your text. Figure H-2 shows a passage of
text that includes parenthetical citations. We have annotated the figure to
show you how the system works. Place the citation in the text where it is relevant and where it disrupts the text the least. Generally, you should place
the citation at the end of the grammatical unit—the sentence or clause—that
contains the material you are documenting.

The purpose of the parenthetical citation is to guide the reader to the corresponding entry in the list of works cited and, when appropriate, to cite
the specific pages of the reference. Some model references follow.

AUTHOR AND DATE

(Asher 1992)

This citation refers the reader to Asher's 1992 work in the list of works
cited. Use this form when you are not citing a specific page.

AUTHOR, DATE, AND PAGE

(Asher 1992, 93)

This citation refers the reader to page 93 of Asher's 1992 work. Use this
form when you're citing a specific page or pages.

DATE AND PAGE

(1992, 97)

Use this form when you have already mentioned the author's name in the
passage leading up to the parenthetical reference—for example, "As Asher's
research shows. . . ."

PAGES ONLY

(324–27)

Use this form when you have mentioned both the author's name and the
date in the passage leading up to the parenthetical reference—for example, "As
Asher's research in 1992 shows. . . ."

Current rhetorical theory indicates that this attempt, through analogy, to call on schemata for newspapers could affect readers' expectations about the writing in the newsletters, which in turn could influence the way these readers process the writing. Genre theory, for example, posits that generic patterns such as those in a newspaper, as part of our "cultural rationality" (Miller 1984, 165), alert readers to ways of perceiving and interpreting documents (Miller 1984, 159). In addition, theories of intertextuality, the concept that all texts contain explicit or implicit traces of other texts (Porter 1986, 34), suggest that creating an analogy between newspapers and newsletters would affect readers' expectations, encouraging them to perceive and interpret material in a particular way (Porter 1986, 38). We must ask, therefore, what readers' expectations about newspapers and hence, by analogy, about the newsletters, might be.

Use specific page reference

Place comma between date and page reference

Place parenthetical notes before any punctuation that ends the material cited

Figure H-2 PARENTHETICAL REFERENCES ON A PAGE: *THE CHICAGO MANUAL OF STYLE*

Source: Adapted with permission from Nancy Roundy Blyler, "Rhetorical Theory and Newsletter Writing," *Journal of Technical Writing and Communication 20* (1990): 144.

GOVERNMENT OR CORPORATE AUTHOR

(Canadian Radio-Television and Telecommunications Commission 1998)

When you have a government agency or corporate division listed as the author in the works cited, you may use the name of the agency or division in your parenthetical citation. If the name is unwieldy, provide a shortened form in parentheses in the list of works cited and use that form in your references, like this:

(CRTC 1998)

TITLE OF WORK

(Producing quality technical information 1986, 14)

Use this form when you have no author's name and have listed the work by its title. As with the author–date reference, omit anything from the parenthetical citation that you have mentioned in the passage leading up to it.

TWO OR THREE AUTHORS

(Berdan and Garcia 1982)

Name all the authors of a work with two or three authors.

FOUR OR MORE AUTHORS

(Odell et al. 1983, 28)

Use first author's name with *et al.* ("and others") to cite a work with four or more authors. However, list all the authors in the list of works cited.

TWO OR MORE WORKS WRITTEN BY THE SAME AUTHOR IN DIFFERENT YEARS

(Jarrett 1992)

(Jarrett 1993)

When you have listed two or more works written by the same author but in different years, the dates will distinguish them.

TWO OR MORE WORKS WRITTEN BY THE SAME AUTHOR IN THE SAME YEAR

(Jarrett 1991a)

(Jarrett 1991b)

To distinguish two or more works written by the same author in the same year, mark the years with lowercase letters, in both the parenthetical citation and the list of works cited.

WORKS CITED   List all the works that you cite in your paper. Figure H–3 illustrates a works cited list following the *Chicago Manual of Style*. We have annotated Figure H–3 to draw your attention to certain distinctive citation features such as capitalization, italics, and punctuation. For example, notice in Figure H–3 and the examples that follow that most titles use sentence capitalization—that is, they capitalize only the first word of a title and proper nouns.

We have categorized the models that follow as Books, Periodicals, and Other.

Books   The following examples illustrate various forms of book citations.

ONE AUTHOR

Day, Robert A. 1992. *Scientific English: A guide for scientists and other professionals*. Phoenix, AZ: Oryx.

TWO OR THREE AUTHORS

Von Koenigseck, Edward, James N. Irvin, and Sharon C. Irvin. 1991. *Technical writing for private industry: The a-to-z of o & m manuals*. Malabar, FL: Krieger.

FOUR OR MORE AUTHORS

Rookard, Frank, Robert Matson, Gerald Fields, and Walter Mazura. 1995. *Communicating in business*. 4th ed. Savannah, GA: Osborn.

In the list of works cited, list all the authors of a work, no matter how many there are.

ANTHOLOGY

Driskill, Linda P., June Ferrill, and Marda Nicholson Steffey, eds. 1992. *Business and managerial communication: New perspectives*. New York: Harcourt Brace Jovanovich.

Place date after author's name

Invert order of first author's name

Use *and*, not ampersand

Use normal order for all author names after the first

For anonymous books and articles, use book or article title and put date after title

Indent second and subsequent lines of a citation three spaces

Use colon before page numbers

Works Cited

Brockmann, R. John. 1986. <u>Writing better computer user documentation.</u> New York: Wiley.

Burnett, Rebecca, and Ann Hill Duin. 1993. Collaboration in technical communication: A research continuum. <u>Technical Communication Quarterly</u> 2: 5–21.

Byrd, David G., Paula R. Feldman, and Phyllis Fleishel. 1986. <u>The microcomputer and business writing.</u> New York: St. Martin's.

<u>Producing quality technical information.</u> 1986. San Jose: IBM.

Lewis, Anthony. 1996. Peace with Arafat. <u>The New York Times.</u> 1 July. America OnLine, 2 July 1996.

Sauer, Beverly L. 1993. Sense and sensibility in technical communication. <u>Journal of Business and Technical Communication</u> 7: 63–83.

For articles and books, capitalize first word of title and subtitle and all proper nouns. Italicize or underline book titles

Italicize or underline periodical titles. Capitalize first and last words and all principal words between. Do not capitalize an article, a preposition, or a coordinating conjunction unless it is a first or last word.

Use arabic numbers for volume numbers, even if periodical uses roman numerals.

Double-space all entries and between entries

Use periods between all major elements of citations

Use inclusive page numbers for articles in periodicals.

Figure H-3 LIST OF WORKS CITED: *THE CHICAGO MANUAL OF STYLE*

Use the abbreviation *ed.* for one editor, *eds.* for two or more. Use *trans.* for one or more translators.

ESSAY IN AN ANTHOLOGY

Faigley, Lester. 1985. Nonacademic writing: The social perspective. In *Writing in nonacademic settings*, edited by Lee Odell & Dixie Goswami. New York: The Guilford Press.

SECOND OR SUBSEQUENT EDITION

Markel, Michael H. 1992. *Technical writing: Situations and strategies.* 3d ed. New York: St. Martin's.

ARTICLE IN A REFERENCE BOOK

Petrochemical. 1975. *The new Columbia encyclopedia.*

When a reference work is well known, you need cite only the name of the article, the name of the reference work, the date of publication, and edition number (if it is not the first). If the work is arranged alphabetically, do not cite page numbers.

For less well-known reference works, give complete information. Cite the author of the article if you have that information; otherwise, begin with the name of the article.

> "Perpetual calendar, 1775–2076." 1989. *The New York Public Library desk reference*. Edited by Paul Fargis and Sheree Bykofsky. New York: Webster's New World. 9–13.

PAMPHLET

> *Cataract: Clouding the lens of sight*. 1989. San Francisco: American Academy of Ophthalmology.

If you know the author of a pamphlet, give complete information in the usual manner.

GOVERNMENT OR CORPORATE PUBLICATION

> Ontario Ministry of Agriculture, Food and Rural Affairs. 1996. *1996/1997 Fruit Production Recommendations*. Toronto: Queen's Printer for Ontario.

Treat government and corporate publications much as you would any book, except that the author is often a government agency or a division within a company. When the corporate name is unwieldy, provide a shortened version in parentheses, which can then be used in the parenthetical citation.

ANONYMOUS BOOK

> *Producing quality technical information*. 1986. San Jose: IBM.

When no human, government, or corporate author is listed, begin with the title of the book.

PROCEEDINGS

> Buehler, Mary Fran. 1984. Rules that shape the technical message: Fidelity, completeness, preciseness. *Proceedings of the 31st International Technical Communication Conference*. Washington, DC: Society for Technical Communication. WE 9–12.

UNPUBLISHED DISSERTATION

> Zhu, A-Xing. 1994. "Soil pattern inference using GIS under fuzzy logic." Diss. U of Toronto.

Abbreviate University as U.

Periodicals The following examples illustrate various forms of periodical citations.

JOURNAL WITH CONTINUOUS PAGINATION

> Barker, Thomas T. 1989. Word processors and invention in technical writing. *The Technical Writing Teacher* 16: 126–35.

Citations for periodicals list the inclusive pages of the article. When page numbers are two digits, use both digits in the second number: 13–14. When page numbers are three digits or more, use only the last two digits in the second number: 324–26, 1034–39.

JOURNAL THAT PAGES ITS ISSUES SEPARATELY

Gardner, David P. 1987. The future of university/industry research. *Perspectives in Computing* 7(1): 4–10.

In this citation, 7 is the volume number, 1 is the issue number, and 4–10 are the inclusive pages of the article.

WEEKLY OR BIWEEKLY MAGAZINE

Caragata, Warren. 1998. "The high cost of healing." *Maclean's*. 15 June, 111.

MONTHLY OR BIMONTHLY MAGAZINE

Beamer, Scott. 1990. "Why you need a charting program." *MacUser* June, 126–38.

NEWSPAPER

McInnes, Craig. 1998. The mystery of the vanishing marmots. *The Globe and Mail* 6 May.

When the masthead of the paper specifies the edition, put that information in your note. What newspapers print frequently changes from edition to edition on the same day.

ANONYMOUS ARTICLE

"Absolute." 1990. *New Yorker* 18 June, 28–29.

When no author is given for an article, begin with the title of the article.

Other   In this section, we show you model citations for computer software, information services, letters, interviews, and two or more entries by the same author.

COMPUTER SOFTWARE

Prometheus Version 1.06. (1993). MacKnowledge Communication Software.

In citing computer programs, give as much information as you have, including the author's name, the city of publication, the publisher, the version number, and so forth.

INFORMATION SERVICE

Berdan, R., and M. Garcia. 1982. *Discourse-sensitive measurement of language development in bilingual children*. Los Alamitos, CA: National Center for Bilingual Research. ERIC ED 234 636.

LETTER

Harris, John S. 1995. Letter to the author. 19 July.

INTERVIEW

Estrin, Herman. 1994. Personal interview. 16 March.

TWO OR MORE WORKS BY THE SAME AUTHOR

Barker, Thomas. 1985. Video field trip: Bringing the real world into the technical writing classroom. *The Technical Writing Teacher* 11: 175–79.

———. 1989. Word processors and invention in technical writing. *The Technical Writing Teacher* 16: 126–35.

When you have two or more works by the same author or authors in your list of works cited, replace the author's name in the second citation with a 3-em dash (or three unspaced hyphens) and alphabetize by title.

Crowhurst, M. 1983a. *Persuasive writing at grades 5, 7, and 11: A cognitive-development perspective.* Paper presented at the annual meeting of the American Educational Research Association, Montreal, Canada.

———. 1983b. *Revision strategies of students at three grade levels.* Final report. Educational Research Institute of British Columbia. ERIC ED 238 009.

When your list of works cited includes two or more works written in the same year by the same author or authors, alphabetize by title, then mark each year with a lowercase letter, beginning with *a*.

Internet Documentation

In this section, we discuss some of the special problems in documenting Internet material, provide model notes and citations, and provide guidance in forming parenthetical references.

Formats for documenting print material usually do not work well for documenting Internet material, for several reasons:

- Internet material seldom has page numbers.
- Publication dates frequently are not provided on the Internet. If they are, they are changeable. That is, many Web sites are works in progress, frequently revised and updated with little or no warning. If the publication date is missing, the date that you accessed the material may be useful and should be included.
- The punctuation used in notes and citations may be mistaken for part of an Internet address.
- Internet addresses must be stated exactly as they're given, with every slash and period in exactly the right place and with no extraneous spaces, punctuation, or misspellings. Improper spacing, incorrect punctuation, or misspellings in a standard citation are usually no more than embarrassing, but similar errors in Internet citations will render them useless.

MODEL NOTES AND CITATIONS   We provide here six models that should cover most of your needs in documenting Internet material, no matter what system of documentation you are using. Whether it is an MLA-style note or an author–date style citation, punctuate the entry as shown in each model. However, if you are using MLA-style notes, put the author's name in normal order and use the indented style shown below in the FTP model. If your citation is in a *Chicago Manual* author–date reference list, transpose the first author's name and use the hanging style of the WWW model shown below.

If the citation is in APA author–date style, transpose the names of all the authors and use the hanging style of the WWW model.

File Transfer Protocol (FTP) Sites   Notes and citations that refer to FTP sites contain the following information:

- Author's or editor's name (if known), followed by a period
- Document title, followed by a period, within quotation marks
- Publication or revision date (if known), followed by a period
- FTP site address, within angle brackets
- Date of access, within parentheses, followed by a period

[1] Jeff Iverson. "Alabama." <ftp://sumex-aim.stanford.edu:info-mac/ _education/alabama-hc.hqx> (6 Sept. 1996).

World Wide Web (WWW) Sites   Notes and citations that refer to World Wide Web sites contain the following information:

- Author's or editor's name (if known), followed by a period
- Document title, followed by a period, within quotation marks
- Title of full work (if known), in italics, followed by a period
- Publication or revision date (if known), followed by a period
- WWW site address, within angle brackets
- Date of access, within parentheses, followed by a period

Waggoner, Ben. "Introduction to the Viruses." *Life on Earth*. 1995. <http://www. ucmp.berkeley.edu/alllife/virus.html> (28 Oct. 1996).

Linkage   Because of the possibility for linking one document to another in Internet systems, showing that link is often the most convenient way to cite a document. The following note shows that the Texas Tech Physics Department Home Page created by Alan Sill can be found on the Nine Planets Home Page located at the University of Arizona at the link named "Many Sites."

[2] Alan Sill. "Texas Tech Physics Department Home Page." Lkd. *The Nine Planets Home Page* at "Many Sites." <http://seds.lpl.arizona.edu/nineplanets/ nineplanets/nineplanets.html> (27 July 1997).

Listserv Messages   Notes and citations for listserv messages contain the following information:

- Author's name (if known), followed by a period
- Author's e-mail address, within angle brackets
- Subject line of message, followed by a period, within quotation marks
- Date of message, followed by a period
- Listserv address, within angle brackets
- Access date, within parentheses, followed by a period

Selber, Stuart. <selber@ttacsl.ttu.edu> "Call for Articles on Managing International Technical and Scientific Communication." 29 Aug. 1996. <CPTSC-L@CLVM. BITNET> (30 Aug. 1996).

E-Mail Messages Notes and citations for e-mail messages contain the following information:

- Author's name, followed by a period
- Author's e-mail address, within angle brackets
- Subject line from message, followed by a period, within quotation marks
- Date of message, followed by a period
- Kind of communication—for example, personal, business, professional—followed by a period
- Date of access, in parentheses, followed by a period

[3] Marlene Ellin. <Mellinab@AOL.com> "Reviews." 10 Sep. 1996. Business communication. (10 Sept. 1996).

Synchronous Communications Notes and citations for synchronous communications (MOOS, MUDS, IRSs, chat rooms, and the like) contain the following information:

- Name of speaker (if known), followed by a period
- Type of communication (group discussion, interview, etc.), followed by a period
- Internet address in angle brackets
- Date of communication, in parentheses, followed by a period

Stephens, Harold. Group discussion. <http://204.31.29.22.8010> (12 Jan. 1997).

PARENTHETICAL REFERENCES When you are using an author–date system, parenthetical citations to Internet material take much the same form we have described previously. Use whatever information you have to work with. If you have an author's or editor's name and a publication date, use both.

Chicago Manual style: (Ellin 1996)

APA style: (Ellin, 1996)

If you do not have a publication date, simply use the author's or editor's name, thus:

(Sill)

If you do not have a name, use whatever comes first in the citation—for example, a title or a shortened title:

(International Professional Communication)

If you have two or more citations to the same person and no publication dates, use letters to distinguish them, both in the list of references and in the parenthetical references.

Figure Documentation

Tables, graphs, and other figures are documented separately from the text. As we explain in Chapter 10, "Graphical Elements," figure sources are documented right with the figure. In general, the form of a figure citation follows that of a note in the note system or of an entry in a list of works cited or list of references, whichever you are using. Because figures include complete documentation, their citations do not appear with the other citations in a paper.

Copyright

Stringent copyright laws protect published work. When you are writing a student report that you do not intend to publish, you need not concern yourself with these laws. If you intend to publish a report, however, you should become familiar with copyright law. You must get permission from the copyright holder to use illustrations and extended quotations. Look for information on the copyright holder on the title page of a publication. A 20-page booklet, *Guide to Copyright*, is available at no charge from Industry Canada (call 819-997-1936).

Ellipsis (*Ell*)

Use three spaced periods to indicate words omitted within a quoted sentence, four spaced periods if the omission occurs at the end of the sentence:

> "As depth decreases, the circular orbits become elliptical and the orbital velocity ... increases as the wave height increases."

> "As the ground swells move across the ocean, they are subject to headwinds or crosswinds...."

You need not show an ellipsis if the context of the quotation makes it clear that it is not complete:

> Wright said the accident had to be considered a "freak of nature."

Exclamation Point (*Exc*)

Place an exclamation point at the end of a startling or exclamatory sentence.

> According to Health Canada, every cigarette smoked shortens the smoker's life by seven minutes!

With the emphasis in technical writing on objectivity, you will seldom use the exclamation point.

Fragmentary Sentence (*Frag*)

Most fragmentary sentences are either verbal phrases or subordinate clauses that the writer mistakes for a complete sentence.

A verbal phrase has in the predicate position a participle, gerund, or infinitive, none of which functions as a complete verb:

> Norton, **depicting** the electromagnetic heart. (participle)

> The **timing** of this announcement about Triptycene. (gerund)

> Braun, in order **to understand** tumor cell growth. (infinitive)

When your fragment is a verbal phrase, either change the verb to a complete verb or repunctuate the sentence so that the phrase is joined to the complete sentence of which it is actually a part.

FRAGMENT

Norton, depicting the electromagnetic heart. She made a mockup of it.

REWRITTEN

Norton, depicting the electromagnetic heart, made a mockup of it.

Subordinate clauses are distinguishable from phrases in that they have complete subjects and complete verbs (rather than verbals) and are introduced by relative pronouns (*who, which, that*) or by subordinating conjunctions (*because, although, since, after, while*). The presence of the relative pronoun or the subordinating conjunction is a signal that the clause is not independent but is part of a more complex sentence unit. Any independent clause can become a subordinate clause with the addition of a relative pronoun or subordinating conjunction.

INDEPENDENT CLAUSE

Women's unemployment rates were higher than men's.

SUBORDINATE CLAUSE

Although women's unemployment rates were higher than men's

Repunctuate subordinate clauses so that they are joined to the complex sentence of which they are a part.

FRAGMENT

Although women's unemployment rates were higher than men's. Now the rates are similar.

REWRITTEN

Although women's unemployment rates were higher than men's, now the rates are similar.

Various kinds of elliptical sentences without a subject or a verb do exist in English, for example, "No!" "Oh?" "Good shot." "Ouch!" "Well, now." These constructions may occasionally be used for stylistic reasons, particularly to represent conversation, but they are seldom needed in technical writing. If you do use such constructions, use them sparingly. Remember that major deviations from normal sentence patterns will probably jar your readers and break their concentration on your report, the last thing that any writer wants.

Hyphen (*Hyphen*)

Hyphens are used to form various compound words and to break up a word that must be carried over to the next line.

Compound Numbers

See "Numbers."

Common Compound Words

Observe dictionary usage in using or omitting the hyphen in compound words.

governor-elect	court-martial
ex-treasurer	Croesus-like
Italian-Canadian	drill-like
pro-American	self-interest

But:

glasslike	wrist watch
neophyte	sweet corn
newspaper	weather map
newsstand	sun lamp
database	prize fight

Compound Words as Modifiers

Use the hyphen between words joined together to modify other words:

a half-spent bullet

an eight-cylinder engine

their too-little-and-too-late methods

Be particularly careful to hyphenate when omitting the hyphen may cause ambiguity:

two-hundred-gallon drums

two hundred-gallon drums

a pink-skinned hamster

Sometimes you have to carry a modifier over to a later word, creating what is called a *suspended hyphen*:

GM cars come with a choice of four-, six-, or eight-cylinder engines.

Word Division

Use a hyphen to break a word that must be carried over to the next line. Words compounded of two roots or a root and an affix are divided at the point of union:

self-/important	wind/jammer
cross-/pollination	desir/able
bladder/wort	anti/dote
summer/time	manage/able

Note: The first two words in this list are always spelled with a hyphen; the remaining words use the hyphen only when the word is divided at the end of a line.

In general, noncompound words of more than one syllable are divided between any two syllables but only between syllables:

aer/o/space	con/clu/sion
sat/is/fac/tion	sym/pa/thy

A syllable of one letter is never set down alone; a syllable of only two letters is seldom allowed to stand alone unless it is a prefix or a suffix, and then only if it is pronounced as spelled:

hello/	elec/tro/type
method/	de/mand
pilot/	ac/cept
many/	walked/
saga/	start/ed

If a consonant is doubled because a suffix is added, include the second consonant with the suffix:

spin/ner	slip/ping
stir/ring	slot/ted

But:

stopped/	pass/ing
lapped/	stall/ing

Because *-ped* is not pronounced as a syllable in the words *stopped* and *lapped*, it should not be carried over. In words like *passing* and *stalling*, both consonants belong to the root, and, therefore, only the suffix *-ing* is carried over.

Italicization (*Ital*)

Italic print is a distinctive typeface, like this sample: *Halifax Chronicle Herald*. All word processing programs have italics. However, when you type or write, you represent italics by underlining, like this:

<u>Halifax Chronicle Herald</u>

Foreign Words

Italicize foreign words that have not yet become a part of the English language:

We suspected him always of holding some *arrière pensée*.

Karl's everlasting *Weltschmerz* makes him a depressing companion.

Also italicize Latin scientific terms.

Cichorium endivia (endive)

Percopsis omiscomaycus (trout-perch)

But do not italicize Latin abbreviations or foreign words that have become a part of the language:

etc.	bourgeois
vs.	status quo

Your dictionary will normally indicate which foreign words are still italicized and which are not.

Words, Letters, and Numbers Used as Such

The words **entrance** and **admission** are not perfectly interchangeable.

Don't forget the **k** in **picnicking**.

His **9**s and **7**s descended below the line of writing.

Titles

Italicize the titles of books, plays, magazines, newspapers, ships, and artistic works:

Concise Oxford Dictionary	*The Free Press*
Othello	*Bluenose*
Canadian Aeronautics and Space Journal	*Mona Lisa*

Misplaced Modifier (*MM*)

As in the case of dangling modifiers, curious sentences result from the modifier's not being placed next to the element modified:

An engine may crack when cold water is poured in unless it is running.

Probably, with a little effort, almost everyone would read this example as intended, but, undeniably, it says that the engine will crack unless the water is running. Move the modifier to make the sentence clear:

Unless it is running, an engine may crack when cold water is poured in.

It should be apparent from the preceding examples that a modifier may be in the wrong position to convey one meaning but in the perfect position to convey a different meaning. In the next example, the placement of *for three years* is either right or wrong. It is in the right position to modify *to work* but in the wrong position to modify *have been trying*.

I have been trying to place him under contract to work here for three years.
(three-year contract)

As the examples suggest, correct placement of modifiers sometimes amounts to more than mere nicety of expression. It can mean the difference between stating falsehood and truth, between saying what you mean and saying something else.

Numbers (*Num*)

There is a good deal of inconsistency in the rules for handling numbers. It is often hard to know whether you should write the number as a word or as a figure. We will give you the general rules. Your instructor or your organization may give you others. As in all matters of format, you must satisfy whomever you are working for at the moment. Do, however, be internally consistent within your reports. Do not handle numbers differently from page to page of a report.

Numbers as Words

Generally, you write out as words numbers from one to nine, and rounded-off large numbers:

> six generators
>
> about a million dollars

However, when you are writing a series of numbers, do not mix up figures and words. Let the larger numbers determine the form used:

> five boys and six girls

But:

> It took us 6 months and 25 days to complete the experiment.

Numbers as Sentence Openers

Do not begin sentences with a figure. If you can, write the number as a word. If this would be cumbersome, write the sentence so as to get the figure out of the beginning position:

> Fifteen months ago, we saw the new wheat for the first time.
>
> We found 350 deficient steering systems.

Compound Number Adjectives

When you write two numbers together in a compound number adjective, spell out the first one or the shorter one to avoid confusing the reader:

> Twenty 10-inch trout
>
> 100 twelve-volt batteries

Hyphens

Two-word numbers are hyphenated on the rare occasions when they are written out:

> Eighty-five boxes

or:

> Eighty-five should be enough.

Numbers as Figures

The general rule here is to write all exact numbers over nine as figures. This rule probably holds more true in technical writing, with its heavy reliance on numbers, than it does in general writing. However, as we noted, rounded-off numbers are commonly written as words. The precise figure could give the reader an impression of exactness that might not be called for.

Certain conventional uses call for figures at all times.

DATES, EXACT SUMS OF MONEY, TIME, ADDRESS

1 January 1996 or January 1, 1996

$3,422.67 **but** about three thousand dollars

1:57 P.M. **but** two o'clock

660 Fuller Road

TECHNICAL UNITS OF MEASUREMENT

6 cu ft

4000 rpm

CROSS-REFERENCES

See page 22.

Refer to Figure 2.

Fractions

When a fraction stands alone, write it as an unhyphenated compound:

two thirds

fifteen thousandths

When a fraction is used as an adjective, you may write it as a hyphenated compound. But if either the numerator or the denominator is hyphenated, do not hyphenate the compound. More commonly, fractions used as adjectives are written as figures.

two-thirds engine speed

twenty-five thousandths

3/4 rpm

Outlining

As illustrated in the accompanying sample outline, an outline has a title, purpose statement, audience statement, and body. We have annotated the sample outline to point out major outlining conventions. Following the sample outline, we provide other major outlining principles. Figure 8-23 earlier in this book provides a comparison of two outline numbering systems. You may wish to refer to it.

Desalination Methods for Mission Use

Purpose: To choose a desalination method for peacekeeping missions located near large bodies of salt water

Audience: Senior officers

First level, use capital roman numeral

Second level, use capital letters

Third level, use arabic numerals

Fourth level, use lowercase letters

Capitalize only first letter of entry and proper nouns

Use no punctuation after entries

I.   Statement of the problem
  A. Need for a choice
  B. Choices available
    1. Electrodialysis
    2. Reverse osmosis
  C. Sources of data
    1. Division manuals
    2. Expert opinion
      a. Journals
      b. Interviews

II. Explanation of criteria
  A. Cost
  B. Purity
  C. Quantity

III. Electrodialysis
  A. Theory of method
  B. Judgement of method
    1. Cost
    2. Purity
    3. Quantity

IV. Reverse osmosis
  A. Theory of method
  B. Judgement of method
    1. Cost
    2. Purity
    3. Quantity

V.   Choice of method

- *Make all entries grammatically parallel.* (See the entry for parallelism.) Do not mix noun phrases with verb phrases, and so forth. A formal outline with a hodgepodge of different grammatical forms will seem to lack— and, in fact, may lack—logic and consistency.

Incorrect	Correct
I. The overall view	I. The overall view
II. To understand the terminal phase	II. The terminal phase
III. About the constant-bearing concept	III. The constant-bearing concept

- *Never have a single division.* Things divide into two or more; so obviously, if you have only one division, you have done no dividing. If you have a "I" you must have a "II." If you have an "A" you must have a "B," and so forth.

Incorrect	Correct
I. Visual capabilities	I. Visual capabilities
A. Acquisition	A. Acquisition
II. Interception and closure rate	B. Interception and closure rate
III. Braking	II. Braking

- Do not have entries for your report's introduction or conclusion. Outline only the body of the report. Of course, the information in your purpose statement belongs in your introduction, and perhaps the information about audience belongs there as well.

- Use substantive statements in your outline entries. That is, use entries such as "Reverse osmosis" or "Judgement of method" that suggest the true substance of your information. Do not use cryptic expressions such as "Example 1" or "Minor premise."

Many word processing programs have an outlining feature. This feature has two advantages. First, you can choose the outlining scheme you want, for example, *I, A, B, 1, 2.* The program automatically writes the appropriate numbers or letters for you, and changes them when you change the outline. Second, you can write your text into the outline.

Parallelism (*Paral*)

When you link elements in a series, they must all be in the same grammatical form. Link an adjective with an adjective, a noun with a noun, a clause with a clause, and so forth. Look at the boldface portion of the sentence below:

> A good test would use **small amounts of plant material, require little time, simple to run, and accurate.**

The series begins with the verbs *use* and *require* and then abruptly switches to the adjectives *simple* and *accurate.* All four elements must be based on the same part of speech. In this case, it's simple to change the last two elements:

> A good test would use small amounts of plant material, require little time, **be simple to run,** and **be accurate.**

Always be careful when you are listing to keep all the elements of the list parallel. In the following example, the third item in the list is not parallel to the first two:

> The process has three stages: (1) the specimen is dried, (2) all potential pollutants are removed, and (3) atomization.

The error is easily corrected:

> The process has three stages: (1) the specimen is dried, (2) all potential pollutants are removed, and (3) the specimen is atomized.

When you start a series, keep track of what you are doing, and finish the series the same way you started it. Nonparallel sentences are at best awkward and off-key. At worst, they can lead to serious misunderstandings.

Parentheses (*Paren*)

Parentheses are used to enclose supplementary details inserted into a sentence. Commas and dashes may also be used in this role, but with some restrictions. You may enclose a complete sentence or several complete sentences within parentheses. But such enclosure would confuse the reader if only commas or dashes were used for the enclosure:

> The violence of these storms can scarcely be exaggerated. (Typhoons and hurricanes generate winds over 125 km an hour and waves 15 metres high.) The study....

Lists

Parentheses are also used to enclose numbers or letters used in listing:

> This general analysis consists of sections on (1) wave generation, (2) wave propagation, (3) wave action near a shoreline, and (4) wave energy.

Punctuation of Parentheses in Sentences

Within a sentence, use no punctuation before the opening parenthesis. Place any marks needed in the sentence after the closing parenthesis:

> If a runway is regularly exposed to crosswinds of over 10 knots (18.6 km/hr), then the runway is considered unsafe.

Do not use any punctuation around parentheses when they come between sentences. Give the statement *inside* the parentheses any punctuation it needs.

Period (*Per*)

Periods have several conventional uses.

End Stop

Place a period at the end of any sentence that is not a question or an exclamation:

> Find maximum average daily temperature and maximum pressure altitude.

Abbreviations

Place a period after abbreviations:

M.D.	etc.
Ph.D.	Jr.

However, some style guides now call for no periods in academic abbreviations such as BA, MD, and PhD.

Decimal Point

Use the period with decimal fractions and as a decimal point between dollars and cents:

.4	$5.60
.05%	$450.23

Pronoun-Antecedent Agreement (*P/ag*)

Pronoun-antecedent agreement is closely related to verb-subject agreement. For example, the problem area concerning the use of collective nouns explained in "Verb-Subject Agreement" is closely related to the proper use of pronouns. When a collective noun is considered singular it takes a singular pronoun as well as a singular verb. Also, such antecedents as *each, everyone, either, neither, anybody, somebody, everybody,* and *no one* take singular pronouns as well as singular verbs:

Everyone had **his** assignment ready.

However, using male pronouns exclusively when the reference may be to both men and women makes the choice of *his* as the pronoun in the preceding example objectionable to many people. Do not choose to solve the problem by introducing a grammatical error, as in this example of incorrect usage:

Everyone had **their** assignment ready.

The use of male and female pronouns together is grammatically correct, if a bit awkward at times:

Everyone had **his or her** assignment ready.

Perhaps the best solution, one that is often applicable, is to use a plural antecedent that allows the use of a neutral plural pronoun, as in this example:

All the students had **their** assignments ready.

The same problem presents itself when we use such nouns as *student* or *human being* in their generic sense; that is, when we use them to stand for all students or all human beings. If used in the singular, such nouns must be followed by singular pronouns:

The **student** seeking a loan must have **his or her** application in by 3 September.

Again, the best solution is to use a plural antecedent:

Students seeking loans must have **their** applications in by 3 September.

See also the entry for sexist usage.

Pronoun Form (*Pron*)

Almost every adult can remember being corrected by parents and elementary school teachers in regard to pronoun form. The common sequence is for the child to say, "Me and Johnny are going swimming," and for the teacher or parent to say patiently, "No, dear, 'Johnny and I are going swimming.'" As a result of this conditioning, **all** objective forms are automatically under suspicion in many adult minds, and the most common pronoun error is for the speaker or writer to use a subjective case pronoun such as *I, he,* or *she* when an objective case pronoun such as *me, him,* or *her* is called for.

Whenever a pronoun is the object of a verb or the object of a preposition, it must be in the objective case:

> It occurred to my colleagues and **me** to check the velocity data on the earthquake waves.
>
> Just between **you** and **me**, the news shook Mary and **him**.

However, use a subjective case pronoun in the predicate nominative position. This rule slightly complicates the use of pronouns after the verb. Normally, the pronoun position after the verb is thought of as objective pronoun territory, but when the verb is a linking verb (chiefly the verb *to be*), the pronoun is called a *predicate noun* rather than an object and is in the subjective case.

> It is **he**.
>
> It was **she** who discovered the mutated fruit fly.

Question Mark (*Ques*)

Place a question mark at the end of every sentence that asks a direct question:

> What is the purpose of this report?

A request that you politely phrase as a question may be followed by either a period or a question mark:

> Will you be sure to return the experimental results as soon as possible.
>
> Will you be sure to return the experimental results as soon as possible?

When you have a question mark within quotation marks, you need no other mark of punctuation:

> "Where am I?" he asked.

Quotation Marks (*Quot*)

Use quotation marks to set off short quotations and certain titles.

Short Quotations

Use quotation marks to enclose quotations that are short enough to work into your own text (normally, fewer than four lines):

> According to Dr. Stockdale, "Ants, wonderful as they are, have many enemies."

When quotations are longer than four lines, set them off by single spacing and indenting them. See the entry for colon for an example of this style. Do not use quotation marks when quotations are set off and indented.

Titles

Place quotation marks around titles of articles from journals and periodicals:

> Salter's article "Infotech '95: Plug and Pray" appeared in *The Report on Business Magazine*.

Single Quotes

When you must use quotation marks within other quotation marks, use single marks (the apostrophe on your keyboard):

"Do you have the same trouble with the distinction between 'venal' and 'venial' that I do?" asked the copy editor.

Punctuation Conventions

The following are the conventions in North America for using punctuation with quotation marks:

COMMAS AND PERIODS   Always place commas and periods inside the quotation marks. There are no exceptions to this rule:

G. D. Brewer wrote "Manned Hypersonic Vehicles."

SEMICOLONS AND COLONS   Always place semicolons and colons outside the quotation marks. There are no exceptions to this rule:

As Dr. Damron points out, "New technology has made photographs easy to fake"; therefore, they are no longer reliable as courtroom evidence.

QUESTION MARKS, EXCLAMATION POINTS, AND DASHES   Place question marks, exclamation points, and dashes inside the quotation marks when they apply *to the quote only or to the quote and the entire sentence at the same time*. Place them outside the quotation marks when they apply to the entire sentence only.

INSIDE

When are we going to find the answer to the question, "What causes clear air turbulence?"

OUTSIDE

Did you read Minna Levine's "Business Statistics"?

Run-on Sentence (*Run-on*)

A run-on sentence is two independent clauses (that is, two complete sentences) put together with only a comma or no punctuation at all between them. Punctuate two independent clauses placed together with a period, semicolon, or a comma and a coordinating conjunction (*and, but, for, nor,* or *yet*). Infrequently, the colon or dash is used also. (There are some exceptions to these rules. See the entry for comma.) The following three examples are punctuated correctly, the first with a period, the second with a semicolon, the third with a comma and a coordinating conjunction:

Check the hydraulic pressure. If it reads below normal, do not turn on the aileron boost.

We will describe the new technology in greater detail; however, first we will say a few words about the principal devices found in electronic circuits.

Ground contact with wood is particularly likely to cause decay, but wood buried far below the ground line will not decay because of a lack of sufficient oxygen.

If the example sentences had only commas or no punctuation at all between the independent clauses, they would be run-on sentences.

Writers most frequently write run-on sentences when they mistake conjunctive adverbs for coordinating conjunctions. The most common conjunctive adverbs are *also, anyway, besides, consequently, furthermore, hence, however, moreover, nevertheless, therefore,* and *too.*

When a conjunctive adverb is used to join two independent clauses, the mark of punctuation most often used is a semicolon (a period is used infrequently), as in this correctly punctuated sentence:

> Ice fish are nearly invisible; however, they do have a few dark spots on their bodies.

Often the sentence will be more effective if it is rewritten completely, making one of the independent clauses a subordinate clause or a phrase.

> RUN-ON SENTENCE
>
> The students at the university are mostly young Newfoundlanders, most of them are between the ages of 18 and 24.
>
> REWRITTEN
>
> The students at the university are mostly young Newfoundlanders between the ages of 18 and 24.

Semicolon (*Semi*)

The semicolon lies between the comma and the period in force. Its use is quite restricted. (See also the entry for run-on sentences.)

Independent Clauses

Place a semicolon between two closely connected independent clauses that are not joined by a coordinating conjunction (*and, but, or, nor, for,* or *yet*):

> The expanding gases formed during burning drive the turbine; the gases are then exhausted through the nozzle.

When independent clauses joined by a coordinating conjunction have internal punctuation, then the comma before the coordinating conjunction may be increased to a semicolon:

> The front lawn has been planted with a Chinese Beauty Tree, a Bechtel Flowering Crab, a Mountain Ash, and assorted small shrubbery, including barberry and cameo roses; but so far nothing has been done to the rear beyond clearing and rough grading.

Series

When a series contains commas as internal punctuation within the parts, use semicolons between the parts:

> Included in the experiment were Peter Moody, a first-year student; Ronnie Szeto, a second-year student; Bonnie Chu, an evening student; and Ruth Leone, a recent graduate.

Sexist Usage (*Sexist*)

Conventional usages often discriminate against or exclude women. For example, a problem often arises when someone is talking about some group in general but refers to members of the group in the singular, as in the following passage:

> The modern secretary has to be an expert with electronic equipment. She has to be able to run a microcomputer and fix a fax machine. On the other hand, her boss still doodles letters on yellow pads. He has yet to come to grips with all the electronic gadgetry in today's office.

This paragraph makes two groundless assumptions: that all secretaries are female and all executives are male. Neither assumption, of course, is valid.

Similarly, in the past, letters began with "Dear Sir" or "Gentlemen." People who delivered mail were "mailmen" and those who protected our streets were "policemen." History books discussed "man's progress" and described how "man had conquered space."

However, of late we have recognized the unfairness of such discriminatory usages. Most organizations and individuals now make a real effort to avoid sexist usages in their documents. How can you avoid such usages once you understand the problem?

Titles of various kinds are fairly easy to deal with. *Firemen* have become *firefighters; policemen, police officers; chairmen, chairpersons* or simply *chairs;* and so forth. We no longer speak of *man's progress* but of *human progress.*

The selection of pronouns when dealing with groups in general sometimes presents more of a problem. One way to deal with it is to move from the singular to the plural. You can speak of *secretaries/they* and *bosses/they*, avoiding the choice of either a male or female pronoun.

You can also write around the problem. You can convert a sentence like the following one from a sexist to a nonsexist statement by replacing the *he* clause with a verbal phrase such as an infinitive or a participle:

> The diver must close the mouthpiece shut-off valve before he runs the test.
>
> The diver must close the mouthpiece shut-off valve before running the test.

If you write instructions in a combination of the second person (you) and the imperative mood, you avoid the problem altogether:

> You must close the mouthpiece shut-off valve before you run the test.
>
> Close the mouthpiece shut-off valve before running the test.

At times, using plural forms or second person or writing around the problem simply won't work. In an insurance contract, for example, you might have to refer to the policyholder. It would be unclear to use a plural form because that might indicate two policyholders when only one is intended. When such is the case, writers have little recourse except to use such phrases as *he or she* or *he/she*. Both are a bit awkward, but they have the advantage of being both precise and nonsexist.

You can use the search program in your word processing program to find sexist language in your own work. Search for male and female pronouns and *man* and *men*. When you find them, check to see if you have used them in a sexist or nonsexist way. If you have used them in a sexist way, correct the problem, but be sure not to introduce inaccuracy or imprecision in doing so.

See also the entry for pronoun-antecedent agreement.

Spelling Error (*Sp*)

The condition of English spelling is chaotic and likely to remain so. George Bernard Shaw once illustrated this chaos by spelling *fish* as *ghoti*. To do so, he took the *gh* from *rough*, the *o* from *women*, and the *ti* from *condition*. If you have a spelling checker in your word processing program, it will help you avoid many spelling errors and typographical errors. Do remember, though, that a spelling checker will not catch the wrong word correctly spelled. That is, it won't warn you when you used *to* for *too*. You may obtain help from the spelling section in a dictionary where the common rules of spelling are explained. You can also buy, rather inexpensively, books that explain the various spelling rules and provide exercises to fix the rules in your mind.

To assist you, we provide a list here of common sound-alike words, each used correctly in a sentence.

I **accept** your gift.
Everyone went **except** Jerry.

His lawyer gave him good **advice**.
His lawyer **advised** him well.

Her cold **affected** her voice.
The **effect** was rather froglike.

He was **already** home by 9 p.m.
When her bag was packed, she was **all ready** to go.

The members of the board stood **all together** on the issue.
Jim was **altogether** pleased with the result of the test.

He gave him **an** aardvark.
The aardvark **and** the anteater look somewhat alike.

The river **breached** the levee, letting the water through.
He loaded the cannon at the **breech**.

Edmonton is the **capital** of Alberta.
Tourists were taking pictures of the **capitol** building.

Always **cite** your sources in a paper.
After the sun rose, we **sighted** the missing children.
She chose land near the river as the **site** for her house.

Burlap is a **coarse** cloth.
She was disappointed, of **course**.

His blue tie **complemented** his gray shirt.
I **complimented** him on his choice of ties.

Most cities have a governing body called a **council**.
The lawyer's **counsel** was to remain quiet.

Being quiet, she said, was the **discreet** thing to do.
Each slice in a loaf of bread is **discrete** from the other slices.

"We must move **forward**," the Prime Minister said.
Many books have **forewords**.

Am I speaking so that you can **hear** me?
He was **here** just a minute ago.

It's obvious why he was here.
The sousaphone and **its** sound are both big and round.

Lead (Pb) has a melting point of 327.5°C.
Joan of Arc **led** the French troops to victory.

Our **principal** goal is to cut the deficit.
Hold to high ethical **principles**.

A thing at rest is **stationary**.
Choose white paper for your **stationery**.

A **straight** line is the shortest distance between two points.
The **Strait** of Gibraltar separates Europe from Africa.

I wonder when **they're** coming.
Are they bringing **their** luggage with them?
Put your luggage **there** in the corner.

He made a careful, **thorough** inspection.
He worked as **though** his life depended on it.
She **thought** until her head ached.

He **threw** the report on her desk.
His report cut **through** all the red tape.

Laurie moved **to** Huntsville.
Gary moved to Huntsville, **too**.
After one comes **two**.

We had two days of hot, sunny **weather**.
Whether he goes or not, I'm going.

Where **were** you on Monday?
The important thing is **we're** here today.
Where are you going tomorrow?

Whose house will you stay at?
Who's coming on the trip with us?

Is that **your** car you're driving?
You're right; it's my car.

Verb Form (*Vb*)

Improper verb form includes a wide variety of linguistic errors ranging from such nonstandard usages as "He seen the show" for "He saw the show" to such esoteric errors as "He was hung by the neck until dead" for "He was hanged by the neck until dead." Normally a few minutes spent with a dictionary will show you the correct verb form. Good dictionaries list the principal parts of the verb after the verb entry.

Verb-Subject Agreement (*V/ag*)

Most of the time, verb–subject agreement presents no difficulty to the writer. For example, in the sentence, "He speaks for us all," only a child or a foreigner learning English might say, "He speak for us all." However, various constructions exist in English that do present agreement problems even for the adult, educated, native speaker of English. These troublesome constructions are examined in the following sections.

Words That Take Singular Verbs

The following words take singular verbs: *each, everyone, either, neither, anybody, somebody.*

Writers rarely have trouble with a sentence such as "No one is going to the game." Problems arise when, as is often the case, a prepositional phrase with a plural object is interposed between the simple subject and the verb, as in this sentence: "Each of *these disposal systems* is a possible contaminant." In this sentence the temptation is to let the object of the preposition, *systems,* govern the verb and write incorrectly, "Each of these disposal systems *are* a possible contaminant."

Compound Subject Joined by *Or* or *Nor*

When a compound subject is joined by *or* or *nor,* the verb agrees with the closer noun or pronoun:

Either the designer or the **builders are** in error.

Either the builders or the **designer is** in error.

In informal and general usage, one might commonly hear, or see, the second sentence as "Either the builders or the designer are in error." In writing you should hold to the more formal usage of the example.

Parenthetical Expressions

Parenthetical expressions introduced by such words as *accompanied by, with, together with,* and *as well as* do not govern the verb:

Mr. Roberts, **as well as** his two assistants, **is** working on the experiment.

Two or More Subjects Joined by *And*

Two or more subjects joined by *and* take a plural verb. Inverted word order does not affect this rule:

Close to Queen's Park **are** the University of Toronto and the Royal Ontario Museum.

Collective Nouns

Collective nouns such as *team, group, class, committee,* and many others take either plural or singular verbs, depending upon the meaning of the sentence. The writer must be sure that any subsequent pronouns agree with the subject and verb:

The **team** is going to receive **its** championship trophy tonight.

The **team** are going to receive **their** football letters tonight.

When the team was considered singular in the first example, the subsequent pronoun was *its*. In the second example the pronoun was *their*.

TECHNICAL REFERENCE BOOKS AND GUIDES

Prepared by Donald J. Barrett
Canadian Edition (1999): Revisions to Canadian Job Information Sources and Appendices A and B by Jey Wolofsky, Ryerson Polytechnic University Library.

APPENDIX A

Even an average library makes a staggering amount of technical information available to its users. You can gain ready access to that information through reference books and reference guides. A **reference book**, such as a dictionary, encyclopedia, or atlas, consolidates a good deal of technical information in one location. With a **reference guide** you can find the reference books, periodicals, and reports published in any specific field from agriculture to zoology. This appendix is a guide to field-specific reference books and field-specific reference guides. The preceding list of subjects covered in this appendix shows the extent of what is available to you and can help you locate the particular works you may need.

Book Guides

You can find information on books in science and technology in standard guides to book publication and general reviewing tools. A few tools devoted specifically to technical publications do exist, but most cover only a small portion of each year's book production, so, in this case, you must use the more general tools. Several of the major guides are listed here and will be found in most libraries.

Books in Print Plus [CD-ROM]. New York: R. R. Bowker. Annual.
> Guide to 1.9 million books available from 50 000+ publishers, including scholarly, popular, adult, juvenile, reprint, and other books on all subjects published or exclusively distributed in the United States.

Books in Print Plus. Canadian edition. [CD-ROM]. New York: R. R. Bowker. Annual.
> Contains bibliographies of 1.5 million+ records for in-print and forthcoming titles from Canada and the United States and covers 2600+ major Canadian publishers and distributors.

Books in Print with Reviews Plus [CD-ROM]. New York: R. R. Bowker. Annual.

Cumulative Book Index [CD-ROM]. Minneapolis, MN: H. W. Wilson.
> Contains 750 000+ citations to English-language books published internationally.

Index to Scientific and Technical Proceedings [CD-ROM]. Philadelphia: Institute for Scientific Information.

Library of Congress Catalog http://lcweb.loc.gov.catalog.

National Library of Canada http://www.amicus.nlc-bnc.ca/app/resanet/introe.htm.

United Nations Documents Index http://www.un.org/Docs.

Reference Books

Most subjects or academic fields have their own literature, often ranging from encyclopedias to indexes, dictionaries, biographical tools, and so on. The amount of literature specific to one subject may vary greatly. When you first approach a field, one principal guide, Nilsen's, is available to assist you in becoming familiar with the literature of the field. The current edition of this guide should be found in every major collection:

Guide to Reference Materials for Canadian Libraries. Kirsti Nilsen, ed. 8th ed. Toronto: Published for the Faculty of Library and Information Science by the University of Toronto, 1992.

Encyclopedias

The encyclopedia, although considered too general by some specialists, is often extremely useful to the researcher in getting under way and learning a field. Several of the encyclopedias for specific subjects are in fact quite detailed and scholarly. The editors and contributors to a well-written special encyclopedia will often be experts in their fields. Of course, the latest developments in a subject would be available only in periodical and report literature. Still, the general works are of great value toward understanding a subject, and they often include bibliographic citations to aid in further research.

Britannica Online. Chicago, IL: Britannica Online, 1995—http://www. eb.com.

The Canadian Encyclopedia. James H. Marsh, ed. 2nd ed. Edmonton: Hurtig Publishers, 1988.

The Canadian & World Encyclopedia [CD-ROM]. Toronto: M&S Multimedia, 1997.

Concise Encyclopedia of Polymer Science and Engineering. Jacqueline T. Kroschwitz, ed. New York: Wiley, 1990.

Dictionary of Organic Compounds: The Constitution and Physical, Chemical, and Other Properties of the Principal Carbon Compounds and their Derivatives, Together with Relevant Literature References. Ian M. Heilbron, ed. 5th rev. ed. 7 vols. New York: Chapman and Hall, 1982. Plus annual suppls. 1985-.
Alphabetical list of compounds, large number of cross-references.

Dictionary of Organic Compounds [CD-ROM]. London: Chapman & Hall Chemical Database, 1994-.

Encyclopaedic Dictionary of Physics. 9 vols, 5 suppls. New York: Pergamon, 1961-.
Scholarly work, alphabetically arranged, articles generally under 3000 words, most with bibliographies. Includes articles on general, nuclear, solid state, molecular, chemical, metal, and vacuum physics. Index, plus a multilingual glossary in six languages.

Encyclopedia of Agricultural Science. Charles J. Arntzen and Ellen M. Ritter, eds. San Diego: Academic Press, 1994.

Encyclopedia of Chemical Technology. Raymond Kirk and Donald Othmer, eds. 25 vols, index, and suppl. 4th ed. New York: Wiley-Interscience, 1991-.
Main subject is chemical technology; about half the articles deal with chemical substances. There are also articles on industrial processes. A bibliography is included for each product, as well as information on properties, sources, manufacture, and uses.

Encyclopedia of Computer Science. Anthony Ralston, Edwin D. Reilly and Caryl Ann Dahlin, eds. New York: Van Nostrand Reinhold, 1993.

Encyclopedia of Environmental Information Sources. Sarojini Balachandran, ed. Detroit: Gale Research, 1993.

Encyclopedia of Materials Science and Engineering. Michael Bever, ed. 8 vols. Cambridge, MA: MIT Press, 1986.
Over 1550 articles to assist in understanding design and development of new processes. Alphabetical topical arrangement. Index volume includes a systematic outline, author citation index, subject index, and materials information sources.

Encyclopedia of Materials Science and Engineering. Supplementary Volume. 1st ed. Robert W. Cahn, ed.

Encyclopedia of Physical Science and Technology. 2nd ed. 18 vols. San Diego: Academic Press, 1992. Supplemental yearbooks.

Covers all aspects of the physical sciences, including electronics, lasers, and optical technology. Over 500 articles, many illustrations, tables, and bibliographic citations. Separate index volume.

Encyclopedia of Physical Sciences and Engineering Information Sources. Martin A. Smith, David E. Wilt, and Judith B. Erickson, eds. 2nd ed. Detroit, MI: Gale Research, 1997.

Encyclopedia of Polymer Science and Engineering. 2nd ed. 17 vols. New York: Wiley, 1985-1988. Plus supplement and index.

Articles designed to present a balanced account of all aspects of polymer science and technology, with bibliographies included.

McGraw-Hill Dictionary of Bioscience. Sybil P. Parker, editor in chief. New York: McGraw-Hill, 1997.

McGraw-Hill Dictionary of Science and Technology [CD-ROM]. New York: McGraw-Hill, 1997.

McGraw-Hill Encyclopedia of Science and Technology. 8th ed. 20 v. + annual suppls. New York: McGraw-Hill, 1997.

Main set includes 7500 articles, kept current by annual supplements. Covers the basic subject matter of all the sciences and their major applications in engineering, agriculture, and other technologies. Separate index volume. Has many diagrams and charts, and complicated subjects are treated in clear and readable language. Contributors identified in index volume.

Van Nostrand's Scientific Encyclopedia. 8th ed. New York: Van Nostrand Reinhold, 1995.

Includes articles on basic and applied sciences. Defines and explains over 17 000 terms, arranged alphabetically with extensive cross-references.

Subject Guides

Bibliographers and librarians have gathered research suggestions and bibliographies for many fields into published guides. It should be remembered that the rapidly changing literature in many subjects partially outdates any guide. Therefore, Nilsen's *Guide to Reference Materials* and other tools listing current books and indexes should be consulted to supplement these guides.

Canadian Sources of Environmental Information. Hull, PQ: Environment Canada. 1986- (Annual).

Chemical Publications, Their Nature and Use. Melvin G. Mellon. 5th ed. New York: McGraw-Hill, 1982.

Describes publications by nature and sources. Identifies primary, secondary, and tertiary sources and evaluates their use by subject. Chapters on manual searching techniques and computer searching of databases.

Computer Select [CD-ROM]. New York: Ziff Communications, 1990- monthly.

Computing Information Directory: a Comprehensive Guide to the Computing Literature. Darlene Myers Hildebrandt, ed. Colville, WA: Hildebrandt, 1990.

Current Contents. Philadelphia: Institute for Scientific Information. Monthly.

Provides multidisciplinary coverage in the life sciences; physical, chemical, and earth sciences; clinical medicine; engineering; computing and technology; social and behavioural sciences; and arts and humanities.

Current Research in the Geological Sciences in Canada. Thomas Elwood Bolton, et al. Ottawa: Energy, Mines and Resources Canada. Annual.

Directory of Environmental Information Sources. Thomas F.P. Sullivan, ed. Rockville, MD: Government Institutes, 1992.

Energy Information Index, 1978-.

The Environment: World Internet Dictionary http://ultrausa.tradenet.it/ links/sc/Environment.html.
Comprehensive links to Canadian and international environmental resources.

Geologic Reference Sources: A Subject and Regional Bibliography to Publications and Maps in the Geological Sciences. Dederick Ward and Marjorie Wheeler. 2nd ed. Metuchen, NJ: Scarecrow, 1981.
Subject bibliography, most items not annotated. Subject and geographic indexes. Section on geologic maps.

How to Find Chemical Information: A Guide for Practicing Chemists, Educators, and Students. Robert E. Maizell. 3rd ed. New York: Wiley, 1998.
Extensive coverage on use of Chemical Abstracts, online databases, patents, and standard literature.

Information Sources in Chemistry. 4th ed. R. T. Bottle. London: Bowker-Saur, 1993.
Subject arrangement, guides to resources and services evaluated.

Information Sources in Physics. Dennis F. Shaw, ed. 3rd ed. London: Butterworths, 1994.
Subject chapters, bibliographic essays, detailed examination of the literature.

Information Sources in Science and Engineering. C. D. Hurt. Littleton, CO: Libraries Unlimited, 1988.
Chapters on the literature of individual disciplines, annotated citations to over 2000 titles.

Information Sources in Science and Technology. Charlie Deuel Hurt. Englewood, CO: Libraries Unlimited, 1998.

Information Sources in the Life Sciences. H. V. Wyatt, ed. London and New Providence: Bowker-Saur, 1997.

The Literature of Agricultural Engineering. Carl W. Hall and Wallace C. Olsen. Ithaca, NY: Cornell University Press, 1993,
Includes bibliographical references and index.

National Standards System: Directory and Index of Standards. Standards Council of Canada. Ottawa: Standards Council of Canada, 1992.

Science and Engineering Literature: A Guide to Reference Sources. Harold R. Malinowsky. 3rd ed. Littleton, CO: Libraries Unlimited, 1980.
Selected evaluative list of basic reference sources, arranged by major subjects such as physics, chemistry, astronomy, and the like.

Science and Technology: An Introduction to the Literature. Denis Grogan. 4th ed. London: Binbley, 1982.
Student guide to structure of the literature of science and technology.

Scientific and Technical Information Sources. Ching-Chih Chen. 2nd ed. Cambridge, MA: MIT Press, 1987.

Arranged by type of publication. Lists materials for each subject field. Annotated evaluative entries.

Scientific and Technical Literature: an Introduction to Forms of Communication. Richard D. Walker and Charlie Deuel Hurt. Chicago: American Library Association, 1990.

Technical Information Sources: A Guide to Patent Specifications, Standards, and Technical Reports Literature. Bernard Houghton. 2nd ed. Hamden, CT: Linnet, 1972.

British emphasis; covers use of patents as source of technical information, use of specifications and reports.

Use of Mathematical Literature. A. R. Dorling, ed. London: Butterworths, 1977.

Describes general literature and use of particular tools, then provides critical accounts by subject experts in their fields. Author and subject indexes.

Using the Biological Literature: A Practical Guide. Elisabeth B. Davis and Diane Schmidt. New York: Dekker, 1995.

Using Science and Technology Information Sources. Ellis Mount and Beatrice Kovacs. Phoenix: Oryx Press, 1991.

Discusses nature and sources of information, textual and nontextual, with 35 chapters on types of sources.

Bibliographies

The literature of a field may often be compiled into bibliographies in connection with other publications, and in some cases as an indication of the work of an agency or company. A guide to bibliographies and examples of other types of compilations are given here.

Bibliographic Index: A Cumulative Bibliography of Bibliographies. 1937-.

Alphabetical subject list of separately published bibliographies and bibliographies appearing in books, pamphlets, and periodicals.

Bibliography of Agriculture. 1942-.

Classified bibliography of current literature received in the National Agricultural Library, with cumulative annual subject and author indexes.

Bibliography and Index of Geology. 1969-.

Index produced by Geological Society of America. Arranged in broad subject categories, with author and subject indexes. Formerly *Bibliography and Index of Geology Exclusive of North America* and *Bibliography of North American Geology*.

Chemical Titles. 1960-.

Author and key word indexes to titles from 700 journals in pure and applied chemistry. A computer-produced bibliography.

DAI (Dissertation Abstracts International) [CD-ROM]. Ann Arbor, MI: University Microfilms. Annual.

A. Humanities and Social Sciences. B. Sciences and Engineering. C. European Abstracts.

GeoRef [CD-ROM]. Boston: SilverPlatter. Quarterly.

Corresponds to *Bibliography of North American Geology, Index of Geology Exclusive of North America,* and *Geological Abstracts.*

Index of Publications, 1959- . Ottawa: Geological Survey of Canada, 1975-.

Index of Selected Publications of the RAND Corporation. 1946-.
Coverage includes unclassified publications of the corporation. Abstracts, listed by subject and author, describe content and indexes.

Science Citation Index [CD-ROM]. Philadelphia: Institute for Scientific Information, 1961-.

Web of Science. Philadelphia: Institute for Scientific Information. http://www. isinet.com/prodserv/citation/websci.html.
Provides Web access to 5000+ journals indexed in *Science Citation Index.* Expanded and exclusive navigational and retrieval functions possible through the combination of citation indexing and enabling Web technology.

Biographies

Identification of authors and significant figures in the scientific and technical areas is frequently a problem. Some of the most notable biographical sources are commented on here. A check of Nilsen's *Guide to Reference Materials* will reveal many more directories in almost every major subject field.

American Men and Women of Science: Physical and Biological Sciences. 17th ed. 8 vols. New York: R. R. Bowker, 1989-1990.
Standard biographical set for 130 000 people in the sciences.

Biography Index. 1946-.
Index to biographical material in books and magazines. Alphabetical, with index by profession and occupation.

Biography Index [CD-ROM]. Norwood, MA: SilverPlatter International. Annual.

The Canadian Who's Who: Incorporating Canadian Men and Women of Toronto: University of Toronto Press. Annual.

Dictionary of Canadian Biography. 24 vols. Toronto: University of Toronto Press, 1966-.

Dictionary of Scientific Biography. 14 vols, suppl. and index. New York: Scribner's, 1970-1980.
Comprehensive: covers historical and current persons in science.

SciTech Reference Plus [CD-ROM]. New York: Bowker. Annual.
Biographical data on American men and women of science.

Who's Who in America: A Biographical Dictionary of Notable Living Men and Women. Chicago: Marquis, 1899-. Biennial.
The standard dictionary of contemporary biographical data. Regional volumes cover persons not of national prominence.

Who's Who in Canada. Toronto: International Press. Annual.

Who's Who in Canadian Business. Toronto: Trans-Canada Press, 1980/81-.

Who's Who in Canadian Business [CD-ROM]. Toronto: Who's Who Publications. Annual.

Who's Who of Canadian Women. Toronto: Trans-Canada Press, 1983–.

Who's Who of Canadian Women [CD-ROM]. Toronto: Who's Who Publications. Annual.

Who's Who in Frontiers of Science and Technology, 1985. 2nd ed. Chicago: Marquis Who's Who, 1985.
> Covers scientists who have distinguished themselves by research in fields representing either new directions in traditional fields or research areas using advanced technologies.

Who's Who in Science in Europe: A New Reference Guide to West European Scientists. 5th ed. 3 vols. New York: Gale Research Service, 1987.
> More than 40 000 entries including natural and physical sciences.

Dictionaries

Definition of terms for the student and scholar is a problem in the sciences, as in any field. A few general guides are available in addition to glossaries for a single field.

Academic Press Dictionary of Science and Technology. Christopher Morris, ed. San Diego: Academic Press, 1992.
> Over 133 000 entries in 124 fields of scientific knowledge.

Chambers Science and Technology Dictionary. Peter M. B. Walker, ed. 4th ed. New York: Cambridge UP, 1988.
> Successor to Chambers Technical Dictionary, completely revised. Dictionary of concise definitions.

Chambers Science and Technology Dictionary. New York: Larousse, 1995.

Concise Chemical and Technical Dictionary. 4th enl. ed. New York: Chemical Publishing, 1986.
> Contains 50 000 brief definitions, including chemical formulas.

A Dictionary of Physical Sciences. John Daintith, ed. New York: Rowman, 1983.
> Includes some diagrams and cross-references.

McGraw-Hill Dictionary of the Life Sciences. Daniel N. Lapedes, ed. New York: McGraw-Hill, 1976.
> Provides vocabulary of the biological sciences and related disciplines. Over 20 000 terms, useful appendices.

McGraw-Hill Dictionary of Physics and Mathematics. Daniel N. Lapedes, ed. New York: McGraw-Hill, 1978.
> More than 20 000 terms, containing both basic vocabulary and current specialized terminology. Illustrated.

McGraw-Hill Dictionary of Scientific and Technical Terms. Sybil P. Parker, ed. 4th ed. New York: McGraw-Hill, 1989.
> Gives almost 100 000 definitions, amplified by 2800 illustrations. Each definition identified with the field of science in which it is primarily used.

Commercial Guides

Access to materials from companies working on a specific product can be facilitated by the use of product association and company address information. The standards are an example of tools that many industries must use to satisfy a contractor's requirements.

Canadian General Standards Board ECAT Electronic Catalogue [COMPUTER DISK]. Ottawa: CGSB, 1990-.

Certified Products Database (CPD) [ONLINE DATABASE]. Rexdale, ON: Canadian Standards Association, 1950-.

> Contains data on 40 000+ products approved for sale or distribution in Canada by the Canadian Standards Association. Information includes CSA Category classification and type, brand names, product manufacturers, model and catalogue numbers and operating characteristics.

Standards Catalogue: Directory and Index of Standards. Ottawa: Standards Council of Canada, 1992.

Thomas Register [CD-ROM] Palo Alto, CA: DIALOG Information Services. Annual http://www.1.thomasregister.com/index.html.

Periodicals

In almost any current research, the latest developments in a field will be published in the current periodicals and professional journals. Your first task as a researcher may be to determine what periodicals are published in a given field. Next, you may want to determine what indexing or abstracting services give access to a specific journal. The guides are the most significant in helping you to locate this type of information.

Ulrich's Plus [CD-ROM]. East Grinstead, UK: Bowker-Saur. Annual. http://www.bowker-saur.com/service/.

> Contains information on 210 000+ periodicals, irregular serials and annuals, new titles, title changes, and cessations, as well as contact information for every listed publisher. Includes annotations, LC classification numbers, 24 search categories, 16 browsable indexes, and 8 display and output formats.

Electronic Resources

The Internet (World Wide Web)

The World Wide Web (The Web, WWW) was developed in Switzerland at CERN (European Particle Physics Laboratory) in 1992 and is perhaps the most powerful and intuitive way of finding information on the Internet. The WWW provides access to information from the Internet using hypertext and multimedia (including audio, graphics and images) to link specific bits of information or entire documents throughout the Internet. When searching the Internet, users need to evaluate informational content. Authority is determined by the qualifications of the author and whether the information has been peer reviewed. Scope relates to whether the information is summary, comprehensive, or in progress. Currency is determined by the date the information was composed or revised and the amount of historical content. Objectivity may be determined by the presence of obvious bias, or whether the information was provided by a special interest or advocacy group or for commercial or marketing purposes.

Computers On, Critical Thinking Off. Janet Martorana and Carol Doyle. *Research Strategies* 14, 3 (Summer 1996):184–191.

Evaluating Information on the Internet. Scott D. Brandt. http://thorplus.lib. purdue.edu/~techman/evaluate.htm.

Evaluating Internet Research Sources. Robert Harris. http://www.sccu.edu/ faculty/R_Harris/eval8lt.htm.

Information Quality: Is the Truth Out There? Serena Fenton. http://ils.unc. edu/~fents/310/.

"Misinformation on the Internet: Applying Evaluation Skills to Online Information." Mary Ann Fitzgerald. *Emergency Librarian* 24, 3 (January–February 1997): 9–14.

"Relevancy and Searching the Internet." D. Scott Brandt. *Computers in Libraries* 16, 8 (September 1996): 35–38.

"Research on the Internet: Inside Risks." J. M. Snyder. *Communications on the ACM* 38, 8 (1995):130.

The Six Quests for the Electronic Grail: Current Approaches to Information Quality in WWW Resources. Matthew T. Ciolek. http://www.educom. edu/web/pubs/review/reviewArticles/32323.html.

Thinking Critically About World Wide Web Resources. Ester Grassian. http:// www.library.ucla.edu/libraries/college/instruct/critical.htm.

CD-ROM

In almost any current research, the latest developments in a field will be published in periodicals and professional journals. This information is available on CD-ROM, which essentially is an electronic index. CD-ROM provides a highly efficient and user-friendly way to access both current and retrospective information. There are 2000 CD-ROM products currently produced. The following CD-ROM databases cover both general and specific fields, and are generally available in university or large public libraries. In most instances, CD-ROM databases are also available in print form.

Sources:

The CD-ROM Directory Worldwide: The Complete Guide to CD-ROM & Multimedia Titles. London: TFPL Multimedia, 1986– (Annual).

CD-ROM in Print: An International Guide to CD-ROM, CD-1, 3DO, MMCD, CD32, Multimedia and Electronic Products. Amy R. Suchowski, ed. Toronto: Gale, 1998– (Annual).

Gale Directory of Databases. Detroit: Gale Research, 1998.

> v.2 CD-ROM, diskette, magnetic tape. handheld, and batch-access database products.

Information in Canada: A Directory of Electronic and Support Resources. Ottawa: Canadian Library Association, 1996- . Annual.

CD-ROM DATABASES

ABI/INFORM Global Full Text, 1971-.

> Contains 800 000+ full text articles from 1000+ periodicals dealing with business and management. Subjects covered include accounting, auditing, economics, computers, engineering management, finance, financial management, health care, law, management science, marketing, advertising, human resources management, labour relations, banking, insurance, public administration and government, real estate and telecommunications.

Applied Science & Technology Index, 1983-.

> Contains 270 000+ citations to journal articles, book reviews and new products in 400+ journals in the areas of aeronautics and space science, chemistry, computer science, construction industry, electric and electronics industry, energy resources and research, food sciences, geology, and chemical, civil, environmental, mining, nuclear and telecommunications engineering.

Biological Abstracts on Compact Disc, 1989-.

> Contains citations with abstracts to journal articles from 6000+ periodicals. Subjects covered include life sciences, bacteriology, behavioural biology, biochemistry, biophysics, botany, food and industrial microbiology, food technology, forestry and forest products, general biology, genetics, pharmacology, physiology, social biology, toxicology and virology.

Business Periodicals OnDisc, 1987-.

> Contains 800 000+ full text journal articles and book reviews in 400+ business periodicals. Subject coverage includes accounting, advertising and marketing, banking and finance, building and construction, chemical industry, communications, computers, economics, electronics, engineering, food industry, government regulations, industrial relations, insurance, international business, management and human resources administration, nuclear energy, occupational health and safety, oil and gas, public relations, publishing, real estate, regulation of industry and transportation.

CCINFODisc CD-ROM Series (Current).

> Contains 25 bibliographic and full text databases covering all aspects of environmental health, occupational health and safety, industrial hygiene and information chemicals, environmental hazards and toxic substances.

Canadian Business and Current Affairs (CBCA) KR Information OnDisc, 1993-.

> Provides full text access to information on Canadian national/local activities and news, politics, social issues, arts, sports, and leisure from 340+ periodicals.

Canadian Business and Current Affairs (CBCA) Full Text Business, 1996-.

> This database provides full text access to 130+ Canadian industry and professional periodicals and incorporates references from corporate continuous disclosure filings and financial documents.

Canadian Business and Current Affairs (CBCA), 1981-.

> Contains 1.65 million+ citations to articles from Canadian sources including 200 business periodicals, 300 popular periodicals and 10 newspapers. Subject coverage includes

product, company, and industry information, government activities, labour news, biographies, reviews, education, health, history, hobbies, music, nature, recreation, science, social issues and travel.

Canadian Constitutional Issues, 1985–1992.

Contains the full texts of articles, editorials, and letters on Canadian constitutional issues, including Confederation, Meech Lake, the Constitution, Charter of Rights, sovereignty association, distinct society, elected senate, and aboriginal rights.

The Canadian Encyclopedia Plus (Annual).

Contains the complete text of The Canadian Encyclopedia, a four volume publication providing 9500+ articles written by 2500 contributors.

Canadian News Disc 1992–.

Contains the full text of Canada's dailies in English and French.

Canadian Patent Index, 1978–1990.

Contains 200 000+ citations to Canadian patents.

Canadian Research Index, 1982–.

Contains references with abstracts to Canadian federal, provincial and municipal publications and references to publications of selected non-profit organizations.

Chemical Abstracts on CD-ROM, 1987–.

Contains citations with abstracts from 8000+ journals. Subject coverage includes chemistry and chemical engineering, applied chemistry, biochemistry, macromolecular chemistry, organic chemistry, and physical, inorganic and analytical chemistry.

Compact Disclosure Canada (Monthly).

Contains financial information on 8000+ Canadian companies. Subject coverage includes income, balance sheet figures and auditing information, names of CEOs and contacts.

Computer Select, 1989–.

Contains full text of journal articles from 120+ computer journals. Subject coverage includes computer hardware and software, data communications, company profiles and a glossary to computer and telecommunications terms.

CPIQ, 1988–.

Contains the complete text of 400+ periodicals published in Canada. Covers current events, news, business, technology, arts and humanities, recreation, and social and health sciences.

Ei Tech Index, 1987–.

Contains citations with abstracts to articles published in 425 international journals covering the fields of engineering and technology.

Energy Information Databases, 1967–.

Contains 87 000+ citations with abstracts to energy-related publications. Subject coverage includes solar energy, bioconversion/biomass, ocean energy, photovoltaics, photoconversion/chemical energy, wind energy, process heat, hybrid/total energy systems, and models and simulations.

Environmental Abstracts on CD-ROM, 1975–.

Contains 250 000+ citations with abstracts to periodical literature dealing with environmental and energy-related topics. Consists of three databases: Acid Rain Abstracts, Energy Information Abstracts, and Environmental Abstracts. Subject coverage includes environment and conservation of natural resources, acid rain, air pollution, urban ecology, land use, and energy resources.

ERIC/EBSCO CD-ROM, 1966–.

Contains 850 000+ citations with abstracts to the journal and report literature in the field of education and related areas. Subject coverage includes all aspects of educational research, including career, adult, vocational, technical and teacher education, special education, reading and communication skills, languages, linguistics, educational management, counselling, library and information science, information resources, urban and rural education, science, mathematics, environment, social studies and social sciences, tests, measurement and evaluation.

Facts on File News Digest on CD-ROM, 1980–.

Contains full text of Facts on File World News Digest providing news summaries of current events worldwide.

General Science Abstracts Full Text, 1984–.

Contains the full text of articles from 40+ periodicals and cover to cover abstracting of all leading journals. Subjects covered include astronomy, atmospheric science, biology, botany, chemistry, conservation, earth science, environment, food, genetics, health, mathematics, medicine, microbiology, nutrition, oceanography, physics, physiology, and zoology.

Geobase, 1980–.

Contains 500 000+ citations with abstracts to 2 000+ journals in the subject areas of physical and human geography, earth sciences, ecology, environmental issues, international development studies and urban planning.

Government Publications Index on InfoTrac, 1976–.

Contains 282 000+ bibliographic descriptions of publications issued by U.S. government agencies, including the U.S. Congress.

MathSci Disc, 1940–.

Contains 1.7 million+ citations with abstracts to subjects in the field of mathematics, statistics and computer science and applications to such fields as physics, engineering, biology and operations research.

METADEX Materials Collection on CD-ROM, 1985–.

Contains 1 million citations with abstracts to published literature relating to materials science and metallurgy. Subject coverage includes polymers, ceramics and composites, structural engineering, technocommercial developments in iron and steel, nonferrous metals and engineering materials.

Moody's Bank & Finance Disc

Moody's Company Data

Moody's Industrial Disc

Moody's International Company Data

Moody's OTC Industrial Disc

Moody's OTC Unlisted Disc

Moody's Public Utility Disc

Moody's Transportation Disc.

Contains current business and financial information on U.S. public companies including financial institutions, industrial corporations, transportation companies and utilities, and 7500+ countries outside the U.S. Subject coverage includes detailed financial statements, capital structure, long-term debt, company history, and business descriptions.

NTIS (National Technical Information Service) on SilverPlatter, 1983-.

Contains bibliographic descriptions of 500 000+ unrestricted technical reports from U.S. and non-U.S. government-sponsored research, development and engineering analyses.

OCLC Computer Library, (Annual).

Contains bibliographic information for 270 000+ materials on computers and computer-related subjects.

PAIS/EBSCO CD-ROM, 1972-.

Contains 400 000+ citations with abstracts to literature on business with emphasis on contemporary social, economic and political issues and public policy. Subject coverage includes economics, business, public administration, sociology and political science.

Predicasts F&S Index Plus Text, 1990.

Contains citations with abstracts and selected full-text articles to international literature on companies, products and industries from 2400+ publications. Subject coverage includes acquisitions and mergers, new products, technology, socio-political and economic factors affecting industries, and financial analyses.

Psychlit/EBSCO CD-ROM, 1974-.

Contains 800 000+ citations with abstracts to journals in psychology and the behavioural sciences and 66 000+ citations to books and relevant book chapters. Subject coverage includes experimental psychology, developmental psychology, communications, social processes, personality, physical and psychological disorders, professional issues, applied psychology, educational psychology, and behavioural literature in such related fields as law, business and medicine.

Reader's Guide Abstracts, 1983-.

Contains citations with abstracts to articles in 240+ popular general interest periodicals published in Canada and the U.S. Subject coverage includes news and current events, business, the arts, sports, fashion, computers, health, politics, hobbies, crafts, food and cooking, education, photography, science, history, home improvement, religion and foreign affairs.

Social Sciences Citation Index Compact Edition with Abstracts, 1986-.

Contains citations with abstracts to significant articles from 1700+ most important social sciences journals and social sciences articles from 3200 journals in the natural, physical and biomedical sciences. Subject coverage includes anthropology, archaeology, ethnic studies, business and finance, communications, computer applications and cybernetics, criminology, demography, economics, educational research, geography, hygiene and public health, information and library science, psychology and psychiatry, sociology and urban planning.

Science Citation Index Compact Edition with Abstracts, 1980-.

Contains citations with abstracts to articles from 3200+ journals from a wide range of scientific and technological disciplines. Subject coverage includes natural, physical, earth, environmental, biomedical and life sciences, chemistry, agriculture, clinical medicine, engineering, technology and applied sciences, and computer and information science.

Computerized Information Retrieval (Online Databases)

Since the 1970s, bibliographic files have been made available for online interactive searching and information retrieval. Normal access is from a local computer terminal to a firm or agency offering access to a database or a system of databases. Charges are calculated on the number of minutes a file is in use and the number of citations received. Citations are usually printed offline and delivered by mail. Many services offer complete text document delivery for an additional charge.

A number of individual database services are now accessible in libraries in compact disc, read-only-memory (CD-ROM) versions. With CD-ROM, there is no charge for line access or printing costs.

Online Databases

Sources:

Fulltext Sources Online: For Periodicals, Newspapers, Newsletters, Newswires & TV/Radio Transcripts. Ruth M. Orenstein, ed. Needham Heights, MA: Bibliodata, 1998 http://www.bibliodata.com.

Covers topics in Science, Technology, Medicine, Law, Finance, Business, Industry, and the popular press.

Gale Directory of Databases. Detroit: Gale Research, 1998.

v.1 Online databases.

GENERAL

EbscoHost.

EbscoHost Academic Search Full Text Elite is a multidisciplinary database that provides the full text of 1000+ journals and abstracts and indexing to 3100+ journals. Subjects covered include business, education, science, and technology.

LEXIS/NEXIS, (Coverage varies by database library).

LEXIS/NEXIS provides mainly full-text information from newspapers, periodicals, wireservices, newsletters, journals, company and industry analyst reports, broadcast transcripts and abstracts from 160+ libraries (or databases). Subject coverage includes current events, business, marketing, financial reports, science and technology, computers, law, medicine and health, and biographies.

ProQuest.

ProQuest provides full text or abstracts and indexing to 4000+ journals. Subject areas include business, computing, information systems, and telecommunications.

SUBJECT-ORIENTED DATABASES

Business & Industry

ABI/Inform

Accounting & Tax Database

Aerospace Database

Annual Reports Abstracts

API Energy Business News Index

Banking Information Source

BCC Market Research

BioCommerce Abstracts and Directory

Business Dateline

Canadian Corporate Names

Canadian Financial Database

Canadian Model History and Forecast Databases

Chemsearch

Chemstats

Commerce Business Daily

D&B (Current)

DunsPrint Canada

Dynamic Information System: Corporate

EconBase

Economic Literature Index

F & S Index

Financial Post Corporation Data

FINDEX

Globalbase

Harvard Business Review

Industry Trends and Analysis

Investext

Kompass (Current)

Management Contents

Marketing and Advertising Reference Service

McGraw-Hill Publications Online

Moody's Corporate Profiles (Current)

PME

Predicasts Forecasts

PROMPT

Report on Business Corporate Database

Small Business Profiles

Standard & Poor's Register (Current)

Thomas Register Online (Current)

Trade & Industry Database

Trademarkscan (various)
WorldScope

Science and Technology
Aerospace Database
AGRICOLA
Architectural Database
Chemical Engineering and Biotechnology Abstracts
CHEMSEARCH
Computer Database
CISTI Online Catalogue
Datapro (Current)
Energyline
Engineered Materials Abstracts
Enviroline
Environmental Bibliography
GeoRef
Information Science Abstracts
Microcomputer Abstracts
Microcomputer Software Guide (Current)
Nuclear Science Abstracts
Paper Chemistry
Publications of the National Research Council Canada
SoftBase: Reviews, Companies and Products (Current)
Standards & Specifications,
Waternet

Atlases and Statistical Guides

Basic data of interest to the technical researcher on many subjects are found in reliable and frequently updated standard guides. The quality atlas generally contains much more than maps of geographical locations. Statistical guides are of great reference importance to original research in economic, industrial, and social questions.

The Canada Year Book. Statistics Canada. Ottawa: Statistics Canada. Annual.

Canadian Environmental Directory. 1991– . Ann Marie Aldighieri. Toronto: Canadian Almanac & Directory Publishing. Annual.

The Canadian Global Almanac. 1987– . Toronto: Global Press. Annual.

Commercial Atlas and Marketing Guide. Chicago: Rand McNally. Annual.
> In addition to maps, contains much statistical data on trade, manufacturing, business, population, and transportation.

Corpus Almanac & Canadian Sourcebook. Don Mills, ON: Southam. Annual.

Europa World Yearbook. London: Europa Publications. Annual.

Macmillan World Reference Atlas. Toronto: Macmillan Canada, 1994.

Mindscape World Atlas and Almanac [CD-ROM]. Novato, CA: Mindscape, 1995.

The National Atlas of Canada. 5th ed. Canada. Energy, Mines and Resources Canada. Ottawa: Energy, Mines and Resources Canada, 1985.

The National Atlas of the United States of America. Washington, DC: U.S. Department of the Interior Geological Survey, 1970.

Outstanding collection of 765 maps, many in colour. Covers general reference and special subjects including landforms, geophysical forces, geology, marine features, soils, climate, water, history, and economic, sociocultural, and administrative data. Maps, data tables, and diagrams.

Statistical Abstract of the United States. 1878-. Washington, DC: Bureau of the Census. Annual.

Official government standard summary of statistics on the social, political, and economic organization of the United States. Excellent source citations, index.

Statistical Atlas of the United States [CD-ROM]. Washington, DC: U.S. Dept. of Commerce, Economics and Statistics Administration, Bureau of Census, Data User Services Division, 1993.

A statistical reference guide to 250+ government and private organization publications and sources on the social, political, and economic organization of the United States.

Statistical Yearbook. Paris: UNESCO. Annual.

Statistics Canada http://www.statcan.ca.

Catalogue: Information Products and Services (IPS).
This catalogue lists all current socio-demographic and economic statistical information and services available from Statistics Canada.

1996 Census Data http://www.statcan.ca/english/census96/list.htm.

Population and Dwelling Counts; The Nations Series; Area Profiles and Basic Summary Tabulations.

Statistics Canada Catalogue. Statistics Canada. Library Services Division. Ottawa: Ministry of Industry, Science, and Technology. Annual.

Contains social, demographic and economic statistical information including print and electronic information sources and services published by Statistics Canada.

The World Almanac and Book of Facts. 1868-. New York: Newspaper Enterprise Association. Annual.

The most comprehensive and generally useful almanac of miscellaneous information. Excellent statistical and news summary coverage.

World Guide [CD-ROM]. Uppsala, Sweden: Interactive Media Group, 1995-.

Canadian Government Information

Canada. Supply and Services Canada. *Guide to Federal Programs and Services.* Ottawa: Supply and Services Canada, 1990- Annual.

Canadian Government Publishing Centre. Government of Canada Publications: Quarterly Catalogue. Hull, PQ: Supply and Services Canada, 1953-.

Canadian Research Index/Microlog. [CD-ROM]. Toronto: Microlog. Quarterly.

Government of Canada Search/FAQ http://www.canada.gc.ca/search/srind. Provides direct links to all existing Federal Government organizations' search engines.

Infosource: Directory of Federal Government Databases. Ottawa: Treasury Board Secretariat. Annual.

Infosource: Sources of Federal Government Information. Ottawa: Government of Canada. Annual.

Land, Brian. "Description and Guide to the Use of Canadian Government Publications." In Politics: *Canada: Problems in Canadian Government.* 7th ed. Toronto: McGraw-Hill Ryerson, 1991.

Scott's Government Index. Don Mills, ON: The Sources, 1995-.

Statistics Canada http://www.statcan.ca (Requires 20/20 Browser [free of charge]).

  Catalogue: Information Products and Services http://www.statcan.ca.
  Current listing of socio-demographic and economic statistical information and services available from Statistics Canada.

  1996 Census Data http://www.statcan.ca/english/census96/lists.htm.
  Provides free of charge: Population and Dwelling Counts; The Nations Series; Area Profiles; Basic Summary Tabulations.

  Strategis http://www.strategis.ic.gc.ca/engdoc/maintxt.html.
  Company information, international business opportunities, trade investments, business information by sector, micro-economic research and statistical analysis, technology, innovation and licensing, business support and services, marketplace services, laws and legislation, human resources, and training and consumer information.

A SELECTED BIBLIOGRAPHY

APPENDIX B

Technical Writing

Allen, Jo. *Writing in the Workplace*. Boston: Allyn & Bacon, 1997.

Anderson, Paul V. *Technical Communication: A Reader-Centered Approach*. 4th ed. Ft. Worth, TX: Harcourt Brace College Publishers, 1998.

Andrews, Deborah C. *Technical Communication in the Global Community*. Upper Saddle River, NJ: Prentice-Hall, 1998.

Blicq, Ron S. and Moretto, Lisa. *Technically Write!* Canadian 5th ed. Scarborough, ON: Prentice-Hall Canada, 1998.

Blum, Deborah, and Knudson, Mary, eds. *A Field Guide to Science Writers: The Official Guide of the National Association of Science Writers*. New York: Oxford University Press, 1997.

Burnett, Rebecca E. *Technical Communications*. 3rd ed. Belmont, CA: Wadsworth, 1994.

Day, Robert A. *How to Write and Publish a Scientific Paper*. 5th ed. Phoenix: Oryx, 1998.

Gershon, Sharon J. *Technical Writing: Process and Product*. 2nd ed. Upper Saddle River, NJ: Prentice-Hall, 1997.

Horton, William Kendall. *Designing and Writing Online Documentation: Helpfiles to Hypertext*. New York: Wiley, 1998.

Killingsworth, M. Jimmie. *Information Action: A Guide to Technical Communication*. Boston: Allyn and Bacon, 1996.

Markel, Michael H. *Technical Communication Essentials*. 1st Canadian ed. Scarborough, ON: Nelson Canada, 1996.

Michaelson, Herbert B. *How to Write and Publish Engineering Papers and Reports*. 3rd ed. Philadelphia: ISI, 1990.

Microsoft Manual of Style for Technical Publications. 2nd ed. Richmond, WA: Microsoft Press, 1998.

Pearsall, Thomas E. *The Elements of Technical Writing*. Boston: Allyn and Bacon, 1997.

Reep, Diana C. *Technical Writing: Principles, Strategies and Readings*. Boston: Allyn & Bacon, 1998.

Roze, Maris. *Technical Communication: The Practical Craft*. 3rd ed. Upper Saddle River, NJ: Prentice-Hall, 1997.

Woolever, Kristin R. *Writing for the Technical Professions*. New York: Longmans, 1998.

Business Communication

Berko, Roy M., et al. *Business Communication in a Changing World.* New York: St. Martin's Press, 1997.

Blundel, Richard. *Effective Business Communication: Principles and Practice for the Information Age.* New York: Prentice-Hall, 1998.

Boone, Louis E., et al. *Contemporary Business Communication.* Canadian ed. Scarborough, ON: Prentice-Hall Canada, 1999.

Ewald, Helen Rothschild, and Rebecca E. Burnett. *Business Communication.* Upper Saddle River, NJ: Prentice-Hall, 1997.

Guffey, Mary Ellen. *Business Communication: Process and Product.* 1st Canadian ed. Toronto: Nelson Canada, 1998.

Hall, Georganna, and Gemmy Allen. *The Internet Guide for Business Communication.* Cincinnati: OHL Southwestern College Pub., 1997.

Leshin, Cynthia B. *Internet Investigations in Business Communications.* Upper Saddle River, NJ: Prentice-Hall, 1998.

Locker, Kitty O. *Business and Administrative Communication.* 4th ed. New York: Irwin/McGraw-Hill, 1998.

Murphy, Herta A. *Effective Business Communication.* 7th ed. New York: McGraw Hill, 1997.

O'Hair, Dan, and Gustav W. Friedrich. *Communication in Business and the Professions.* 3rd ed. Boston: Houghton-Mifflin, 1998.

Roebuck, Deborah Britt. *Improving Business Communication Skills.* 2nd ed. Upper Saddle River, NJ: Prentice-Hall, 1998.

Satterwhite, Marilyn L. *Business Communication at Work.* New York: Glencoe/McGraw-Hill, 1998.

Thill, John V. *Excellence in Business Communication.* 4th ed. Upper Saddle River, NJ: Prentice-Hall, 1998.

Treece, Malra, and Betty A. Kleen. *Successful Communication for Business and Management.* Upper Saddle River, NJ: Prentice-Hall, 1998.

Writing in General

Angel, David, and Brent D. Heslop. *The Elements of E-Mail Style: Communicating Effectively via Electronic Mail.* Reading, MA: Addison-Wesley, 1994.

Day, Henry Noble. *The Art of Discourse: A System of Rhetoric.* New York: Scholar's Facsimiles & Reprints, 1998.

Elbow, Peter. *Writing with Power.* 2nd ed. New York: Oxford University Press, 1998.

Kinneavy, James L. *A Theory of Discourse.* New York: Norton, 1980.

Meiser, Mary Jordan. *Good Writing!* 2nd ed. Boston: Allyn & Bacon, 1998.

Stull, Andrew T. *English on the Internet: A Student's Guide.* Upper Saddle River, NJ: Prentice-Hall, 1998.

Van Buren, Robert, and Mary Fran Buehler. *The Levels of Edit.* 2nd ed. Pasadena, CA: JPL, California Institute of Technology, 1980.

Williams, Joseph M. *Style: Toward Clarity and Grace.* Chicago: University of Chicago Press, 1990.

The Internet

Horton, William K. *The Web Page Design Cookbook: All the Ingredients You Need to Create 5-Star Web Pages.* New York: Wiley, 1996.

Manger, Jason. *The Essential Internet Information Guide.* New York: McGraw-Hill, 1995.

Negroponte, Nicholas. *Being Digital.* New York: Random House, 1995.

Shea, Virginia. *Netiquette.* San Francisco: Albion, 1994.

Swartz, Mark. *Get Wired, You're Hired: The Canadian Guide to Job Hunting Online.* Scarborough, Ontario: Prentice Hall Canada, 1997.

International Communication

Chen, Guo-Ming. *Foundations of Intercultural Communication.* Boston: Allyn & Bacon, 1998.

Dodd, Carley H. *Dynamics of Intercultural Communication.* 5th ed. Boston: McGraw-Hill, 1998.

Galloway-Thomas, Carolyn. *Intercultural Communication: Roots and Routes.* Boston: Allyn & Bacon, 1998.

Gudykunst, William B. *Bridging Differences: Effective Intergroup Communication.* 3rd ed. Thousand Oaks, CA: Sage Publications, 1998.

Leigh, James W. *Communicating for Cultural Competence.* Boston: Allyn & Bacon, 1998.

Lustig, Myron M. *Intercultural Competence: Interpersonal Communication Across Cultures.* 3rd ed. New York: Longman, 1998.

Mead, Richard. *International Management: Cross-Cultural Dimensions.* 2nd ed. Malden, MA: Blackwell Business, 1998.

Usage

Fee, Margery, and Janice McAlpine. *Guide to Canadian English Usage.* Toronto: Oxford University Press, 1997.

Fowler, Henry Watson. *The New Fowler's Modern English Usage.* 3rd ed. Toronto: Clarendon Press, 1996.

Style Manuals

American Psychological Association. *Publication Manual of the American Psychological Association.* 4th ed. Washington, DC: American Psychological Association, 1994.

The Canadian Style: A Guide to Writing and Editing. Rev. and expanded ed. Toronto, ON: Dundurn Press, 1997.

CBE Style Manual Committee. *Council of Biology Editors Style Manual.* 5th ed. Arlington, VA: Council of Biology Editors, 1983.

Chicago Manual of Style. 14th ed. Chicago: University of Chicago Press, 1993.

Columbia Online Style: MLA Style Citations of Electronic Sources http://www.cos.usf.edu/english/walker/mla.html.

Gibaldi, Joseph. *MLA Handbook for Writers of Research Papers.* 4th ed. New York: Modern Language Association of America, 1995.

Li, Xia, and Nancy B. Crane. *Electronic Styles: A Handbook for Citing Electronic Information.* 2nd ed. Medford, NJ: Information Today, 1996.

Turabian, Kate. A *Manual for Writers of Term Papers, Theses and Dissertations.* 6th ed. Chicago: University of Chicago Press, 1996.

Web Extension to American Psychological Association Style (WEAPAS) http://www.beadsland.com/weapas.

Speech

Becker, Dennis, and Paula Norkum Becker. *Speaking Skills for Business Careers.* Homewood, IL: Irwin Mirror Press, 1993.

Beebe, Steven A., and Susan Beebe. *Public Speaking: An Audience-Centered Approach.* 3rd ed. Boston: Allyn & Bacon, 1997.

DeVito, Joseph A. *The Elements of Public Speaking.* 6th ed. New York: Longman, 1997.

Lucas, Stephen. *The Art of Public Speaking.* 6th ed. Boston: McGraw-Hill, 1998.

Logic

Boolos, George. *Logic, Logic, Logic.* Upper Saddle River, NJ: Prentice-Hall, 1998.

Copi, Irving M., and Carl Cohen. *Introduction to Logic.* 10th ed. Upper Saddle River, NJ: Prentice-Hall, 1998.

DeBono, Edward. *The Use of Lateral Thinking.* London: Jonathan Cape, 1967.

LeBlanc, Jill E. *Thinking Clearly: A Guide to Critical Reasoning.* New York: W. W. Norton, 1998.

Graphics

Duff, Jon M., and James L. Mohler. *Graphics and Web Page Design*. Indianapolis, IN: Sams.net, 1996.

Govil-Pai, Shalini. *Learning Computer Graphics*. New York: Springer, 1998.

Lewis, Clarence, and Harold Langford. *Symbolic Logic*. 2nd ed. New York: Dover, 1959.

Pitts, Natanya, et al. *HTML Style Sheets Design Guide*. Scottsdale, AZ: Coriolis Group Books, 1998.

Sakawa, Hayashi, and Kazuhiro Hayase. *Internet.home.page.design*. 1st U.S. ed. Carson, CA: Books Nippon USA, 1997.

Weinman, Lynda. *Creative HTML Design*. Indianapolis: New Rivers Pub., 1998.

Library Research

Barzun, Jacques, and Henry F. Graff. *The Modern Researcher*. 5th ed. Boston: Houghton Mifflin, 1992.

Hurt, Charles Deuel. *Information Sources in Science and Technology*. 3rd ed. Englewood, CO: Libraries Unlimited, 1998.

Mann, Thomas. *The Oxford Guide to Library Research*. New York: Oxford University Press, 1998.

CHAPTER NOTES

Chapter 1: An Overview of Technical Writing

[1] Paul V. Anderson, "What Survey Research Tells Us about Writing at Work," *Writing in Nonacademic Settings*, eds. Lee Odell and Dixie Goswami (New York: Guilford, 1985) 30.

[2] Anderson 40.

[3] Anderson 54.

[4] Philip W. Swain, "Giving Power to Words," *American Journal of Physics* 13 (1945) 320.

Chapter 2: Composing

[1] Fred L. Luconi, "Artificial Intelligence," *Vital Speeches of the Day 52* (1986) 605.

[2] Terry Winograd of Stanford University, as quoted in Bob Ryan, "A1 in Identity Crisis," *Byte* (June 1991) 241-42.

[3] Stephen S. Hall, "Aplysia and Hermissenda," *Science 85* (1985) 33.

[4] Lester Faigley and Thomas P. Miller, "What We Learn From Writing on the Job," *College English* 44 (1982) 562-63.

[5] Lee Odell, Dixie Goswami, Anne-Herrington, and Doris Quick, "Studying Writing in Non-Academic Settings," *New Essays in Technical and Scientific Communication: Research, Theory, Practice,* eds. Paul V. Anderson, R. John Brockmann, and Carolyn R. Miller (Farmingdale, NY: Baywood, 1983) 27-28.

[6] For the concept we are indebted to Victoria M. Winkler, "The Role of Models in Technical and Scientific Writing," *New Essays in Technical and Scientific Communication: Research, Theory, Practice,* cds. Paul V. Anderson, R. John Brockmann, and Carolyn R. Miller (Farmington, NY: Baywood, 1983) 111-22.

[7] Blaine McKee, "Do Professional Writers Use an Outline When They Write?" *Technical Communication* (1st Quarter 1972) 10-13.

[8] Ontario Hydro, *Report Writing Guide* (prepared by the Management Training Section, Staff Resources and Development Division, 1984) 16.

[9] Lillian Bridwell and Ann Duin, "Looking In-Depth at Writers: Computers as Writing Medium and Research Tool." *Writing On-Line: Using Computers in the Teaching of Writing,* ed. J. L. Collins and E. A. Sommers (Montclair, NJ: Boyton/Cook, 1985) 119.

[10] Eric Brown," Word Processing and the Three Bears," *PC World* (Dec. 1985) 197.

[11] In writing this section on ethical considerations, we have drawn upon the following books and articles: John Bryan, "Down the Slippery Slope: Ethics and the Technical Writer as Marketer," *Technical Communication Quarterly* (Winter 1992) 73-88; William K. Franken, *Ethics* (Englewood Cliffs, NJ: Prentice-Hall, 1963); Dean G. Hall and Bonnie A. Nelson, "Integrating Professional Ethics into the Technical Writing Course," *Journal of Technical Writing and Communication* 17 (1987) 45-61; Mike Markel, "A Basic Unit on Ethics for Technical Communicators," *Journal of Technical Writing and Communication* 21 (1991) 327-50; H. Lee Shimberg, "Ethics and Rhetoric in Technical Writing," *Technical Communication* (4th Quarter 1978) 16-18; and Arthur E. Walzer, "The Ethics of False Implicature in Technical and Professional Writing," *Journal of Technical Writing and Communication* 19 (1989) 149-60.

[12] George F. R. Ellis, as quoted in W. Wayt Gibbs, "Profile: George F. R. Ellis: Thinking Globally, Acting Universally," *Scientific American* (October 1995): 55.

[13] Society for Technical Communication, "Code for Communicators," *Technical Communication and Ethics*, eds. R. John Brockmann and Fern Rook (Washington, DC: STC, 1989) 93.

[14] International Association of Business Communicators, "Code of Ethics," *Technical Communication and Ethics*, eds. R. John Brockmann and Fern Rook (Washington, DC: STC, 1989) 95–96.

[15] *Honor in Science* (New Haven, CT: Sigma Xi, 1988).

[16] In writing this section on ethical graphics, we have drawn upon Edward R. Tufte, *The Visual Display of Quantitative Information* (Cheshire, CT: Graphics Press, 1983) 53–87.

[17] *Radon Control in New Homes* (Ottawa: CMHC, 1988).

Chapter 3: Writing Collaboratively

[1] In this chapter we are indebted to the following: Rebecca E. Burnett, "Substantive Conflict in a Cooperative Context: A Way to Improve the Collaborative Planning of Workplace Documents," *Technical Communication* 38 (1991) 532-39; Mary Beth Debs, "Collaborative Writing in Industry," *Technical Writing: Theory and Practice*, eds. Bertie E. Fearing and W. Keats Sparrow (New York: Modern Language Association, 1989) 33-42; and *Collaborative Writing in Industry: Investigations in Theory and Practice*, eds. Mary M. Lay and William M. Karis (Amityville, NY: Baywood, 1991). In the latter anthology we are particularly indebted to David K. Farkas, "Collaborative Writing, Software Development, and the Universe of Collaborative Activity," 13-30; James R. Weber, "The Construction of Multi-Authored Texts in One Laboratory Setting," 49-64; Barbara Couture and Jone Rymer, "Discourse Interaction between Writer and Supervisor: A Primary Collaboration in Workplace Writing," 87-108; Ann Hill Duin, Linda A. Jorn, and Mark S. DeBower, "Collaborative Writing: Courseware and Telecommunications," 146-69; and William Van Pelt and Alice Gillam, "Peer Collaboration and the Computer-Assisted Classroom: Bridging the Gap between Academia and the Workplace," 170-206.

[2] For more on revising collaboratively, see Edgar R. Thompson, "Ensuring the Success of Peer Revision Groups," *Focus on Collaborative Learning*, ed. Jeff Golub (Urbana, IL: NCTE, 1988) 109-16.

Chapter 4: Writing for Your Readers

[1] Human Resources Development Canada, Education Support Branch, *Profile of Post-Secondary Education in Canada, 1993 Edition*. Also, Jillian Oderkirk, "Educational Achievement: An International Comparison," Canadian Social Trends (Statistics Canada, Autumn 1993) 9.

[2] Kevin Churchill, Barb Shipley, & Lynn McLaughlin, *Clear Writing: What Is It? How Do You Do It?* (Ontario Ministry of Agriculture, Food, & Rural Affairs, rpt. February 1995) 1.

[3] Mary B. Coney, "The Use of the Reader in Technical Writing," *Journal of Technical Writing and Communication* 8 (1978) 104.

[4] Coney 104.

[5] Michael OReilly, "The World's Biggest Thermometer," *SkyNews: The Canadian Magazine of Astronomy and Stargazing* 1.2 (July/August 1995) 26. Michael OReilly is a freelance journalist specializing in science, medicine, and technology.

[6] Michael Ryan and James Tankard, Jr., "Problem Areas in Science News Writing," *Journal of Technical Writing and Communication* 4 (1974) 230.

[7] J.J. Degan, "Microwave Resonance Isolators," *Bell Laboratories Record* (April, 1966) 123.

[8] For material in this section we are indebted to Janice C. Redish, "Understanding Readers," *Techniques for Technical Communicators*, eds. Carol M. Barnum and Saul Carliner (New York: Macmillan, 1993) 14-41.

[9] U.S. Geological Survey, *Our Changing Continent* (Washington, DC: GPO, 1991) 6-7.

[10] Thomas N. Huckin, "A Cognitive Approach to Readability," *New Essays in Technical and Scientific Communication*, eds. Paul V. Anderson, R. John Brockmann, and Carolyn R. Miller (Farmingdale, NY: Baywood, 1983) 99.

[11] Mark Nichols, "Feeling the Heat," *Maclean's* (April 24, 1995) 52.

[12] James W. Souther, "Identifying the Informational Needs of Readers: A Management Responsibility," *IEEE Transactions on Professional Communication* PC-28 (1985) 10.

[13] Souther 10.

[14] Souther 10.

[15] Souther 10.

[16] Thomas E. Pinelli, Virginia M. Cordle, and Raymond F. Vondran, "The Function of Report Components in the Screening and Reading of Technical Reports," *Journal of Technical Writing and Communication* 14 (1984) 89.

[17] Ontario Hydro, *Understanding Ionizing Radiation*, "Let's Give Tomorrow a Hand" Series (1992) 5.

[18] Kim Guttormson & Bud Robertson, "Operation Overbite," *The Globe and Mail* (June 24, 1995) D8.

[19] Allen Hammond, "Limits of the Medium," *SIPIscope* 11.2 (1983) 6-7.

[20] See Ann Hill Duin, "How People Read: Implications for Writers," and Wayne Slater, "Current Theory and Research on What Constitutes Readable Expository Text," *The Technical Writing Teacher* 15 (1988) 185-93, 195-206.

[21] Ryan and Tankard 233.

[22] David F. Cope, "Nuclear Power: A Basic Briefing," *Mechanical Engineering* 89 (1967) 50.

[23] Junko Torii et al., "Effect of Time of Day on Adaptive Response to a 4-Week Aerobic Exercise Program," *The Journal of Sports Medicine and Physical Fitness* (December, 1992) 350-51.

[24] Lester Faigley, "Nonacademic Writing: The Social Perspective," *Writing in Nonacademic Settings*, eds. Lee Odell and Dixie Goswami (New York: Guilford, 1985) 238.

[25] The material about cultural differences in this section is based on William B. Gudykunst, *Bridging Differences: Effective Intergroup Communication* (Newbury Park, CA: Sage, 1991); Lisa Hoecklin, *Managing Cultural Differences: Strategies for Competitive Advantage* (Reading, MA: 1995); Lisa Hoecklin and Geert Hofstede, *Cultures and Organizations: Software of the Mind* (London: McGraw-Hill, 1991); Richard Mead, *Cross-Cultural Management Communication* (Chichester, England: John Wiley & Sons, 1991); Franz Trompenaars, *Riding the Waves of Culture* (London: The Economist Books, 1993).

Chapter 5: Achieving a Readable Style

[1] *The Climates of Canada* (Ottawa: Minister of Supply and Services Canada, 1990) 110.

[2] Wallace Immen, "A Swell System of Tiny Hearts," *The Globe and Mail* (June 28, 1995) A 11.

[3] Janice C. Redish and Jack Selzer, "The Place of Readability Formulas in Technical Communication," *Technical Communication* (4th Quarter 1985) 49.

[4] Francis Christensen, "Notes Toward a New Rhetoric," *College English* (October 1963) 7-18.

[5] Daniel B. Felker et al., *Guidelines for Document Designers* (Washington, DC: American Institutes for Research, 1981) 47-48.

[6] As quoted in Felker et al. 64.

[7] As revised in Felker et al. 65.

[8] As quoted in Janice C. Redish, *The Language of Bureaucracy* (Washington, DC: American Institutes for Research, 1981) 1.

[9] CBE Style Manual Committee, *CBE Style Manual*, 5th ed. (Bethesda, MD: Council of Biology Editors, Inc., 1983) 38.

[10] *CBE Style Manual* 38.

[11] For a perceptive essay on elegant variation, see H.W. Fowler, *A Dictionary of Modern English Usage*, 2nd rev. ed. (New York: Oxford UP, 1950) 130-33.

[12] Examples of owners' policy, Ontario Automobile Policy forms OPF.1 (approved by the Insurance Commissioner for use on or after January 1, 1994) and OAP1 (after March 31, 1995).

[13] *CBE Style Manual* 36-37.

[14] "Planners Outlaw Jargon," *Plain English* (April, 1981) 1.

[15] Keith Stelling, "Our Native Herbs," *Alive* 150, 48-50. Keith Stelling is editor of the *Canadian Journal of Herbalism*.

Chapter 6: Arrangement Strategies

[1] Alan Nixon, *Canada's Nuclear Fuel Industry: An Overview* (Library of Parliament Research Branch, Science and Technology Division, November 1993) 3-4. Reproduced with the permission of the Minister of Supply and Services Canada, 1995.

[2] Wallace Immen, "Global Warming — Weather Thou Goest?" *The Globe and Mail* (June 3, 1995) D8.

[3] Margaret Visser, "It's Snowing What to Say," *Saturday Night* (February 1994) 30.

[4] David Suzuki, "Racing to Reach the Genome," *Inventing the Future* (Toronto: Stoddart, 1989) 47. Reprinted with the permission of Stoddart Publishing Co. Limited, Don Mills, Ont.

[5] "Ministry of Northern Development and Mines, Ontario 1994." *ROCK ONtario* (Ontario Ministry of Northern Development and Mines, ROCK ON Series 1) 23-24. © Queen's Printer for Ontario, 1994.

[6] Ontario Ministry of Agriculture and Food, *Production Recommendations for Nursery and Landscape Plants* (© Queen's Printer for Ontario, 1994) 124. Reproduced with permission.

[7] Environment Canada, *Tornadoes* (1988) 1.

[8] "Ministry of Northern Development and Mines, Ontario 1994." *ROCK ONtario* (Ontario Ministry of Northern Development and Mines, ROCK ON Series 1) 61. © Queen's Printer for Ontario, 1994.

[9] AECL, FusionCanada, *Fusion: Energy for the Future.* (MacPhee Technical Corporation, 1991) 7.

[10] Roberta Bondar, *Touching the Earth* (Toronto: Key Porter Books, 1994) 37-38. Used with permission.

[11] Canadian Space Agency, *Canadarm: A Canadian Symbol* (1992) 2-3.

[12] Harish M. Verma, *Geology and Fossils of the Craigleith Area* (Ontario Ministry of Natural Resources, 1979) 8-10.

[13] Debra J. Reid and Suzanne M. Hendricks, "Consumer Understanding and Use of Fat and Cholesterol Information on Food Labels," *Canadian Journal of Public Health* 85.5 (September/October 1994) 334-35.

[14] U.S. National Aeronautics and Space Administration, *Viking: The Exploration of Mars* (Washington, DC: GPO, 1984) 6.

[15] Joel Gurin, "In the Beginning," *Science* 80 (July/August, 1980) 50.

[16] For a more detailed explanation of Toulmin logic, see Steven Toulmin, Richard Rieke, and Allan Janik, *An Introduction to Reasoning*, 2nd ed. (New York: Macmillan, 1984).

[17] Based on Maren Oelbermann and Michael Milburn, "The Mysteries of the Animal Mind," *Nature Canada* (Summer 1995) 35-40.

Chapter 8: Document Design

[1] For a rationale for teaching design, see Stephen A. Bernhardt, "Seeing the Text," *College Composition and Communication* 37 (1986) 66–78. For a research-based summary of document design principles for paper documents, see Philippa J. Benson, "Writing Visually: Design Considerations in Technical Publications," *Technical Communication* 32, 4 (1985) 35–39.

[2] Janice C. Redish, "Understanding Readers," *Techniques for Technical Communicators*, eds. Carol Barnum and Saul Carliner (New York: Macmillan, 1993) 14–41.

[3] William Horton lists many types of online documentation in his book, *Designing and Writing Online Documentation*, 2nd ed. (New York: Wiley, 1994).

[4] R. Kruk and P. Muter, "Reading of Continuous Text on Video Screens," *Human Factors* 26.3 (1984) 339–45; John Gould, "Why Is Reading Slower from CRT Screens Than from Paper?" *Proceedings of the Human Factors Society, 30th Annual Meeting* (Dayton, OH, Human Factors Society, 1986) 834–35.

[5] Thomas N. Huckin, "A Cognitive Approach to Readability," *New Essays in Technical and Scientific Communication: Research, Theory, and Practice*, eds. Paul V. Anderson, R. John Brockmann, and Carolyn R. Miller (Farmingdale, NY: Baywood, 1983) 90–101; Janice C. Redish, Robin M. Battison, and Edward S. Gold, "Making Information Accessible to Readers," *Writing in Nonacademic Settings*, eds. Lee Odell and Dixie Goswami (New York: Guilford, 1985) 129–53.

[6] These books will give you more information about designing effective paper documents: Jan V. White, *Graphic Design for the Electronic Age* (New York: Watson-Guptill, 1988); and John Miles, *Design for Desktop Publishing* (San Francisco; Chronicle Books, 1987). These books will give you more information about designing effective online documents, help screens, and World Wide Web pages: Horton, *Online*; William K. Horton, Lee Taylor, Arthur Ignacio, and Nancy L. Hoft, *The World Wide Web Cookbook*, (New York: Wiley, 1996). For information on the WWW about designing Web pages, check the links that are available through the home page of the Society for Technical Communication at http://stc.org.

[7] For more information on page layout, including many thumbnail sketches of grids, see the work of Elizabeth Keyes: Elizabeth Keyes, "Typography, Color, and Information Structure," *Technical Communication* 40. 4 (1993) 638–54; and Elizabeth Keyes, David Sykes, and Elaine Lewis, "Technology + Design + Research = Information Design," *Text, ConText, and HyperText*, ed. Edward Barrett (Cambridge, MA: MIT Press, 1988) 251–64.

[8] White 20.

[9] Rolf F. Rehe, *Typography: How to Make It Most Legible*, 3rd ed. (Carmel, IN: Design Research International, 1979) 34; Keyes; Keyes, Sykes, and Lewis.

[10] M. Gregory and E. C. Poulton, "Even Versus Uneven Right Margins and the Rate of Comprehension in Reading," *Ergonomics* (1970): 427–34; Rehe, 34.

[11] M. A. Tinker, Legibility of Print (Ames, IA: Iowa State UP, 1969); J. Foster and P. Coles, "An Experimental Study of Typographical Cueing in Printed Text," *Ergonomics* (1977) 57–66.

[12] For more on using colour effectively, see also Gerald M. Murch, "Using Color Effectively: Designing to Human Specifications," *Technical Communication* 32. 4 (1985) 14–20; Horton, *Online*, 241–45; Horton et al., *Web Cookbook*, 242–43 and 420–21.

[13] Linda Flower, John R. Hayes, and Heidi Swarts, "Revising Functional Documents: The Scenario Principle," *New Essays in Technical and Scientific Communication: Research, Theory, and Practice*, eds. Paul V. Anderson, R. John Brockmann, and Carolyn R. Miller (Farmingdale, NY: Baywood, 1983) 41–58.

[14] White, 95–106; Miles, 42–46.

Chapter 9: Design Elements

[1] M. Jimmie Killingsworth and Betsy G. Jones, "Division of Labor or Integrated Teams: A Crux in the Management of Technical Communication?" *Technical Communication* 36 (1989) 210.

[2] The Petroleum Resources Communication Foundation. *Our Petroleum Challenge: The New Era* (Calgary: PRCF) 1.

[3] *Our Petroleum Challenge.*

[4] Environment Ontario, *The New AQI: A Broader Measure of Air Quality.* (Updated booklet now available).

[5] David R. Russell, "The Ethics of Teaching Ethics in Professional Communication: The Case of Engineering Publicity at MIT in the 1920s," *Journal of Business and Technical Communication* 7 (1993) 84-85. Reprinted by permission.

[6] Pthalates in Food (Chicago: Institute of Food Technologists, 1974) 1.

[7] Russell 107.

[8] A. Groot and R.A. Haig, "Take Advantage of Advance Growth When Planning Harvesting Operations," *Frontline: Forestry Canada Technical Note No. 4* (1991).

[9] Karen Davison, "The Quality of Dietary Information on the World Wide Web," *Journal of the Canadian Dietetic Association.* Vol 57 No. 4 (Winter 1996) 137-141. Reprinted with permission from the *Canadian Journal of Dietetic Practice and Research* (formerly the *Journal of the Canadian Dietetic Association*), a publication of Dieticians of Canada.

Chapter 12: The Strategies and Communications of the Job Hunt

[1] In writing this chapter, we have drawn upon materials from Human Resources Development Canada and from The Canadian Association of Career Educators and Employers. Earlier editions were indebted to two U.S. Department of Labor publications, *Job Search Guide: Strategies for Professionals* (Washington, DC: GPO, 1993) and *Tips for Finding the Right Job* (Washington, DC: GPO, 1992).

[2] Canadian Association of Career Educators and Employers, *Career Options in Science and Engineering* (1997-98) 25.

[3] Mark Swartz, "The Wired Work Search," *Career Options in Science and Engineering* (1997-98) 8-10. See Also Mark Swartz, *Get Wired, You're Hired: The Canadian Guide to Job Hunting Online* (Scarborough, ON: Prentice-Hall Canada, Inc., 1997).

[4] *Job Search Guide* 22.

[5] Jane L. Anton, Michael L. Russell, and the Research Committee of the Western College Placement Association, *Employer Attitudes and Opinions Regarding Potential College Graduate Employees* (Hayward, CA: Western College Placement Association, 1974) 10.

[6] Jennifer Gay, Staffing and Organizational Developments Coordinator, MPR Teltech, Burnaby, B.C. Quoted in *Science and Engineering Career Options: The Graduate Recruitment Annual* 1995–96 (Toronto: CACEE, 1995) 9.

[7] *Career Options in Science and Engineering* (1997–98) 47.

Chapter 15: Instructions

[1] G.B. Harrison, *Profession of English* (New York: Harcourt, 1962) 149.

[2] The questions posed here are based on questions presented by Janice C. Redish, Robbin M. Battison, and Edward S. Gold, " Making Information Accessible to Readers," *Writing in Nonacademic Settings*, eds. Lee Odell and Dixie Goswami (New York: Guilford, 1985) 139–43.

[3] Redish, Battison, and Gold 134.

[4] Ontario Ministry of Labour, Health and Safety Division, *Designated Substances in the Workplace: A Guide to the Lead Regulation* (1985, rev. 1988) 4–5.

[5] Ontario Ministry of Environment and Energy, *Where and How to Caulk and Weatherstrip* (Toronto: MEE, n.d.) 14–15.

[6] Shoe box for Sebago Docksiders.

[7] Kathryn Coonrod, "Why Should Technical Communicators Care About Product Liability?" *STC Intercom* (February, 1993) 5.

[8] Charles H. Sides, *How to Write Papers and Reports About Computer Technology* (Philadelphia: ISI, 1984) 70.

[9] U.S. Department of Agriculture, *Simple Home Repairs: Inside* (Washington, DC: GPO, 1986) 7–8.

[10] *Simple Home Repairs: Inside* 16.

[11] Protocol analysis material furnished by Professor Victoria Mikelonis, U of Minnesota, St. Paul, MN.

Chapter 17: Oral Reports

[1] These introspections were compiled at a session of the National Training Laboratory in Group Development that one of the authors attended in Bethel, Maine.

[2] The material on visual aids has been especially prepared for this chapter by Professor James Connolly of the University of Minnesota.

Part V: Handbook

[1] Minna Levine, "Business Statistics," *MacUser* (April 1990) 128.

[2] Levine 120.

INDEX

Planning and Revision Checklists

The following questions are a summary of the key points in Chapter 2, "Composing," and Chapter 3, "Writing Collaboratively." They provide a planning and revision checklist for composing. Questions that apply to collaborative writing only are preceded by an asterisk.

SITUATIONAL ANALYSIS
* ★ Has the group appointed a recorder to capture the group's ideas during the planning process?
* What is your topic?
* Why are you writing about this topic? What is your purpose (or purposes)?
* What are your readers' educational levels? What are their knowledge and experience in the subject matter area?
* What will your readers do with the information? What is their purpose?
* Do your readers have any expectations as to style and tone? Serious, light, formal?
* What is your relationship to your readers? How will this relationship affect your approach to them?
* What are your readers' attitudes about what you are going to say?

DISCOVERY
* What discovery approach can you use? Brainstorming? Using arrangement patterns? Other?
* Are there documents similar to the one you are planning that would help you?
* Do you have notes or journal entries available?
* What questions are your readers likely to want answered?
* Do you have all the information you need? If not, where can you find it? People? Library? Laboratory research?

ARRANGEMENT
* Are there standard arrangement patterns that would help you, such as instructions, argument, proposals?
* Will you need to modify any such standard pattern to suit your needs?
* Do you need a formal outline?
* When completed, does your organizational plan fit your topic, material, purpose, and audience?
* What headings and subheadings will you use to reveal your organization and content to your readers?
* Is everything in your plan relevant to your topic, purpose, and audience?
* If you have a formal outline, does it follow outlining conventions? Entries grammatically parallel? Each section divided at least into two parts? Correct capitalization? Entries substantive?
* ★ When planning is completed, does the group have an organizational plan sufficiently complete to serve as a basis for evaluation?

DRAFTING
* ★ How will the group approach the drafting stage?
  By dividing the work among different writers?
  By writing together as a group?
  By assigning the work to one person?

* Has the group agreed on format features such as spacing, typography, table and graph design, headings, and documentation?
* Has the group set deadlines for the work to be completed?
* Should the group appoint a coordinator for the project?
• Do you have a comfortable place to work?
• Where in your organizational plan can you begin confidently?

REVISION
• Have you stated clearly and specifically the purpose of the report?
• Have you put into the report everything required? Do you have sufficient supporting evidence? Have you stated the implications of your information clearly?
• Are all your facts and numbers accurate?
• Have you answered the questions your readers are likely to have?
• Does the report contain anything that you would do well to cut out?
• Does your organization suit the needs of your content and your audience?
• Are your paragraphs clear, well organized, and of reasonable length? Are there suitable transitions from one point to the next?
• Is your prose style clear and readable?
• Is your tone appropriate to your audience?
• Are all your statements ethical? For example, have you avoided making ambiguous statements or statements that deliberately lead the reader to faulty inferences?
• Are your graphs clear and accurate? Are they well placed? Do they present your information honestly?
• Is your document readable, accessible, and visually effective?
• Are there people you should share your draft with—for example, members of the target audience—before going on to a final draft?

EDITING
• Have you checked thoroughly for misspellings and other mechanical errors?
• Have you included all the formal elements your report needs?
• Are format features such as headings, margins, spacing, typefaces, and documentation consistent throughout the draft?
• Are your headings and titles clear, properly worded, and parallel? Do your headings in the text match those in the table of contents?
• Is your documentation system the one required? Have you documented wherever appropriate?
• Have you keyed the tables and figures into your text and have you sufficiently discussed them?
• Are all parts and pages of the manuscript in the correct order?
• Will the format of the typed report be functional, clear, and attractive?
• Does your manuscript satisfy stylebook specifications governing it?
• Have you included required notices, distribution lists, and identifying code numbers?
• Do you have written permission to reproduce extended quotations or other matter under copyright? (Necessary only when your work is to be published or copyrighted.)
• While you were composing the manuscript, did you have any doubts or misgivings that you should now check out?
• Have you edited your manuscript for matters both large and small?
• What remains to be done, such as proofreading final copy?

Proofreader's Marks

∧	Insert here the addition or correction indicated in margin.
out - see copy	Something omitted at point indicated in text; see copy.
ℒ	Take out; delete matter indicated.
ͻ	Close up; no space.
ℰ	Take out character indicated in text and close up.
#	Insert a space here; increase spacing.
¶	Make a paragraph here.
no ¶	No paragraph; "run in" same paragraph.
tr	Transpose letters or words indicated in text.
∿	Transpose these letters.
⌐⌐	Transpose these words.
Ⓠ	Marginal question to author.
Ⓢⓟ	Spell out.
stet	Let it stand; restore crossed-out letters or words.
....	Retain letters of words above these dots.
⍀	Insert comma.
⊙	Insert period.
(:)	Insert colon.
(;)	Insert semicolon.
⌄	Insert apostrophe.
=/	Insert hyphen.
?/	Insert question mark.
ℊ ʺ	Insert quotation marks.
!	Insert exclamation mark.
(/)	Insert parentheses.
[/]	Insert brackets.
]	Move to right.
[	Move to left.
⊓	Raise.
⊔	Lower.
ᘒ	Upside down; reverse.
×	Character appears battered; examine.
ital.	Change to italic type.
rom.	Change to roman type.
caps	Put in capitals.
sm caps	Put in small capitals.
lc	Put in lowercase (small letters).
___	Under a letter or word, set in italic type.
=	Under a letter or word, set in small capitals.
≡	Under a letter or word, set in capitals.
∿∿∿	Under a letter or word, set in boldface type.
//	Line up properly.
⸗	Straighten line.